PROFESSIONAL
PRACTICE FOR
BUILDING WORKS

PROFESSIONAL PRACTICE FOR BUILDING WORKS

by

Ian A. Melville, F.R.I.C.S.

and

Ian A. Gordon, F.R.I.C.S.

1983

⊖G

THE ESTATES GAZETTE LIMITED
151 Wardour Street London
W1V 4BN

First published 1983

Text set in 10/11 pt Linotron 202 Baskerville, printed and bound
in Great Britain at The Pitman Press, Bath

Preface

Our principal reason for writing this book is the firm belief we hold that advances in technology against the background of a changing society will not, in themselves, ensure the satisfactory completion of building works. Just as important as the skills deployed on a project are the procedures adopted by the architect or surveyor and, in particular, the personal qualities of firmness and tact used in his relations with others. The reasons for holding this belief are fully elaborated in the Introduction.

It is hoped that the book will prove of value to all those who fulfill the role of designer and specifier between the initiator of the building works and the building contractor. The range of such people, however, is wide and it has been difficult to select a suitable conglomerate term for use throughout to embrace all such practitioners. We have chosen "architect and surveyor" since apart from those of both sexes to whom the description does literally apply, both qualified and approaching qualification and presumably forming the bulk of the readership, it has to include those designers who cannot call themselves architects, because they are not registered, and management surveyors as well as building surveyors. The professional practice described is appropriate to both the private and public sector but the law has been restricted to that applicable to England and Wales except to point the occasional contrast with the law in Scotland.

In compiling this book we have drawn upon various sources of material but in particular the publications of the Royal Institution of Chartered Surveyors, Surveyors Publications, RIBA Publications Ltd, the British Standards Institution, Crown Copyright publications by permission of the Controller of Her Majesty's Stationery Office including those of the Building Research Establishment, the National House Building Council and the National Building Specification, to whom due acknowledgements are made. The source of material extracted from such publications is quoted in each case throughout the text.

We also wish to thank Mr. Leonard Moseley, FRICS, FFB Director of Studies at the College of Estate Management not only for

v

his general encouragement but for making a number of valuable suggestions regarding aspects to be included. We also wish to thank Mr. Anthony L. Poole, FRICS a past President of the Building Surveyor's Division of the RICS for kindly reading the section relating to party walls and for his valuable comments.

London
December 1982

IAN A. MELVILLE
IAN A. GORDON

Contents

CONTENTS

A paged list of contents appears at the beginning of each Chapter

Introduction

ALTHOUGH there are now three times as many professional architects and surveyors dealing with building works than there were 40 years ago, it is a regrettable fact of life that the public hold a large proportion of such professionals at a fairly low level of esteem. The opportunities made available for qualification in the professions by the more liberal allocation of grants for full and part-time study have been matched, until recently, by a high level of demand for new and refurbished buildings to make up for the losses caused by the Second World War, the neglect of the inter-war years and the desire for better accommodation, generated by a higher standard of living. Much of the new work comprised in the large scale redevelopments of the immediate post war period has, however, been found to have serious structural defects or to provide unhealthy and unpleasant living conditions while much of the refurbished work, to which the public turned after large scale development was found to be socially unacceptable, has been carried out to poor and shoddy standards. All this has happened paradoxically during a period when scientific and technical research has provided the professionals dealing with building work with an abundance of advice. Rectification is currently costing vast sums of money and the public, understandably, feels let down particularly when, as owners in the form of rate and taxpayers, it has to meet those costs.

The reasons for the high incidence of failures in the post war building programme, and the often poor standards offered by the building industry, are many and diverse, while the responsibility for their occurrence is diffuse. It is not fair to put all the blame on the professional advisers, although many who should accept some of the responsibility have strong reasons of their own for endeavouring to do just that. The professionals have been pressurised from all sides to adopt new, speedier, and cheaper methods of building so that the public, central and local government, must all accept some of the responsibility. The market at the same time has been flooded with new untried materials and techniques, so that building owners, instead of the suppliers, have had to pay dearly for establishing that many were not the marvels they were claimed to be. The contracting industry has failed to supply the skilled labour and supervision needed for many projects because the conditions it provides for its employees have tended to turn the skilled and reliable away into other more secure and lucrative industries. When confronted with its failures the industry has, furthermore, tended to vanish into the realms of dissolution and reformation. Research has, perhaps, been ill-directed and tended to follow, with an inquest on what has gone wrong, rather than lead by way of the anticipation of problems. It is hardly surprising, in the circumstances, that matters went sadly wrong but surprising that they did so to such an extent. Nevertheless, there is a feeling that if some of the older "crustier" members of the professions had been around over this period with the attitudes and manners from the "steadier" times (not necessarily better, but certainly different) of pre-1940, the failures would not have happened to such an extent and standards would not have dropped so low. Clients would have had "No" said to them much more often and contractors would have been told "that will not do" on many more occasions. If some failures occurred, they would have been categorised as "unsuccessful experiments" for which no possible blame could be attached to the professionals concerned. It would seem to be this lack of firmness and, to a certain extent, guile which has landed the professions dealing with building in their present plight.

However, in general, the professionals of the pre-1940 era were very different in outlook. In many cases they could afford to say "No" because the backing of private means enabled them to be more independent. The professions were generally held in higher esteem, whether justifiably or not is of no account, and advice gratefully accepted, and willingly paid for, by clients who in many cases behaved more like patrons. Over the last 40 years, however, the professional in private practice has had to be very watchful as to where the next fee is coming from so as to keep his head above water and, if in employment, whether privately or by a public authority, has had to watch his prospects. Pressures have therefore, accordingly, provided at times compromise situations and advice has been tailored to clients views and requirements with the result that, however unjustified it may seem to many, the professionals engaged in building must also accept some of the blame themselves for the sorry results and the poor esteem in which they are now held. To restore that esteem requires the adoption of much more hard professionalism on the part of architects and surveyors towards clients, other professionals, contractors and officials. This applies to architects and surveyors in both the private and the public sector since both serve clients in precisely the same way, whether the clients are in the form of fee or salary payers, and the professional responsibility is the same to both. If a stronger line is not taken and there is no improvement clients will, understandably, turn more frequently to other methods of obtaining building work. For example, many contractors offer package deals, where the design and site control fee is disguised in the overall cost but where it may be felt that the contractor exercises more responsibility in his outlook, as he is virtually selling a completed product and cannot shift the blame on to anyone else, if something should go wrong. After all much building work was done in the past, and plenty still gets done satisfactorily, without the interference of professional architects and surveyors. If there is a return to such earlier procedures in this regard, as was more common in the mid 19th century, before the RIBA and RICS were even founded, then instead of witnessing any further enlargement in the numbers of architects and surveyors, there will be a diminution. For those who genuinely believe that the best interests of clients are served by the employment of a professional to advise upon and control building work, this would be regrettable. Even so, it may have to be accepted that package deals are probably the most appropriate method for those clients requiring the cheapest work, very urgent work, or work where the quality of design is of little consequence.

Of course, it goes without saying that, if professional advisers are engaged, clients will only be satisfied if good advice and a sound service is provided and if a degree of professional competence is exercised. All too frequently it is found that sound building practice is neglected, advice derived from research ignored, the new untried product specified in preference to a proven standard product and innovation practiced for the mere sake of it. Some will say that no "progress" will ever be made if the architect or surveyor is not allowed the freedom to use new methods and materials as he thinks fit, and, instead, is required to use only tried and trusted methods, but this attitude is to ignore the whole point of the argument. It is only right and proper that new materials, methods and techniques should be tried out over a period of time and that some architects and surveyors should be involved in such work on behalf of research authorities controlled by central government or, perhaps, even some of the major contracting organisations. It is when such materials and methods are introduced by architects and surveyors themselves without a full explanation of the risks involved, and matters go wrong that clients are justifiably outraged. If the risks are fully explained to lay clients, be they an individual, a company, trustees, a local authority Council committee or administrators, most will settle for something of which it is reasonably possible to be sure will provide a satisfactory performance over the years, even if it means the client has to accept a scheme on a smaller scale than would have been the case if a less expensive, innovatory, scheme had been adopted. Technical skill must be presumed to be provided for architects and surveyors by the study courses leading to qualification by examination and it is not the aim of this book to deal with technical competence as such. Instead it is intended to stress that by following certain procedures, it is more likely that acquired technical skill will be exercised in a manner likely to lead to a satisfactory outcome for the project at the end of the day, together with a contented client who might possibly come back in the future for further building work.

It might be said that proper procedures are set out by the professional societies in their conditions of appointment, or engagement, describing the professional services which clients may expect to receive from architects and surveyors, the various practice notes issued by the societies, and such publications as the RIBA Handbook of Architectural Practice and Management, with derivative Manuals such as the Architects Job Book along with RICS publications on Building Management and Contract Administration. Much useful advice is given in such publications but they do tend to be the fruits of committee deliberations and, as a result, are somewhat bland. They lack explanation, in many instances, of why it is recommended that matters should proceed in a certain way and, in all cases, they assume that everyone involved will act reasonably and follow set procedures. No mention is made in such publications of rogue clients (either in the form of individuals, companies, administrators or committees), rogue consultants or contractors, yet all appear in real life, to say nothing of fellow professionals who follow less than ideal practices. It can be of help if such characters are recognised in advance before they cause too much damage. The contrast between good and bad helps to highlight the merits of good procedure and therefore much can and will be made of what can go wrong if bad procedures are followed. Cautionary tales relevant to current conditions will, it is considered, help to clothe the bare bones of official advice.

The extent to which aspects of professional practice are involved on a particular project depends, to a great extent, on the size and character of the proposed building works. To trace every facet which may arise on the very largest of jobs would tend to make the book even larger and, possibly, dilute the message. On the other hand if procedures for only the simplest and smallest of jobs were to be followed, then much of importance would be omitted. Furthermore, in current conditions, it is essential to cover the procedures involved not only in new work but also in the repair and alteration of existing buildings. In consequence, where it has been thought helpful to relate the advice being given to work on a specific project, a medium sized scheme of repairs, alteration and extension to an existing semi-detached residential, or small commercial building, has been selected. Such a project would not, in the ordinary run of events, always require the services of a quantity surveyor, and consulting structural or heating engineer although the possibility and special aspects of procedure if they are engaged on the project, are taken into account. Nominated contractors are envisaged as being engaged for the sample project and the fact that the property on which the work is to be carried out is semi-detached, and to be extended, permits the relationships with neighbours to be discussed.

The book is presented in five parts following, roughly telescoped, Work Stages as set out in both the RIBA Architects Appointment 1982 and the RICS Conditions of Engagement 1981. Part 1 deals with the architect's and surveyor's relationships with various different types of client, his duties in the broader sense and his appointment for a project. Part 2 covers client's requirements for building works and feasibility studies to ascertain whether those requirements are practicable, both from the physical and financial aspect, including advice on suitable contract forms and tendering procedures, and the report to the client. Part 3 sets out methods of preparing the documentation necessary to describe and illustrate the proposals, the emphasis here being on completeness of the information to enable reasonable accuracy to be obtained on tendering, and the avoidance of delays once work has begun. Ensuring that the client obtains what he wants, and what he is paying for, takes up a substantial amount of space in Part 4 "The Work in Progress", since this is considered to be a substantial area of weakness in professional relationships at the present time. Practical completion of the work signifies the commencement of Part 5, which not only deals with the steps necessary to secure the remedying of minor faults and the issue of the Final Certificate on settlement of the account when works are completed satisfactorily, but also covers the settlement of disputes, by arbitration if possible, and those situations where it is impossible to secure the completion of the works for some reason or other. In discussing the relationship between client and architect or surveyor, it must be assumed that the latter are qualified and in practice, either privately on their own account or in employment, in either the private or public sectors, and in those instances where such a relationship can be said to exist. Those employed, for example, by property development companies do not come into this category and unless acting in the capacity of "expert" clients, are best treated as "developers" or "owners" as the case may be; business men, rather than professionals, in other words. There is no place in the book for those relationships involving the setting up of a practice or a professional unit in an authority, obtaining business or work, or running an office organisation. That would involve a book on practice management and it is not intended to consider such aspects except where the lack of suitable and appropriate office managerial skills may impinge on the professional practice involved in arranging for the satisfactory completion of building works. Obviously professional practice does not affect architects and surveyors, in the true sense, until they have completed their full time studies and accordingly the book is directed, and it is hoped will be of value, to the younger practitioner and to those in process of taking the Test of Professional Competence of the RICS and the Professional Practice Examination of the RIBA.

Part 1
The Appointment

Chapter 1
Clients, Responsibilities and the Law

CONTENTS

3

Clients

THE individuals and organisations owning an interest in property who require building work carried out are very varied indeed. Work will be required from the wealthiest to the poorest of individuals and from the largest to the smallest of organisations. The appointment of an architect or surveyor to set out such work on paper and to supervise the operations on site, however, is by no means a forgone conclusion. Much will depend upon the attitude of the initiator of the proposal and on the extent and character of the intended work.

Many individual owners of property tend to think of professional architects and surveyors as "expensive" and very often they cannot see the need for the payment of fees to describe and supervise work which they think, often erroneously, that they can carry out unaided. Very often and quite reasonably the proposed work, whoever it may be for, consists mainly of repair or renewal with a minimum of alteration which can be described simply by word of mouth either by the owner himself or his representative. Even quite large structures in industry and agriculture provided they comprise run-of-the-mill routine requirements where aesthetic considerations may be of little consequence can be put up by contractors after discussion with a works engineer or farm manager or purchased perhaps from a catalogue much in the same way as a house owner buys a garage for delivery and erection by the supplier. Furthermore there persists a long standing tradition of house building carried out by contractors using fairly standard designs modified to suit a particular market and concentrating on structural types within their range of capabilities. It is often considered by these contractors that the introduction of an architect or surveyor in a supervisory role merely leads to "complications" which could well increase the cost of the product. Professional architects or surveyors may deplore all this activity carried on without their involvement but must accept the fact that individuals, organisations and contractors between them can produce satisfactory building work without their help. They have done so for a long time in the past, certainly well before the time when the professional architect or surveyor in the form as known today became established, and will no doubt continue to do so in the future.

Very often, however, individuals and the smaller organisation or company turn to professional architects or surveyors on the first occasion when they believe that there is a prospect of being overcharged by a contractor or in circumstances when they are not

5

quite sure of what it is they wish to have done and believe that the expertise of a professional will assist in bringing order to a confused mind. Unflattering as it may seem to architects and surveyors they are often approached not for the high minded reasons many would wish to think. Many cherish the view for example, of how reliable is their judgement, how invaluable and skilful they are and how indispensable to any owner contemplating building works whereas in truth the owner may only be looking upon the professional as a form of buffer between himself and an avaricious contractor. Fortunately many owners come to realise just how valuable the professional service can be but the number who do so will depend to a great extent on the quality of the service they obtain.

That building owners have increasingly found the need for the services of professionals over the last 40 years is evidenced by their increase in numbers. While there has been some increase in the number of architects and surveyors in private practice on their own account and, correspondingly, also in the numbers of architects and surveyors employed in such practices, the most substantial increase has been in the numbers employed directly by private companies, central and local Government and by the Nationalised Industries. Such organisations not only utilise the services of those architects and surveyors which they employ directly but may also commission work from outside private practices, the method by which most public sector work was originally carried out in the period before 1940. It is worth mentioning, however, that such organisations without necessarily commissioning work or employing architectural or surveying staff directly can still even now, and on occasions do, obtain new buildings through the method of the "package deal".

Because of the current widespread use of both architects and surveyors in private practice and in direct employment it is necessary to consider owners who have work carried out from two separate aspects. In the first place they must be considered as commissioners of work and in the second place they need to be considered as employers. Conversely the responsibilities of architects and surveyors, their duties and relationships must be thought of in relation to the owner in two separate guises, as commissioner and as employer. It must be made quite clear, however, that the owner, in whatever manifestation he may appear, is entitled to the same standard of service and advice from his professional advisers irrespective of whether he is a commissioner of work or an employer. It goes without saying that this service must be satisfactory if the professions are to stay at the numbers of today or even to grow in size.

Up to now the individual or organisation proposing to carry out building works has been referred to as the building owner and indeed this is right and proper since ownership of an interest in land or buildings is a sensible pre-requisite for having works carried out, to put it no higher. Not many will wish to do and pay for work on property in the ownership of someone else, although it has been known to happen. When it comes to entering into a contract with the builder who agrees to carry out the work the building owner may be referred to in a number of different ways depending on the form of contract being used. For example in the Joint Contract Tribunal Form he will be known as "the employer", in the forms used by Central Government, GC/Works/1 and GC/Works/2, he will be known as "the authority", while in the Institution of Civil Engineer's Form of Contract he will be referred to as "the promoter". However, in his relationship with the professional adviser the building owner has always been known as the "client" and is referred to as such in the Architect's Appointment issued by the Royal Institute of British Architects and the Conditions of Engagement issued by the Royal Institution of Chartered Surveyors. Whoever or whatever organisation wishes to have works carried out will henceforth be referred to as "the client" irrespective of whether he, or it, is, paying fees to an architect or surveyor in private practice or a salary to an architect or surveyor in his, or it's, employment and throughout all stages of the project. As will be seen later there is a contract between the client and the architect or surveyor whatever the relationship between the two may be. The contract is perhaps more apparent and more easily recognisable in the case of commissions to architects or surveyors in private practice but it is nonetheless real in the contract of employment between a company or organisation and a professional architect or surveyor.

It will be noted that throughout the singular "client" is used rather than the plural "clients" even though for example the "client" may in fact be a partnership or an organisation. There are two reasons for this. In the first place it is most essential for the architect or surveyor to receive his instructions and to have all contact with the client through one focal point. It does not matter whether he is acting for a group of people such as a committee managing a large block of flats, a charitable concern or a committee of a local authority, "they" should always be looked upon as a corporate entity speaking through one person. In the second place it is a vital component in the ethos of professionalism that an adviser cannot have two clients involved in the same project in view of the possibility of a clash of interests. In the rare cases when there are two clients on a particular project it is preferable for one to be made subservient to the other and kept in the background with all the instructions flowing from the principal client. In other cases it is probably better for two professional advisers to be appointed since it must be accepted that no two clients interests are identical and the professional adviser must always avoid the danger of being caught between two conflicting viewpoints and in the invidious, difficult and dangerous position of weighing the balance.

Two of the most essential requirements in any client for the successful completion of building repairs or construction work are that in the first place he has the authority to take decisions and secondly the authority to release the finance that will be required to pay the contractor and the professional advisers at the required intervals. Repair and construction contracts are unique in that effective administration requires not only major but many minor decisions to be taken, often at short notice, with finance readily available both on long and short call. It is often thought that smaller contracts in the private sector are the most vulnerable due to failures on both these aspects and certainly every architect or surveyor at some time or other is likely to experience a case where a building contract, confidently entered into, falls into some unexpected difficulty. The case of a confident business man suddenly called away when his house is being extended, normally so ordered and precise, but who leaves behind a wife unable to take decisions and without the financial control to enable her to release monies at the times provided for in the contract is an obvious example. On the other hand it must not be assumed that simply because the client is a local authority or a government department that all will necessarily be well. The organisation may look impressive but the actual machinery for ensuring that decisions are taken promptly and that money payments are discharged at the appropriate dates might be entirely lacking. The efficiency of the client is by no means guaranteed by increasing size.

By considering the various types of client likely to be encountered by the architect and surveyor both in private practice and in employment it is possible to see how each meets up with these two essential requirements. It is possible also to consider whether there is any course of action which the architect or surveyor can take, or should take, to ensure so far as it is possible to do that they fulfil these requirements before embarking on services on the client's behalf. The various types of client can best be considered to begin with from the point of view of the architect or surveyor in private practice commencing with the smallest and reviewing the possible client in increasing order of size.

If asked, most architects and surveyors would probably say straight away that their idea of "the client" who comes to mind immediately is the man or woman who wishes to build or extensively repair, extend or convert his or her own private dwelling house or, similarly, the entrepreneurial director of a firm who wishes to build, extend or alter business premises and seeks out a professional adviser to give assistance in the traditional way. An individual, with drive, honesty and the appropriate capital available is likely to make a good client since he will impress his views upon his advisers, listen to what they have to say and, in his own self-interest, change his mind when he is persuaded that he is wrong. By the same token his advisers will be in no doubt where their duty lies and, under the influence of a man with brisk businesslike methods, are likely to react with similar efficiency. This case, however, can be contrasted with that where the individual is mean and crafty and will go to any lengths to save a few pounds. Such a man is never likely to tell his advisers the whole story, be addicted to the introduction of less than efficient help whether professional or constructional purely for cheapness and, worst of all, land himself and everyone else in a situation where no one is fully responsible for anything and everyone is supposedly responsible for the mistakes which have been made. A man such as this having produced a disaster will then stand aside and blame everyone else for he, depend upon it, is never in the wrong. Some such clients can, with good fortune, be detected at an initial meeting or very early on at the instruction stage and this might enable the opportunity to arise for the architect or surveyor to suggest that the client might be better served elsewhere. Even if not detected early on, and this will often be the case with the more wily of the breed who will be at pains to show all sweetness and reasonableness in the early stages, such an individual will need to be tied down with very great care by way of written agreement to define the relevant spheres of authority. It should be made clear at this stage that a distinction should be drawn between a requirement to carry out building works within reasonable cost effective yardsticks to produce value for money on the client's behalf on the one hand and downright cheeseparing meanness on the other. The former is a discipline to which all architects and surveyors must respond favourably while the professional will learn to recognise very quickly in the latter case that the clients own best interests are not necessarily being served by mere compliance with his every whim. This is a point which, however, will require further elaboration since borderline cases can prove difficult and require the exercise of considerable tact if the charge of arrogance is to be avoided.

The good client will allow the architect or surveyor to investigate his standing both as regards authority for taking decisions and on finance and will freely produce the required documents. It goes without saying that the larger the proposed contract the easier this type of enquiry can be and it is on the smaller contracts that the surveyor or architect may have to use particular discretion. The client must also realise that in certain cases the contractor will naturally wish to make his own enquiries and not merely proceed on the surveyor's assurance that the client is "obviously a man of means". Once the money is known to be there however, and it is known that he has authority to act, in the case of the individual usually because he owns the premises, proof of the ability to take quick firm decisions can only be awaited upon with gloom or cheerful expectancy, depending upon the temperament of the professional adviser, until the works start. It is by no means the housewife mentioned previously who is the most cautious in issuing instructions nor is it the man in charge of a large business or the running of a local authority department who is necessarily the most bold. It can be amusing in some cases and totally disconcerting in others to find that any pre-judged stereotyped assessment of the way people are likely to act under the pressure of the requirement to make quick decisions can be totally blown to the wind. The lady of supposedly no business sense can be splendidly decisive while the man who conducts a commercial empire can sometimes tend to duck away from decisions being used, perhaps, to sheltering behind subordinates, to do so. It is a fact that the need to take speedy decisions sometimes involving quite large sums of the clients own money is likely to bring out to the full the client's temperament to his professional advisers in a very short space of time. As an example advisers acting for an individual holding high office under the Crown made the elementary mistake of sitting back and confidently expecting Napoleonic decisions to be made but were taken aback to find that the decisions were not forthcoming. It then dawned upon them that the client, while expert at amassing all the necessary information upon which a decision was to be taken, would far rather act as advocate than judge. The experience finally grew rather depressing with letters from the client containing such expressions as "provided I have your total, complete and categorical assurance that this will be so . . ." providing a commentary on a contract from which, in the end, no one extracted any particular satisfaction.

The ideal individual client knows his own mind and organises his affairs so as to ensure that his wishes will be obeyed and that he gets what he wants. Whether on large or small contracts, he will ensure that everyone employed by him including consultants, independent or otherwise, knows his part with precision and that they can expect a firm rebuke if they are guilty of either exceeding the authority granted to them or of sloppy conduct. In a large management team, in particular, it is vital that everyone knows his part and the organisation and determination to ensure that everyone does achieve this derives partly from administrative ability on the one hand and partly from the natural gift both to direct and inspire. If present in the client all to the good and no architect or surveyor should find it difficult to form a part of the client's team. If lacking in the client then these qualities are, with advantage, to be developed and exercised by the architect or surveyor to a greater or lesser degree, depending on the disclosed attributes of the client. It can, however, be seen that in some cases with a very "strong" client indeed professional advisers and contractors may find themselves "dragooned", hopefully in the best sense of the term.

A "strong" client with pronounced views, for example, on how alterations to a building should be carried out or on the appearance of an extension may be convinced, with some reason, of his own ability to "go it alone" and turn himself into what is in effect a management contractor purchasing materials, taking on labour as and when he needs it, paying it promptly and dismissing it with efficient despatch to make way for the next group. In the case of a clear sighted and resolute man this type of operation can work brilliantly. In such circumstances, however, it is interesting to discover that the employer not only knows or gets to know intimately everyone who is responsible for decisions on the site but makes sure that the various personalities are not allowed to conflict. He also works extremely hard visiting Town Halls, attending on the site and generally being everywhere at once. A factory owner who conducted just this type of operation was extremely proud of being able to do without professional help but added in the very next breath that he would never attempt such a thing again as the loss of his own personal time had "cost him a fortune". However such a man, due to shortage of time or other reasons, may not be able to arrange for the work to be carried out in this way and will consider that it is up to the professionals he employs in these circumstances merely to produce what he wants, provided always that it is possible to do so. The professional advisers will not be thanked for being "difficult" and for trying to impose their own ideas. This type of client, however, is comparatively rare but when he does appear it will be just those attributes of administrative ability and the capacity to direct and inspire which will be sought in the professional advisers he instructs.

It is always a relief for an architect or surveyor to know that the client has gone to some pains in arriving at his selection of advisers possibly by enquiry and recommendation and has made his choice knowing that that the firm concerned offers a particular skill. On the other hand architects and surveyors must have every sympathy with the "inexperienced" client who attempts to decide on an appointment lacking the experience or warnings of friends or contacts who have been involved in the building process before. The various "package deals" offered by different companies or contractors, "design and build" contracts or "fixed fee" contracts, might all have their appeal, as already discussed, against what might seem to be the more troublesome business of either procuring names of suitable architects or surveyors from either the Royal Institute of British Architects or the Royal Institution of Chartered Surveyors or trying to select from the discreet range of advertisements for consultancy services which are now permitted.

There are many individual clients who have no idea at all of the services which are available from an architect or surveyor, nor have they any idea whatever of what can be achieved by way of improvement, extension or major repair to buildings and are, understandably, also totally ignorant of building costs. Such clients need particular care, help and consideration by the architect or surveyor as they may have totally unrealistic expectations. In these cases every effort must be made to ascertain the amount available for spending on the project by enquiry from the prospective client. If by discreet questioning the client is still coy about revealing the amount available then it is probably best to explain, with some approximately costed examples, what can be done within broad bands of expenditure and for the client to ponder on these for a while. If the architect or surveyor is able to use real examples so much the better and even more so if the prospective client can actually go and see the completed work. It is important with the uninitiated prospective client to ensure that he is clear in his own mind about the character of the services which can be provided and, if the prospective client is able to explain what he requires to be done, that he is provided with the best of approximate costs of the project with typical fees given separately but all merely as a guide and with stress put upon the fact that payments both for the works and for fees are always staged. It has been known for clients to initiate work in the mistaken belief that it need not be paid for until entirely completed. An honest and straightforward opinion of what can be carried out for various sums of money must be given, erring, preferably on the cautious side. It is no use misleading the prospective client and indeed very wrong to do so, into thinking that he can get more work done for his money than is reasonably certain on the principle that "oh well, the client will pay up in the end when the time comes since he is probably keeping some finance back in reserve".

It will be disastrous for all concerned if there are in fact no reserves and as a result cannot meet progress payments towards the end of the contract. Needless to say in all these discussions if the project is quite modest the prospective client's reaction to the fee aspect may well be quite marked and he may never be seen again. It should go without saying that the approaches of all prospective clients should be treated with equal courtesy. Appearances can be very deceptive. The wealthy can sometimes look the shabbiest, the smartest may turn out to be comparatively poor. The inarticulate, voluble and flashy all need treating with caution alike and a client with a title can present problems by the way in which he or she is viewed by others. He or she, it is true, may be a little vague, possessing money and therefore unaware of the pressing need of quite small sums of this commodity in others but, equally, the titled client may have vary little money in the form of disposable cash, however resounding the name. The contractor may make a wrong assumption and it is the job of the architect or surveyor to dispel, as tactfully as possible, any illusions on either side. Similar comments apply to those in the entertainments industry. Seemingly absurdly rich in a very short time the general public quite simply fail to appreciate the spectre of the tax man behind every successful artist or artiste with the requirement of continued success as the only alternative to impoverishment.

Some detailed consideration has been given to the individual client from the point of view of his ability to meet the two essential requirements of decision taking and making payments. It will be necessary to return to the individual client again later to see how the actual stages of introduction and acceptance of instructions are handled by the architect or surveyor but in the meantime some consideration needs to be given to other types of client in relation to these two essential areas of decision taking and financial control.

Some architects or surveyors would probably say that the most difficult of clients can be those groups of individuals formed into clubs or associations. Sports clubs, tenants associations, charitable or religious organisations are examples which come to mind. The individual members elected on to the various governing committees are generally fairly forceful characters and there is seldom any love lost between them. Some committees often have such difficulty in reaching a satisfactory decision that their final conclusions are so riddled with compromises as to be almost useless. Even if all members of the committee agree that something should be done the remainder of the membership will take a delight in scoring points off the committee members. On other occasions a comparatively docile committee will fall into the hands of a dominant member who is only too pleased to give out all sorts of instructions without prior consultation with other members. Unfortunately if the true standing

13

of the members is not examined beforehand it may be found that "the first class chap who has them all eating out of his hand" may unexpectedly vanish elsewhere, leaving the situation in the control of a number of lesser lights, all of whom form factions and promptly disagree with each other so that no decisions are forthcoming at a very crucial stage of the project.

The architect or surveyor when asked to accept instructions from the committee of any organisation must try to ensure that one person and one person only is responsible for acting as "client" and from whom the architect or surveyor will receive his instructions and to whom he will refer for decisions as necessary during the progress of the works. The same person should also be required to arrange for the necessary payments to be made on the issue of the architect's or surveyor's certificate. All too often it will be found that when it comes to making payments another committee is involved knowing little of the ins and outs of the building process and inclined to raise questions rather than issue a cheque. This can lead to an impossible situation for the architect or surveyor when he is unexpectedly required to answer queries which may be directed to him from two different sources.

During the past decade architects and surveyors in private practice have been increasingly involved in work for Housing Associations both for new work and in respect of older property due for refurbishment and conversion into self-contained units. For a number of years approval to a scheme including all the contract documentation had to be obtained from the Housing Corporation. This has been changed so that the particular Housing Association concerned is now made responsible for the adequacy of the contract documentation on being provided with a copy of the Housing Corporation "Scheme Work Guide". This provides detailed guidance, which is updated at intervals, on the relationship between Housing Associations and their professional advisers and has to be followed by architects and surveyors carrying out such work.

Moving up the scale in size, architects or surveyors obtaining work from companies larger than those in the control of an individual will find that there is usually a manager in a responsible position who can be empowered to take decisions and to authorise payment. He may be either a director or an employee. If this is not the case, and it will usually be apparent at one of the early meetings whether such a situation exists or not, then the architect or surveyor must ensure that the situation is clarified at an early date and that he avoids becoming embroiled with any broad discussions or arguments among the company directors on general policy. Of course this is not to say that he should avoid meeting the other directors at all times. The Board will no doubt wish to meet its architect or surveyor at intervals during the course of the project and one obvious occasion may well be at the completion of the design stage when a presentation can be arranged for the benefit of a fully assembled Board gathering and perhaps for formal Board approval to be given.

From companies in general it is necessary to distinguish two types for their particular attributes in relation to their dealings with architects and surveyors. Generally most companies are in business in fields totally unrelated to building and accordingly rely implicitly on the architect or surveyor to advise them on all aspects in the same way as is normally necessary when dealing with a lay individual. Sometimes, however, companies with large property holdings and with their own staff architects or surveyors will approach outside architects or surveyors in private practice on a consultancy basis, perhaps because the proposed project will stretch their own resources beyond safe limits or perhaps because the project is of a specialist nature more appropriate to the skills of the practice selected for the task. In such cases the private architect or surveyor will be in a fortunate position in some respects in that he will have as a client, more often than not, a professional architect or surveyor from the firm concerned. This is because invariably the company will expect their own staff to liaise with and instruct the private consultant. This should hopefully make relations with the client proceed in a somewhat smoother manner since the staff architect or surveyor should be aware of the consultants need for full, firm and clear instructions and may probably have gone some considerable way himself to formulating these before the consultant is even appointed. Against this advantage the consultant may find that he is involved with a crabby autocratic personality who is out of date in both his knowledge and his attitudes and with whom the architect or surveyor finds it impossible to relate.

The Architects in Industry and Commerce Group of the Royal Institute of British Architects published a document in September 1971 entitled "The Working Relationship between Architects in Industry and Private Practice" which is reproduced in the RIBA Architectural Practice and Management Handbook (4th revised edition 1980). This document outlines various factors to be taken into consideration in such situations in relation to the defining of respective responsibilities, terms of appointment and the actions to be taken by both parties at various stages of the work. Stress is put on obtaining clear agreement in writing on the responsibilities between the parties, on copyright and on any additional indemnity required should any responsibilities be shared. Under the terms of

15

appointment the document indicates that the "client architect" in these circumstances can nominate consultants and quantity surveyors who may be from his own organisation. The avoidance of a division of responsibility on supervision is indicated as being of considerable importance as is the responsibility of the consultant architect or building surveyor on financial control. The document has very clearly been prepared by and from the point of view of "client architects", but provides a suitable aide memoire for consultants on points to consider when an appointment of this nature is under discussion. Certainly an architect or surveyor should consider very seriously whether to accept any invitation to participate in a project where responsibilities are to be divided, where the client's own staff consultants are employed or where it is proposed that client's own building systems are to be used. Consultant architects and surveyors should be careful not to become confused and to treat such appointments as different from any other. Complete and total responsibility should be retained as though the job had been commenced completely from scratch for a lay client, consultants nominated by and not inflicted on the architect or surveyor and building systems or materials used only if the architect or surveyor would have used them in the first place. If such conditions are not acceptable to the client company or its professional staff then it is possible that the company's best interests would be served by consulting someone else or perhaps by an enlargement of its own staff to cope with the work.

Difficulties of the nature described above can also arise, or possibly even increase in connection with appointments from companies whose business it is to trade in buildings, either property investment companies or developers of entirely new buildings or refurbishments. Sometimes the buildings so provided are intended to be held as long term investments and then there will be the need to strike a good balance between reasonable standards of design and construction, economy and speed. Large well established companies of this nature have no problems generally on taking decisions and arranging for the necessary finance to be available. Such companies can, however, impose a very demanding standard on their professional advisers. They are not just an expert client in the normal sense but one with a distinctly commercial and often critical eye particularly of anything involving delay. Speed and efficiency loom high in the considerations of such firms. The less well established of them, however, may have economy in the forefront of their considerations since they are less likely to be in the business of holding properties for investment but will be intending to sell the building at a price which will give the highest profit possible. Whereas speed will be important many of the decisions will be taken with a view to obtaining the maximum amount of space or the maximum number of units in the cheapest form of construction possible. There may well be a reluctance, however, to adopt a decision on features which will detract from the appearance so that it becomes too obvious that the whole scheme is a cut price job and accordingly pressures will often be put on the architect or surveyor to save on hidden constructional details or to adopt finishes which may provide a surface glitter but possess no staying power. In these circumstances the architect or surveyor may find himself in a difficult position. The client should, after all, be provided with what he requires but is this a case where, if the architect or surveyor allows decisions to be taken if not entirely against his better judgement then perhaps on the borderline, he will find himself associated, as many have done in the past, with a scheme that becomes notorious for its faults rather than its merits? Such a scheme may at best provide merely a substantial profit for the developer at the expense of everyone else involved. It is as well therefore for the architect or surveyor to learn at an early stage in his career to recognise such clients as soon as they appear. They are often clients who move from one professional adviser to another with a degree of rapidity and if they do appear dubious then it is sensible for the architect or surveyor to enquire who has been engaged on other schemes for the same company, to view these schemes and to talk with the professional advisers engaged. It may, of course, be that the change of advisers has been made quite validly out of a desire for variety in the various schemes or because of dissatisfaction of past performance and all will be well. However there is a natural tendency in all concerns to stick with advisers that satisfy rather than change and accordingly it is more likely that this is a case of the advisers declining to be associated with another scheme for the same company. In this case the newly approached architect or surveyor needs to be very cautious. It will probably be difficult to penetrate the veil that usually surrounds schemes that have proved to be difficult and ascertain what precisely went wrong but it may be possible to make an intelligent guess even if the original professional advisers are not all that forthcoming. Much will depend on the former consultants themselves. If they are fairly well established and feel they have been "caught" they might be eager to warn others. Some however would probably not wish it to be thought that anything could possibly go wrong with schemes with which they were associated and be reluctant to talk about the circumstances.

The architect or surveyor now selected may cherish the belief that he is just the adviser for such a client and maybe can "cure" the company of its cheap and shoddy outlook by tying the client with a detailed agreement to cover the scope of the appointment but experience suggests that this is not really possible. The sort of conditions which the architect or surveyor would wish to include, for example a free hand over design and costs, even possibly within certain limitations, would be unlikely to be agreed by the client company. Clients do indeed have the last word and accordingly it is best not to even try and serve known unreasonable clients. It is far better to steer clear of them entirely. Such clients will always be able to find someone willing and possibly even able to do their work for them so that no grief need be shed that some members of the community are being deprived of professional services because of the intransigence of a coterie of architects and surveyors in a particular locality.

Mention has been made earlier of a document prepared by the Architects in Industry and Commerce Group of the RIBA on the relationship between architects or surveyors provided with commissions by companies when those companies have their own architectural or surveying staff to convey instructions to those commissioned. The Society of Chief County Architects of Local Authorities after consultation with the RIBA and the Association of Consultant Architects published a similar document in May 1976 entitled "The Relationship between Public and Private Architect" in order to foster a sound relationship between local authorities and private architects undertaking commissions. Not all local authorities employ architects and surveyors on their permanent staff but all have at least some permanent officers with whom the private architect or surveyor will need to work when undertaking a commission from a committee of a local authority. This document correctly places the authority's architect or surveyor, if one is employed, as "expert representative of the client" with full responsibility devolving on the private architect or surveyor. It is stated that he should recommend which private architects should be invited to act or be consulted (a hint of nepotism here and putting the official architect perhaps in an invidious position of patronage in many respects). This document is also reproduced in the RIBA Handbook of Architectural Practice and Management and contains two useful Appendices, one with twenty four headings for setting out the administrative procedures usually necessary in appointments of this nature, the other providing a form of monthly financial statement. There is useful advice in this Report, more so than in the case of the Architects in Industry and Commerce Group document, since it suggests that consultants are best appointed by mutual agreement or even on the preference of the private architect and if there is a suggestion of utilising a client sponsored system of building, the private architect has the opportunity of recommending the use of an alternative, if he considers the clients preferred system to be unsatisfactory for the purpose, before accepting responsibility for using the client's system.

Certainly any private architect or surveyor accepting instructions for local authority work will be well advised to study the Report and follow the recommendations, since useful guidelines are included for making sure that both the official architect, representing the client, and the private architect or surveyor undertaking the project know the boundaries of their responsibilities. It is the muddying of these boundaries that often causes difficulties. Basically the concentration, as it should be, is on how, as "expert client", the official architect can assist the private architect by understanding and appreciating the sort of information he requires and having it ready on time to ease the path forward but without undertaking any of the responsibilities of the private architect to prepare and present the scheme, deal with the consultants, obtain estimates, see that the project is built properly and settle the account. Having said that, and the architect or surveyor following all the recommendations, it does not necessarily mean that all will run smoothly. One aspect of local authority work not mentioned so far is the need to comply with cost yardsticks, cost limits, cost formulae and the like laid down by the central government Department administering the enabling Act under which the local authority is working on the particular project. A private architect or surveyor working for a local authority must reconcile himself to this form of control or decide at a very early stage whether such constraints are acceptable or not within the ambit of his own expertise. Such a discipline should cause no particular problem and indeed should work as a challenge in many respects and controls of this nature are clearly a fact of life to prevent profligate expenditure when central government funds are deployed for the benefit of local authorities. Notwithstanding, the administration of such controls has come in for a degree of criticism in that at times they have been used too rigidly without consideration for the individual requirements of difficult schemes. Their use has also been questioned as not providing the correct solution to all problems in that initial cost becomes all important to the detriment of costs in use and subsequent maintenance. Cost yardsticks are blamed by many for much dismal and unhealthy local authority housing schemes and although it would be wrong to accept this as the only reason, since innovation, poor design and bad workmanship are probably equally to blame, it is undoubtedly true to say that yardsticks are probably not in the best interests of the community when they are applied in the rigid manner of the past.

If an architect or surveyor is mindful of accepting a commission where cost controls are involved he should ascertain their full implications before accepting the work. He will need to know that what is proposed can be satisfactorily completed to the brief within the limits, otherwise he must take steps in advance to see whether it is possible to negotiate something better to satisfy what he feels to be the requirements for finance. If this is not possible then he needs to consider his own professional standing very carefully before becoming associated with the project. Blind acceptance of what is laid down which results in a scheme of which nobody can be proud is, as previously mentioned, more than likely to damage an architect's or surveyor's reputation rather than enhance it.

Difficulties over cost limits are just as likely to be present when private architects accept commissions from central government Departments to the extent that there are cost limits on educational buildings, hospital and prison buildings and the buildings for the more routine requirements of housing civil servants and members of the armed forces. Usually there are design requirements and standards laid down by the Departments concerned, Education and Science, Health and Social Security, the Home Office or the Department of the Environment through the Property Services Agency and a form of cost limit agreed with the Treasury since public accountability through Parliament looms as large as a concern for quality.

It is seldom that a private architect or surveyor will have direct access to the "client", that is the actual occupiers or users of the proposed building when engaged on a commission for central government. Many commisions arise because the permanent resources of the Department concerned are overstretched and are unable to undertake the project. Even so they are seldom so overstretched as to be unable to supply an architect or surveyor to act either as project manager, a role for architects or surveyors of which more will be said later, or as a consultant liaison officer between the actual occupiers and the private architect or surveyor and thus become in effect the expert client. There is no comparable document along the lines of those produced by the Architects in Industry and Commerce Group or the Society of Chief Architects of Local Authorities previously discussed for governing the relationships and fields of responsibility as between the central government architect or surveyor and the private architect or surveyor. There are however administrative procedures which have to be followed as a requirement of the appointment for a commission. These vary from

Department to Department but those for the Property Services Agency, the building arm for the Department of the Environment which not only arranges for the accommodation of most civil servants and members of the armed forces but also acts in the same capacity on an agency basis for a number of other organisations, are governed by a Commissions Code dealing with the appointment of consultants in various disciplines relating to the building process. The section dealing with architects and surveyors follows closely the requirements and practices of the RIBA Conditions of Engagement on Work Stages etc., but there is invariably a consultant liaison officer or Project Manager internally appointed who not only acts as expert client but has an overall responsibility for the financial control of the project to ensure that value for money is obtained. Consultants are required to use PSA Method of Building Components and there is a PSA Standard Specification so that prospective consultants would no doubt wish to consider these requirements in advance of accepting any commission to ascertain whether they were acceptable. Furthermore all central Government Building work is carried out utilising its own forms of building contract, Forms GC/Works/1, General Conditions of Government Contracts for Building and Civil Engineering Works and aC/Works/2, the minor works version, being the most familiar, unlike Local Authorities who normally use the Joint Contract Tribunal Forms in Local Authority Editions. A Consultants Procedural Guide is made available to all those who undertake commissions explaining the various methods and procedures of working.

There are usually no problems in obtaining decisions on a project for central government and in the main it will be expected that all stages of work are carefully followed with authorisation clearly expressed in writing before the consultant proceeds to the next stage. Similarly there should be no difficulty in arranging for the payments on the issue of certificates although as is to be expected a close control will need to be kept on the progress of the contract in regard to cost.

The final type of client who needs consideration in this by no means wholly exhaustive review is the state nationalised industry. Amongst others these include the power undertakings of gas and electricity, the transport undertakings, the Post Office and British Telecom, which are all large users of buildings throughout the country and with a need for architectural and building surveying services. The state industries are independent to the extent that they can adopt and develop their own means of providing such services in a way which suits them best although ultimately they are responsible through a Minister to Parliament and their overall expenditure is controlled through limits placed on their borrowing powers. Most state industries over the years have built up a professional staff to carry out, in some cases, nearly all their new or refurbishment work or alternatively a proportion of the work, leaving the remainder to be carried out by privately employed consultant architects or building surveyors. In the case of British Telecom the legacy of the time when the Post Office was a department of central government lingers on in that the Property Services Agency, as successor to the Ministry of Works, continues in some cases to act as agents to procure building works although there is an increasing tendency for private consultants to be employed.

As in the case of central and local government and the larger private companies, privately commissioned architects and surveyors will usually find that their contact with the commissioning organisation will possibly be through a fellow professional. Accordingly the same care needs to be taken over the terms of the appointment, the division of responsibilities, the use of other consultants, briefing, decision taking and financial control as in the case of commissions accepted from other organisations. In the smaller sized organisations or even in the regional areas of the larger bodies where there is no professional to act as expert client it is vital to ensure that a single member of the organisation is appointed to act as liaison officer through whom all instructions, decisions and approvals are channelled and to whom all certificates are presented by the contractor. Obviously the person delegated to act in this capacity within the organisation must be senior enough to fulfil the function in a satisfactory manner otherwise if, for example, he is only acting as a "postman" to collect and convey messages there could be disastrous delays to the contract.

As mentioned, the larger companies, local authorities, central government and the nationalised industries are substantial employers of professional architects and surveyors themselves. Indeed it is the growth of employment by these bodies that has been primarily responsible for the considerable increase in the membership of the professional institutions for architects and surveyors over the last forty years. Because they are employed does not make such architects and surveyors any less professional and the responsibilities and duties to the client employer remain the same, irrespective, as we shall see, both in the general sense and in the specific sense of dealing with building works as in the case of a privately engaged architect or surveyor vis-a-vis his client.

Responsibilities and The Law

Once a private architect or surveyor is appointed he becomes an agent of his employer and as such immediately assumes responsibilities. The professional ethos is such that the client places confidence in the judgement and integrity of his adviser and accordingly the law expects the relationship to be one of the utmost good faith. The prime responsibility must be to the client to the exclusion of other interests so long as the commission has been accepted and subsists. The RIBA Handbook of Architectural Practice and Management (4th revised edition 1980) talks about the architect's responsibilities to society first and the client second with responsibilities to the profession, the design team, his own organisation and the remainder of the building team bringing up the rear. This is absolute nonsense and while regard may be had to supra-client values in the long term interests of society and the environment they count for nothing if they run counter to the client's instructions and if the client cannot be persuaded to change his mind. The only thing the architect or surveyor can do in these circumstances is to resign. Before taking such a drastic step however he must seriously consider whether by doing so he might be considered in the eyes of the law to be perverse and high handed and if the client suffers loss as a result he may well consider taking action against the architect or surveyor for recovery of that loss.

As far as the law of agency is concerned architects and surveyors in private practice are no different from any other professional person. Solicitors, accountants and engineers are other examples in similar circumstances empowered to set up a contractual relationship between their principal and third parties. The creation of the relationship of principal and agent may be set up either by express appointment on the one hand or by implication of the law on the other which might arise from a number of different circumstances. The relationship may also be established by the subsequent ratification of an unauthorised act. In most cases relating to new building works or substantial conversion and refurbishment works the relationship is a contractual one and the architect or surveyor would be described at law as a special agent, one who is appointed to perform a particular commission after which his authority comes to an end. In the case of surveyors who manage estates of properties for their clients they would be known as general agents since they have a continuous authority not only to collect rents but also in the disbursement of clients' money by arranging and paying for repairs to be carried out. It would probably be the case that the general authority would extend only to effecting routine repairs not major alterations or improvements so that a surveyor would always need to be careful not to exceed that authority. It is quite possible of course, to have both a general agency and a special agency relationship vesting in the same surveyor at the same time when he is both managing the estate and carrying out a major scheme on one particular property on the estate.

Sometimes the relationship of principal and agent can be set up or extended in times of a real emergency concerning a building and where it is impossible to obtain instructions from the owner. Under the doctrine of "agent of necessity" the law will imply that the owner has consented to the creation of an agency in order to allow an architect or surveyor to act so as to prevent a dangerous situation arising. For example if an architect or surveyor was dealing with one of two adjoining houses and a potentially dangerous situation arose from some outside and totally unconnected source, an agency of necessity could be created vis-a-vis the adjoining owner if he was absent and the architect or surveyor took steps to protect both houses at the same time, as he might well need to do, in view of the connection between the two. His own special agency relationship with his client would also of necessity be extended to the extent of the cost of the emergency work needed to the house being worked upon should his own client by chance also be away at the time.

The position of the architect or surveyor as agent so far as third parties, usually the contractors, are concerned, where the building owner is either named or not named on a contract, however formed, is of particular concern in regard to personal liability. Where the architect or surveyor makes it clear that he is acting in the capacity as agent and gives the name or description of his client the general rule is that the agent himself incurs no liability or obligations in the law of contract as distinct from tort. The contract is assumed at law to have been made direct between the client and the builder. What is needed are the words "on behalf of . . ." or "on account of . . ." or "as agent for . . .". When the architect or surveyor instructs a contractor "as agent" but without disclosing the name or description of his client the position is generally the same since he has made it clear that he is not the principal. It is when he gives the instructions merely using his own name and professional qualifications or just adds the one word "agent" more in a descriptive sense as distinct from "as agent" representing a personal capacity that he is in serious danger of having to accept personal liability for the contract should anything go wrong. If the contractor has no way of telling that the architect or surveyor is acting "as agent", the doctrine of the undisclosed principal will apply. Should the contractors have a genuine cause of action they can elect to sue either the architect or the surveyor or the undisclosed building owner if he can be found. The danger to the architect or surveyor is well illustrated by the case of a chartered civil engineer who obtained an estimate for work from contractors and accepted by a letter signed with his own name and qualifications only. When the building owners went bankrupt the contractors were successful in suing the engineer for the price of their work even though they probably knew full well that he was only acting as an agent.[1] The written contract in this case in the form of a letter showed the engineer as principal and that was the determining factor.

A professional man contracting in the above way without disclosing his principal's name or description or that he is acting as agent can harm his principal's interests since if the latter should have a cause of action against the contractor he could only pursue this if the agent's authority existed at the time the contract was made and also if the contract so made was within the terms of and not incompatible with the terms of the agency. If the building owner suffered loss because of this the architect or surveyor could find himself liable.

It is appropriate to mention that there has been a tendency over the years to extend the personal liability of agents even where the agent makes it quite clear that he is contracting on behalf of others. This has affected brokers in a number of the commodity markets and, of course, an auctioneer has for long been responsible for the due performance of the contract for sale even though he, more obviously than most, is an agent. It may not be long before a contractor succeeds against an agent, clearly purporting to contract as such, whose principal goes bankrupt before works are completed on the basis that the agent owed a duty of care to the contractor to ensure that his principal had sufficient funds before entering into the contract on his behalf in the first place. It will be seen later that contractors, wisely, very often investigate the financial status of their customers and there are now very sound reasons why architects and surveyors should do the same whenever there is any doubt about the resources of the client (particularly as, in any event, the fee will be lost, either in whole or in part, if the client does go bankrupt). Obviously, although the fee will not be saved, the personal liability to the contractor might be resisted by insisting that the building owner signs all contracts himself, which most architects and surveyors do require in respect of the larger contracts, so that there is no question of an inducement by the architect or surveyor on the contractor to enter into any contract except at his own risk.

The general principles of an agent's responsibilities to his principal can be summarised at this stage since it will be necessary to relate these in far greater detail to the various proceedings which

---

(1) *Sika Contracts Ltd* v. *B. L. Gill and Closeglen Properties Ltd.* (1978) 9 Building Law Reports 11.

arise during the course of a typical commission and to examine how easy it is for the basic principles to become muddied and confused. The duties and obligations of the agent are:

(a) To exercise due diligence.
(b) To exercise the skill he purports to possess.
(c) To render all accounts as required.
(d) Never to allow his own interests to conflict with those of his principal.
(e) Not to delegate his duties to a sub-agent without express or implied authority.
(f) Not to make use of confidential information obtained during the course of his duties.
(g) To comply with his instructions wherever possible and notify his principal if it is not possible to do so.

Breach of (d) above, where bribery is involved, renders the agreement between principal and agent voidable at the option of the principal.

Not all the duties and obligations are one way and correspondingly the principal has certain duties to his agent which can be summarised as follows:

(a) To pay the remuneration and expenses as agreed or as customary or reasonable in the circumstances.
(b) To indemnify the agent against losses arising from the execution of his authority or in the performance of any unauthorised act subsequently ratified.
(c) To give clear and unambiguous directions.

Even though printed Conditions of Engagement may be used or some other formal written documentation to define the contract between the principal and the agent any of the above items not specifically included would be implied by law. Obviously it is more convenient to use ready printed conditions when these are available and consideration in detail will be given in the next chapter to those currently available for use by architects and surveyors. However before discussing some of the implied terms not usually mentioned in printed conditions it is as well to point out that engagements can be terminated by notice or by revocation in the case of the principal or by notice or renunciation in the case of the agent. Otherwise the agency is terminated on completion of the commission in the case of a special agency for a new building or a major refurbishment or by the expiration of the period stipulated by a contract for a general agency of management. Of course an agency can also be terminated by mutual agreement or may perforce need to be terminated in the case of death, lunacy, or bankruptcy of either principal or agent or dissolution in cases where the principal is a corporation. It can also be terminated by destruction of the subject matter, for example a fire destroying the property being refurbished, or by the contract becoming unlawful. As mentioned, however, summary termination whether by the architect or the principal may be a breach of the contract itself and any loss caused as a result to either party may have to be made good. If no period for notice of termination is stipulated in the contract, "reasonable" notice must be given to avoid such a claim. Reasonable in such circumstances can be very much a matter of argument. If an agent's authority is terminated but he continues to act contractors and suppliers are entitled to assume he is still giving instructions on behalf of the building owner who will continue to incur expenditure until such time as notice of revocation is given to all third parties by the building owner.

Generally, while it is true that the instructions given by an agent are binding upon the principal this always pre-supposes that the agent is acting within his authority. Untold difficulties can arise if this is not so, as already mentioned in regard to personal liability, so that it is obviously vital for there to be an absolutely clear understanding between principal and agent as to the extent of the agent's authority and for the architect or surveyor to be careful to ensure that further authority is obtained when circumstances not envisaged originally are introduced to alter the situation.

While an employed architect or surveyor has not quite the same relationship between himself and his principal as has the architect or surveyor in private practice the concept of agency is still very relevant. While it is to be hoped that wider issues will be taken into account by larger companies, local and central government and the nationalised industries rather than pure self-interest, there is unfortunately no guarantee that this will be the case and indeed many such organisations have been found to be despoilers of the worst kind and to indulge in dictatorial practices that reflect little credit on the officers concerned, pressurised though they may be by directors, councillors and the like. It is for the professional architect or surveyor to weigh up what is required by his client employer and to carry out those instructions only as far as he is able to do so satisfactorily within his own professional concepts of what is right and what is wrong. If he feels that he is being manoeuvred or pressurised into doing something which he feels is incorrect in any one of many possible different ways but also in much the same way as the pressures exerted by a client on a private architect or surveyor, he must first of all endeavour to put his own employer on the right track by persuasion, escalating the matter through to his chief officer

27

if that proves to be necessary. It will be found surprising how many administrators councillors or business executives can be persuaded to change their views provided the architect or surveyor exercises a degree of firmness and tact. Not many employers will deliberately flout the advice of their professional advisers and will often back off surprisingly quickly in such a confrontation, bruised, but without suffering any permanent damage. After all, the professionals are employed to give advice and provided the professionals ensure that they retain that status and do not become mere servants and docile implementers of decisions it will be found that the views and advice will be listened to, accepted and acted upon. On occasions, however, no amount of persuasion will convince the employer of the wrong headedness of his views since he will be determined on a course of action and instruct his professional advisers to put it into effect. The professional can then find himself in a very difficult position. The trouble is that, more often than not, when the course of action has been completed or when it is under way and the accusations are flying about, the particular administrator, councillor or business executive originally involved will have moved on to fresh fields, leaving the finger of scorn or blame to be pointed in the direction of the professional. If he had been in private practice the architect or surveyor may not have considered taking on the job in the first place but if he had done so and the situation had developed unfavourably in this way then he could always have resigned his commission putting up with any financial loss involved. The employed architect or surveyor can of course do this as well by resigning from his employment. This is admittedly a very strong form of protest but a course of action which has been taken on occasions. However unlike the architect or surveyor in private practice the remuneration from the post is probably the only source of income for the employed professional who will not, obviously, have other commissions on hand to provide his livelihood. On the other hand by resigning he will be free to publicise his views, provided these do not clash with any undertaking he may have signed in the past, for example the Official Secrets Act, and will be able to demonstrate his independence of mind. Publication is usually what is feared by people who are up to something with dubious undertones so that often the mere threat of resignation and the warning of future publication is sufficient to bring the offenders to heel. To avoid either the threat or the taking of such an extreme measure as resignation resort is sometimes had to the "inspired leak" as a way of publicising something thought not to be all it should be. For the professional to be the source of such a leak amounts to a breach of faith which is unprofessional in itself. Employers rightly regard this as a breach also of the normal conditions of employment and take a severe view of such happenings. It is no use the professional saying that in some circumstances the end justifies the means because professionals cannot expect to be treated with respect and consideration if they themselves adopt unprofessional practices.

Faced with the determination to proceed and instructions to put matters in hand the architect or surveyor could ask to be transferred to other work but this could only be done in cases where a particular officer holds strong individual views which may not necessarily be shared by others and accordingly there are others who could take his place. However such a difficulty between architects might be referred to the Salaried Practice Advisory and Conciliation Panel in such circumstances which might be able to resolve the issue. If all professionals are agreed then of course the matter will be in the hands of the Chief Officer by this stage. Chief Officers vary of course and indeed some become so divorced from the actual work that they tend to lose their professional outlook. There is a lot to be said in these circumstances for such architects and surveyors to abandon the pretence of being professionals at all and embrace titles and practices more suited to their administrative or managerial functions. If the Chief Officer however retains in full his professional outlook and backs his staff then there will be a major policy dispute within the organisation concerned. It might be appropriate in these circumstances for the dispute to be referred to the associations already mentioned of architects in private companies or local authorities who might be able to assist or alternatively the matter could be referred to either of the professional institutions for advice and possibly support. If total impasse is reached and the professionals are unable, perhaps for financial reasons, to resign then, before matters are implemented in what will amount to a situation of duress, the architects or surveyors will wish to see, as a matter of record, that the dispute is noted officially either, for example, in Council minutes or company minutes and also perhaps in personnel files for future reference if need be if and when any furore arises.

Mention has already been made of the Society of Chief Architects of Local Authorities and its report on the relationship of architects in local authorities with consultant architects. The Society has also joined with the Royal Institution of Chartered Surveyors and the Chartered Institute of Public Finance and Accountancy to produce a useful statement and practical guide dated May 1982 entitled "The Control of Building Projects" covering the role of professional officers in local government. In tabular form the guide sets out the various stages of a building project and describes the involvement of designer, be he architect or surveyor, quantity surveyor and auditor.

It stresses the need for proper checks on procedures and the necessity for reports on progress to committee at appropriate times with a view to avoiding the lack of financial control evidenced in certain local authority projects as ascertained by the Chief Inspector of Audit in 1979. Following the stages and procedures laid down in the guide will provide considerable assistance to the architect or surveyor in establishing and retaining firm control on a project.

Matters of integrity and the utmost good faith extend of course into the relationships between the architect or surveyor and other individuals apart from the client whether in the public or private sector. Neither architect or surveyor can be taking a secret profit out of some relationship unknown to the client or the employer. For example any self interest must be disclosed and any connection by an architect or surveyor with contractors of any sort must be clearly disclosed. Even with disclosure it is better to avoid totally any involvement with firms where the architect or surveyor may have a personal relationship or a relation working therein.

Contractors often wish to show their appreciation of obtaining work from clients by the provision of entertainment or gifts to the architects or surveyors involved. It may seem churlish or even rude to decline such offers and indeed there is probably likely to be no harm at all in the acceptance of such provided they are of reasonable proportions. It is certainly unfair to impute improper motives to all the providers of such entertainment or gifts and the suspicion must be that contractors very often offer because it has been expected of them in the past. It is known that not all like such customs and some contractors of sterner stuff have turned away entirely from the practice. The trouble has always been in deciding what is reasonable and what is not and accordingly it is better in all cases to adopt the view that it is no part of the professional man's life to allow even the possibility of a suggestion of undue influence to enter into it. The same applies to any suggestion of the exercise of influence and this could arise in the case of taking say the local planning officer out to lunch. The architect or surveyor could not in the circumstances even wish it to be thought that this had been done to influence the outcome of a planning application submitted on behalf of the client. This may seem to be a stuffy outlook but on balance the adoption of a cool businesslike arrangement with all contacts is far less likely to lead to difficulties. It remains a fact so far as some contractors are concerned that those offering the most lavish hospitality and the largest gifts are those also most likely to be producing the poorest standards of workmanship and also very probably introducing novel and dubious items into their accounts and expressing the deepest shock when such items are eventually struck out. It should not of course be necessary to indicate that real and substantial departures from the principles of good faith come into the realms of fraud when criminal proceedings may become involved. It is a regrettable fact of life that architects and surveyors have been despatched to gaol not only for taking bribes but for offering them as well. It has been from the bench that the sternest strictures and reminders of professional standards have been laid down, particularly in recent years.

In accepting a commission to arrange for and supervise building work the architect or surveyor accepts a responsibility to exercise sound judgement, to display an adequate degree of competence and to devote sufficient time for the proper completion of the task. As the RIBA booklet Architect's Appointment 1982 puts it at paragraph 3.1 a normal condition to apply to an architects appointment is that "the architect will exercise reasonable skill and care in conformity with the normal standards of the architect's profession". If an architect or surveyor does not consider that he is competent enough to carry out the work envisaged by a particular commission or has insufficient time to do the work properly then he would be ill advised to accept it. This is not to say, of course, that an architect or surveyor is required to know everything about every aspect of the work envisaged before he starts on a commission. It is simply not possible to know everything and it is often necessary to carry out some research as the requirements develop during the course of a commission so as to be able to cope with all the problems as they arise. In assessing whether due competence has been applied on a particular job, should the matter ever be called in question in an action for breach of contract either in the case of an engagement of a private architect or surveyor or in the case of an employee (there is an implied duty in the contract of employment of every professional architect or surveyor that a proper degree of care and skill will be exercised), the Courts would expect to find the standard of an average architect or surveyor. The skill to be expected from a youngster recently out of college but having passed his Test of Professional Competence would not be sufficient but on the other hand neither would the skill of a wily old bird, with forty years of experience behind him in that particular type of work, be required. Accordingly it has often been said in the past that an error of judgement which an ordinary middle aged architect or surveyor, say half way through his career might make may be said to be permissable, without any liability being incurred for the consequences. The danger in this idea, however, lies in trying to show that the error of judgement was one that would be made by an ordinary average architect or surveyor and that is very

31

seldom possible. With hindsight most errors of judgement look just like plain silly mistakes.

The leading case on the standard of care to be expected from professional men is *Bolam* v. *Friern Barnet Hospital Management Committee* (1957) WLR 582 where it was said "the test is the standard of the ordinary skilled man exercising and professing to have that special skill; a man need not possess the highest expert skill; it is well established law that it is sufficient if he exercises the ordinary skill of an ordinary competent man exercising that particular art". Perhaps the restatement of well established law at that time in such phraseology lulled practitioners into thinking that they would be quite safe merely by exercising an ordinary sort of skill but in fact the Courts have paid architects and surveyors the compliment of expecting from them the very highest of standards much in the same way as the public through a period of reasonable affluence and the availability of education have come to expect more of a professional adviser as the years have gone by.

The law is still the same at present as re-stated in the Bolam case and the basic principle has not been altered since by those cases where warranties have been given, either express or implied, to the client as for example in the case of *Greaves and Co. (Contractors) Ltd.* v. *Baynham Meikle and Partners* (1975) 1 WLR 1095.[2] Here contractors engaged by an oil company to erect a warehouse to be used for storing oil drums, which were to be moved around by fork lift trucks, employed engineers (the defendants) to design the structure. Serious cracks developed in the structure due to vibration in use; the contractors had no defence and turned on the engineers on the basis that it was known to them for what purpose the warehouse was to be used and therefore they were liable for the defects (said to cost £100,000 to put right) as it was maintained that there was an implied warranty that their design would be fit for its purpose. The Court was careful to stress that consulting engineers could not be expected to guarantee a correct result every time but in this particular case a warranty could be implied from the facts. Perhaps if the engineers had been brought in just to design the structure of a warehouse for letting they would not have been liable even though most professional engineers, one would have thought, would know that goods were moved around by fork lift trucks nowadays.

As recently as 1980 this principle was upheld in two cases which will be referred to again later for other points of liability. In cases brought by two house owners, a Mr. Balcomb and a Mr. Pethy-

_____

(2) Also reported in the Estates Gazette 20 September 1975 at Page 823.

bridge, against Wards Construction (Medway) Ltd. and Hurst, Pierce and Malcolm a firm of consulting engineers,[3] the possibility of an implied warranty having been given by the consulting engineers was investigated by the Court and rejected since the engineers did not construct or even supervise the construction of the foundations. As it happened the rejection did not help the engineers who were found totally liable for the damage on two other lines of argument.

Accordingly it seems unlikely that the standard of care will be changed since it is long established law and it is interesting to note that it can be extended in the case of building work to designers who are not professionally qualified as exemplified in another High Court case.[4] In this a firm of estate agents, surveyors and valuers employed an architectural draughtsman who prepared plans of a bungalow for a client and for which the firm charged a fee of £31.50 in 1968. The plans showed foundations taken only down to a comparatively shallow depth but the firm were not employed to supervise the work of a local builder who increased the depth of the foundations with the approval of the building inspector. Shortly after occupying the bungalow the owner cut down two elm trees which were very near the house and the subsequent swelling of the soil below the house caused severe damage necessitating partial rebuilding and underpinning in 1973. The judge held that the estate agents were liable for 40% of the damage amounting to £5,591 plus interest of £1,000 for breach of contract and negligence with the builder liable for another 40% and the local authority the remaining 20%.

There is therefore no question of strict liability arising as it does on parts of the continent. The liability is for carelessness and the onus of proof lies with the plaintiff to show that there was some want of care on the part of the professional concerned. However a successful defence to a charge that due skill and competence have not been exercised is difficult, and is likely to require one or both of the following types of argument:

(a) that the matter complained of is so abstruse that hardly anyone other than an expert in that particular field would have known about it.

(b) that when the actions complained of were carried out they were in accordance with general practice at the time.

An example of the first argument is apparent in the case of *B. L. Holdings Ltd.* v. *Robert J. Wood and Partners* (1981)[5] where the Court of

(3) Estates Gazette 5 September 1981 Page 765.
(4) *Oxborrow* v. *Godfrey Davis (Artscape) Ltd., Tompkins, Homer and Ley Ltd. and Tendring District Council.* Architects Journal 14 January 1981 Page 68.
(5) 12 BLR 3.

Appeal reversed the finding of a lower court by concluding that a firm of architects were not liable for negligence arising out of some confusion over the need or otherwise for an Office Development Permit. In 1970 the architects were instructed to design a speculative office building by developers in Brighton to be the most commercially attractive as possible without the need for an Office Development Permit, required at the time for all schemes over 10,000 square feet. The scheme as prepared and built satisfied the criteria only if the parking space and caretaker's flat were excluded from the area calculations. Planning permission had however been granted in 1970 but when the building was completed in 1973 it was suggested that an Office Development Permit was required and if that was so the planning permission obtained earlier was invalid. The offices could not be let as a result and the developers brought an action against their architects for negligence and breach of contract. The Court of Appeal's view was that the architect was not negligent in relying on the local authority officer's statements and the planning permission obtained even though at the time he admitted he thought they might not be correct at law. The Court stated that the architect was entitled to take the view that the Council had discretion in such matters as area calculations and was not negligent in so doing as most architects (and even some lawyers) would do the same in similar circumstances.

Exhaustive search through reported cases has failed to unearth more than one successful use of the second argument which in itself is symptomatic of the difficulty in resisting claims of negligence. However in the case of *Acrecrest Ltd.* v. *W. S. Hattrell and Partners* (1979)[6] referred to again later in regard to other aspects of the law, the Judge considered whether a firm of architects should have been aware of the danger of Dutch Elm disease when designing the foundations of two storey blocks of flats built near elm trees in 1971. The incidence of the disease necessitated the felling of a number of trees after the blocks had been constructed causing the ground to heave upwards as the clay soil expanded with the moisture formerly taken up by the trees. The Judge held that neither the architects nor the local authority inspector could have been expected at that time to foresee soil heave due to the need to cut down trees because of the disease and accordingly could not be found negligent on that account. Nevertheless he found both to be negligent in not providing foundations to a sufficient depth knowing that fruit trees had been cut down over the building site before construction had begun and knowing that there were other trees nearby suggesting a need for foundations throughout the site to a greater depth than normal.

(6) Estates Gazette 15 December 1979 Page 1107.

A defence that work was carried out in accordance with general practice at the time is not an easy one to sustain. If any architect or surveyor utilising novel, or even just fashionable but ill-considered forms of construction, which subsequently proves to be faulty seeks to show that he was not negligent on the grounds that "everyone" was using such techniques at the time he is likely to find himself faced with strong arguments to the contrary. At any particular time there will always be practitioners available to say that they would not have used such methods under any circumstances. Such practitioners will be able to cite many instances where more traditional methods had been used successfully at the time. The contrast between the prudent and successful and the proportion of practitioners who, with hindsight, will have been made to appear almost reckless will not be lost on the court. Furthermore there are always the remarks made by their Lordships in the House of Lords case of *Independent Broadcasting Authority* v. *EMI Electronics Ltd. and BICC Construction Ltd.*[7] to consider. In this case the defendants demonstrated that they had designed a transmitting mast, which subsequently collapsed, to the limits of sophisticated knowledge current at the time but were told that when innovating techniques are used even greater care than normal must be taken.

The difficulties found in resisting claims has resulted in the situation that most claims never indeed reach the Courts and are settled by the insurers to whom most architects and surveyors in the private sector wisely pay substantial premiums for cover against just such an eventuality.

What of claims for want of skill and competence exercised by employees be they of private practice companies, nationalised industries, local or central government where it is thought that the taking out of insurance against claims being made against an individual is comparatively rare? It is not always appreciated by employees that they can be sued in negligence as individuals by any person who suffers loss through their actions. It is usual however for employees to shelter behind their employer and indeed since there is so much a better chance of getting something out of an employer than the employee it is usually the employer who gets sued in fact. However as we have seen the professional man also owes a duty to his employer to exercise care and skill in the performance of his duties and if he does not do so and his employer suffers loss then he can be held liable. That more employers do not pursue actions against the members of staff who let them down badly in this manner is perhaps understandable. Perhaps they do not wish to be considered vindictive employers or perhaps, more realistically, they

(7) 14 BLR 1.

are not too keen on taking the weekly deductions out of salary which is probably the only way they will be able to obtain damages if they are successful in any action. However the principle of liability is well established and it may be that we shall see more such cases in view of the spate of building failures which have occurred and which can be attributed to carelessness and mistakes in design. The case of *Tryer* v. *District Auditor of Monmouth* (1973)[8] is a case demonstrating the principle though it concerned a quantity surveyor. The High Court in that case found that a surcharge of £12,794 imposed by the District Auditor in 1973 to be reasonable on the evidence and refused to grant any relief. It was held that a quantity surveyor employed by the Council had by his negligence and misconduct lost the Council £29,000 by certifying (a function often performed by architects and surveyors on smaller jobs) overpayments to a contractor who subsequently went bankrupt making it impossible for the Council to recover the money other than by way of a small dividend on winding up. The quantity surveyor pleaded heavy pressure of work and that he acted in the position of arbitrator in issuing interim certificates and therefore could not be held liable or alternatively that he had acted reasonably. The Court however could find no merit in either argument or any reason to upset the District Auditor's view that the standard of care exercised by the quantity surveyor fell far below what the Council was entitled to expect from a man with his professional qualification as a chartered surveyor. Bearing in mind that this case was in 1973, if the quantity surveyor was unable to meet the surcharge out of capital and was not insured, he could still well be making payment by instalments.

It is generally overlooked by employees that they should carry insurance to cover any loss suffered by their employer through the employees mistakes or carelessness particularly since as discussed the standard expected of professionals is high and it is so easy for anyone to make an error of judgement which in the eye of the Courts would look like carelessness or a silly mistake. Not many employees do in fact insure mainly because it never seems to occur to them to do so. They practice in the belief that their employer would never sue in such circumstances although the employer might reprimand or discipline them in some other form. Clearly in view of the Tyrer case it would be unwise to rely on this as there must be times when it is the public duty of the employer to take all necessary action to recover a loss. Alternatively another view is often held that to carry insurance would merely encourage the employer to sue and a staff association or Union would help in any event to resist such action. This too seems unwise since a Union would find difficulty in

(8) Estates Gazette 18 May 1974 Page 973.

justifying the expenditure of its funds on defending someone who by that time is probably recognised all round as careless.

It might be thought that the professional bodies would do something about any element of incompetence complained about by lay clients but in fact although both the RIBA and the RICS receive correspondence on this topic from time to time, understandably perhaps, there has been a general reluctance of assembled architects and surveyors to pronounce on the performance of their brethren. It is however worthwhile to look at the Codes of Professional Conduct laid down by the two Institutes to see whether the point is covered at all.

The RIBA Code of Professional Conduct in the edition applicable from 1 January 1981 and reprinted with amendments in December 1981 and June 1982 is a comparatively slim twelve page booklet containing three principles and a number of rules applicable to each coupled with a series of notes. In the preface it is said that the object is to promote the standard of professional conduct or self-discipline in the interest of the public. A typical member of the public might well wish to substitute "the members" instead of "the public" but this would perhaps be less than just in the case of the RIBA Code than it would be with the equivalent code of the RICS, although the latter makes no pretensions similar to the carefully composed phraseology of the three principles in the RIBA Code where a quick read tends to gloss over the true underlying meaning. The three principles set out in the RIBA Code are as follows:

Principle 1

"A member shall faithfully carry out the duties which he undertakes. He shall also have a proper regard for the interests both of those who commission and of those who may be expected to use or enjoy the product of his work."

Under Principle 1 there is a note to the effect that an architect is "advised" to arrange that his resources are adequate and properly directed to carry out any work. Among the rules following this Principle one provides for a written agreement or contract for an architect's services preferably making use of the RIBA Architect's Appointment 1982 to define the terms and another provides that he shall interpret the conditions of a building contract with fairness. Some of this is a bit muddled because when it comes down to brass tacks the architect's duty is to his client and "the proper regard to others" and "fairness" is only applicable when it suits the client otherwise it is inapplicable.

Principle 2

"A member shall avoid actions and situations inconsistent with his professional obligations or likely to raise doubts about his integrity."

This Principle is of course very laudable and follows changes in the Rules of Conduct in 1980 to allow architects to take directorships in companies, for example contracting organisations. The rules include a warning and requirement not to accept bribes or to improperly influence the granting of planning consents or statutory approvals, also, presumably, by the giving of bribes. Declarations are required of self interest which might conflict and if the architect is now to be involved with a company he has to be able to declare that that involvement is subsidiary to his practice as an architect. He must not supervise works as an independent architect if he or his employer is the contractor and neither must he represent any combined contracting and consultancy business as though the latter element purported to be independent. He must not practice with any person disqualified from membership of the RIBA or other professional body. He is given the alternative if conflicting interests do arise of withdrawing, removing the source of conflict or declaring it and continuing only with the full agreement of the parties concerned. The final rule under this Principle requires him not to act in disregard to the professional qualifications of others and requires members who employ other architects to define their conditions of employment, authority, responsibility and liability.

Principle 3

"A member shall rely only on ability and achievement as the basis for his advancement."

The main consequences of this principle embodied in the rules which follow is that the architect must not give bribes to get work, must not quote fees without invitation and furthermore he must not revise his fee quotation to take account of the fee quoted by another architect. A member must not seek to supplant another and there is control on the type of advertising which can be produced, together with a bar on entering architectural design competitions other than those held under RIBA regulations.

The Rules of Conduct of the RICS in the edition first published in 1973 and revised in July 1981 have of course to provide for the various differing disciplines contained within that Institution. Apart from the Rules of Conduct covered by Bye-Laws there are a series of Regulations describing in greater detail some aspects of what is acceptable and what is not in relation to those separate disciplines but none specifically directed to surveyors dealing with building works. In the Rules of Conduct there are none of the fine Principles expressed in the RIBA Code. The Rules of Conduct Bye-Law 24 cover the following items set out here in summary form:

(1) No conduct unbefitting a chartered surveyor.
(2) No connection with any business considered to be incompatible with membership.
(3) Conflicting interests both with a surveyor's own and those with another client for whom he may be acting must be declared.
(4) No practising under limited liability or with a sleeping partner who has all the money.
(5) Will be liable for the actions of his partners or staff if he knew about them.
(6) No offering of gifts to secure work or offering to do work cheaper than another surveyor, pay to others for the introduction of work and no working on the basis that the fee will be related to the success achieved if the work relates to judicial or quasi-judicial proceedings.
(7) No soliciting except to regular clients and then not if it is known that the particular work has been entrusted to someone else.
(8) Keep the client's money separately from the firm's and account properly for it at the due time.
(9) No practising under a name, style or title likely to prejudice the surveyor's professional status or the reputation of the Institution.
(10) Provides a saving clause to the extent that the Bye-Law shall not be construed as restricting a surveyor acting as an estate agent with respect to matters contained in the Restriction on Agreements (Estate Agents) Order 1970, which of course prevented agents selling residential property combining together to agree fees between themselves.

At the time of writing there are proposals in hand to amend the RICS Bye-Laws to the extent of allowing members to compete on the basis of fees.

Anyone can call himself a surveyor and indeed the ordinary member of the public usually has an understandable difficulty in identifying which type of surveyor does what. Also, as discussed, anyone can engage in design and supervisory services for building work on a consultancy basis. Only those registered with the Architects Registration Council of the United Kingdom (ARCUK) established under the Architects (Registration) Act 1931 can however call themselves "architects". The Council has its own Code of Professional Conduct which is similar but not identical to that of the

RIBA to which not all registered architects belong. Not one of the Codes of Professional Conduct, however, say a word about incompetence or even about exercising a due degree of competence and it is of interest to quote from the RIBA Handbook of Architectural Practice and Management some of the main "examples of breaches of the ARCUK Code which the Discipline Committee of ARCUK found to constitute "disgraceful conduct in a professional respect":

(a) Soliciting business.
(b) Soliciting business by means of letters to local authorities.
(c) Accepting hospitality to such an extent that it was likely to affect the judgement of a local authority architect.
(d) Involvement in a firm carrying on business as estate agents and being a substantial shareholder in a building company.
(e) Giving substantial sums of money with a view to the introduction of work.
(f) Taking part as a developer in a project for which he was the architect and thereby his remuneration was not solely by way of fees.
(g) Acting as manager of a company engaged in the development of land.
(h) Being the proprietor, with his wife, of a building company whilst practising as an architect.

An informed cynic from the lay public might with some reason consider much of this trivia, without actually condoning it, when compared with the horrors of foundation failures, leaking roofs, condensation and the like, not to mention aspects of high rise design causing misery to thousands of users. Is this in itself not a more serious breach of say Principle 1 of the RIBA Code than a lot of the other matters described as disgraceful? Yet no one has been reprimanded in relation to such matters even when found by the Courts to be responsible. It is hardly surprising the building professions are held in poor esteem when the members collectively as banded together in professional institutions fail to monitor the competence of their members, rather than describing as disgraceful those items which concern the architects and surveyors as distinct from the public.

Generally it will be observed that the professional organisations take the view that, in the absence of any crime, it is best left to the Courts to establish whether an architect or surveyor has been negligent or not after hearing evidence from experts on the general practice in relation to the matter complained of and of the law. As we shall see later while there is provision in the RIBA Architect's Appointment 1982 and the Conditions of Engagement of the RICS for arbitration on any dispute arising out of an appointment made under the Conditions of Appointment or Engagement respectively it is unlikely that any client taking legal advice on a matter of negligence would be allowed by his solicitor to permit the matter to proceed before an arbitrator.

In Chapter 4 an outline will be provided of the various aspects of the law governing building works which need to be considered on most projects, in particular on the typical job envisaged by this book. Failure to make such consideration may amount to negligence in relation to the commission and give rise to a claim for loss in breach of contract between the architect or surveyor and his client. What must not be forgotten nowadays, however, is that the architect or surveyor's duty extends to other parties who may suffer damage and with whom the architect or surveyor has no contractual relationship.

Not only have the Courts, encouraged by the increased availability of insurance over the last twenty years or so, tended to accept the proposition that practically any mistake made by architects or surveyors to which loss can be attributed amounts to carelessness or negligence for which the architect or surveyor will be liable to pay compensation, they have also widely extended the range of people who can claim such compensation and the period of time over which such a claim can be made. At one time the architect or surveyor was only thought to be liable to his client in contract for not performing what he undertook to do but the law of tort has now become so extended that it has become increasingly difficult to find someone to whom the architect or surveyor does not owe a duty of care. If anyone is injured either physically or financially as a result of an architect or surveyor's mistake or carelessness then it is likely that he would have a good cause of action for compensation. This could be a subsequent owner of a building who need have taken no trouble to have a survey carried out under the principle of caveat emptor, (let the buyer beware), a tenant, an adjoining owner, some person or an organisation that lends money on the security of the property or a passer by. The list is almost endless and the Courts have given little sympathy to pleas that the damage or injury to the person or organisation concerned was too remote and not reasonably in contemplation or forseeable. It is commonly held by the Courts for example that since properties change hands, are let, are invariably used as security for loans, such happenings or occurrences are all forseeable to anybody doing work on or having a responsibility in relation to buildings, be they contractors, local authority inspectors as well as architects or surveyors.

The case which really changed the law was *Hedley Byrne and Co. Ltd.* v. *Heller and Partners Ltd.* (1963) 2 All ER 575. Up to that time actions in negligence could not succeed if the act complained of consisted of an expression in words as opposed to deeds, or the outcome produced a financial loss as opposed to physical damage. It made no difference that the negligent person knew that others might rely on his advice or that he knew or ought to have known that the advice was wrong. That case concerned a reference by bankers given recklessly so that the aggrieved party suffered loss and its outcome changed the law to the extent that if someone who provides written advice knows or ought to have known that reliance will be placed on that advice he will be liable if it is shown to be made without due care and financial or physical loss is suffered as a result.

Rumblings of what might be in store for professional architects and surveyors came very soon after the Hedley Byrne case. In a case the year before *Clayton* v. *Woodman and Sons (Builders) Ltd.* (1962) 1QB 533, the Court of Appeal had found a builder alone liable for the absence of adequate timbering when a workman was injured on site but a year later, after the Hedley Byrne decision, came to quite a different conclusion in the case of *Clay* v. *Crump and Sons Ltd.* (1963) 1QB 533.[9] On that occasion the architect was found to be 42% liable, the demolition contractor 38% and the workman's employers 20% by the Court of Appeal after a wall, which had purposely been left standing after demolition of the remainder of the premises, collapsed. It was said that the architect ought reasonably to have foreseen that the builder's workmen would be affected by his carelessness in ordering the wall to be left as it was.

Furthermore with only his client to think about an architect or surveyor until quite recently could throw away his plans and specification and file papers safe in the knowledge that once six years had elapsed he was secure from any claims in regard to any mistakes he might have made in any particular commission for a new building or the refurbishment of an old building. If the property on which the work had been carried out was sold by his client before the six years had elapsed then it was possible to put the papers away even earlier since a subsequent owner would have no possible action in contract and no cause of action in tort unless there had been an element of fraud and concealment of bad work originally to the extent of preventing a new owner from even knowing that there was anything wrong. This happy situation on the time aspect came about through the passing of section 26 of the Limitation Act 1939 which barred any action brought by an aggrieved party if his cause of action accrued more than six years before the issue of the writ in cases of breach of contract or an action in tort. This provision in the

(9) Also reported in the Estates Gazette 21 September 1963 Page 835.

Act had been framed with the idea of preventing the Courts becoming clogged with stale actions but it also came to be thought by some as a way whereby a wrongdoer could escape the consequences of his action provided nobody noticed anything wrong for six years. The Courts have now shown that even with the law as it is this idea was quite wrong. Although section 26 of the 1939 Act has been carried forward as section 32 of the Limitation Act 1980 and therefore the law is still the same, the Courts fairly quickly recognised the injustice of cases where the six year period had run out before the plaintiff even knew a wrong had been done to him and for this reason developed the notion of a "concealed fraud" particularly on building work in regard to the way foundations had been formed and reinforcement had been placed in concrete.

With the law of contract as it stands with a six year limitation period it is usually a simple matter to determine when the cause of action "accrued" because that is when the architect or surveyor made the mistake so that a building owner has to move within the six years of that happening if he wishes to sue his professional adviser under the contract. It is when it comes to dealing with the tort of negligence that the Courts have gradually extended both the range of people who must be considered to be owed a duty of care by the architect or surveyor and have widened the earlier interpretations of when "the cause of action accrued". Accepting, as must now be the case, that any professional man who gives advice on the safety of buildings or materials owes a duty to all who may suffer injury or loss in the event of that advice being bad[10] the Courts have considered arguments as to whether the cause of action should accrue either at:

(a) The time when the wrongful act took place.
(b) The time when the plaintiff suffered damage or
(c) The time when he knew or should have known that he had suffered damage as a result of the wrongful act.

Since, particularly on commissions for work concerning new buildings, a considerable amount of construction which could ultimately effect the new building's stability is promptly covered up it is perhaps not surprising that most of the cases which have led to developments in the law have involved settlements attributed to foundation failure often some considerable time after completion. Indeed in the Dutton case referred to in the footnote on this page the

---

(10) As per Lord Denning in *Dutton* v. *Bognor Regis Urban District Council* (1972) 1 QB 373 following the decision of *Hedley Byrne and Co.* v. *Heller and Partners* (1963) 2 All ER 575.

house in question was built on a rubbish tip and although no architect or surveyor was involved it was held that the damage was done and the wrongful act took place when the foundations were badly constructed and accordingly the cause of action by Mrs. Dutton against the Local Authority whose building inspector had passed the foundations ran from that date, not later when the cracks became manifest. As it happens Mrs. Dutton was out of time but to back his view Lord Denning quoted an earlier case of *Baggot* v. *Stevens Scanlon and Partners* (1966) 1 QB 197 where it was held that a firm of surveyors were not liable for negligent supervision of drainage work when the cause of action in contract was brought over seven years after the drains were laid. In the Dutton case Lord Denning also considered whether the builder who formed the defective foundations of the house was also liable in the same way as the building inspector and came to the conclusion that the building inspector could not be liable unless it was held that the builder was liable in the first place. Accordingly if the builder had still been involved in the action he too would have been held liable but as it happened Mrs. Dutton had already settled her claim against the builder outside the Court action, possibly for a sum much smaller than the Court would have awarded.

Three years later Lord Denning in 1976, had, after much thought and discussion with his fellow judges, changed his views in the case of *Sparham-Souter and Others* v. *Town and Country Developments (Essex) Ltd. and Another* (1976) 1 QB 858.[11] In this case it was alleged that the foundations were inadequate to support the load of houses completed in 1965. Cracks appeared about two to three years after completion and the Court held that the limitation period ran from the date when the damage was discovered or ought reasonably to have been discovered (situation (c) on the previous page). This change of view by the Court of Appeal enabled the case of *Anns* v. *The London Borough of Merton* (1978) AC 728[12] which had just been decided by the Court of Appeal on the basis of the earlier Dutton case and which had effectively deprived owners of maisonettes, built in 1962 over an old cellar which had been filled with uncompacted rubble, of any cause of action because the cracking did not begin to appear until 1970, to proceed for decision by the House of Lords. The highest Court in the land then proceeded to confirm the views expressed on the liabilities of builders and building inspectors in the Dutton case and seemed to agree with the decision given on the Sparham-Souter case in the Court of Appeal that the limitation

(11) Also reported in the Estates Gazette 29 January 1977 Page 309.
(12) Also reported in the Estates Gazette 13 and 20 August 1977 at Pages 523 and 591.

period for such cases should run from when the damage was discovered. Lord Denning had said "the only person to sustain the damage was the man who owned the house at the time when the house sank and the cracks appeared. It is only at that time that he can be reasonably expected to know that he has a cause of action . . . it may seem hard on the builder or the council's surveyor that he may find himself sued many years after he left the works but it would be harder on the householder that he should be without remedy."

The only puzzling thing about the above sane and sensible statement is that it had taken so long to appear and to effect a change in the law and, in fact, to bring it in line with long established law in Scotland. It is quite evident that until recently the scales have been weighted heavily against the owners of property which developed cracks due to the mistakes and carelessness of designers, builders and local authority inspectors. The alteration in the Court's view however is in line, although somewhat belatedly, with numerous other changes and social developments. Many privileges created by self interest have been rightly whittled away over recent years.

Further cases since have only confirmed the impression that no holds are barred when it comes to a struggle for redress. A case, *Batty and Another* v. *Metropolitan Realisations Ltd. and Others* (1978) 1 QB 554, 2 All ER 445[13] concerning a house built on an unstable hill in 1971 considered to be unsaleable following movement in 1974 found the owner successfully suing the vendors, who were the developers, in contract for breach of warranty and in tort for negligence and the builders for negligence in tort for the full replacement value with costs plus an extra sum to cover the wife's distress, put at £250.

In another case *Acrecrest Ltd.* v. *W. S. Hattrell and Partners and Another*[14] involving flats built in 1972 on a clay soil where trees had been felled and where the ground subsequently became swollen and heaved upwards, the freehold owners successfully sued the architects for the cost of repairs.

The architects in turn sought to associate the local authority as being responsible by approving the plans. They were however only partly successful to the extent of recovering 25% of the damages, it being held that the building inspector only had a limited expertise and was by no means on a par with a civil engineer, architect or surveyor.

Yet a further case, *Eames London Estates Ltd. and Others* v. *North Hertfordshire District Council and Others*[15] shows the extent to a greater

(13) Also reported in the Estates Gazette 1 April 1978 Page 43.
(14) Estates Gazette 15 December 1979 Page 1107.
(15) Estates Gazette 8 August 1981 Page 491.

degree than earlier cases of who can sue and who can be sued. The case concerned an industrial building designed by an architect and built in 1965 to his specification but on ground of variable consolidation with the result that it started to settle at different rates in 1971 but alarmingly so by 1976. The original developers had retained the freehold until 1973 when they had sold it to the first plaintiffs, the second plaintiffs being the original tenants who were still in occupation. The two plaintiffs sued the original developers, their architect, the builder and the local authority. As one commentator has put it, the buck in cases of this nature is not to be passed but to be divided up between the negligent parties, in this action to the extent of $22\frac{1}{2}$% each with the exception of the architect who had $32\frac{1}{2}$% awarded against him. It was said that the architect who had specified the loading on and the design of the foundations could not waive liability on the basis that the local authority had agreed with him. The developers were under a duty on a warranty, following on from the Dutton and Batty cases to ensure the land was satisfactory for the proposed development and were not excused because they employed an architect. The builders who were also strictly liable for breach of statutory duty in accordance with the decision in the Anns case, because it is the builder's duty to comply with the Building Regulations, were also liable in negligence for continuing to lay foundations when they should have realised the danger and were not excused because they acted on the instructions of the architect or that their work was approved by the building inspector. A further interesting feature was that it was held that a company could sue even though the Building Regulations are intended to protect human health and safety. On the aspect of the limitation period a further extension of the period was gained to the extent that while cracks became apparent in 1971 it was not until 1976 that the actual cause was determined and accordingly it was held that the cause of action accrued when reasonable skill and diligence determined that symptoms which had begun to appear earlier really were serious.

Of course what we do not learn from the reported cases was what subsequently might happen to the parties. For example in the Eames case the action was brought by the current owners and tenants of the factory but, arising out of that, it is found that the original developer has suffered loss through the negligence of his architect, as also proved in the course of the action, and the builder also through following the instructions of the architect. Adding the $22\frac{1}{2}$% of the damages awarded against each of these parties to the $32\frac{1}{2}$% awarded to the architect would make the architect liable for a total of $77\frac{1}{2}$% which would no doubt have to be paid out to compensate the developer and the builder for their loss since the architect would have no possible defence. Similar circumstances arose in two cases where house owners, a Mr. Balcombe and a Mr. Pethybridge, sued the developers, Wards Construction (Medway) Ltd.[16] and civil engineers employed by them, of two houses which they had bought on an estate in 1972. These houses required substantial repair in 1974 but by the time the action was brought were considered worthless due to the soil below the foundations swelling following the clearance of trees. The builders admitted liability under contract but the Judge went on to find the civil engineers also liable for breach of contract to the developers, for failing to exercise professional skill, and also in tort for breach of duty of care. The engineers were also found liable in tort to the house owners and as, furthermore, he found there to be no contributing negligence by the builders, the civil engineers were held liable for all the damages and costs. It was mentioned in the course of the hearing that another eight houses were in a similar state because of the lack of deep foundations and it must be assumed therefore that following the outcome of the Balcombe and Pethybridge cases the civil engineers would be expected to reimburse the owners of those houses for their loss. It is not therefore really surprising that some clients insist upon their professional advisers being insured because they are concerned that there should be sufficient resources to provide compensation to them in case the need should arise.

It is partly at the instance of the Secretary of State for the Environment that the Law Reform Committee, through its Sub-Committee on Latent Damage, is considering at the time of writing the law regarding negligence claims involving latent defects and the limitation period because of the possible liability of local authorities, many years hence, for the actions of their building inspectors. No doubt there has also been some pressure from professional bodies because, of course, limitation periods affect professional people other than architects or surveyors likely to be caught up in negligence claims and there is no doubt that professional people feel highly exposed and unsettled at the possibility of being sued by all and sundry up to and even beyond the grave in time. On the other hand from the consumer's point of view such pressures sound like special pleading for there is every reason to suppose that the public fully supports the Courts in gradually tipping the balance away from the unreasonable advantages which professionals, who had been careless, previously enjoyed. The public might well say that professional architects and surveyors need have no worry about

(16) Estates Gazette 5 September 1981 Page 765.

claims if they did their work properly and did not make mistakes and, anyway, they can always insure. The last point however overlooks the fact that the cost of insurance is considerable and is an overhead to a practice, the cost of which has to be covered by the fees charged eventually to the client.

Renewed pressure is likely to be brought upon the Law Reform Committee to produce a sensible recommendation on the limitation period, and for the Government to act upon it, now that the House of Lords[17] has recently clarified its view on the decision it reached in the Anns case discussed on Page 44. The House has now stated that the limitation period, as the law stands at the end of 1982, runs from the date the cracks appeared (situation (b) on Page 43), not when it is believed that the cracks are a result of a negligent action, as had previously been thought and on which basis cases subsequent to Anns had been decided. This clarification, and the decision flowing from it, has harshly deprived plaintiffs of their remedy against consulting engineers, because the plaintiffs took two years to establish that cracks, which had appeared in a chimney, were the result of a negligent act and not due to other causes. Those two years made all the difference between success and failure and since the plaintiffs had no way, it appears, of knowing, during that period, that the cracks were the result of a negligent act, it is hardly surprising that there are now even more urgent calls for a positive legislative ruling on the subject before their Lordships reach yet another decision.

Professional architects and surveyors sometimes cite continental practice where, in France for example, developers designers and builders all warrant new buildings for just ten years from construction date but are held strictly liable for structural and weatherproofing defects within that time without the need for the aggrieved party to prove negligence or other fault against the other parties to the contract. Insurance is compulsory by law for the benefit of the owner by the payment of a single premium on completion, which obviates the danger to the owner which may arise from liquidation by any of those who may be responsible for defects. Accordingly if something should go wrong the owner has immediate access to finance to make good his loss. The unravelling of responsibilities can then take its course through the Courts or by arbitration and the damages paid out to the owner under the insurance policy apportioned among the insurers of those found responsible for the damage and loss.

Since English Courts have almost got round to the notion of strict

(17) Pirelli General Cable Works Ltd v. Oscar Faber and Partners (1982).

liability in regard to errors made by architects and surveyors, despite the protestation that the law remains unchanged, there might be some advantages in adopting the continental system provided insurance costs came down as well. They might just do so since operating a "claim" insurance, as is done now, involving the need for extensive investigation to establish liability, is much more expensive than merely investigating a loss to establish whether it is genuine or not. However the ten year period is thought by many to be much too short to provide a really worthwhile benefit to owners even although the National House Building Council operates a similar insurance scheme for the purchasers of new houses from builder members of the Council, although from the third to the tenth year this cover is limited to major defects in the load bearing structure and there is an upper limit on the amount which can be claimed. Perhaps twenty years would be better since, as will have been observed from the cases quoted, it can take some considerable time to establish the full extent of serious defects.

Insurance of the type available in France is obtainable in this country but, just as in France before such insurance is granted, the insurance company has to be satisfied with the proposed design and details of construction and will of necessity inspect the works during their progress either with its own staff or utilising consultants appointed for the purpose. Obviously, since the scheme is not in general vogue here, costs are high. In France the scheme is much more sophisticated and there is an organisation providing technical advice to insurers on construction matters and relating methods of construction to premiums, somewhat similar to the Fire Offices Committee in this country which has its own Fire Insurers Research and Testing Organisation for testing the fire resisting period of various materials and components. In this manner innovatory methods and proprietary products are certified before they will be accepted for insurance cover. Short term cover can be obtained in France for new methods of construction pending evaluation. Experience in this country has shown that even methods recommended by the worthiest of bodies are not necessarily good long term solutions to problems and no doubt the French have found the same thing to be true. At least, however, the risk is then carried fair and squarely by the insurers after their evaluation is complete and they are, after all, in business for just that purpose. The risk is not carried by an innocent owner unaware of what has been done or by a hard pressed architect or surveyor perhaps trying to be just too original.

A step towards the compulsory insurance of professionals would be logical for the legislature to initiate. Past Governments have found it possible to require compulsory third party insurance for drivers and obligatory insurance for employers and it would not be difficult to require such insurance for all those providing services in the field of design for buildings. Coupled perhaps with a move towards strict liability, insurance might prove to be cheaper since those practising members who are not insured now would be brought in. These at present do not get sued if they make a mistake for the simple reason that aggrieved parties would not find it worthwhile. That does not, however, alter the fact that such practitioners do nothing to enhance the reputation of the professions dealing with building unless they can put their hands on their hearts and say they never make a single mistake. Perhaps some can but it is very doubtful.

Compulsory insurance seems a much more likely trend for the future than say the idea of private practices becoming limited liability companies. This is no real help since although the company as such may escape liability it is unlikely that the individual concerned would escape if he was negligent, particularly if any action against him was found in tort. Similarly endeavouring to place exclusion clauses in contracts of engagement, besides risking contravention of the Unfair Contract Terms Act 1977, would normally be resisted and indeed thought of derisively by prospective clients. Furthermore even if agreed they would provide no protection in an action in tort.

Generally it is thought unlikely that any proposal for going back on the now newly established rights of third parties would be successful. More likely there will have to be easier arrangements for access to compensation, as on the continent, where as we have seen this involves a scheme of compulsory insurance. This in turn will mean that insurers will have to become more closely involved in controlling standards of construction. Universal application of this idea to all new building and major refurbishment and improvement work as distinct from simple renewal or repair leads almost logically to the withering away of much of the building control work currently in the hands of local authorities who could perhaps merely be concerned with siting, along with space and environmental standards. Even these latter items could be dealt with by the designer certifying to the insurance company that the building complies. In this way the system maintained by local authorities in controlling building work could vanish, to be replaced by certification and insurance, the cost of which would fall entirely on those wishing to build. Similarly the current liability incurred by local authorities in their statutory duty to consider whether foundations should be inspected will be neatly transferred to others. Cries that such a proposal would provide an even more inhibiting factor to architectural freedom of expression than the current system of building control could safely be ignored in view of the present control systems past failure to curb such expression and innovatory construction for the ultimate benefit of all the users. What needs to be stated, and which those who complain loudest about the extent of architects and surveyors liability do not seem to always appreciate, is that such liability would not arise if mistakes were not made so frequently. Mistakes cannot always be avoided even in the best of regulated systems and the incidence of some is probably inevitable. The trouble is that there have been far too many over the last few decades and building owners and taxpayers have suffered vast losses with sometimes little redress being available. A substantial increase in the standard of competence coupled with ready redress by ease of access to insurance seems to be the course most likely to be successful for both the building professions and owners.

Nothing has been said so far of the possible liability of an architect or surveyor under the Defective Premises Act 1972. The Act concerns building work in dwellings and Section 1 of the Act states that it is the duty of a person taking on the work of providing a dwelling, be he builder or developer to see that it is completed in a workmanlike manner so that it will be fit for habitation. Other provisions extended rights of action for defective building work of any sort causing injury to persons, to subsequent owners and others who might be affected and made landlords more liable for defects in their premises. This was the response of the legislature to the spate of defects in houses put up by private developers and builders which came to light in the 1960's together with defects in other buildings. To date however it has not been pleaded very frequently in reported cases dealing with defects for the simple reason that the Court's extension of liability and the adjustments made to the limitation periods since the Act was passed has enabled easier redress to be obtained under the normal common law rights of an aggrieved party in contract or tort. Furthermore redress under the Act is not available when schemes approved by the Secretary of State for the Environment to provide a guarantee for work is available to purchasers and the NHBC scheme comes in this category. Perhaps the time has come for a new Act to take account of the developments which have taken place in this field of law since the Act was passed and which have resulted in it being overtaken by events.

Chapter 2
Conditions of Engagement

CONTENTS

CLIENTS with their desirable and not so desirable characteristics have been considered and the basic responsibilities of architects and surveyors to clients in both the private and public sectors have now been discussed in the widest sense. It is now necessary to look at how the duties and responsibilities might be defined in relation to a specific job as between architect or surveyor and private client, a section of this book which relates for obvious reasons only to architects or surveyors in private practice, not to those in employment. In the case of the latter the client is "captive" and the conditions of engagement are to be found in the contract of employment and such administrative regulations and requirements as are made by the particular organisation concerned. The basic importance of the fee as being central to the contract does not appear in the same sense as exists for the private practitioner, although, as we shall see, the concept of notional fees is increasingly used to measure the cost effectiveness of employed staff, i.e. how much does it "cost" the employer in salaries, overheads and national insurance payments to have work carried out by staff as against the employment of consultants.

For the simplest of jobs, say for example, where an individual company or local authority owns a property now requiring repair and perhaps a small element of renewal, the owner or a representative of the owning organisation may approach an architect or surveyor either by letter or telephone and ask what his charges would be to inspect, prepare details of the necessary work, obtain competitive estimates, place an order, supervise the work and settle the account. To a member of the Royal Institution of Chartered Surveyors such a request would pose no problems and could be confirmed as to the duties to be undertaken and the fee quoted in accordance with Scale 33 of the Scale of Professional Charges for Building Surveying Services in the 1981 edition, published by the Institution, at a recommended 10% on the amount expended on the work or at an hourly rate if that method of charging was preferred, merely by letter. Provided all went well it is not thought that any difficulty should arise since on receipt of instructions to proceed from the client a valid contractual relationship would subsist. If matters did go awry then the Courts would need to hear evidence on the customary way in which such contracts are performed and would imply any other conditions, not mentioned in the exchange of correspondence, provided they were reasonable to both parties and the Court considered them necessary for the proper completion of the work.

It will be noted that only a member of the RICS has been mentioned in the above paragraph. This is because there is clearer guidance in the printed Conditions of Engagement for Building Surveying Services in the 1981 edition published by the RICS than in the RIBA Architect's Appointment which since 1 July 1982 has replaced the former mandatory conditions published by the Royal Institute of British Architects. A member of the RIBA, on receiving a request of the above nature, would have to negotiate a fee on a time basis or alternatively negotiate a percentage fee, perhaps based on the recommended sliding scale for repairs and alterations according to the classification of the building and the likely cost of the work. Since architects are no longer required by their professional body to follow printed Conditions of Engagement in every eventuality it does seem sensible for all architects and surveyors services in relation to building works to be carried out now on a comparatively uniform basis. Accordingly it is wise for both architects and surveyors to treat the guidance of both professional bodies as a basis for general use and to limit variations from the normal conditions to very exceptional cases. They are in fact very similar in character and this course is indeed recommended by both the Royal Institute of British Architects and the Royal Institution of Chartered Surveyors.

Obviously all practising architects and surveyors must be in possession of the latest edition of guidance on appointments or engagements at all times for dissemination to clients. All remarks, however, must be considered as referring to the editions mentioned above. The RIBA Architect's Appointment and the RICS Conditions as mentioned above are broadly similar particularly when dealing with work of a similar character although the RICS Conditions are considerably fuller in scope since, of course, they cover the far greater range of services provided by building surveyors.

In relation to building works to both existing and for new buildings both the RIBA Architect's Appointment and the RICS Conditions provide for Work Stages and these will be discussed in greater detail as the study of professional practice for building works progresses from inception to completion. What requires stressing to the client at this stage are the General Conditions to obtain his agreement both to these and to the arrangement for charging. Many clients will not know the first thing about either and accordingly there is not an atom of use in the RICS set of Conditions stating that the Conditions will apply unless otherwise agreed if the client has never even seen them and does not even know of their existence.

Both the RIBA Architect's Appointment and the RICS Conditions devote three to four pages to general matters, and it is possible to discern agreement between the two on what constitutes the general responsibilities. It is now fortunate, in a booklet intended to be handed to clients, that the new RIBA Architect's Appointment no longer starts off with remuneration as did the former mandatory Conditions of Engagement. The former placing of this item merely fueled the cynical idea amongst certain sections of society that the first thing a professional man thinks about when he sees a client is the fee. Be that as it may, both the RIBA Architect's Appointment and the RICS Conditions generally agree on the extent of the responsibilities of architects and surveyors in relation to building works though here and there there are some surprising differences.

Client's Authority

The RIBA Architect's Appointment states that the architect must have the authority of his client before initiating any service or Work stage. However the RICS Conditions in the 1979 edition merely stated that "the surveyor shall be deemed to have the authority of the client to give all necessary instructions for the proper performance of the service required by the client". The former is surely correct and it is a significant that the 1981 edition of the RICS Conditions omitted this sentence and substituted words to the effect that the surveyor's responsibility (not "authority") depends on the scope of the service provided, on the detailed instructions and the general circumstances of the relationship. It is easy to see what could happen if a client allowed a surveyor such freedom as expressed in the 1979 edition of the Conditions. For example if a client wished to convert a house into three flats and instructed a surveyor to arrange for the work to be carried out and the surveyor promptly did so at vast expense without further reference to the client, it could only be expected that the client would pay a reasonable sum to do the work not a sum inflated by some madcap scheme. As we shall see a client's specific authority is an essential requirement before proceeding on every stage of work which involves expenditure for the client either for building work or fees.

Modifications

Both the RIBA Architect's Appointment and the RICS Conditions require the client to be consulted and his approval obtained before any "material" or "major" changes in the approved design relating specifically to design, cost or construction programme are made. The question may well arise, of course, as to what is "material" or "major" in particular circumstances. It is implied in the RIBA

Architect's Appointment that some modifications can be made without reference and even that major modifications can be made "during construction for constructional reasons" provided the client is informed without delay. In the RICS Conditions the surveyor shall have the client's authority for making such modification as he deems necessary provided no material change in design, no cost increase or time taken on the works is thereby occasioned. Again there is the word "material" which will have different meanings to different people and accordingly it is considered sensible for all architects and surveyors to refer *all* changes in design and all variations which involve an increase in costs or a lengthening of the contract time to the client for approval unless some prior arrangement, say an upper limit on cost variations, has been agreed in writing with the client. It can be a salutory experience to be left holding the bill for an unauthorised extra pressed, by the contractor and ignored by the client, however necessary it may have been in the architect or surveyor's view for the proper completion of the works. Chapter 11 will discuss the arrangements to be made while works are in progress to eliminate such a possibility arising.

Inspections

Both the Architect's Appointment and the RICS Conditions make requirements that architects and surveyors make "visits at intervals appropriate to the stage of construction" or "periodic" inspections of work in progress, not "exhaustive" or "continuous" or "frequent" or "constant" inspections. If the latter are required by the client or by the size or nature of the work provision is made for the appointment of a resident architect or surveyor or a Clerk of Works whose costs shall be met by the client but who will be under the control of the architect or surveyor. As discussed in greater detail in Chapter 11, the word "periodic" will have different meanings to different people as will the period of "appropriate" intervals between inspections and does not comprise an adequate description of what is in fact required to protect the client's interests. A shrewd client may well require the word "periodic" to be amplified in advance. Other clients can become obsessive about the frequency of inspections particularly if they themsleves are either living or working in another part of the same building and can see and, what is often worse, hear what is going on. Invariably such clients consider the number of inspections being carried out by the architect or surveyor inadequate.

Depending on the character and size of the job the requirement on inspections to protect the client's interests will vary considerably. In the typical jobs envisaged in this book a combination of detailed inspections at set stages before work is covered up and spot random checks at irregular intervals is required. "Periodic" tends to give the impression of, say, a once weekly visit at a set time and that would be totally insufficient to protect the client's interests in the vast majority of cases. In this respect the new RIBA Architect's Appointment gives a better impression with its reference to "the architect will visit at intervals appropriate to the stage of construction" but even so is not ideal.

Specialists and Consultants

Both the RIBA Architect's Appointment and the RICS Conditions rightly point out that the normal services of architects and surveyors do not extend to quantity surveying, structural, civil, mechanical or electrical engineering, heating and ventilating engineering or similar specialist consultant's services. The RIBA Architect's Appointment says "the architect will advise on the need for independent consultants" but the RICS Conditions only state "the surveyor may". The RIBA Architect's Appointment is more forthright in requiring that the architect shall have the authority to co-ordinate and integrate their work, however employed, but states that they should be nominated by either party with the agreement of the other but can be appointed and paid by the client or by the architect on behalf of the client. This is undoubtedly a more straightforward arrangement and the RICS Conditions, while saying nothing about nomination or approval by the surveyor, only that he deems it necessary for such appointments to be made, also envisages appointments being made in this way. The 1981 RICS Conditions now accept the surveyor's responsibility for the direction and integration of consultants work whereas the 1979 edition made no mention of this. One would have thought it must surely have been the responsibility of a consultant when appointed direct to see that his work integrated with that of the architect or surveyor and to accept responsibility to the client for this aspect of his work but this was not always the case in the past. Both the RIBA and the RICS now make it clear where the responsibility for such co-ordination and integration should lie regardless of how such consultants are appointed. Neither architects or surveyors however accept responsibility for the design, competence, inspection or performance of the work entrusted to the consultant.

Both the RIBA Architect's Appointment and the RICS Conditions, as to be expected, are united by way of indicating that, whether the specialist service is available from within the particular architect or surveyor's practice or not, the fees will be extra. The RIBA Architect's Appointment also provides that the fees will be those of the relevant professional body to the extent that if provided from within a single firm they shall be the sum of the appropriate fees for the individual professional services rendered.

A particular point to make here is that there is no abatement of the architect's or surveyor's fee on account of the employment of specialist consultants, a point which on occasions causes some surprise to clients. In the client's view this amounts to double charging in that a percentage of the total cost is payable to the architect or surveyor with another fee on the cost of the specialist's work, included in the total cost, payable to the consultant. The argument for charging in this way is that the architect or surveyor has had the task of integrating the consultant's services which function justifies the charge. It must be left to the discretion of individual architects and surveyors whether they wish to follow this practice or to adjust their fee to reflect a reduction, either in whole or in part, in the total cost of the project equivalent to the total cost of the specialist's work, a procedure which is by no means uncommon.

Specialist sub-contractors and Suppliers

Both the RIBA Architect's Appointment and the RICS Conditions mention the possible recommendation by the architect or surveyor of specialist sub-contractors and suppliers for design and execution of part of the work. There is a divergence, however, between the two in that the RIBA Architect's Appointment provides for the architect to be responsible for co-ordination and integration but not for the detailed design, proper execution or performance of the work entrusted to the specialist sub-contractors or suppliers and accordingly there is no responsibility for inspecting the quality. The RICS Conditions on the other hand while agreeing on the latter aspect of disclaimer and also on the responsibility for integration or direction, although this is phrased as being through the main contactor, provides for the surveyor to be responsible for monitoring the work in the same way as the work of the main contractor.

It is interesting to note however that on this occasion the architects fee under the RIBA Architect's Appointment is abated to the extent of being charged on the total construction cost less any nominated sub-contractors design fees for work on which consultants would otherwise have to be employed. If such fees are not known the architect is to estimate a suitable reduction from the total construction cost.

Copyright

Copyright is, on balance, of more importance to architects than it is to surveyors and appropriately more paragraphs are devoted to this subject in the RIBA Architect's Appointment than in the Conditions of Engagement published by the RICS. Generally unless otherwise agreed the copyright in all drawings, specifications and documents prepared by architects or surveyors and the work executed from them remain the property of the architect or surveyor concerned. The RICS Conditions have an addition concerning the exception for designs prepared for the Crown as provided in the Copyright Act 1956 which used to appear in the pre-1982 Conditions and which, although not mentioned now, applies to all architects and surveyors as well as everyone else. The RIBA Architect's Appointment also provides for circumstances where partial services only are supplied, including the case where the client wishes to build the design but does not require detailed design, tenders or supervision.

Delay and Changes in Instructions

Both the RIBA Architect's Appointment and the RICS Conditions make provision for changes and any resultant delay but in a slightly different form. In the RICS Conditions "changes or delays in instructions by the client and delays arising from the bankruptcy or liquidation of the contractor, delays in construction or any other matter beyond the surveyor's control which cause additional work or expense to the surveyor may give rise to an additional fee". The RIBA Architect's Appointment provides for additional charges for a few more reasons than mere changes or delays in instructions or construction, for example delays caused by changes in interpretation or enactment or revision of laws, delays resulting from defects or deficiencies in the work or any other cause beyond the control of the architect.

Disputes

Both the Architect's Appointment and the RICS Conditions provide for the reference by agreement of any differences or disputes between client and architect or surveyor to arbitration. Both also provide for the actual appointment of an arbitrator by agreement or failing agreement by the President of the Chartered Institute of Arbitrators. Since the President of the Institute is likely to appoint an arbitrator who is an architect or surveyor as well as a member of the Institute many clients would not necessarily consider this to be the fairest way of settling disputes although no doubt the client could represent to the President that in his view a solicitor, for example, should be appointed instead. Some clients may prefer to delete the provision with a view to deciding, should a dispute arise, whether arbitration or Court proceedings were likely to produce the better outcome.

Before proceeding to a consideration of how remuneration is dealt with in both the RIBA Architect's Appointment and the RICS Conditions it is worth noting that the RICS Conditions cover two points of general substance which until July 1982 were not mentioned in the Conditions published by the RIBA and a further point common to both. The fact that the surveyor cannot assign the whole or any part of his duties without the prior approval of his client under his Conditions of Engagement is now also specifically stated in the Architect's Appointment. Of course, it would apply by implication under the general law of agency to both even if not set out in the Conditions. Indeed this aspect would probably be much more relevant in the case of architects in view of the more personal nature of the design element in their work. The other item in the RICS Conditions is in the form of a pre-requisite directed to the client to the extent that the "surveyor shall be entitled to receive from his client all information necessary to perform the duties for which he is being retained". Strangely such words were not previously included in the RIBA Conditions but since there is no harm in including them even though the point is again a matter of the general law of agency they have now been incorporated in the 1982 Architect's Appointment. However such wording may represent no more than a pious hope in the face of a "difficult" client determined to keep information to himself. The sentence revolves around the word "necessary". Who is to say what is "necessary"? Again any difficulties may have to be resolved around a consideration of what is reasonable or not.

Both the RIBA Architect's Appointment and the RICS Conditions do however find a place for a mention of postponement or determination of the engagement in a form by either party at any time on the expiry of reasonable notice, although in the case of the architect terminating his appointment this is expressed as being only in cases of force majeure making it impracticable to carry out any of the agreed services. Once again the question could always arise as to what constitutes reasonable notice. Termination by the client can presumably take place for no reason at all, even, presumably, at his mere whim but clearly if, as a result of the termination, either party suffers loss then that could amount to a breach of the contract giving rise to a claim for compensation, unless of course the termination had been brought about by a breach of the conditions by the other party.

Remuneration

The recommended remuneration for both architects and surveyors for building works until July 1982 was identical but, as now set out in the RIBA Architect's Appointment and the RICS Conditions (although basically similar and based on a sliding scale according to the total construction cost with a differentiation between new works and works to existing buildings), has some differences not only in the recommended percentage scales but also because the RIBA scales are now related to eight different building types in five separate classes. As mentioned previously however, another publication of the RICS, the Scales of Professional Charges, provides, in its March 1980 reprint, for a fee of 10% on the amount expended or a charge based on the time involved for repairs to and maintenance of property. Note (ii) to this Scale 33 states that the scale will not apply where working drawings are required and that in these circumstances "the RIBA scale should be used". This is a strange statement when the RICS had already published the Conditions of Engagement for Building Surveying Services and these are referred to in Scale 35 even although it is acknowledged that both the RICS and the RIBA have the same scales for new building work and refurbishing works to existing buildings. It is interesting to note the point where the distinction arises between "repairs and maintenance" as far as fees are concerned. While it is possible to carry out quite a fair amount of refurbishing work to a building without working drawings there does come a time when these are really necessary and at that point a different fee scale comes into operation.

The fees for building work, being a percentage of total construction costs, are, of course, designed to keep pace with inflation, in that as costs rise and architects and surveyors expenses rise roughly in line, so do the fees. The sliding scale recognises the undoubted fact that for many small jobs as much work needs to be done by the architect or surveyor as is needed to see through to completion a much larger job. A diet of very small jobs is not likely to be very profitable unless the expenses of the architect or surveyor are low. Adjustments were made previously in this regard in 1971 when the percentage charges for work under £25,000 were increased and those for work over £750,000 reduced and the RIBA has made further adjustments now in 1982.

The scales of charges shown in the RIBA Architect's Appointment 1982 are now only recommended charges in contrast to those set out in the earlier RIBA Conditions which were the minimum and were mandatory since member architects were not permitted to quote lesser fee rates. In the case of RICS members, quoted charges have always been recommended scales, not mandatory, and accordingly can be varied upwards or downwards. Both architects and surveyors can if they wish and if they obtain their client's prior agreement charge higher percentage rates than those quoted in the respective professional institutes published guidance. This indeed may be necessary on small complicated jobs or where work is being carried out to buildings of historical interest or where an architect or surveyor feels he has a special flair for the work and can bring that little extra special something to the jobs and the market, in the form of the clients, will bear it. Usually in the latter case the architect or surveyor will be in the happy position of having in effect a "waiting list".

Despite various studies by the professional organisations and in the 1960's by the Prices and Incomes Board it was not found possible to find or devise a fairer method of charging than by a percentage rate on construction costs. In fact, of course, the preparation of working drawings, the writing of specifications, obtaining tenders, supervising work and settling accounts follows a reasonably predictable pattern in "normal" circumstances and the amount of work carried out by the architect or surveyor is clearly related to the sheer volume as reflected in the cost of the project. Indeed central government has accepted the scale of charges set out in both the RIBA and RICS Conditions as being a fair method of assessing fees on its own commissions to private architects and surveyors in the past although there are indications that an element of bargaining on fees may be introduced in future. Notwithstanding this, however, there are aspects of the work involved in most projects, particularly in the early stages, which are not predictable as to amount and for which it is necessary to charge fees on a different basis. Since the work will vary considerably depending on the nature of each job no set fee can be laid down and accordingly the work is charged for on a time basis.

It will be apparent from the items mentioned in the previous paragraph as being covered by the scale fee that other items not mentioned such as examining and discussing client's requirements, initial appraisals, preliminary investigations to existing buildings are the sort of matters which are unpredictable in scope and accordingly require, at the commencement of every job, an agreement with the client on an acceptable basis of time charging for the architects or surveyors services.

The RICS Conditions give no indication whatever on a method of determining what might constitute a fair method of time charging merely stating that "all relevant factors including the complexity and character of the work, the experience and responsibility of the surveyor must be considered in assessing the charge". The RIBA Architect's Appointment 1982 is much more helpful in this regard and provides guidance on charging for technical staff other than principals to whom the same sort of vague words, however, are applied as in the RICS Conditions. The minimum hourly rate put forward is 15 pence per hour for each £100 of gross annual salary. Accordingly for someone in receipt of a gross annual salary of £10,000 defined to include bonus payments and the employer's share of other overheads such as national insurance, occupational pension schemes, private medical schemes and other emoluments such as car and accommodation allowances, the hourly charge would be £15. This gives a useful indication of what might also be charged for principals' time which could be based on what the principal might expect to be able to take out of the firm by way of profits each year calculated roughly in accordance with the definition of gross annual salary used for calculating hourly rates for assistants. In assessing the rate at which time should be charged the RIBA Architect's Appointment states that all relevant factors should be considered including the complexity of the work, the qualifications, experience and responsibility of the staff member and the character of any negotiations with which he might be involved.

Although the RICS Conditions do not give guidance on methods of assessing time charges for building works the full Scales of Professional Charges published by the RICS, which although abrogated as from March 1982 for all work except Building and Quantity Surveying, give some indication in respect of other branches of the surveying profession. For example Scale 34 provides for the assessment of hourly charges for assistants engaged on planning work at precisely the same rate as quoted in the RIBA Conditions, 15 pence per hour for every £100 of gross annual remuneration. To be included in the gross remuneration are the employer's national insurance contributions, staff and graduated pension contributions and similar payments, all adding up to the cost of a particular employee. Principals time on the other hand is stated as being charged on an hourly rate agreed with the client according to the professional status and qualifications of the member concerned and the circumstances of the case.

Scales 36 and 37 which govern quantity surveying services and are therefore still extant by RICS members for building works and which are effective from 1 March 1980 provide a different basis for time charging in relation to assistant's services. This method involves taking the annual cost of the member of staff, including salary and bonus, but excluding expenses, plus all employers contributions in pursuance of the terms of employment of the member of staff and dividing by 1650 to arrive at the hourly rate. To the figure so derived is added 145% to cover overheads and this gives the hourly figure for charging to the client. If the total annual cost of a member of the staff is £10,000 then this calculation produces an hourly charge of £14.85 not too dissimilar from that produced by the method given in the RIBA Architect's Appointment booklet or the RICS scale 34 for planning work. Here again for quantity surveyor's services, principal's time is charged by arrangement according to the circumstances including the professional status and qualifications of the quantity surveyor except as stated when he is doing work normally carried out by a member of his staff when the charge should be on an hourly time basis equivalent to that of a senior assistant as set out above.

It is apt to point out here that the quantity surveyor's scale indicates that the time charges are for use where other paragraphs of the scale, fees based on percentages of the cost, form a significant proportion of the overall fee. In all other cases an increased rate of time charging may be agreed.

It is interesting to note, in passing, that assistants time on quantity surveying services for civil engineering works (Scale 38), on a scale effective from 1 July 1971, used a divisor of 1750 instead of 1650 as on the scale for quantity surveying services for building works, to arrive at an hourly cost from an annual cost and an uplift of 125% instead of 145%. The difference in the two scales no doubt reflects the reduction in the average hours worked over a year during the last decade (on the basis of a 35 hour working week for 50 weeks, which surely must have been over optimistic at any time let alone ten years ago, to 47 weeks, a not over generous figure even now) and the proportionate increase in overheads as against salaries which seems to have been recognised by the Price Commission which agreed an increase of 12½% effective from 1 January 1977 on this scale to be levied as a surcharge. Again, using a member of staff with £10,000 as his gross annual salary this produces an hourly charge of £14.46 on Scale 38.

Yet another method of calculating time charges which has been adopted in the past is that of arriving at a daily figure by taking this at 1% of gross annual salary, again as defined previously to include all employer contributions. For an assistant costing his employer £10,000 per annum this produces a daily charge of £100. Taking the working day at 7 hours produces an hourly charge of £14.29. A working day of 7 hours is probably rather optimistic; with breaks and the usual interruptions it is doubtful whether much more than 6 hours is spent on actual productive work in the normal 09.00 to 17.00 hours office day and using this figure would give an hourly charge of £16.66. However taking 7 hours produces a figure not wildly different from that produced by the other two methods of calculation but since that derived from the RIBA Architect's Appointment 1982 is slightly higher than the other two it is probable that most surveyors dealing with building works would favour the use of that scale if such could be agreed with the client.

Of course it is always possible to produce hourly charges from first principles by adding together all the overheads of the firm and relating the total costs proportionally to the total number of hours worked by all members of the staff and the principals. Many firms do indeed keep such calculations up to date. The minimum recommended charges set out in the RIBA Architect's Appointment and the time charges set out as recommended in the RICS scales are intended to apply to an "average" sized practice, if there is such a thing, with "average" expenses and may be thought inadequate for a large well known practice with heavy administrative overheads and palatial offices. On the other hand the staff of such a practice would presumably be earning commensurately higher salaries and the principals would certainly have much higher expectations than those of an average practice.

What is important and which is rightly stressed in both sets of Conditions is that such charges should be agreed with the client in advance. Private clients in paid employment themselves and probably earning more than twice the assistant's salary mentioned previously of £10,000 per annum never fail to gasp with astonishment when quoted hourly figures of around £15 per hour, totally, or conveniently, forgetting that it is not just the gross annual salary paid to staff that has to be taken into account but all the overheads such as premises, rates, fuel, postage, telephones and, of course, accounts and clerical staff as well; the list can seem endless. Depending on the size and location of a practice it is necessary to multiply the gross hourly cost of staff by something like $2\frac{1}{4}$ to $2\frac{1}{2}$ (as mentioned in the RICS scales for quantity surveying services) for average sized practices to provide for these overheads. As mentioned previously for larger practices the multiplier may need to be higher, ranging perhaps up to the 3–4 times as charged by one central government agency for its services to clients because of the need to pay for a heavy burden of unproductive administration staff.

While the level of time charging must be a matter for each individual practice it is useful to look at the likely total costs that might arise on the typical job envisaged in this book to ascertain the recommended fee under the guidance issued by both professional institutes which would be payable in consequence and review the amount of time which could be devoted to the project. It may be thought that this should be considered more closely in relation to the Feasibility Study to be discussed in greater detail in Chapter 6 since it is only when the architect or surveyor can begin to get to grips with the project that he will be able to gauge its full extent. However it remains a business necessity, insofar as many clients are concerned, to be able to answer this question soon after the very first meeting or talk with the client. It is necessary not only to be able to quote the level of time charging to be made but also to know whether work can be done at the recommended scale fee. Consideration of one way in which the typical job might materialise in greater detail will help to underline this point as well as many of the other points already made in this chapter.

The typical job envisaged in this book is the professional administration of a small to medium sized building contract but this, of course, covers such a wide range of possibilities that it is necessary to see, in the minds eye, what is regarded as a suitable project which can cover a reasonable number of the points of interest likely to arise. The project envisaged could concern a surveyor or architect whether in the public or private sector who is asked to advise first upon the feasibility and then to implement an appropriate building contract for the complete repair of a neglected house structure together with the construction of an extension anywhere in Britain whether it be London, Maidstone or Nottingham. The structure is sound enough to be refurbished, but preliminary feasibility shows that the accommodation is cramped for the purpose required necessitating alteration and the erection of a new extension at the rear. There are various complications. Part of the original internal structure of the cellar was replaced or reinforced in concrete due, it is thought, to air raid precautions in 1940 while the remainder of the interior ranges from a state of fair preservation to bad dilapidation. The main structure, which is listed under Grade II is semi-detached with another property, and the site is closely surrounded by other buildings. This is the starting point and the rest follows from here.

Irrespective of whether the architect or surveyor is in the public or private sector, instructions to deal with a case such as this are likely to arise in one of three ways:

1. As a completely new job.
2. As a continuation from some advice upon structure or allied

matters given at some time in the past, perhaps anything from one to five years ago.
3. As an extension of an existing duty to deal with the property as part of a continuous process in the management of an estate. An instance might be where the property has formed part of a larger complex of buildings for which the money to rehabilitate the structure has only now been made available.

It is tempting to say that the easiest category for the practising architect or surveyor to deal with is (1) above as the whole field of feasibility can be entered into with totally fresh enthusiasm, each logical step following another so that the documents relating to the contract are compiled on a firm base of full and up-to-date information. All too often, as the practitioner whether in the private or public sector will appreciate only too well, a long past history of investigations for various purposes whether partial or full may have been involved under category (2) possibly accompanied by so many abortive meetings that the architect or surveyor may groan at the thought of returning once again to a familiar old problem with little or no feeling of motivation. His task of commencing a feasibility study may be horribly complicated by previous efforts in this field either by himself or others and his client may wish to force upon him, understandably, from economic reasons, the result of old investigations or tests or old plans or drawings compiled by someone else. The tendency may be in such a case to take the least line of resistance and cut corners with results that can be profoundly embarrassing at a later stage. In the final category (3) above, familiarity may again breed contempt, but the managing surveyor may have the drawback that sums of money may have been spent in a sporadic manner in the past to deal with various aspects of disrepair and his new refurbishment brief might be a partial one only on the impeccable administrative grounds that since some works of repair have been carried out fairly recently, irrespective of their quality or the purpose for which they were intended, feasibility can now therefore be confined to those parts where money has not been recently spent.

A little thought however, reveals that there is one important factor missing in this rather superficial assessment. The enormous advantage that the architect or surveyor would have under category (2) and (3), is his knowledge of the client, whatever his or her make-up and whether it be single or collective. Such knowledge need not necessarily imply great enthusiasm but nevertheless must be a considerable advantage. Since no previous knowledge of the client is more likely to occur in the private sector rather than the public, it can be more appropriate to take a particular case in point from that sector. This might for example concern the managing director of a manufacturing company situated near the centre of a market town which has expanded rapidly in recent years. He has acquired the property described earlier, in spite of the cost of doing so, since it is conveniently placed for the works and, with his budding international contacts, he wishes to provide sufficient accommodation not only for his family but also for entertaining. He is likely to be a busy man and is always likely to wish to appear to be so, since few manufacturing contacts are gained by an inert outlook on life. The first meeting therefore between the managing director and his professional adviser may not be particularly productive. It has probably been arranged at fairly short notice to give an impression of efficiency at one or other of their offices and although each will attempt to gain some idea of the basic temperament and character of the other, neither party is likely to give much away. The prospective client is naturally anxious to give an impression of being both busy and commanding so that the real answers required by each party may not therefore be at once to hand. What the managing director really wants to know is, firstly, whether his architect or surveyor is capable, secondly, whether he will follow his wishes and, thirdly, whether he will conduct the whole contract in a prompt and business like way without dragging matters out at endless cost. The architect or surveyor on the other hand would really like to know the answers to a good many more complex and indefinable questions. His thought processes are likely to run much more on the lines of "I am likely to have to work with this man for quite a long time. . . . There he is walking round the room waving his hands in the air . . . I am not sure that I can really take it. . . . What sort of a man is he? . . . Does he really know what he wants? . . . Will he listen to advice? . . . All he has really done so far is to tell me about himself and the rapid growth of his company and go on and on about business efficiency. . . . I wonder if he has had some past unfortunate experience or whether, like some, he adopts the view that anyone in a profession is out of date, inefficient and costly".

Architects and surveyors all have their own view about how initial discussions are best carried out. Some say a luncheon or supper table is helpful while others abhor any such suggestion. One thing is certain, however, in a case such as this and that is that the professional adviser really has to find out the answers to a number of important points, some of them clearly personal, right at the outset. Some of these may seem obvious but a failure to ask them or an omission of some of the answers can be a cause of great embarrassment later. The questions might be listed as follows:

1. The name and occupation of the client.
2. The nature of the project proposed.
3. Does he or she really know what is wanted?
4. Does he or she have sole say or are they influenced or beholden to others?
5. Is a cheap, middle range or Rolls Royce job expected?
6. Has he or she any conception of what can be obtained in money terms?
7. Has he or she a good grasp of what is likely to be required by way of feasibility, applications for consents and like matters or only the vaguest idea?
8. Is it important that the project be completed by a particular date?
9. Is there any proposed budget?
10. Can he or she pay for the work without undue difficulty or is the whole matter dependent upon fairly fragile financing arrangements? In short, can the client pay the required sums on the due dates without difficulty?
11. Have any advisers been employed on the project before this and are there any plans, investigations and results or other documents which the client requires to be used. Was a structural survey carried out before the property was purhased?
12. Has the client any "in-house" staff such as tradesmen or supervisors or does he or she wish to employ a particular labour force or contractor?
13. Does the surveyor or architect think that he likes the client and will get on well with him or her and vice versa?

All these questions are important, particularly the last, as the relationship with a client with whom the architect or surveyor gets on well may well overcome many other faults or black marks in the answers to the queries listed above whereas the cards are heavily stacked against an uncongenial relationship proving fruitful. Nevertheless, having said this, unsatisfactory replies to any of the above questions could be fatal to the project. If the client lacks authority or requires a cheap and nasty job which the surveyor or architect could not tolerate, the interview will be speedily concluded, contrasted with the case, equally profitless, where discussion lasts for hours until the realisation slowly dawns upon the professional adviser that the client is incapable of formulating a brief. An arbitrary date for the completion of the work in too short a time will frustrate the project, as will a rigid and insufficient budget, or the client's inability to meet progress payments in cash. Such a case might occur when the client is due to receive a large sum of money at a certain time but expects the whole of the work to be completed beforehand. Finally, there is the danger of the architect or surveyor being involved with in-house staff or a pet contractor which the client wishes to employ. This is always an extremely awkward situation. Although authority may be vested in him on paper it may well not exist in fact and an architect or surveyor who loses control of the work is in a miserable and impossible situation.

It may be thought with some reason that the prospective client should put a list of questions to his surveyor or architect in order to ascertain his qualities and capabilities. In fact he rarely does so. Few people like to spend endless hours interviewing prospective professional advisers, although some have been known to have this quirk in their makeup, but in the vast majority of cases the client, once he has satisfied himself usually by recommendation as to his professional adviser's competence, proceeds to the million dollar question – the amount of the fee. This question is of such overriding importance with most private and company clients that other matters seem to pale into insignificance beside it.

The question at the outset of a complicated project "how much are you going to charge me" is always an embarrassment no matter how many years the architect or surveyor has spent in practice. The reason for this is, of course, that like all professional questions that are difficult to answer, the information on which to arrive at a correct assessment is normally lacking. The experienced practitioner will delay giving an answer for as long as possible while he finds out as much as he can beforehand or until he sees a frown beginning to form on his client's face. It is true that the RIBA Architect's Appointment and the RICS Conditions of Engagement are helpful to some extent as already discussed and these can be proferred either with a winning smile or a serious look combined with a suggestion that the booklet repays detailed study. The reaction however, of the client is rarely helpful. The booklet is either slipped into a briefcase which is then snapped shut, or turned over in puzzled fingers and returned with the comment "I can't read all that – just tell me the answer". In any event, neither booklet provides the actual time charges which it will be necessary to quote and agree and it could be dangerous to the commission's profitability for the architect or surveyor to quote the recommended scale fee without at least seeing what the project is likely to involve.

The nettle of quoting fees accordingly has got to be grasped at this stage. If one ignores the most superficial enquiries that are sometimes received in the office such as when the secretary to a businessman telephones a number of surveyors or architects merely to describe the project in a few words and asks what they would charge, unhappily a not uncommon practice and one that, since it is totally meaningless, should be countered by an offer to quote on a full consideration of all the facts, one can pass to the next stage and return to our managing director. Once the initial interview is over, more or less successfully as the case may be, the request to quote a fee can be parried with the counter-suggestion of making a quick visit to the site to be followed by the writing of a letter setting out the fees, costs and likely expenses in broad terms. This is likely to be received with a nod of acceptance coupled with the comment "as long as I receive the letter fairly quickly . . .". The next stage is therefore an inspection by the architect or surveyor. This, as part of the service in order to provide a quotation of fees must be carried out free of charge and indeed it would be a most unfortunate introduction to any client to insist upon charging for such an inspection at the outset of the relationship. The visit is normally a short one and is designed to concentrate the mind of the architect or surveyor upon the initial steps to be taken.

Inspection of the property described earlier in this section is likely to be instructive and the architect or surveyor will busily write notes while he prods and peers through the interior of the building and prowls around the outside. Often he will be delighted to come across a caretaker or adjoining owner or occupier who can give him a great deal of information. His notes might be on the following lines:

1. The property consists of a large semi-detached Victorian structure with cellar, entrance and two upper floors and attic accommodation. It is of brick, built about 1890 with a partly slated and partly tiled roof constructed on the Manor Road frontage of a long (approximately 200 ft) site. What appears to be a Georgian addition at the rear is, or was, in fact a small detached house served by the footpath known as Bridle Passage before the Georgian buildings to Manor Road were re-developed in Victorian times. The whole structure contains sixteen rooms and the derelict cellar accommodation.

2. Structural problems include progressive settlement of the rear (north east) corner of the main Victorian structure (drains and tree roots) and the advanced failure of the brick walls of the Georgian section which is a write-off. Internal problems include failure in the stud partitions, sagging of the roof-slopes, bad dry rot and total neglect everywhere one looks.

3. The most unusual feature of the property is the war-time concrete construction in the cellar. This looks, surprisingly, good and would cost a fortune to replace just for the sake of it.

4. There is a nasty possibility of made up ground at the rear.
5. The extension needed is possible but the site is enclosed to a surprising degree by other buildings. Rights of light? What about Bridle Passage, is there a right of way?
6. Major Scott ("The Limes" – detached on eastern side) is a tree fanatic. He may cause problems. He was informative. He said that the property attached to ours on the western side is occupied by a very elderly lady in her nineties who is bedridden having been (so he says) abandoned by her family and living now with a single nurse companion. This brings up problems over the party wall in the event of an extension being built. He also said that all the local houses were Leasehold only – the Freeholds owned by the South-water Estate. He had been served with a schedule of dilapidations but was going to fight it to the House of Lords. Note: Do not assume the property to be Freehold. Enquire whether freehold purchased under Leasehold Reform Act or is property still Leasehold?

Return to the office and enquiries by telephone reveal a few uncomfortable facts. The managing director is only too keen to give the name of his solicitor who reveals that the property is Freehold in one sense but not in another. Notice was served under the Leasehold Reform Act eighteen months ago but the claim is being disputed as the freeholders are reluctant, to say the least of it, to see the estate broken up and there is no immediate prospect of any agreement of terms. Enquiries of the owners solicitor on the right of way means that he will have to obtain a sight of the Deeds regarding the question of Bridle Passage and will 'phone back. Enquiry of the local Council reveals that the land at the rear of the house is indeed made up ground and this explains the lack of recent additions to the estate generally which had been a source of puzzlement. The enquiry also establishes that it is the small Georgian portion which is listed, not the main Victorian building, but that all the property is in a Conservation area.

The inspection, together with the opening interview with the prospective client will now enable the architect or surveyor to consider whether for the predictable work involved and its character in respect of both the alteration and refurbishment of the original building and the construction of the new extension the recommended scale fees are likely to be sufficient to cover the cost and to show a profit. Having regard to the fair overall size of both parts of the project it is thought that the minimum scale would probably be acceptable and would accordingly be quoted with reference to the

Conditions. However it should not be forgotten that the scales for both work to existing buildings and the scales for new work apply to a project of this nature since the extension, being substantially independent, counts as a new building and it would be inequitable to charge at the higher rate for the whole of the work. Quite justifiably, however, that part of the work which marries new to old should be charged in with the alteration and refurbishment at the higher rate. Clause 4.18 of the RIBA Architect's Appointment 1982 provides for this work of connection to be charged separately as for a new commission of equal value but this would only be in cases where no major alterations were being carried out in the existing building.

Although in this case the recommended scales would probably be acceptable there are many instances where higher scales would be justifiable. If the existing building had been Georgian instead of Victorian where the client might make stipulations in regard to the careful matching of new to old or where the extension was very small in relation to the main building are two examples which come to mind.

What of the unpredictable work which, in the case of this project would consist of the initial feasibility study and, if this showed that the client's intentions could be broadly fulfilled, a subsequent survey and drawings of the existing building and the site for the extension, together with the work involved on obtaining listed building consent, party wall agreements, negotiations on rights of light and the obtaining of lessor's consent not covered by the normal predictable work stages set out in the Conditions of Engagement? Obviously just because the scope of the work is unpredictable the architect or surveyor will endeavour in the first instance to cover this aspect by quoting hourly charges for the various categories of staff likely to be involved including if necessary those of any other disciplines. The only difficulty with this form of quotation however is that it is meaningless in terms of total money liability to the average client and, of course, if agreed by the client, could in effect amount to an open ended commitment. Depending on the size of the project and the financial means of the client an open ended commitment of this nature may not be acceptable. Indeed the more stringent the finances the less likely is it to be so. Accordingly the client may expect and ask for either of the following, both of which could be acceptable alternatives to the architect or surveyor in lieu of time charges though obviously both will involve him in an additional degree of care in the preparation of the estimate. In the case of a large complicated job, however, he may have to insist on the client's acceptance of the second alternative if he is to be able to fulfil the task properly of preparing a worthwhile feasibility study.

(a) a firm quotation for the feasibility study and other matters likely to be involved if this should prove acceptable (even if other quotations have to await completion of the feasibility study);

(b) maximum limits on expenditure on time charges for the various items involved based on the architects or surveyors considered estimate of the total cost but with a requirement to refer back to the client if the limit is likely to be exceeded.

If a firm quotation is required by now the shape of all the problems should be emerging and the surveyor or architect can work out the hours likely to be spent on the site by himself and any assistants and the hours which will be required to make the initial enquiries and accordingly be able to calculate what sort of fee he will require for the feasibility study, not forgetting the out of pocket expenses likely to be incurred. These may be required to pay for a wide range of professional assistance that may be necessary, for example a structural engineer, heating and ventilating engineer and even perhaps a quantity surveyor as well as technical help by plumbers in testing existing installations. Builders time is also likely to be a charge on the study for general attendance on the architect or surveyor as well as perhaps the structural engineer and heating consultant. The architect or surveyor's own time in meeting such consultants must also not be overlooked.

It is at this stage that the architect or surveyor must give thought to compiling the actual letter dealing with the subject of fees and expenses. A procedure often found useful is to dictate the letter in draft form setting out the original brief as it has been explained by the prospective client together with the various stages that the job will require with any of the stages related to the times when payment of fees will be needed. Actual figures can be left out of the draft, for the time being, the wording being concerned with the practical progression of the whole matter from start to finish without some vital element being overlooked. Subsequent thought can result in the figures being entered in ink on the draft and the final letter being typed after fresh consideration. The advantage of this method of procedure is twofold. On the one hand some care is accordingly and rightly given to a letter that will form the basis of the contract between client and architect or surveyor for a large amount of time and money to say the least of it. On the other hand if the progressive stages are clearly defined and priced, it means that, should a crisis of personality occur between the architect or surveyor and his client, the agreed level of fees up to each progressive stage in the project will be set out and this will reduce any subsequent acrimony as against other occasions when, as often happens, insufficient agreement has been reached on the subject of fees. Since the only other document relating to the basic contract is likely to be a two line letter of acceptance from the client if he feels that the proposals are reasonable, the wording of the initial architect or surveyor's letter is all important.

The skeleton of the letter should be drafted having regard to the particular requirements of the case. There is little point in having a standard form, although the RIBA do publish such a form suitable for simple new work cases, as this often sounds impersonal or off the point to private clients and the advantage of a letter is to be specifically aimed at the particular project under discussion and to sound businesslike and interested. Since the architect or surveyor may already have given his client the RIBA Architect's Appointment booklet or a set of the RICS Conditions of Engagement the letter can be stated as being taken in conjunction with the conditions as set out therein. If, however, it is suspected that the client has probably never looked at, or lost, the booklet, a further copy can be enclosed.

The skeleton of the letter might therefore be as follows:

1. Reference to the original telephone call and subsequent meeting or meetings with the client and repetition as far as possible in the client's own words, if he has written a letter, as to the terms of the architect or surveyor's brief.
2. For carrying out the initial feasibility study involving:
   (i) A full structural survey.
   (ii) Additional attendances to meet specialist's representatives and contractors.
   (iii) Initial enquiries into statutory and other requirements.
   (iv) Report to client setting out approximate costs and time scale.
   To Fee:
   Either:
   (a) Firm quotation fee or
   (b) Estimated fee not to be exceeded without prior approval.
   (c) On time charge at so much per hour.
   Plus VAT
   Specialists costs and expenses.
   Travelling and out of pocket expenses.
3. Carrying out a measured survey of the existing buildings and producing a survey drawing including, where necessary, levels.
   To Fee:
   Either: (a) (b) or (c) as above.
   Plus VAT

4. Serving Notices upon and negotiating with adjoining owners, agreeing awards and schedules of condition in respect
of party walls. Investigating aspects of rights of light and
reporting. Submitting details to Lessors and obtaining approval (other than legal work).
   To Fee:
      Either (b) or (c) as above.
   Plus VAT
   To further costs and expenses.
   Special Note: As initiator of the work you will be required to
   pay the fees of architects or surveyors appointed to act for
   adjoining owners estimated at £ ....

5. Preparing and presenting to you, for approval, outline
sketch design. Preparing full working drawings incorporating any advice given by consultants and/or specialists, if
retained, and submitting applications for planning, building
regulation and other statutory consents. Obtaining estimates from any necessary nominated sub-contractors and/
or suppliers. Preparing specifications and/or a schedule of
information for the preparation of Bills of Quantities. Advising the client of procedures for the selection of contractors
and, if appropriate, submitting documents for tender and
advising on tenders received; Requesting authority to
proceed.
   To Fee on the basis of work to existing buildings work
   costing £............
      and new work costing £............ . Total Fee £............
      Three quarters of total fee........................
                                              £............
         Plus VAT   ....
         Further costs and expenses ....

6. Advising the successful contractor of appointment. Supplying all necessary information to the contractor, arranging
the commencement of the works, preparing contract documents as necessary and examining the contractor's programme. Monitoring the progress of the work with periodic
site visits (as set out in the Conditions of Engagement),
supplying all information to the contractor for completion of
the contract in accordance with the contract documents.
Administering the contract during the progress of the work
including the issue of payment certificates, architect's or
surveyor's instructions and variation orders. Accepting the
completed project on behalf of the client, preparing and/or
checking final accounts, advising on any defects and conse-

quential liability for remedial works under the terms of the contract, and ensuring their rectification and issuing the final certificate. Preparing or obtaining record drawings, if required, showing the services as installed. Supplying initial guidance on maintenance.

To Balance of Fees set out in paragraph 5 above £...........
Plus VAT   ....
Final costs and expenses   ....
LESS Fee for Feasibility Study   ....

The above schedule closely follows the guidance of the professional institutes varied slightly to cater for a project that is geared to both an altered existing building with considerable new work in an extension. The variable factors not covered would, of course comprise initial advice to the client as to the need for consultants to be employed, or a quantity surveyor for example, and if it was obvious that these would be required then it would be appropriate to include mention of their fees in addition, even though consultants will be required to give their own estimate before appointment. The Conditions of Engagement relating to such matters as expenses, disputes, separate or ancillary services and charges (Part 4 in the RIBA Architect's Appointment and section 3 of the RICS Conditions of Engagement) could be specifically referred to in the letter as being applicable. If the architect or surveyor suspects from his knowledge of the client that he is likely to have to make a number of personal supplementary visits, he should state an hourly rate at the end of the schedule for "any extra visits above the number normally envisaged if requested by yourself only would be charged for at the hourly rate of £........". It would be strange if the wife of the managing director had not by now appeared on the scene and it would be odder still if the architect or surveyor had not deliberately taken the opportunity of meeting her and the incorporation of an hourly rate charged would be the surveyor's or architect's only weapon against too much indiscriminate use of his time. Cases have been known where professional advisers have made similar charges against letters and telephone calls for the same reason.

The mention of hourly rates again, however, does introduce an essential requirement for the architect or surveyor whenever these are levied by prior agreement on fixed rates. As discussed earlier, charging by this method is not popular with clients not only because the client has no idea whether the final bill will be £200 or £2,000, but also because the method is open to abuse by the unscrupulous. Accordingly it is essential for the architect or surveyor to keep accurate diary records of the dates and of the hours spent on each date on the work by the various staff concerned and not for reliance to be placed on memory. The RIBA publish a form for this purpose which is useful and paragraph 4.15 of the Architect's Appointment requires records to be kept and for these to be made available to the client on reasonable request. There is, furthermore, a duty to see that work is allocated to the appropriate level of staff. A client, for example, should not be expected to pay at a senior assistant's rate for work which could properly have been done by a junior assistant. If the work cannot be allocated properly because the junior assistant is away unwell and the senior assistant has to do the work himself it would only be correct to charge the senior assistants time at the junior's rate. The client has a right to expect an itemised account showing the dates on which hours were worked on his behalf and by which of the staff concerned. Not to send an itemised account is to risk a query which if accurate records have not been kept, could prove embarrassing to answer.

Accurate records of the time spent on all jobs is of course a useful tool towards the assessment of the profitability of the work under-taken, despite the general reluctance of staff to treat such recording systems seriously. Mention has been made of the need to check that the methods of time charging by a practice or organisation do indeed produce the hourly rates to meet the cost of staff, accom-modation and services and yet still leave a margin of profit. What-ever method is used to produce the correct hourly rates is immaterial provided the results are satisfactory. Those hourly rates and an accurate record of time spent by all concerned on a job can, of course, be used to calculate whether a job done on scale fees is also profitable. If the amount which would have been charged to the client, should the work have been done on a time basis, far exceed the amount produced by the scale fee then there would be something radically wrong with the organisation and methods of the practice. A few jobs carried out on the same basis would see the demise of the practice if such jobs were the staple fare. A regular comparison in this manner, however, of all the work carried out by the practice is a useful guide as to whether all work should or should not be carried out at the minimum scale fee. Perhaps higher percentage scales should be charged depending on the type of new work, on the character of an old building to be altered, on the type of client or on whether premises are to remain occupied while works are being carried out, otherwise the work may not prove to be profitable. It may simply be whether a particular architect or surveyor wishes, quite legitimately to specialise and to devote that much more care and attention to individual jobs than is the case with other architects or surveyors. In such cases a client may well be prepared to pay more for the extra time taken over his commission to produce a "Rolls Royce" job. Architects and surveyors can often learn a great deal from interior designers in their expectation of a much higher level of anticipated attendance on site to ensure implementation of their ideas in a satisfactory way and for which they can command a much higher pro-rata fee.

An extension of the reasoning behind these comparisons enables the architect or surveyor, once the approximate cost of the project has been assessed, to prepare a work programme to show the amount of hours which can be devoted to the project by the various staff concerned in order to show a profit at the end of the day. For example to use purely hypothetical figures for the alterations and new extension which comprise the typical job envisaged in this book, let us assume that the alterations to the existing building will cost £45,000 and the new extension £75,000. We shall see how such figures may be produced for the Feasibility Study at a later stage.

Up to 1 July 1982 the mandatory scale fees of the RIBA and the recommended scale fees of the RICS were identical. The scales were divided into two sections, one for work to new buildings the other for work to existing buildings, minimum fees within each section being quoted for various levels of total construction costs. With the abandonment of mandatory fees the RIBA have published a new more elaborate range of recommended fees based on five classifications of eight building types, the precise recommended percentage fee being ascertainable for new works and for works to existing buildings by reference to two graphs for total constructional costs ranging from £20,000 to £5 m. Accordingly the recommended scales of the two professional bodies at the time of writing are different. It is probable that the RICS will bring its recommended scales into line with those of the RIBA in due course, particularly as to do so would provide for an increase over those applying previously but account has to be taken here of the divergence which exists at the present time.

Under the RIBA recommended scales applicable from July 1982 the fee for the typical job envisaged would be as follows on the assumption that the architect would not feel the need to charge at a higher percentage rate because the building is in a conservation area (as suggested may be the case in paragraph 4.21 of the Architects Appointment) and that he is prepared to include the cost of the connection of the existing building to the new extension within the total cost of the works of alteration for the purpose of the fee calculation and not treat it as a separate commission as he could do under paragraph 4.18 of the Architects Appointment.

Works to Existing Building:
	£
On total cost of work to a	
Class 5 residential building	
13⅞ on £45,000	6243.75

New Works:
On total cost of work to a	
Class 5 residential building	
8⅝% on £75,000	6468.75

Total fee on project completed in	
accordance with costs provided in	
Feasibility Study	£12,712.50

It is possible to quote such precise percentages as set out above since interpolation in the graphs enables this to be done in contrast to the broader bands which applied to the mandatory scales in the pre-1982 Conditions of Engagement and which still apply to the scales in the RICS Conditions of Engagement. No doubt, however, in quoting fees the architect would probably have sought to round the percentages up to perhaps 14% and 9% respectively in the circumstances of this case while the client, suitably armed with a copy of the RIBA Architects Appointment booklet 1982 might have endeavoured to persuade the architect to do the work for rounded down fees. In the current climate of bargaining and competition the architect at the time of quoting fees would have had to have the possibility of such competition in mind while the client, if he was obtaining various quotations, would have to weigh up the effect on the final outcome of, what might seem to many, foolish cheeseparing by bargaining on fees instead of using as a criteria for selection the quality of work of the architect being considered.

It will be noted on comparison between the fees for the typical job set out above with those set out below that the RIBA scales now produce quite substantially higher fees for the comparatively small scale work envisaged than the current RICS scales. This is so even in the case postulated where the surveyor has decided to quote a scale 1% above the minimum recommended and the client has thought sufficiently highly of him to accept. This difference reflects the view that with the rapid increase in building costs over recent years smaller jobs on the old scales have become increasingly unprofitable and reinforces the belief that the RICS will not be long behind the RIBA in increasing the level of fees for the smaller scale work.

With the additional 1% above the recommended scale, the fee for the typical job envisaged under the RICS conditions of Engagement 1981 would be:

Works to Existing Building: £

On total cost of work over £25,000	10%	
Plus 1%	1%	
	11% on £45,000	4950

New Works:

On work costing in total between £25,000 and £750,000	6%	
Plus 1%	1%	
	7% on £75,000	5250

Total fee on project completed in
accordance with costs provided in
Feasibility Study   £10,200

and this total fee will be used in the assessments which follow where the resources which can be devoted to the job in the surveyor's office will be discussed. Obviously the same reasoning using different figures can be applied however on the total fee derived from the RIBA Scales.

If we assume that in addition to the surveyor working on the project himself, there will also be a qualified assistant paid a gross annual salary of £11,000 including all emoluments and a draughtsman paid £6,000, these could be charged at 15 pence per hour for each £100 of gross annual salary, namely £16.50 for the qualified assistant and £9.00 per hour for the draughtsman. No doubt the surveyor's own expectations will be somewhat higher and perhaps £30.00 per hour would not be unreasonable to assume as his personal hourly charge. If again it is assumed that to complete the project satisfactorily the qualified assistant needs to spend twice the number of hours that either his principal or junior spends, it is possible to ascertain an average hourly rate thus:

$$1 \times £30.00 = £30.00$$
$$2 \times £16.50 = £33.00$$
$$1 \times £9.00 = £9.00$$
$$£72.00 \div 4 = £18.00 \text{ per hour}$$

Total hours to be spent on the project to produce a satisfactory outcome can be calculated as:

Total Fee ÷ average hourly rate = £10,200 ÷ £18 = 566·66 hours divisible between the three professional staff approximately as follows:

141 hours at £30.00 =	£4,230
282 hours at £16.50 =	£4,653
141 hours at £9.00 =	£1,269
Total Fee	£10,152

With the division of labour on the project as set out above it will be seen that in order to achieve a reasonable return (that being the premise in the hourly rates charged) the principal and the junior should be spending no more than about 20 days or four weeks each on the project while the qualified assistant can spend 40 days or about eight weeks since on him will fall the bulk of the work involved in settling the details of the design, preparing the drawings and specification, arranging the contract, site supervision and settling the account.

Of course the proportion of staff time at different levels to be devoted to a project will vary from job to job and from practice to practice but experience from previous schemes will provide the guide for the assessment of needs and the deployment of principals and staff on a new project. Whatever assessment is made in advance, and the above method is adaptable for different numbers and levels of staff and any proportion of involvement, it is essential at the conclusion of the project to match the scale fee income with the time spent, as recorded, so that any glaring anomalies can be recognised for future avoidance and correction. This is important and applies to work carried out both by the private sector and by architects and surveyors in employment by companies, local and central authorities and the nationalised industries. In cases where architects and surveyors are employed however, hourly rates will be calculated ignoring an element of profit, if work is being done for the organisation itself and not for outsiders, and the figures used to compare the cost of having work done by the employed staff against the expense of employing outside consultants.

It may be that some work in all organisations, even the best regulated, has to be carried out at less than a desirable level of profit and perhaps some even at a loss. That may be the price of obtaining further work of a more profitable nature in the private sector or of fulfilling a public service or providing a social service in some areas of the public sector.

Within an organisation, however, it is important to be able to identify non-profitable work so that it can be reviewed in a wider context. It could be that such projects can be safely contained and amalgamated with work showing a more than average rate of profit to produce satisfactory overall figures. On the other hand it may be shown that projects without such balancing factors and of a particular size and type need to be charged at higher than minimum recommended scale fees. If the market will not accept charges higher than the minimum then it may be that such projects are more appropriate for the routine package deal. Under such circumstances the cheaper house extensions and loft conversions come to mind, rather than the individual attention to design and detail provided by the architect or surveyor. The individual attention to problems does not come cheap and clients for such professional services tend to be more concerned with quality rather than pure space and financial considerations.

It should be obvious that a client will only pay the agreed fee on the completion of the project. Part only of the fee will be payable if the project is abandoned at various stages as set out in both the RIBA Architect's Appointment and the RICS Conditions of Engagement. These also provide for part payment of the fee at various stages of the work programme as it proceeds and this can be amplified by agreement on large projects if the architect or surveyor wishes to have his fees paid by, say, monthly instalments.

Having said all the foregoing about fees it is important, once the level has been agreed, for the architect or surveyor to forget all about the subject until the project is completed. Although there may be provision for collection as the work proceeds this should be done automatically. There is considerable danger to the completion of a satisfactory job if there is the sort of comparison of income and time spent on a job during its progress. This is liable to lead to the situation where a conscious decision is taken that the project is not paying and involving too much time to the extent that everyone engaged must spend less time on it. The professional outlook should be that once rates and fees have been agreed nothing should come in the way of completing the job in the most satisfactory manner irrespective of the time and effort involved. As we shall see in the case of the building contract the best thing to do with any agreement on fees and conditions of engagement is within reason to put it in a drawer and forget about it. That done, undivided concentration can then be given to satisfying the client's requirements in all respects.

So far, consideration has been given to the various aspects which need to be taken into account when the almost inevitable question of fees arises in discussion with a prospective private client. It has been seen that an architect or surveyor would rather turn aside the full question until he has had the opportunity of carrying out a Feasibility Study by which time he will be able to assess whether the project merits a charge of more than the minimum fee scales laid down. The Feasibility Study he would prefer to carry out would be on an agreed hourly rate time basis, preferably with no upper limit on expenditure, but agreeing to a prior limit not to be exceeded without authority if the client insists on an arrangement of this nature. For clients with really limited means the architect or surveyor may find himself being asked to quote a total fee for the Feasibility Study, so that the client will know in advance, as he does when requiring a structural survey on purchasing a property, the full extent of his liability. Since in such cases the project will probably be fairly small, the architect or surveyor will probably in the circumstances be able to quote a fee for the purpose.

It is only right and proper that the fee for a Feasibility Study should be paid by the client within a short time of the receipt of the Study. The client will obtain such information, the full extent of which will be described later, as to enable him to decide whether to proceed with the project or not. If he does not proceed then the contract between client and architect or surveyor will be completed on payment of the fee. If the project is to continue then, depending on the arrangement entered into earlier, payment of the fee will be taken as part payment on partial completion of the contract or a new contract will be set up if the original instructions only extended, as would be preferred by the architect or surveyor in most cases, to the Feasibility Study itself. What will often be forgotten, however, is that on submission of the account for the final instalment of fees on completion of the project, a reduction should in most cases be made for the amount of the fee in respect of the Feasibility Study. Although, as discussed, it has to be charged on a different basis, it is still part of the design process and as such should become incorporated as part of the scale fee levied on the total cost of the completed project and not left charged as an extra on that scale fee. If this deduction is not made clients will maintain that there has been an element of double charging. Good work done at the time of the Feasbility Study will save a vast amount of time at later stages and there can be very few cases where the making of such an allowance will operate unfairly against an architect or surveyor. Total changes in the client's instructions might be one case where it may well be justified to charge separately and in addition to the scale fee for a Feasibility Study. This would probably be because a complete change would in effect amount to a requirement for an additional Feasibility Study.

It is always necessary to draw clients' attention to the fact that expenses involved in travelling, printing of plans etc. are not included in the fee. If a project is some distance away from the architect or surveyor's office this may be an element which may affect a client's decision on whom to employ. If the client favours a particular architect or surveyor to carry out the project he may well consider the extra cost worthwhile. Another suitable reminder to be provided to the client is that fees are exclusive of VAT so that the addition of VAT at the current rate on the architect or surveyor's account is an item for which he should allow.

Obviously with the typical job envisaged in this book finance would probably not be too critical a factor, so that it is more likely that after the initial inspection and quotation of fees and time charges a contract for the services of the architect or surveyor can be drawn up with the client. If this wording gives the impression of a need for formal documentation, as for example, arises in the case of a building contract under the JCT Form or a lease or hire purchase agreement nothing could be further from the truth. Many such contracts are made orally, others on the flimsiest of documentation by way of letters often phrased in the vaguest of terms. Most contracts formed in such a nature proceed satisfactorily and are concluded on the rendering of an account by the architect or surveyor and payment by the client. Such easy going arrangements more often than not develop over a period of time and through a trust established between a practice and a particular client. Notwithstanding such relationships, it is recommended, and clearly much more businesslike, to have an agreement in writing as to the extent of the architect's and surveyor's duties, his remuneration and the mode of payment and this is a requirement for members of the RIBA, though not for those of the RICS although obviously recommended.

Because of the requirement for a written agreement the RIBA publish a suitable Form of Agreement together with the appropriate relevant Schedule of Services and Fees for completion between a building owner and his architect. There is no need, however, to use this Form of Agreement, a specimen of which appears at the end of the RIBA Architect's Appointment 1982 but it does provide a useful guide to what should be included in any letter of appointment for either architects or surveyors. Obviously the respective Conditions in the Architects Appointment 1982 or the RICS Conditions of Engagement will need to be referred to and there must be a quotation as we have seen for the hourly rates to be charged for work not covered by percentage scale fees. Obviously a copy of the appropriate Architect's Appointment or RICS Conditions must be attached to the letter and the Form of Agreement if one is used. It is advisable to send two copies of the Agreement Form, letter and Conditions so that one copy can be returned signed by the client who can retain one copy for his own records. Signing and returning will signify the commencement of the contract between the building owner and the architect or surveyor and will enable the architect or surveyor to embark either on the main part of the project or perhaps, as already discussed, on the Fasibility Study if the agreement has been made before this has been carried out.

Part 2
Feasibility

Chapter 3

Briefing and Preliminary Investigations

Contents

CLIENTS vary enormously in the degree of confidence with which they are able to express their requirements for building works. Whether a high degree of self confidence is well placed or not is another matter. The house buyer who is downcast to find that the designs in a glossy magazine prepared for a film director in Mayfair do not translate well to a terraced house in the suburbs will either react angrily, when this sad fact is pointed out, or will recover well if he or she detects signs of a positive solution emerging from the architect or surveyor. In the first case little can be done, since someone with a fixed idea cannot really be helped. In the second case, however, the architect or surveyor really fulfils a function when, at the end of the project, the client, looking at the original glossy magazine decides how well his adviser has solved the problem and what an improvement has been made over the designs for the film director.

Any client, however, can be forgiven for disliking a purely negative approach in his architect or surveyor. The company director who produces a Continental design as an example for his new light industrial building will be scathing if his architect's or surveyor's viewpoint is one merely of glum passivity, "I suppose we could build it like that but it will be very expensive". If the reaction is far more positive, "this design has some really excellent features which we could certainly use but we could save quite a lot of money by altering such and such . . ." the client's response is far more likely to be one of interested attention.

In what is basically a "one to one" relationship, the architect or surveyor has one enormous advantage or disadvantage whichever way one likes to look at the situation. He will either get on well with his client or he will not. He will certainly know within a very short time whether this is so but it does at least mean that, from the point of view of administration, he will know the person with whom he is dealing and, however odd his client may be, at least he will be in no doubt as to what is happening. Real problems arise, however, when the architect or surveyor deals with an organisation rather than a single client. Contract administration under such circumstances assumes a totally different character and it is to this aspect of the matter that the next section will be devoted. Dealing with a large firm requires particular thought and consideration beforehand. On the one hand there may be the expert client in the form of an organisation or company employing in-house architects or surveyors but not yet having the capacity to carry out the project within its own resources. In such cases professionals in the organisation may already have gone to considerable trouble to ascertain from other branches of the organisation what is actually required. Sometimes it is only when the full requirements have been assembled is it realised that the full resources necessary for the project's completion are not available. The commissioned architect or surveyor in these circumstances will probably be fortunate in inheriting a fully considered, detailed, brief and having as his contact another professional. However, if clarity alone was the prime consideration instructions received from a development company might also be completely satisfactory but, as discussed in Chapter 1, such clarity may have its disadvantages when it is extended to include precise instructions on how matters are to be arranged and the materials to be used with the aim of keeping costs to a minimum and to derive maximum profit to the exclusion of most other considerations. However the architect or surveyor's attitude to this type of client should already have been settled. At the other end of the spectrum there will be clients who have only the vaguest idea of what they wish to have done and no idea at all of what can be provided with the money which they have available.

It is in the circumstances of a clients unfamiliarity with what can be done where the architect or surveyor accepts the greatest responsibility for discussing and settling the brief with the client. A Brief may be said to be an assembly of information both in general and specific terms prepared for the purpose of the design of new buildings or the alteration and refurbishment of existing buildings. Initial discussion with a prospective client will have ascertained basic ownership details and financial capability. It will be the purpose of the brief to set out the size, character and style of the accommodation that it is hoped can be provided within that capability and the purpose of the feasibility study to confirm whether what is required is possible or not.

Briefs will take as many different forms as there are clients and different types of jobs, from the poorest requirements of the uninitiated private client to the highly detailed and technical brief from the expert client. It is the duty, however, of the architect or surveyor to establish what is really required. This forms a very vital part of the service provided by architects and surveyors. Performed satisfactorily it can set the seal on a successful commission whereas failure to ascertain what is required will lead at the end of the day to complaints that the outcome was not what had been intended or expected. Such comments are an indictment of the architect or surveyor not a sign of failure in the client. Admittedly the occasional client may be delighted in the outcome, finding that he has something he likes which he did not initially know he even wanted. It has been said in the past that this is the mark of the successful commission but it smacks too much of a dilettante "hit and miss" outlook at variance with the need for sound business relationships in current conditions. It can only be again stressed that client's money is his own and the duty of the architect or surveyor is to ascertain, so far as is humanly possible, how the client wishes that money to be spent. To do otherwise is to mistake the architect or surveyor's true role in building matters, certainly as seen by the lay public. To impose upon a client an architect or surveyor's own subjective views of what the client should have and to ignore, or fail to take the trouble to find out, the client's views, is an example of the arrogance of which there have been all too many complaints in the last two decades. Strangely enough it probably offers a greater challenge to the technical skill and competence of the architect or surveyor to follow a tightly reined Brief and yet produce something with that little extra special character which makes the client happy at the thought that he consulted an architect or surveyor in the first place and did not, after all, just go to a builder or take up one of the package deals on offer. Accordingly subjective views should be purged from the mind and, in the absence of a prior prepared Brief, the architect or surveyor's role at this stage should be one of listener and recorder coupled with the interpolation of well considered questions designed to elucidate the information necessary to formulate a complete Brief for the feasibility stage, recognising that if the project proceeds to actual work much further refinement of the Brief will be necessary. For example, at this stage, nobody is concerned with what make or design of sanitary fittings is required, only the number, nor what type of door furniture, yet in many cases these sort of details may loom quite large in both client and architect or surveyor's minds when in fact they should not.

Of course, having said that, it is the duty of the architect or surveyor to settle the terms of the brief, it remains the responsibility of the client to take the decisions which, as discussed in Chapter 1, for some clients can prove quite difficult. It is therefore wise for all architects and surveyors to be as sure, as it is possible to be, that clients have genuinely devoted the necessary time and consideration to the task in order to reach suitable conclusions. It is better, if this consideration does not seem to have been made, to proceed slowly so as to avoid premature starts on ill-considered schemes resulting in abortive work. When due consideration has been given, or at least, it seems that no further progress can be made, it is important to ensure that the Brief, as settled, is duly recorded as agreed so that at the time of the agreement both client and architect or surveyor are in possession of an identical document for reference purposes.

Sometimes, in the case of architects and surveyors in employment, the lines of decision taking and responsibility become blurred so that it is difficult to determine who is the client and at times it may even seem that the architect or surveyor almost assumes the role of client himself. This can be an exceptionally dangerous situation for the professional man in which to find himself. If he encounters attitudes in the company or authority for whom he is working such as "Oh, you know what we want" or "We will leave it all to you; you know best", flattered though he may be, he will find himself taking on a function which is more likely to produce brickbats for him rather than an accolade at the end of a job. Far better he should say to the manufacturing division, transport division, housing or education committee or department or whatever "it will be your building and your people will be using it – what is it you wish to have" and proceed from that point.

In the better organised larger authorities undertaking a fair amount of building work, forms are often produced for the various client divisions within the organisation the completion of which may serve to initiate a scheme. The forms require answers to a wide range of questions before the matter is progressed by the architect or surveyor. These forms, at times, even serve to forestall an ill-considered idea that further accommodation is required. For example a re-organisation of work or improved utilisation of existing space might entirely obviate the necessity for further accommodation.

If the need for further accommodation has definitely been established, then this might be phrased, of course, within a time scale which in turn will govern the form the solution will take. For example new accommodation required in three to four years time, in an area where land is available, obviously suggests that the solution will be found in a new building. In a dense inner city area a similar solution might be achieved by demolition of old derelict buildings and rebuilding or alternatively by alteration and refurbishment of existing premises. A requirement phrased within a shorter time scale, say two years might still be solved by minor alteration and refurbishment of existing premises although clearly such a scheme would have to be relatively straightforward. An urgent demand would have to be satisfied as best it could by the taking of premises available on the market, virtually as they stand, because little could be done by way of fitting out to newly built or refurbished premises in under a year or eighteen months unless the client was able to call upon and had the trust and confidence in professional advisers and contractors to embark upon one of the more open ended types of contract to effect speed of operation as are discussed in Chapter 5 and where decisions are taken, drawings produced and contractor's work proceeds as a rapid progression. However it is the concern of this book to concentrate on what are called "Preliminary" and "Basic Services" in Part 1 of the RIBA Architect's Appointment 1982. The first two "Work Stages" are described thus:

PRELIMINARY SERVICES

WORK STAGE A: Inception

Brief	1.1 Discuss the client's requirements including time-scale and any financial limits: assess these and give general advice on how to proceed: agree the architect's services.
Information to be provided by the client	1.2 Obtain from the client information on ownership and any lessors and lessees of the site, any existing buildings on the site, boundary fences and other enclosures, and any known easements, encroachments, underground services, rights of way, rights of support and other relevant matters.
Site appraisal	1.3 Visit the site and carry out an initial appraisal.
Advice on other consultants' services	1.4 Advise on the need for other consultants' services and on the scope of these services.
Design work by specialist firms	1.5 Advise on the need for specialist contractors, sub-contractors and suppliers to design and execute part of the works to comply with the architect's requirements.
Site staff	1.6 Advise on the need for site staff.
Timetable and fee basis	1.7 Prepare where required an outline timetable and fee basis for further services for the client's approval.

WORK STAGE B: Feasibility

Feasibility studies	1.8 Carry out such studies as may be necessary to determine the feasibility of the client's requirements; review with the client alterna-

tive design and construction approaches and cost implications; advise on the need to obtain planning permissions, approvals under building acts or regulations, and other similar statutory requirements.

This description of the first two Work Stages is considerably different from the two comparatively brief paragraphs covering these stages which appeared in the 1971 Edition of the RIBA Conditions of Engagement which, with amendments in subsequent years, remained in use until June 1982. There was no mention previously under Stage A: Inception of information from the client, visiting the site or advice on site staff some of which might be thought more appropriate in any event to Stage B: Feasibility. Fortunately the Introduction to the RIBA Architect's Appointment 1982 states that the sequence of work stages may be varied, or two or more work stages may be combined to suit particular circumstances, because it would certainly seem that most circumstances would require such variations.

The description for the first two Work Stages in the pre-1982 RIBA Conditions closely matched those which appear in the current 1981 edition of the RICS Conditions of Engagement for New Works set out below:

2.1.2.   New Buildings

Stage A
Discussing the client's requirements, giving general advice and outlining possible courses of action.

Stage B
Visiting the property and carrying out an initial technical appraisal including making preliminary enquiries of the local authority regarding statutory requirements. This appraisal may include advice on the need for consultants, an approximation of cost, an outline timetable for completion of works and suggested contract procedures to be adopted.

Although perhaps open to criticism because of their comparative brevity the above description of the first two Work Stages is probably sufficient to initiate a project yet also trigger off the need to cover any additional aspects in the agreement between architect or surveyor and client according to particular circumstances. By endeavouring to be more comprehensive than formerly the RIBA may yet still not have succeeded in covering all possible points. It will be noted however that visiting the property, a highly important requirement, did in fact appear in the RICS Conditions and its omission from the earlier RIBA Conditions has now been corrected, albeit by including it under Inception rather than Feasibility.

For building works to existing buildings (alterations, conversion, improvements, additions to buildings and rehabilitation works) the initial Work Stages are set out as follows in the RICS Conditions of Engagement, 1981 edition:

Stage A

Discussing the client's requirements, giving general advice and outlining possible courses of action.

Stage B

(i) Visiting the property and carrying out an initial technical appraisal, including making preliminary enquiries of the local authority regarding statutory requirements and reporting to the client. This appraisal may include advice on the need for consultants, an approximation of cost, an outline timetable for completion of works and suggested contract procedures to be adopted.

(ii) Carrying out a measured survey of existing buildings and producing a survey drawing including, where necessary, levels.

Stage B (ii) regarding the survey of existing buildings will be dealt with in greater detail in Chapter 7 on Drawings, in Part 3, Project Documentation. Although there may be cases where it is necessary to carry out a survey and produce drawings of existing buildings before it is possible to produce a Feasibility Report it is thought that such circumstances are comparatively rare. As discussed later in Chapter 7, surveys and drawings are expensive and it would not be reasonable to commit a client to such expenditure until a Feasibility Report had shown that it was possible to produce, from the existing building, the scheme as proposed to date. What will be required in most cases and which should be sufficient for the purpose will be sketch plans, either based on existing drawings, if there are any, or produced by pacing distances and preparing a plan to an approximate scale only in outline. While it is convenient to mention the measured survey in the RICS Conditions at this point along with survey drawings, probably because as for the other work covered by

Stages A and B the charge for these items would be on a time basis, it seems a curious omission not to mention specifically the need to carry out a structural survey as part of the Feasibility Study. Perhaps however visiting the property and carrying out an initial appraisal is intended to cover this aspect although the wording does conjure up something far less than what is normally found to be necessary. It would seem therefore that the RICS Conditions have got matters round the wrong way in mentioning the need for measured surveys yet failing to mention the need for a structural survey.

Although it could be said that a reasonably full Brief could be prepared with a time scale and that this could be handed out to professional advisers who could be left to provide a solution in one of perhaps a number of alternative possibilities, without further reference back to the client, in practice this is seldom done. Much more likely is the steady progression through the various work stages in conjunction with the client and, as far as the typical job envisaged by this book is concerned, it is interesting to observe that completion of some parts of Stage A, Inception, has in fact already taken place. It is also of interest to note that the RIBA Architect's Appointment 1982 on Preliminary Services omits all reference to the headnote to the description of "Normal Services" which appeared in the pre-1982 edition of the RIBA Conditions and which provided that such initial consultations "may be given free of charge". This omission is curious. Both the method of approach and the fact that normal business relations in nearly all circumstances dictate that such initial enquiries, (amounting in fact to whether there is employment or not for an architect or surveyor) need to be provided without charge have been covered in Chapter 2, so that at this stage it is of concern to establish a further Brief sufficient for a Feasibility Study to be carried out.

With Stage B having been reached it will usually be known whether the Feasibility Study is to be carried out for a building project on a new site already owned by the client or one in process of being purchased, usually the outcome of the Study determining whether the purchase proceeds or not, or whether it is to relate to an existing structure, once again either already owned by the client or marked down as a possibility for purchase.

Although, as already mentioned, Briefs will take as many forms as there are projects, it remains true that certain features will crop up regularly. The features will be grouped according to whether the building is to be used for residential, office, industrial, laboratory, storage or any other purpose or combination of purposes. In all cases it will be necessary to establish a focal point with address and telephone number for dealing with queries in the preparation of the Brief and for agreeing any amendments to the agreed Brief should this be found necessary during the course of preparation of the Feasibility Study.

For a new residential building on a virgin site items of information which the architect or surveyor will need from the client will include, among others, the following:

(i) the floor area required; this will probably be expressed in terms of the number of occupants, and their ages together with the number of rooms. It will be up to the architect or surveyor to translate this information into net and gross areas in discussion with the client.

(ii) the number of storeys; the architect or surveyor will need also to know whether he is to cater for any disabilities in the proposed occupants, for example an inability to negotiate stairs or steps.

(iii) any preferences in relation to aspect or environmental conditions.

(iv) requirements for sanitary accommodation.

(v) requirements for special leisure activities.

(vi) requirements for garaging and parking of vehicles.

(vii) any special security requirements.

(viii) any marked preferences for heating systems or fuel to be used.

(ix) requirements for landscaping.

(x) Total amount available to cover total costs including fees.

(xi) Any time limit on the requirement.

In the case of an existing building which is to be extensively refurbished much the same information is required from the client but, of course, it will need, in the Feasibility Study, to be related to the existing buildings and whether the building will be satisfactory for the purpose in size or will require extension.

For a building to be erected for use for office purposes the information required takes on a somewhat different form but the items which might typically be requested from clients could include details of the following:

(i) staff numbers to be accommodated categorised into
Male.
Female.
Grades of each of the above.
Space entitlement of each (if not standardised within the client's organisation discussion would be needed to resolve this aspect with the client).

101

    (ii) Whether space to be open plan or cellular.

   (iii) Grouping of staff – the identity, size and composition of units.

   (iv) Any unusual or special office machinery requirements involving higher floor loadings than normal, unusual ceiling heights or special services.

    (v) Filing and retrieval systems. Post room facilities.

   (vi) Telecom switchboard and Telex facilities.

  (vii) Computer facilities.

 (viii) Catering facilities – restaurant, canteen, tea points and vending machines.

   (ix) Conference room and cinema requirement.

    (x) Interview rooms.

   (xi) Libraries.

  (xii) Reception areas, public spaces, waiting rooms, exhibition space.

 (xiii) First aid facilities. Medical room.

 (xiv) Reprographic facilities.

  (xv) Security facilities and staff accommodation.

 (xvi) Strongrooms or safes.

(xvii) Garaging and parking space. Loading facilities.

 (xix) Sports and staff social facilities.

  (xx) Waste disposal methods – collection.

 (xxi) Preferences for particular environmental characteristics, air conditioning for example.

Most of the above information becomes translated into an overall space need but of course specific sectional requirements determine layout, circulation, access etc. Client's preferences can be expressed in their answers to particular queries.

For work to an existing building there would be a need to gather all the information required in a similar manner with a view to the layout of the accommodation required being arranged within the specific areas available and all of it within the constraints of the existing overall building envelope if at all possible. Here again, however, the outcome of the Feasibility Study may suggest the need for a suitable extension, if what is available from the existing building is insufficient to satisfy the requirements, and the Study would then need to proceed to discuss the possibility of providing this necessary enlargement.

If the development or refurbishment is to be undertaken for a developer then, of course, more likely than not there will be no tenant for whose occupation the project is to be specifically designed. Instead the developer will almost certainly have canvassed the market as to what are the current "selling points" in the office field and direct the architect or surveyor to incorporate these and perhaps to adopt other constructional features to his specific requirements. From his own experience, either to a lesser or greater degree, the architect or surveyor may know of the former but should, in any event, be able to discourse on the latter.

Whereas residential and office buildings designed for speculative development tend to follow a reasonably well worn path and even those designed or refurbished for a known tenant with specific needs have many features in common this is not always the case with industrial buildings. It is true that the advent of electrical power, the fork lift truck and other mechanical innovations have made many of the light industrial premises erected as speculative developments look very similar and indeed almost indistinguishable from warehouses. Such premises are often suitable with minimum adaption for many of the requirements of light industry today. It is often only when such buildings, available fairly readily on the open market, are unsuitable or even when older pre-war light industrial buildings, which in many ways adapt more easily, are found unsuitable, that an architect or surveyor is approached to design or adapt premises to suit the more specialised requirements of a particular manufacturer. Generally in the case of work for manufacturers there will be a greater need for the architect or surveyor to take special steps to establish and understand the production processes involved in the particular concern for whom the work is to be carried out. He will also need to study existing production conditions at first hand, or similar plants elsewhere, and listen carefully to criticisms of those conditions with a view to improving on what has been done before. If he takes this extra trouble to find out for himself and not rely merely on word of mouth descriptions from others, even though they may be employed by the organisation, this will pay hands down in the long run and he will be able to design for the particular production processes far better as a result. In effect he will be carrying out a "user requirement study" of which more will be said later.

A mere mention only at this point may be made to show how some of the production processes may impinge on a building structure. There may for example be a need for:

(a) Special environments for certain operations; for example paint booths or dust free rooms requiring high levels of ventilation, temperature, humidity and fine dust controls.
(b) Vibration or sound proofing for heavy presses or stampers.
(c) Structure borne mechanical handling equipment for example overhead cranes, monorails or conveyors.

(d) Fume, acid or alkali precipitators.

(e) Special areas for toxic, corrosive or radio-active processes perhaps necessitating special protection for floors, separate washroom and rest areas, air filtration and with fumes and effluents requiring special disposal.

(f) Precautions against fire or explosion hazard, perhaps necessitating a sprinkler installation or special areas left clear of all other features around particularly sensitive buildings.

(g) Special facilities for loading and unloading; a raised dock perhaps with special levellers or drive-in facilities. Special provision may be needed for hopper vehicles.

The service requirements for production and processing can be considerable and need to be taken into account in assessing the position of structural members when it comes to designing new premises or ascertaining whether existing premises will be satisfactory. A mention of a few possibilities will illustrate the range which may be encountered:

(a) Electrical power; there may be different power requirements for different areas of the production process and preferred positions for power outlets, isolators and switch gear.

(b) Lighting levels may need special care; for example some processes require colour correction while some machinery can interact with the frequency of the lighting making machinery appear stationary even when in operation.

(c) Extra ventilation may be necessary because of heat gain from the production proceses as well as the production services.

(d) Effluents may need special treatment apart from normal "domestic" requirements of grease traps and petrol interceptors.

(e) While natural gas may be required for space heating and boilers it may also be required for production processes and there may also be requirements for other types of gas with consequential storage problems.

(f) Water may need to be preheated, filtered and softened for the processes involved.

(g) There may be a need for compressed air, either dried or perhaps even lubricated, in the production process with the necessary plant for its production and treatment with consequential noise control for compressor plant.

It will of course be appreciated that the larger the project the greater the number of people who are likely to become involved both from the architect or surveyor's own office and also from the client's organisation together with, possibly, consultants on management and production processes employed by the client, all of whom will be feeding information to the architect or surveyor on what will be required from the new or refurbished existing buildings. The consultants employed by the client may well have been introduced in advance of the design team to consider and advise upon the client's operational activities. On the other hand the investigations and enquiries by the architect or surveyor may bring to a head recognition of the need for such consultants to be appointed.

Consultants appointed to advise on the client's own operational activities are quite distinct from those consultants whom the architect or surveyor may well feel he needs to advise the client to appoint for the duration of the Feasibility Study. These appointments may be necessary so as to enable the architect or surveyor to have the full resources of allied disciplines in the building field, for example structural engineer, mechanical services and electrical engineer possibly also acoustic and even landscape consultants along with a quantity surveyor to advise on difficulties and costs, since obviously on large projects feasibility applies equally to the disciplines practiced by these professionals as well as to the architect or surveyor. If the architect or surveyor neglects to enlist such advice when it is necessary and instead makes guesses or assumptions in relation to work more properly the province of other disciplines he could find himself dangerously too far wide of the mark in his report on Feasibility. If for no other reason than the natural affront felt by one professional when another from a different discipline encroaches on his territory, the architect or surveyor should be very wary of stepping into other's shoes in this respect otherwise he may find himself under criticism at a later date. Only the architect or surveyor knows when it is necessary to call in these other specialists but clearly this must be in nearly all cases other than the comparatively straightforward when the architect or surveyor is certain he can speak on all the aspects required by the Feasibility Study from his own experience. A client is entitled to place reliance on the architect or surveyor's judgement on the need for other consultants at this stage and the corollary applies in that the client should be prepared to take the advice given.

For projects beyond the personal experience of the architect or surveyor, or beyond his capability to acquire that experience in connection with the particular project, there will be a definite need for special consultants as already discussed. For the very large project or the project to be used for a comparatively unfamiliar purpose where the needs are not to be met by a stereotyped solution of simple space, there will probably be the need for a full "User

Requirement Study". The User Requirement Study is a process of identifying purpose in terms of activities and human needs and analysing their affect on design. Its purposes are to state the design problem as precisely as possible, clarify implications for both client and design team and specify the required performance of the building. It begins by establishing the facts about the people and activities to be accommodated and ends with recommendations for an environment and an arrangement of space suited for comfort and efficiency.

As discussed in relation to the design of industrial premises an understanding of function is best derived from operational research and work study. On the other hand an understanding of human needs from physiology, psychology and sociology which, if not in so many words, forms a vital part in the basic training of architects and surveyors as designers. When there is little known about the type of building needed, the User Requirement Study is of necessity a component part in the preparation of the Brief. It should be obvious that this process is in fact adopted by all architects and surveyors in the solution of all design problems. Adoption however tends to be subconscious in the case of the more routine demands of residential, office, storage or industrial developments. Even when the developments are of a more complex nature, for example for school, hospital, transport or public utility undertakings and these are for public authorities there may well be requirements and standards laid down from a central development department within the authority or laid down by central government. Even public authorities can have a need, at times, to produce fairly unique buildings and it is for these occasions and in the case of jobs for private clients that the full range of user employment studies will be adopted for special new process works, research laboratories, leisure complexes and the like. The eventual aim will be to produce a building which will enable its occupants to carry out their activities economically and conveniently while at the same time providing an environment suited to human needs both individually and collectively. The architect or surveyor will, of necessity, need in his design to counter the way in which the activities or processes carried on within the building impinge upon the occupants carrying out those activities.

It is necessary for both clients, occupants and any specialist consultants as well as the architect or surveyor to participate in the User Requirement Study. The importance of method cannot be overstressed to clarify objectives, to help create good relationships and to disseminate all the varied aspects of required information while ordered method will help to overcome any tendency towards the formation of subjective judgements.

The information obtained from a User Requirement Study should be organised to:

(a) Identify facts leading to a definition of the standards of space and conditions.

(b) Interpret those facts as they affect building by specifying the amount of space required for each activity and the physical conditions needed in each case and

(c) guide decisions by analysing the data affecting the arrangement of the plan and the choice of fabric and mechanism.

In practice the User Requirement Study can be utilised in three ways:

(a) For assisting normal design when a Brief has been prepared in basic outline form, perhaps purely from the client's viewpoint, but which needs developing even though this development may have to be within parameters set by the client.

(b) For developing and setting a standard when it is assumed that no reliable standards or information exist on area requirements, environmental conditions or even costs. The results might in these circumstances establish a policy and a range of standards for future use by a large organisation.

(c) For reviewing existing standards when these, to an extent, have been called in question or when there are new circumstances to allow for. Generally the study in these circumstances will result in a revision of existing standards for future use.

Studies can be carried out in roughly three ranges of depth depending on the circumstances of a particular job and whether it forms a prelude to others of a similar nature:

(a) A comparatively shallow study is often referred to as a "practice" study although it is in fact, more used for single jobs and normal work. It deals only with group activities on the basis that individuals' activities are well known within the group and with documented standards.

(b) The deepest in detail would be the "research" study dealing with individual activities and could be required for an entirely new type of building or, at the commencement of a large building programme, perhaps, for what at the commencement are comparatively novel buildings. In this case a comprehensive reference on the subject will be required for future use elsewhere. Clearly the costs of such studies are high and it is to be expected that such costs would be spread over the whole programme.

(c) A study at a sort of half way house stage may be considered a "special" study and where, in the main, most activities are well known and documented there remain activities and requirements which are not fully understood.

The key to the control of detail is the size of the group of persons examined in each activity. The nearer to the individual the greater the depth and, of course, decisions on the depth of the study need to be taken at the outset.

The method of going about a User Requirement Study will vary in regard to details on collecting facts, their classification and analysis according to individual requirements and preferences but the objectives remain the same. These follow a logical sequence of thinking through four stages from statement and investigation to interpretation and recommendation thus:

(1) The basic problem forms the "statement" and must represent the view of the client at top level of management. The statement provides a description of the people who will use the building, their corporate purpose and how they are organised functionally to achieve their objectives.

(2) An objective identification and analysis of facts is the requirement for a logical investigation involving all the users, their activities and all the equipment, materials furniture and fittings which they use.

(3) Relating the facts to the problems of the building provides the logical interpretation and involves the participation of the client with his consultants if necessary and all the design team. The data from the investigation duly interpreted determines the space requirements and the environmental conditions for each activity.

(4) The skilled judgement of all members of the design team may be needed for the recommendations on the requirements. It will be here that the judgement and design skill of the members in planning the arrangement of space, the choice of materials for the fabric and the selection of mechanical systems will be brought to the fore so that the client can be advised properly on what he really requires and so that eventually it can all be incorporated in the agreed Brief.

Facts and the details of activities required for the Study will be ascertained by a series of surveys. Members of the team may in fact take part or sit-in on activities, make notes, collect documents, take photographs, make drawings or tape record; all the time asking questions such as "What is done?", "Why is it done?", "How often is it done?", "What do you use in doing it?". The client will often have items such as schedules, statistics of personnel, production figures and accounts which will be useful, while observation and discussion will produce the remainder. Joint observation and joint discussion sometimes helps to reduce any tendency to subjective viewpoints which may surface if too much reliance is placed on the individual.

It may be at the stage of concluding the User Requirement Study when the full details of space requirements are known, together with the requirements for environmental conditions that the client will wish to have a very broad outline of likely cost. He may need to have this so that he can determine what effect a reduction in cost will have on the amount of space which will eventually be available or on the quality of the environment which will be provided in a new building or refurbishment, for example if air conditioning is omitted. He may then be able to gauge whether these reductions and omissions will have a significant effect on the efficiency of the activities undertaken in the proposed building. Obviously this is a sensible assessment to make before finally settling the Brief. Such assessments at this stage can, however, only be made on the very broadest of basis of cost comparisons. The architect or surveyor will need to have the services of a quantity surveyor to hand for this purpose since reliance on his own experience, supported perhaps by a study of the comparative cost tables provided in the building price books, a few of which are indicated in the Bibliography, would be insufficient for the purpose and indeed positively dangerous. Extreme care is needed in using these pricing books for approximate costings by way of reading all the "small print" and exercising considerable skill and care in making the necessary adjustments to reflect the differences between the project under consideration and the typical job envisaged by the author compiler of the pricing book. There is furthermore the consideration of inflation and it should always be made quite clear whether the figures quoted by the quantity surveyor are approximate current costs, as may possibly be required for DCF calculations, or approximate costs projected forward to an estimated practical completion date for the whole project.

The Brief settled, agreed and signed between the parties, the architect or surveyor can now give his full attention to ascertaining whether the requirements expressed in that Brief can be satisfied by a new building on a defined site or in an existing building refurbished for the purpose or as postulated in the typical job envisaged in this book by a combination of refurbishment of an existing building with the construction of a new extension.

What is of vital importance in terms of professional practice at this stage is that both client and architect or surveyor know and understand the requirements of the Brief and the extent and degree of detail to which the Feasibility Study is to be taken, however difficult and time consuming the steps necessary to reach that stage have been. Furthermore, the client will know precisely to what extent he is committed financially in ascertaining whether what he wants done can indeed be done and the architect or surveyor knows exactly to what extent his financial authority extends, both in respect of the amount of work he is to do and the fee he can expect, together with the extent to which he can employ consultants without further reference to the client, even if, when the project proceeds, such consultants would be employed directly by the client.

Whatever the circumstances of the project, there are bound to be physical features to be examined and analysed by the architect or surveyor, the condition and circumstances of which will influence the conclusions reached in the Feasibility Study. In the case of a new building proposed for a designated site or on a site to be acquired the Feasibility Study will require a full range of investigations regarding its topography and geology carried out in detail and to the depth necessary to determine whether what is proposed can be built and, having regard to the characteristics of the site, the effect of the cost of suitable foundations on the total cost of the project. Obviously the site itself cannot be considered in isolation and regard must be had to neighbouring sites and the availability of infrastructure, suitable roads, adequate sewers, public utility mains etc. in the immediate area.

The question will undoubtedly arise in the architect or surveyor's mind when considering a site for a new building as to whether it is necessary at Feasibility Study stage to have a soil survey carried out. There can be no hard and fast rule on this aspect and each case must be considered on its merits. Projects for sites in built-up areas where there are buildings not too dissimilar in character to that proposed, standing nearby without obvious blemish, and where the architect or surveyor is familiar with the area and the local geology suggest that the expense of a soil survey at Feasibility Stage would be unwarranted. A study of Ordnance Survey plans, a talk with the local Building Inspector or District Surveyor would probably be sufficient in the circumstances though, of course, it would be essential for such a survey to be carried out before the foundations were designed in detail when the project goes ahead.

At the other end of the scale there will be schemes for building on sites where the surroundings are either devoid of other buildings or where the existing buildings are of a character totally dissimilar from the structure envisaged. While it may be true to say that it is possible to provide a building in almost any situation given the scope of modern materials and engineering, feasibility is also about cost and at this stage the architect or surveyor must determine (with engineering advice from a consultant if necessary) the type of foundations which will be required so that the approximate cost can be included. Such costs on unsuitable sites can be prohibitive and may at times be the making or breaking of a scheme. Obviously in these circumstances a full soil survey is necessary at Feasibility Stage with approval to the cost being obtained from the client.

There will, of course, be cases where doubts arise somewhere between these two situations and then it will be necessary for the architect or surveyor to discuss an acceptable approach with the client. The client might be advised on these occasions that, in order to save the cost of the soil survey at this stage, the Feasibility Study will assume that the worst possible circumstances exist and approximate costs gauged accordingly. If the project goes ahead actual costs should at least not be exceeded in respect of the foundations and if changes are found to be necessary at the design stage as against the arrangement allowed for in the Feasibility Study, this should only be reflected in a lower contract sum than that envisaged by the anticipated contract sum set out in the Study. What is obviously unwise, and thoroughly bad practice, is to assume without reference to the client, the cheapest of foundations in the Feasibility Study and for the client to be led to believe the scheme can be carried out for less cost than what might in fact be the case.

For most schemes it will not probably be found necessary to carry out a soil survey but, even so, there may be times when the site is littered with old walls and foundations, or perhaps machine bases, and then it will probably be necessary to obtain the services of a quantity surveyor to give an approximate estimate for clearing these items as would be the case for the clearance of existing trees and vegetation.

As discussed in greater detail in the next Chapter in the case of every site, whether owned by the client or being purchased, the opportunity must be taken of examining the deeds to see that there are no restrictions on its use and to ensure that there are no rights exercisable over the site by others which would inhibit its development as intended. However, just as essential is a full physical inspection of the land to be used for building with such aspects in mind, since not all restrictions on the possible future use of the site are necessarily recorded in the deeds. For example, rights of light and support to buildings can be acquired over the years, as can a

111

right of way when passage over the site has been allowed to be used over a period of time. Evidence of such rights may be apparent on the site without a mention being made in the deeds and such evidence may need to be followed up with further enquiry and investigation into the facts so that some conclusion can be drawn in the Feasibility Study.

Some of the other aspects relating to preliminary investigations of the site for a Feasibility Study which may need consideration include, according to circumstances, the topography and geology, the elevation and degree of exposure, the water table and flood risk, the type and quality of top soil (assuming no soil survey is to be carried out) any grouping of trees or mature trees likely to be the subject of preservation orders or, because of their shape and character and condition, likely to be required for retention under planning for amenity purposes, the natural drainage pattern and last, but not least in times when old industrial and the poorer sites are being pressed into use, the presence of toxic materials.

Some features on an existing site which could affect costs of development could include existing roads, for example, which need diversion, existing public utilities such as sewers, gas, water or electricity mains, telephone cables to be relocated, existing gullies or streams to be diverted, bridged or piped and, if present, perhaps the re-routing of rights of way, although this can only be done with the agreement of the users.

The Meteorological Office may need to be approached if industrial processes are involved or if environmental conditions may affect services within the building. Information such as the velocity and direction of the prevailing winds, the risk of airborne pollution from any adjoining areas, or risk to any adjoining neighbourhood, anticipated minimum and maximum temperature and humidity levels, with appropriate averages and peak rainfall, so that the effect of any climatic extremes can be gauged on the site.

All developments require to be served by the public utilities and the presence or lack of some, or all, could be critical to the progress of a scheme. For example where utility services are available queries need to be raised on their condition and capacity. If they are not present then enquiries need to be made on the proximity and capacity of the nearest available and if this is inadequate then the distance to the nearest of suitable capacity. Water supply may be equally critical to a scheme. A potable supply from the Authority will be needed but there may also be a requirement for cooling water from natural sources necessitating enquiries relating to amounts which can be extracted, any conditions and any requirements as to how it is to be returned. Apart from cooling purposes process water may also be required as part of the industrial process itself.

The capacity of sewers in relation to the projected quantity of waste products whether it be domestic, industrial or merely surface water can also be very critical and extensive enquiries may need to be made into this aspect together with ascertaining whether there are any restrictions on quantity or type of effluent.

Where there are buildings on the site which are to be re-used and refurbished there will, of course, be a need for a structural survey to be carried out as part of the Feasibility Study. If the Feasibility Study is for a property which is being purchased then in many respects it will be an extended version of the more normal structural survey carried out for a prospective purchaser who merely wishes to use the premises as they exist without major alteration. Even if the client already owns the property the structural survey will present a new assessment of the property for the purposes for which it is proposed to be used. It will probably tell the client a great deal about the property of which he was not previously aware.

The character and scale of the property and whether it is occupied or not will govern to a great extent whether the vendor, in the case of a property up for sale, will allow tests to be carried out and the opening up of the structure to permit examination of hidden structural features. If the property is already owned then clearly no trouble should be experienced in this respect but if it is not possible to open up, whatever the ownership, then the consequences and possibilities need to be spelt out to the client together with some approximate estimating on costs likely to be incurred should conditions be as bad as could possibly be expected when it comes to detailed design stage and the time for assumptions is past.

Certainly whenever possible considerable care needs to be taken to establish as much information as possible about the existing structure. This may extend from the mere taking up of floor boards to the removal of beam casings or the hacking off of plaster through to the removal of old roof coverings to examine the underlay and sub-structure below or to taking core samples for the examination of reinforced concrete work whether in the form of columns, beams or floor slabs. This latter aspect of modern structural surveying and engineering work is perhaps worth some amplification.

The scare over the use of High Alumina Cement in the later 1960's and 1970's had one rather fortunate by-product. This was the advance in diagnostic techniques for investigating the adequacy or otherwise of concrete members. Tests for existing concrete structures have always been available but these have now been extended and the techniques of examination are much more sophisticated than they used to be. Non-destructive tests such as differential thermal analysis can determine the degree of conversion while the more sophisticated ultra-sonic pulse velocity tests are able to provide a general guide on the residual strength of the material. However the tests can often be only of a limited nature and the results have to be interpreted with caution. A rather better known procedure provides for the drilling of concrete cores for compressive strength testing with related UPV readings and provides more consistent results for analysis and is perhaps the method most widely employed today. A further technique is provided by the use of the BRE pull-out test which comprises the drilling of small diameter holes into a beam and inserting a small self-locking anchor bolt. The force to overcome the grip of the bolt is then measured and compared with information compiled by the BRE. A further additional non-destructive method has now also been developed in the United States called the Windsor Probe Test. In this case a small gun drives a metal rod into the concrete by means of a precisely metered charge of explosive. The length of the exposed section of the probe is then measured, a relationship being found with the hardness of the aggregate and the resultant compressive strength of the concrete. With all this advance in diagnostic ability, it is now possible to work out methods of saving structures, hitherto thought to be unsafe, by the provision of structural sub-frames linked to subsequent monitoring devices, such as UPV Transducer heads, permanently installed so as to register any significant changes in comparative residual strength. The engineer simply arrives at the site with his portable digital indicator, plugs this into a permanent socket outlet from a purposely concealed cable and takes readings at appropriate intervals.

There are now a number of engineers who are skilled in diagnostic techniques and who specialise in repairs to defective structures which were once thought to be totally worthless. Information regarding failure in concrete structures is now broadcast much more widely. This is just as well in view of the never ending series of defects in buildings which almost daily receive coverage in the newspapers. The effects, for example, of Calcium Chloride on the reinforcement in concrete, once publicised, have not been forgotten and the use of this additive is now severely restricted. Its legacy, however, lives on in a number of post war buildings where severe spalling occurs to the structural elements all indicating that Calcium Chloride was probably added to the water or cement when the concrete was mixed in order to accelerate the initial set, particularly in cold weather, in quantities with no adequate measuring so that the results were disastrous. Calcium Chloride has been described by a leading engineer as "the cancer of concrete". When spalling or rust stains are evident on the exterior of a beam, these are the final, not the initial indications of failure. Major loss of strength in the structural member concerned will have already occurred.

In 1972 the blast from a bomb affected the structure of a building in Northern Ireland. This, in itself, was not perhaps surprising, but the results of the subsequent investigation certainly were. The woodwool permanent shuttering had been blown away leaving large areas of the solid structure with no concrete to speak of surrounding the reinforcement. Further investigations were carried out to build-ings in this country and it was found that this particular type of defect was widespread. Recently a completed office building in South West London had to be abandoned and it was found that what had clearly happened was that the concrete simply had not surrounded and, in some cases, even penetrated between the reinforcing rods so that failure was inevitable. Whether this was due to the fact that the concrete was insufficiently liquid or whether the aggregate was incorrectly specified, having regard to the diameter and spacing of the rods, does not particularly concern us here. What does concern us is the fact that in an age when techniques are available to deliver pre-mixed concrete in order to do away with the variations and problems associated with the old hand mixing methods, and even when mechanical means of vibration are avail-able to take out the drudgery and uncertainties of shovelling and tamping concrete on building sites, nevertheless, major defects still occur. If the laying of concrete is not soundly and adequately supervised, whether in foundation work or in-situ beams or col-umns, failures will result. The architect or surveyor must be vigilant in the supervision of concrete construction as discussed later in Chapter 12.

It may be wondered why, in an increasingly technological age, so many failures should continue to occur. Continued reports of failures in buildings however point to the inescapable fact that the large majority of problems are caused by faulty workmanship and insufficient supervision, not in the materials themselves or the plant and machinery deployed on the building site. The same rules apply in the case of a large concrete framed building to a single in-situ concrete beam. The consequences of failure are no less damaging to the professional advisers in either case. Accordingly, therefore, the appropriate British Standard Codes of Practice relating to the structural use of reinforced, pre-stressed and pre-cast concrete in buildings repay close study. It should be added that these publica-tions are extremely helpful to the architect or surveyor when examining existing reinforced concrete work. In such cases the architect or surveyor will, of course, call in a structural engineer since knowledge about concrete is a case where a little knowledge is a dangerous thing. The architect or surveyor will obviously rely upon the engineer for all that is necessary but he should not automatically expect that the engineer will solve all the problems in isolation and the architect or surveyor should attempt to learn as much as he can about concrete construction so that the two professionals can act together.

It should not be assumed that modern diagnostic aids to discover faults in old buildings are a matter for the engineer alone. An example of one particular aid now adopted by the larger firms of building surveyors concerns the various types of fibre optic probes. Such equipment developed by the medical profession has been adapted to give information, hitherto impossible to obtain without expensive opening up of old structures, of those areas that are concealed or inaccessible. The use of such probes has covered obvious examples such as timber framed buildings or cavity walls or, for example, the condition of structural timbers to the roofs of a large Victorian complex of flats. The construction in this case was unusual to say the least, as the timbers were incorporated in a sandwich type flat roof structure with concrete above and below so that the cost of investigation by traditional means would have been prohibitive. Insertion of the optical probe gave much information about the extent of decay of the main bearers which, deprived of ventilation and subject to isolated occurrences of damp penetration were found to be in variable condition ranging from sound to completely rotted.

The apparatus developed comprises a light source box containing a projector-type bulb capable of being connected to an electric mains supply or battery. Since the box also contains reflectors, cooling fan, variable light output control, extension lead and plug, it is fairly heavy and requires a carrying sling. There is a light guide cable with anular bunches of optic fibres and an integral connection to the probe. The diameter and length of the probe and its focussing eye piece can vary but the optic fibres carry the light along the probe to illuminate the dark area to be examined and a series of prisms and lenses carry the image to the focussing eye piece. The equipment is completed by an extension lead and a $\frac{1}{2}''$ drill for use where access has to be obtained. The bulk of the light source box and the need to drill holes are obvious limiting factors for the fibre optic probe type of investigation but much valuable information can be obtained regarding the need for a greater or lesser amount of opening up of the structure.

The architect and surveyor's "gadgets" comprising moisture meters, cover meters for ascertaining the cover to reinforcement, air velocity meters, vibration recorders, clinometers, aggregate testing hammers, chloride ion testers, metal detectors for finding covered drainage inspection chambers and electronic detectors for detecting underground service pipe runs are all of fairly recent origin. Nevertheless they can form valuable aids in diagnostic work that can save a great deal of clients money.

Apart from close consideration being given to the structural condition of premises having regard to their proposed use considerable care will need to be given to the special arrangements and the condition of services to see whether these will satisfy the requirements of the brief or more usually in the case of the services, whether they can be renewed in such a way together with other features to provide the environmental conditions required. There is, of course, a limit provided not only by the physical features but also by cost on what can be done to bring older buildings up to the standards achievable in entirely new buildings.

In particular, for domestic or commercial office buildings, those requirements mentioned as possibilities for inclusion in the brief earlier in this Chapter will need to be reconsidered in the light of what is found. For example a requirement for the use of heavy office machinery or even just office use in a former residential building will require an ascertainment of floor loading capability by an engineer experienced in such work if the architect or surveyor himself is not sufficiently experienced on this aspect. In the case of the industrial buildings it may be a question of deciding whether the structure of say a fairly modern single storey building will be capable of taking the load of mechanical handling equipment or complicated services. If not the cost of such strengthening work or replacement needs to be included in the Feasibility Study. Too much of such work needed to an existing building will, of course, bring the feasibility of the project into question vis-a-vis the cost of the provision of an entirely new building.

It is not possible to discuss or even mention most of the possibilities which have to be considered governing the physical relationship of a site to the new proposed buildings or the circumstances related to an existing building to be converted, adapted and improved; perhaps also extended, so that the site of the extension needs close consideration as well. Mention has been made earlier of the likely requirements of a brief relating to office and residential projects but reference should be made to various works of study and Handbooks on residential, office, factory, hotel, hostel, library or leisure building design, a few of which are mentioned in the Bibliography commencing at Page 671 if the architect or surveyor's own study field or experience needs reinforcing.

Whereas projects are of all sorts and sizes and the solutions to the problems posed by architects and surveyors are equally varied all come within the restraints of the legislation current at the time they are conceived. This legislation both national and local is diverse and complicated and although there are indications at the time of writing of endeavours being made to simplify both regulations and the administration involved it is certain that a substantial amount of control will always remain. This is for the simple reason that a consensus of opinion requires that a degree of social responsibility must apply to most building projects in view of their inevitable visual effect on others and by the nature of their use and the effect this may have on near neighbours.

The architect and surveyor's knowledge of this legislation is, along with his knowledge of design and building construction, one of the main reasons why clients approach professional advisers who are expected by the law to have a considerably greater knowledge of the legal constraints on building and the use of buildings than builders themselves. It is an element of the building process which has grown considerably over the last thirty years to take up a far larger proportion of time and effort than it did before and the consequences of failure to give the proper advice have, as a result, become much more severe. It is to this aspect that attention must now be given as the Feasibility Study must be prepared against this background of constraints governing not only what can be done but also, very much, the cost of compliance.

Chapter 4

The Law Governing Building Works

CONTENTS

119

ARCHITECTS and surveyors are likely to have a greater or lesser knowledge of legal matters and law according to the nature of their practices. There are some architects and surveyors, usually well into middle age, who specialise in various aspects of diagnostic work who are asked to give opinions on various matters relating to buildings and who constantly appear in the Courts as expert witnesses. The knowledge that such experts obtain is highly specialised and is beyond the scope of most general practice architects or surveyors, most particularly in their knowledge of the way that litigation solicitors work and the general structure of the Courts. They will know for example the difference in a case heard in the County Court from one heard in the High Court and the general nature of matters relating to appeals. They will be in such close and continuous contact with solicitors that they will identify completely with the problems of litigation and will be expert in producing proofs of evidence. They will be likely to know intimately the procedure of tribunals and, since this type of practice very often involves a quasi-judicial side as well, are likely to be expert in the practice and procedure of arbitrations and similar hearings. It is obvious therefore and would be admitted freely by such experts that their knowledge and experience in other fields such as, for example, the supervision of building work on the site is bound to wither and that other matters outside their increasingly specialised field may pass them by.

By the same token, a senior partner in a large practice firm of architects or surveyors may acquire specialised knowledge that is vital to the success of the partnership but is so different in form and character to that gained by the specialised expert witness that these two people might, to all intents and purposes, be in entirely different professions. This senior partner may have close knowledge of the law relating to partnerships, which is a specialised field in itself, and matters relating to employment which have provided a vast growth field for legislation in recent years. In a substantial practice knowledge of the statutory provisions relating to employment protection may affect every member of a large work force combining all grades of manual, clerical and professional staff. The partner in a large firm delegated to deal with matters relating to staffing will probably have a small devoted department under him but would himself have to be familiar with the legislation relating to employment generally, the rules relating to wages and salaries and lastly with the legislation relating to the termination of employment.

There are in addition a number of miscellaneous matters that he would also have to know about. The mutual duties of employer and employee formerly rooted in common law have been altered by the provisions of the Employment Protection (Consolidation) Act 1978. This imposes statutory rights and duties in certain cases but these are overlapped by a number of provisions ranging from the Sex Discrimination Act 1975, the Race Relations Act 1976, with the setting up of the Commission for Racial Equality, to the Wages Council set up under the Employment Protection Act 1975. Since the introduction of the Rules of Equal Pay in 1975 under the Equal Pay Act 1970, there are a number of provisions relating, for example, to maternity pay but most of the important legislative provisions have concentrated on protection for the employee during or on termination of employment. The rules relating to redundancy and unfair dismissal are complicated and must be followed by the employer prior to a possible hearing before an Industrial Tribunal. The original Employment Protection Act of 1975 was amended under the Employment Protection (Consolidation) Act 1978 and with the introduction of ACAS (The Advisory, Conciliation and Arbitration Service) a conciliation officer is introduced to any pending case once a claim is made. An employer's position would have been prejudiced before the conciliation officer even telephones him if he had not taken the proper steps under the 1978 Act.

The above comments merely serve to illustrate the point that two architects or surveyors who studied together can end up with totally disimilar areas of specialised knowledge that have hardly any relationship with each other. The illustration may seem a trifle obvious but to carry the point further it is possible to contrast two architects or surveyors in the public and private sector respectively. The first might have specialist knowledge as an insider of planning law, for example, or public health law but is unlikely to have specialised knowledge of each. In a planning department he might deal with matters relating to planning consents such as applications, material change in use, conditions relating to consents and the area of enforcement. He is unlikely to have the knowledge of a colleague in another office of matters under the Public Health Acts such as the use of abatement notices and detailed knowledge of Building Regulations. An architect or surveyor in private practice, however, dealing frequently with repairs and conversions is likely to have a general knowledge of the whole field without the degree of specialisation required by either officer in the public service. It is no longer true, however, to say in general that the architect or surveyor in the public sector acts in an advisory capacity only while his counterpart in private practice gets things done. At certain periods during the last decade it can be said that the reverse is more likely to be true and the architect or surveyor in the public sector may have a much more detailed knowledge of matters relating to building contracts, particularly of the larger variety, than his colleague in private practice. It is for example extremely rare for a private practitioner to have knowledge of the trade unions and labour relations Acts and the workings of the National Joint Consultative Committee for Building. His colleague however, might be an expert on such matters.

It is reasonable to enquire what general fields of legal knowledge should be acquired by the architect or surveyor who wishes to undertake the work of designing new buildings or converting and repairing buildings but who has no wish to over-specialise. A fair question but the only answer which can be given is that there is no such thing as a "general field of legal knowledge". A surveyor or architect in general practice might find himself suddenly and unexpectedly caught up in events beyond his control and find himself thrust unwillingly into the witness box. Illness or staff changes may involve him in a nightmare world of pay and employment problems that are totally unfamiliar to him, whether the practice is large or small. A surveyor in the public sector might be transferred or have change thrust upon him so that his familiar specialised skills are lost while new ones have to be painfully acquired. Those government officers running contracts being undertaken by medium sized or large contracting firms may find that they acquire some detailed knowledge in an unexpected direction; that relating to company law for example.

Captain Queeg said "you can't assume a goddam thing in the Navy"[1] and the same thing, regrettably, is true of professional practice. Captain Queeg's equivalent of the naval regulations is the complex web of statutory law that exists at present, extended and made even more complicated by delegated legislation produced by bodies which have been given authority by Parliament to enact laws. Such delegated or subordinate legislation may be in the form of statutory instruments such as the Building Regulations or made by local or other authorities in the form of by-laws. It is in the specialised areas of delegated legislation that the legal fraternity expect a great deal from architects and surveyors. They confidently assume that, in matters relating to buildings, architects and surveyors are masters of delegated legislation i.e. the fine print. Indeed, if certain statutes are designed for specialist reasons, lawyers, other than certain barristers waiting in the wings to pounce when matters

(1) "The Caine Mutiny" by Herman Wouk.

go wrong, will dismiss whole statutes as being the architect's or surveyor's province. An example is the London Building Acts (Amendment) Act 1939.

The usual easy assumption made by the lay public is that the acquisition of specialised legal knowledge is simply a matter of burning the midnight oil. If this were so there would be a large number of weary but infallible architects and surveyors. That this is not and cannot be so is due to more complex factors. An eminent authority recently described sections of the Housing Act 1980 as being "totally incomprehensible" and comments made in later chapters relating to the early ups and downs of what was for a long time known as the RIBA Contract Form, now more properly the "JCT" Form, give apt illustration of the difficulties of professional men engaged in building work who venture into the legal world. In spite of the loud recriminations as to who is responsible, masses of ill-considered, haphazard and badly drafted measures pass from being Bills to become Acts and surround the normal citizen, who is often only barely aware of them, like a minefield. Yet the professional architect or surveyor is supposed not only to know about all relevant legislation but to act upon it even if, upon the introduction of a new Act, solicitors shrug their shoulders and wait in the side-lines interested to see if the architects or surveyors will prove to be right or wrong. Many will remember the complications which arose upon the introduction of the Building Regulations and the need for waivers and the general disorganisation that followed. The queues will be remembered in local authority offices while puzzled local government officers scratched their heads as to whether timber staircases could be retained in Georgian buildings or not. The professional architect or surveyor cannot reasonably expect help from solicitors when new legislation relating to buildings is introduced.

It would not be quite so bad if the form in which legislation appeared was constant. There is, however, a regrettable modern tendency for provisions formerly relating to Housing Act matters to pop up in Town and Country Planning Acts and vice versa. The difficulty often presented by a particular provision is to find out its source of origin. The architect or surveyor dealing with problems relating to trees for example, will have to trace relevant provisions from Section 60 of Part IV of the Town and Country Planning Act 1971 which re-enacted earlier procedure in making and confirming tree preservation orders. The architect's or surveyor's simple expectation of finding a codified Act of Parliament under the heading of "Trees" will not be fulfilled. The main authority, reasonably enough, for Improvement Grants is to be found in the various

Housing Acts notably the 1969 Act but the whole field of listed building consent, for example, is far more complex. The term "Listed Building" refers to the procedure laid down under various Acts of Parliament for protecting special buildings of "architectural or historic interest". Although the Department of the Environment and its predecessors have been listing buildings of special architectural or historical interest since the end of the Second World War and the process is continuing, albeit very slowly, at the present time, the desire to prevent the wholesale wastage and destruction of ancient monuments and historic buildings finds its roots at the end of the last century. The Ancient Monuments Act of 1882, a modest measure relating to burial mounds, stone circles and objects of antiquity had been preceded in 1877 by the formation of the Society for the Protection of Ancient Buildings. This society was followed much later by the formation of the Georgian Group in 1937 and the Victorian Society in 1958. The enormous growth of preservation societies and environmental groups now in existence owes much to the work carried out by these forbears in this field and indeed these three societies along with the Ancient Monuments Society and the Council of British Archaeology and the Royal Commission on Historical Monuments have to be notified of any application for the demolition of a listed building. The variety of Acts of Parliament and the numerous consultative bodies typify in this particular instance the problems of the professional architect and surveyor.

It is all the knowledge built up by an architect or surveyor by experience and by continual reading during his professional career that will enable him to give a truly professional service to his clients on legal matters. As students, all architects and surveyors learn the basic rules of how the Planning Acts and the Building Regulations control building work but it is the ease with which certain practitioners weave their way through the legislation which distinguishes the interested and experienced architect or surveyor from the one who has learned enough to pass his examinations but then sits back and fails either to keep up to date or at least to take a responsible interest in his profession. Clients value the services of professionals in particular who can clearly differentiate between genuine requirements made by authorities and "try ons" made either cynically by experienced officials or sometimes by inexperienced subordinates out of ignorance. They also appreciate the firm advice which enables them to carry out certain projects without even applying for permission because their architect or surveyor can say "Oh yes the case of so and so showed that that particular section of whatever Act does not apply to what you wish to do". One architect of national fame is said to have acquired much business by means of a reputation which ascribes to him the ability to get more office space on a site under the Planning Acts than can others. Be that as it may many practices do indeed build up a reputation for a satisfactory performance on certain types of work and, as such, for dealing well with the requirements of certain types of client. The private architects or surveyors specialising in office buildings for developer clients is one such example just quoted but there are many others in firms who have a reputation for sound industrial buildings or good housing for developers. There is a keenness in the outlook of such practices to provide the client with schemes which do not become bogged down by technicalities of planning or building control involving costly delays; what goes forward for formal approval is likely to be accepted straight away because of the designer's familiarity with the requirements and his sure knowledge of what is and what is not acceptable. Furthermore the end product is one which will be readily acceptable to prospective tenants or purchasers on the market. Equally there are other practices which develop a flair for school, local authority housing work or the design of hospitals while other architects or surveyors, without building anything new in their entire career, concentrate on the repair, restoration, refurbishment and conversion of older buildings for modern useage. The latter in particular develop a knowledge of how older buildings and modern legislation have to be brought together and their services have become much more generally valued as the tendency to preserve has grown over the years. A sudden switch into an area of work novel to some of these practices can cause a great deal of heartache and the burning of the midnight oil on necessary background study by the staff involved.

At the top of the scale, however, there will be found large offices in both the private and public sectors, sometimes arranged on a multi-disciplinary basis, who are prepared to tackle practically any type of work for any type of client. These are usually able to call upon considerable reserves of talent and resources within the organisation and have the capital structure and background security to enable them to devote considerable long term investment into novel and often very unfamiliar types of project. Since there is often very little experience in such cases to fall back upon and client with architect or surveyor are, to some extent, in a pioneering role, the results on occasions can be extremely variable but, as discussed earlier, the architects or surveyors involved should have already ensured that their position vis-a-vis the client is absolutely clear so that there are no accusations of blame to be cast around.

There is no real substitute for a solution in building matters based on past experience, i.e. a repeat of something proved right on an earlier job or the conscious alteration to make it right for a solution that went somewhat wrong on a previous occasion. There is a considerable responsibility therefore resting on the older and more experienced members of the building professions to watch over the activities of the less experienced and this applies as much to the handling of solutions to the problems posed by the legislative control of building work as to matters of physical building construction. The younger inexperienced members have a responsibility too, of course, in that while they may be, in many respects, more up-to-date in their knowledge of current legislation, coming recently from college, they need to continue in the early years of a practice with a considerable amount of background reading. By doing so they will assimilate the finer points and clothe the bare bones of the general knowledge of both technical and legal matters which they will have acquired in order to secure their qualificatons. Of course, this is where the smaller practice, or working unit forming part of a larger authority, scores over the massive practice or local authority office where staff come and go, there is lax control from above, comparatively little contact between older and younger personnel and where everybody does a little bit on every job rather than a great deal on one job. Continuity is important on all building jobs, but obviously not always possible. In substitution the Job Book is required, and its importance cannot be overstressed, in order to maintain a complete record of all enquiries made and discussions held from inception onwards and in particular at Feasibility Stage with local planning officers, building inspectors, the District Surveyor and other inspectors administering differing aspects of the legislation. Such discussions do not bind Council or Authorities but the architect or surveyor will by the nature of the discussion and the views expressed by the officer concerned need to gauge the likely outcome of the later formal application for consent, or what lines of approach need to be adopted to gain the approvals necessary. The Job Book retains the continuity in this regard if there are any changes of staff and, of course, operates as an aide-memoire even if there are no changes.

Generally it is not necessary at Feasibility Stage to make any formal applications since the combination of the knowledge and experience of the architect or surveyor coupled with the investigations and discussions with officials will provide the answer in most cases to whether the project will be feasible or not. Of course if this is not the case it may be necessary to make a formal consent and await the outcome before the Feasibility Study is submitted to the client. Such an application would of course be in respect of the principle rather than the detail of a project. One example might be where there are doubts under planning control on whether a project might be approved on grounds of use of a site as distinct from any aspect of design and appearance. As will be seen there are provisions whereby outline approval covering the principle of a scheme can be obtained prior to the submission of details and it is appropriate to commence any review of the legislation controlling building with a consideration of the Town and Country Planning Acts. Even so it is still necessary to give prior consideration to the ordinary legal rights of others which may exist in a freehold site, and most certainly do so in a leasehold site, but for convenience these will be grouped together at the end of this chapter.

Town and Country Planning

Although Town and Country Planning Acts were passed before 1947 they were, in the main, of an adoptive nature and few local authorities were sufficiently interested to exercise control over local development or to indulge to any degree in positive planning. The destruction of the Second World War changed attitudes and the Town and Country Planning Act 1947 altered that situation and required all local planning authorities to prepare schemes. The controlling Act in power at the time of writing is the Town and Country Planning Act 1971 and this requires planning authorities at county and local level to prepare structure and local plans for their areas with a degree of public participation. These plans relate to current and future uses and how the local authority sees its area developing over the years, what it would like to see encouraged or discouraged and its ideas, if any, for helping to implement such proposals. "Zoning", setting out suitable uses for areas and "plot ratio", governing the scale of development, are not so rigidly applied now as they were at one time and more general trends and intentions are inclined to be put forward nowadays. All "development" with a few exceptions now requires planning permission, it tacitly being understood that any development which fitted in with the proposals of the structure or local plans would have a good chance of approval. There are various Statutory Instruments in force amplifying the provisions of the 1971 Act and deriving their authority for doing so from the principal Act.

Every architect or surveyor must be knowledgeable on, and familiar with, the definition of development in S22 of the principal Act since it includes not only building works on land amongst other activities such as mining but also the change of use of a building as well. The section in sub-paragraph (2) goes on to describe specific operations which do not constitute development while under the provisions of S24 the Secretary of State for the Environment has made the Town and Country Planning General Development Order 1977. This has been amended by further Statutory Instruments in 1980 and 1981, but sets out a list of operations for which it may be taken that planning permission is granted. These operations are generally known as "permitted development" and consist mainly of extensions to existing buildings and some changes of use and are included to avoid overloading the administrative system with a myriad of applications for minor works and changes.

There is also the Town and Country Planning (Use Classes) Order 1972 which closely defines various uses, setting them out in Schedules of Classes which group uses of a like nature together. A change from one use to another within the same class is not regarded as a change of use requiring planning permission.

It is inconceivable that any architect or surveyor could be in practice without possessing or having ready access at least to the Act and the two Orders referred to above as far as planning law is concerned. There are other peripheral Acts and many other Statutory Orders relating to procedures on planning matters to which access at least should be readily available as required, but the above are so fundamental that possession and study will facilitate ready answers to many of the problems posed by clients. What the inexperienced architect or surveyor may not realise, however, is that, as perhaps only to be expected, there is a considerable amount of case law on the subject of what constitutes development and whether an activity should be included in one Use Class or another. Digests of cases are available, and reference to works in the Bibliography will help in cases of doubt, but there is little doubt that keeping an eye on cases as they are reported in the Press and professional journals is the best way of being able to deal promptly and fluently with queries. For really knotty problems, of course, the client may have to be advised to obtain the opinion of one of the Counsel who specialise in planning law.

The principal Act does provide in S55 for applications to be made to determine whether planning permission is required or not. This is a very useful provision, as already discussed, and there is furthermore under S42 additional provision for the making of applications and permissions to be given on an "outline" basis. Obviously where the Feasibility of a project is in doubt from the planning point of view it would be essential, before going too far, to make one or other of such applications bearing in mind that charges are now made on planning applications and provided for by S87 of the Local Government Planning and Land Act 1980 to the scale set out in The Town and Country Planning (Fees for Applications and Deemed Applications) Amendment Regulations 1982 and that notification may need to be given to superior owners as required by S27 of the principal Act of 1971, a point not to be overlooked, otherwise the application will not be entertained or alternatively any permission given in error will be of no effect.

It must be borne in mind however that a planning authority may refuse to entertain an application in outline if, in its opinion, the development is one where the siting and appearance of the proposed buildings are all important. This can apply to developments in conservation areas and to works on listed historic buildings and in these cases the local planning authority would be entitled to refuse to consider the application until further details were submitted.

A refusal of outline planning permission would of course necessitate a reference back by the architect or surveyor to the client as to whether an appeal to the Secretary of State for the Environment should be made. While in most circumstances the responsible client, architect or surveyor will find that an application does not reach the stage when consideration of whether to appeal or not is necessary (simply because they will have taken the trouble to be aware of local plans and sensitive local feelings and, having taken all these aspects into consideration, will have framed the application with a view to obtaining approval rather than a refusal) there will be occasions when difficult officials or a difficult local authority will be encountered. Notification of an appeal in these cases will sometimes lead to discussions and the opportunity to negotiate terms for a compromise application acceptable to both sides.

Listed Buildings or Buildings in a Conservation Area

While all the above considerations apply to every application or proposal for development, certain categories of work require special treatment. As already mentioned certain buildings are listed by the Secretary of State for the Environment under S54 of the Town and Country Planning Act 1971. The buildings on the Statutory List are graded as follows:

Grade I   :   Buildings of National Importance.

Grade II* :   Buildings of Special Architectural or Historical interest which merit special consideration for their interiors.

Grade II   :   Buildings of Special Architectural or Historical interest.

Having regard to the fact that the criteria for selection now extends through Victorian and Edwardian buildings of quality and character to a number of types of differing styles built between 1914 and

1939 it is obvious that a check must be carried out before any building is altered with the list held by the Local Authority to see whether the building is listed or not, even although owners and occupiers should have been notified at the time of listing.

Even if the building is not on the Statutory List the check must be extended to ascertain whether the building is in a Conservation Area. Areas of special architectural or historic interest, as distinct from individual buildings, are to be preserved and under the Town and Country Amenities Act 1974 local planning authorities designate such areas as Conservation Areas. There are now thousands of such areas dotted throughout the country and the effect on any proposal to demolish or extensively alter or extend a building in a Conservation Area is much the same as though the building was listed since, in fact, Listed Building Consent is required. The regulations governing Listed Building consent are set out in the Town and Country Planning (Listed Buildings and Buildings in Conservation Areas) Regulations 1977. These require that all the notices and certificates as for a normal planning application have to be served in addition to all details of the proposed work, while the local planning authority must advertise the proposals in the local press stating where the proposals can be examined for a further period of twenty one days thereafter as well as displaying a Notice on the property for seven days. In considering whether to give consent the local planning authority is expected to follow criteria suggested in the Department of the Environment Circular 23/77 where there is also a list of certain works in Conservation Areas which do not require Listed Building consent.

Ancient Monuments

It is unlikely, so far as occupied buildings are concerned, that any which the architect or surveyor will be invited to deal with will be scheduled as Ancient Monuments under the Act of that name, dated 1913, since occupied houses are specifically excluded from scheduling. However bare sites are occasionally found to be encumbered by the presence of scheduled barrows, mounds or archaeological sites. Old barns or industrial buildings also may become involved if only by being attached to the historic remains at some time in the past. Scheduling requires the Department of the Environment to become directly responsible for the protection of the Monument and for making any rules for its use or repair. The local planning authority would be guided by the Ancient Monuments Branch of the Department of the Environment in considering any application, which has to be made under the provisions of The Ancient Monuments and Archaeological Areas Act 1979, relating to any proposed works.

131

Tree Preservation

Trees, both as individual fine specimens and in groups, are protected nowadays along with buildings of special architectural or historic interest and ancient monuments. It cannot be assumed therefore that a single tree or group of trees which may be in the way of a proposed development can be cut down at the mere whim of the developer, architect or surveyor. It is therefore necessary to check whether any trees on the site are the subject of a Tree Preservation Order with the Local Authority at Feasibility stage.

The procedure for making Tree Preservation Orders was consolidated in Part IV of the Town and Country Planning Act 1971 and there have been additional provisions relating to trees in the Town and Country Amenities Act 1974, S8 and S10, and in the Local Government and Planning Act 1980. Briefly the provisions provide that:

(1) Local Planning Authorities make Tree Preservation Orders which prohibit the cutting down, lopping or wilful destruction of trees without consent.

(2) Six weeks' Notice must be given to the Local Planning Authority if it is proposed to remove any tree in excess of 75mm in diameter in a Conservation Area, the particulars of the Notice to be maintained in a register open to the public so as to give the authority time to consider whether a Tree Preservation Order should be made.

It is clear therefore that before any consideration in the Feasibility Study is even given to actual building construction, or alterations to an existing building, a substantial amount of research will be needed into the site itself, if vacant, and both the site and the existing buildings if the site of the proposed project is already developed. The legal background exemplified in the deeds and as can be ascertained from the site itself in regard to rights thereon or in relation to neighbours, as we shall see, will also need a substantial amount of research at Feasibility Stage. Furthermore the planning aspects generally related to the use of proposed or existing buildings and possibly the bulk of any new development will need to be discussed. In relation to the typical job envisaged in this book as described in Chapter 2 involving the change of use, alteration and extension of a listed building with mature trees in the existing garden, it would soon become apparent that little progress could be made in discussions with local officials and perhaps local amenity groups until an outline scheme at least, giving a fair impression of what the final effect will be, can be made available as a basis for consultation. In these circumstances, it is not thought that an outline application would be entertained unless it was limited to change of use only and unless also the existing structure had been empty and decaying for some time and the Local Planning Authority was concerned that something should be done; a change of use being the only likely possibility to secure this. The Brief to the architect or surveyor and instructions for expenditure would of necessity have had to be formulated with this in mind. It may be that the Feasibility Study may have to be extended to include the stage of Outline Proposals (Stage C in the RIBA Architect's Appointment 1982 and RICS Conditions for both New Works and Works to Existing Buildings) if, because of the sensitivity of the scheme, it is not possible to gauge the amount of work which it will be necessary to carry out to obtain Listed Building Consent or, at the very least, a fair indication that such consent will be forthcoming.

Control of Construction

Legislation to protect the safety and health of the occupants of buildings has a long history and has generally been extended over the years to become the complicated morass of detail it is at the time of writing. While most people would agree that legislation has probably been a beneficial force in preventing the serious loss of life that has occurred through structural building failures in other countries (it is significant that Ronan Point, a block of flats, part of which collapsed after a gas explosion, was constructed as a special case outside the scope of the legislation existing at the time it was built) it is also true to say that all the legislation does not appear to have significantly reduced the number of faults in buildings which, if not exactly making many of them physically dangerous in which to live, have certainly made them uncomfortable and in many cases downright unhealthy. As such the scope and character of building control legislation is currently under critical examination and it is likely that substantial changes will be made soon.

Outside Inner London the legislation relating to the construction of buildings is in two complementary parts, an Act of Parliament in broad terms giving power to a Minister to make the detailed rules and regulations which are published in a Statutory Instrument. There are different enabling Acts for England and Wales, taken together, and for Scotland and Northern Ireland and the statutory instruments containing the Building Regulations are of different dates for each and contain different requirements. The current set of Regulations for England and Wales is dated 1976 with an amendment effective in 1979, those for Scotland are dated originally from 1971 with subsequent amendments and those for Northern Ireland are dated 1973.

In Inner London the enabling legislation is the London Building Act 1930 with amending Acts in 1935 and 1939. Under the principal Act the Greater London Council has the power to make Constructional By-Laws the current edition being dated 1972 with amendments dated 1974.

Regulations relating to construction are capable of being expressed in three different ways as follows:

Specific	:	These set down requirements in a precise specific manner and accordingly tend to lack flexibility.
Functional	:	These set out what is required of a part of a building and usually in conjunction there are schedules of forms of construction which would satisfy the requirement. Clearly these are more flexible than specific requirements and it is always open to architects and indeed any other applicants to show that some other form of construction meets the requirements equally. Sometimes also the "deemed to satisfy" construction shown in the Schedules may be varied or extended to include work in accordance with the requirements laid down in a particular British Standard or British Standard Code of Practice.
Performance	:	These set down requirements in the form of criteria to be satisfied by tests. They tend to be more complex and are limited by the availability of suitable tests.

As time has gone on so has the number and complexity of the Regulations grown so that of necessity the practising architect and surveyor needs not only his copy of the Regulations and Amendments but also the books which purport to act as Guides through the complex provisions of the Regulations and also those British Standards and Codes of Practice providing the details of the deemed to satisfy provisions set out therein. It is a difficult, time consuming and expensive matter to keep up to date in such matters, but clearly the architect who can not only do that (an essential pre-requisite for anyone in practice) but who can also advise his client positively and cogently on the meaning of the Regulations and can also talk authoritatively to the Building

Inspectors on the staff of the Local Authorities who administer the Regulations has a distinct advantage over his colleagues.

Most certainly it is necessary for all architects and surveyors to know the exemptions for new buildings and the partial exemptions; for the way in which the Regulations are applied to alterations and extension work to existing buildings and how they apply on a change of use of existing buildings and when the full effect of the Regulations may be brought into play in relation to such work.

In relation to works to existing buildings it is important that architects and surveyors are fully aware of the powers of relaxation contained in S6 of the Public Health Act 1961, the enabling Act for the Building Regulations in England and Wales, and similar powers in the other enabling Acts. Local Authorities can entertain applications for relaxation when it can be shown that the enforcement of the Regulations to the particular circumstances is unreasonable except in relation to Part D (Structural Stability) and Section 2 of Part E (means of escape in case of fire) when applied to certain large buildings or structures. The Local Authority is allowed two months to give a decision on an application and if it fails to issue a decision in that time the application is held to be unsuccessful. There is then a further month allowed for an appeal to the Secretary of State. The Secretary of State has issued advice to Local Authorities that such relaxations in respect of buildings of special architectural or historic interest should be dealt with sympathetically and even in relation to other old buildings it is not unusual for approval to be given for the relaxation of requirements for fire resisting construction of floors and walls, separation, compartmentation, room heights, window areas etc to be granted. A digest of relaxations allowed on appeal by the Secretary of State is published by the Department of the Environment and is essential reading for those dealing with older buildings.

Before work can be put in hand under the Building Regulations approval must be obtained. Obviously at Feasibility Stage it is necessary to discuss with the local Building Inspector any particular points which it is considered may be of concern and to keep a careful record of the comments made. It is important to be forward and outgoing in these discussions since it is better to be made aware of difficulties at this stage rather than later. If the Building Inspector is being shown a sketch plan and appears to miss a point of likely difficulty it is best to draw his attention to it. He is sure to notice it at the time of formal submission.

In London, although only a Notice is required to be served on the District Surveyor two days before work commences, it is obviously advisable to follow the same practice. Furthermore if structural calculations are involved it is obvious that far more than two days is necessary to obtain approval.

Unfortunately for architects and surveyors and their clients the Building Regulations and the London Building Constructional By-laws are not the only examples of legislation controlling the construction of buildings and a mention must be made of the following national Acts which may also have some relevance depending on circumstances:

The Public Health Act 1936.
The Office Shops and Railway Premises Act 1968.
The Factories Act 1961.
The Fire Precautions Act 1971.
The Highway Acts 1959 and 1971.
The Clean Air Acts 1956 to 1968.
The Health and Safety at Work Act 1974.
The Licencing Act 1964.

There are a number of other Acts as well relating to building generally and some others to specific types of building. The Department of Environment publishes a Building Design and Construction Guide to Statutory Provisions at regular intervals covering the General Acts and the Statutory Provisions made under them and which effect building work in England and Wales. This Guide does not, however, cover local Acts and By-laws so that it is always necessary to check in any event with local authority officers on the scope of such local legislation if any.

It may be, for example, that the architect or surveyor's client runs a business or uses buildings to store materials which involve one or other of the licencing procedures controlled by local magistrates or local authorities which in turn incorporate requirements relating to buildings or structures for the safety of the occupants or users and the users of neighbouring premises. These premises include theatres, cinemas, hotels, public houses and restaurants, premises to be used for public dancing, singing, music or other public entertainment, premises used for the keeping of petroleum, premises concerned with any business involved in the preparation of food, premises providing accommodation for animals and, while the list is by no means exhaustive, certain premises used for specific industrial or commercial processes for example involving the use of alkalis or explosives or even dry cleaning fluids. The likely requirements of the licences issued for these various purposes need to be taken into account in the Feasibility Study.

Statutory Undertakings and Public Utilities

Mention has been made earlier of the need to consider the mains of statutory undertakers supplying the utilities when examining the existing site or the existing buildings. Of course in the Feasibility Study it is necessary also to take into account the availability and costs involved in supplying the project with the services which will be required for its day to day running together with the costs involved in complying with the requirements of the statutory undertakers in regard to connections and installations.

Water authorities for instance are only required to supply domestic consumers with water and even then there are certain conditions governing when they will or will not supply premises. Other users may have to pay for the water main to be run to the site. Temporary supplies may also need to be negotiated and it is essential to obtain and study the Water Authority's By-laws and regulations for the storage and use of water, since the requirements of these will effect the ultimate cost.

Gas and Electricity Boards need to be approached with details of the proposals including the purpose of the intended building and the anticipated load on the supply of both gas and electricity. The requirements for the connection to the main, types of cables, pipes and fittings etc need to be ascertained and for electricity whether the client will be expected to pay for any sub-stations or overhead cables. It is totally unwise to assume that existing mains servicing a site or an existing building are satisfactory for a proposed use, even with domestic buildings or that a connection will be made at a nominal charge.

Similar assumptions in regard to drainage are equally dangerous and it is always essential when making enquiries to explain as fully and as early as possible what is proposed so that consideration can be given to the adequacy of the existing drains and sewers to cope with the discharge from the proposed development. If there are no adequate existing sewers it may be that the cost of providing a private drainage system will have to be contrasted with the cost, as indicated by the local authority, for running the new drains and sewers which may be required.

Provisional enquiries will also need to be made with the Local Highway Authority to obtain an approximate figure for inclusion in the Feasibility Study for any works regarding sight lines, crossings over the footway, any street lighting which may be required and full details of required types of construction and drainage if the proposed development includes any road intended for adoption by the local authority.

Most architects and surveyors tend to think of telephones as being very much the clients concern but this can no longer be said to be the case as the ready availability of modern communications systems is of vital concern to practically all occupiers. Provision must be made in the design for such installations and the cost, even at Feasibility Stage needs to be taken into account in relation to the clients requirements as expressed in the Brief. These need to be discussed with the local manager's office of British Telecommunications.

Control of Building Works by Others

Many an architect or surveyor, to his cost, has assumed that once all statutory consents are obtained there is nothing to stop a development proceeding only to feel outrage when a neighbour or superior owner threatens to, or even obtains, an injunction from the Courts to stop the work until the proposals can be properly investigated. If the architect or surveyor is lucky in these circumstances it will be found that the only cost has been delay, critical and expensive though that may have been. On other occasions there may have to be costly changes in design, even although the Local Planning Authority was quite happy with the proposals, or compensation paid to aggrieved parties for the scheme to proceed without alteration. The feeling of outrage felt by the architect or surveyor will be minimal compared with the effect on the wallet of the client who may with justification, feel that he ought to be able to recover the additional expense to which he has been put from someone else. He may take the view that professional advisers should not allow him to proceed on the basis of assumptions and it takes little stretch of the imagination to guess who the client will have lined up for carrying the can in these circumstances.

The rights of others are an aspect of equal importance in the law governing the control of building works as are statutory requirements, yet they are frequently overlooked. It is at the Feasibility stage that the architect or surveyor needs to make the appropriate enquiries and with the knowledge gained from his site examination give due consideration to the effect of the proposed development on others. The client, if he already owns the site or building will not necessarily think to involve this solicitor in the project unless he is actively reminded to do so by the architect or surveyor. It is not sufficient however, for the architect or surveyor to rely upon the solicitor to give clearance in all respects and it is his duty to see all the documents relating to title so that he can establish for his own satisfaction:

(a) Whether the land and/or buildings are freehold or leasehold and whether any other person has rights over them.
(b) The details of any registered restrictions on the use of the land, for example, restrictive covenants, charges, conditions attached by previous planning consents, easements, building lines, highway improvement lines and local authority restrictions.
(c) The details of boundaries, their description and position, details of adjoining owners with their rights and interests with a view to giving consideration to any possible rights of support to buildings, rights of light or rights of way.
(d) If the property has been recently purchased the architect or surveyor should see the replies to all searches and enquiries with a view to establishing local conditions and known proposals for the surrounding area; for example compulsory purchase orders, development proposals for housing, educational, industrial or highway proposals and the operation of such statutes as the Clean Air Acts etc.

While examination of the documents is obviously necessary, the architect or surveyor is advised not to place too much reliance upon them. For one thing they cannot tell the whole story as in the case of, say, an occupier of part of the land or buildings holding over under an old tenancy, while for another they may be plainly in error. One of the more diverting tasks of a conveyancing solicitor is, upon receiving a new set of deeds, to point out problems and inconsistencies. There will however, be cases where even he will be unable to help and a prime example is in the case of boundaries. While it has always been established law that there is no obligation on any property owner to fence his land or even indeed to define the boundaries (unless he has an obligation as the result of an easement or covenant or under the terms of a statute) it is rare that boundaries are not marked in some way or other by an artificial feature such as a brick wall, fences, or adjoining building or a natural feature such as a river.

The architect or surveyor who, in his early years in practice, eagerly unties the red ribbon with which a packet of deeds is secured, expecting to find all the answers relating to boundaries such as their exact position or ownership finds that his enthusiasm tends to wane as the years pass by. Not only are the deeds generally lacking in the sort of information that the architect or surveyor hopes to find but they can be downright misleading at the same time. He may indeed find a plan, probably crudely prepared in the case of unregistered land which, by its very appearance, gives him little confidence. He then may refer to the parcels clause in the deed which is supposed to define the physical extent of the land conveyed but which may be of little or no help. There are even cases where obvious inconsistencies occur. In such instances, the words used in the parcels clause should be examined. If it is stated that the land is "more particularly delineated" in the plan attached then the plan itself is all important. However, where a plan is stated as being "for identification purposes only" the verbal description must stand whatever the contents of the plan. On very many occasions architects and surveyors have puzzled their heads over badly drawn plans and inadequate descriptions. Even where plans have been prepared by professionals in the case of new buildings, errors are still apparent due perhaps to a variation in design not having been recorded. However by far the vast majority of plans in deeds are not professionally prepared and the sheer difficulty and volume of time that has to be spent trying to unravel boundary disputes is known to only those architects or surveyors who have been so involved.

It is a mystery why the old question normally asked by solicitors "have you checked the boundaries" seems to have fallen into disuse. Admittedly, the situation is rather better in the case of registered land where the definition is used in conjunction with a 'filed plan' usually based on the Ordnance Survey National Grid maps, to a scale of 1 : 1250 (1 : 2500 in some rural areas). Although the existence of a properly prepared plan is obviously helpful the disadvantages are, firstly, that the plan is subordinate to the verbal description under section 76 of the Land Registration Act 1925 and, secondly, the scale of the plan is so small as to make disputes over any but the most simple cases impossible to solve. On many occasions architects and surveyors have obtained 'blown up' copies of the plan using all types of ingenius calculations to solve problems over boundaries only to retire baffled in the end.

Legal disputes over boundaries are generally lengthy and, in consequence, painful. The Court will first look at the title deeds and then, having come to the same conclusion reached by everyone else, that the deeds are of little assistance, will then apply certain tried and tested legal presumptions. For example, where boundaries shown or described in the title deeds obviously differ from those on the ground, it is most likely that an error has occurred in the course of a conveyancing transaction. If both parties agree that a mistake has been made it is possible for the documents to be amended but in other cases one party only can ask for the documents to be rectified by the Courts. In the case of registered titles rectification, when supported by actual occupation, is an overriding interest in land and will therefore be binding upon a purchaser. Rectification however, is available only in cases where both parties can be shown to be mistaken as to the contents of the deeds. Where one party only makes a mistake rectification is not normally ordered, unless it can be established that the other party knew of the mistake and stood to gain by it.

A not uncommon problem found by architects and surveyors is where a boundary line has been altered by agreement possibly to overcome a problem relating to a party wall but where this has never been recorded in the deeds. Even very small strips of land, of say 100 to 200mm in width should be properly conveyed in the same manner as larger areas but this, for some reason, is often forgotten. Even where no land changes hands a written memorandum and an application to the Land Register for rectification of the boundary is obviously desirable.

Complications however, can occur where one owner encourages his neighbour to believe that a boundary is situated in a particular place but then at a much later stage wishes the original boundary line to be restored. He may be prevented from doing so by the doctrine of estoppel. In a case where one of the owners of two adjacent plots agreed that his neighbour should construct a garage so that the new outer garage wall would form the boundary, the encroachment on what was the true boundary was in fact considerable. Later however, when it was found that the true boundary line was not as had been thought and application was made to the Courts for the boundary line to be restored to its former position, the doctrine of estoppel took effect. The Court decided that neither the original owner nor his successor in title could ask for the new boundary line to be altered.[2] Furthermore, since the right to hold land can be lost by neglect where, for example, someone encroaches upon a boundary and no action against him is taken for a long period of time, restitution can become difficult and in excess of twelve years will be impossible.

It is hoped that if this section of the book points to one lesson above others, it is the need for the architect or surveyor to trace out boundaries very carefully on the site and make sure that he knows the true position. It is by no means unheard of for a scheme involving the construction of an addition built along the line of a supposed boundary to be totally frustrated when the adjoining owner produces sufficient proof to suggest that the boundary line may be incorrect. Architects or surveyors who then, undaunted, proceed with the project as originally planned are reckless indeed.

Another notable example of a case where possible restrictions on a building project will not necessarily be revealed by an examination of the deeds is in connection with rights of light. Such rights, in the

---

(2) *Hopgood* v. *Brown* (1955) 1 ALL ER 550.

form of a negative easement are conferred by the Prescription Act 1832 and under the provisions of that Act are acquired, but not necessarily recorded, over a period of nineteen years and one day of uninterrupted use (extended to twenty-seven years by the Rights of Light Act 1959 to allow for the duration of the Second World War where appropriate) and if there is a proposal to extend an existing building or to construct a new building, careful examination of the adjoining structures and in particular their windows is necessary together with an assessment of the age of the window openings and whether the proposed development is likely to obstruct the light to the extent of giving rise to an actionable nuisance. It is the extent of the obstruction which can be built with impunity which may be of particular interest and concern at the Feasibility stage. It is here, and in similar situations where there is doubt about what can or cannot be done, that in addition to his knowledge of legislation the architect or surveyor will find a knowledge of case law and, in particular, that element of recent provenance which at any particular time has yet to find its way into text books, particularly useful. Judicial precedent as expressed in case law is as important in building matters as it is in other walks of life and the architect or surveyor who confines or concentrates his knowledge on legislation alone will miss much that is important. The underlying theme of judicial precedent is that all cases should be treated in the same way as previous cases of a like nature. Therefore if, for example, the new proposed development is going to interfere with another property's light but to an extent similar to that pertaining in another situation where the developer had successfully resisted an action at law to curtail the proposals, it follows that the new development should be able to proceed with impunity. Even apart from the difficulty of comparing one case with another, to see whether they are analogous or not, every so often such assumptions will be upset when the judicial precedents set down by previous cases are ignored or even overturned. Glum faces may be produced all round as architects and surveyors are forced to revise their previously held notions on the subject and acclimatise to the new situation.

A comparatively recent case on the easement of the right to light illustrates this point. Architects and surveyors might confidently and reasonably expect that the law of easements, which of all common law matters is the most rooted in past history, by now to be almost beyond change. It is certainly true that in the Ellenborough Park case in 1956 the four main characteristics of an easement were re-stated.[3] These are in the first place that there must be a

(3) Ch 131 per the judgement of Sir Raymond Evershed MR.

dominant and a serviant tenement, secondly that the easement must accommodate the dominant tenement, thirdly that the dominant and servient owners must be different persons and lastly that a right over land cannot amount to an easement unless it is capable of forming the subject matter of a grant. An easement is incidental to land and is not personal to the owner and must serve as an extension of the enjoyment of the dominant tenement. The principle that a right over land cannot amount to an easement unless it is capable of forming the subject matter of a grant rules out a number of situations which might at first glance be thought of as easements such as a delightful prospect of the Downs, the automatic right to privacy or the right to sunlight, protection from the weather and a general right to air or light.

There is much confusion over the principle of "negative" easements. One cannot, in fact, acquire a natural right of access to maintain a wall built on a boundary.

An easement might be acquired by specific grant, by implication, by statute, by necessity or by prescription. Thus if a building has been erected long enough to acquire an easement of support, an adjoining owner may only remove support at his peril. While an owner has a natural right to the support of his land this does not automatically include the right to the support of a building unless an easement has been acquired. The acquisition of an easement is a matter of fact. Architects and surveyors are mainly concerned with prescriptive rights. These may arise in three ways. Firstly since time immemorial by Common Law, secondly by the concept of the modern lost grant and finally by the Prescription Act of 1832. The right must be enjoyed openly and not secretly (nec vi, nec clam, nec precario).

As many architects and surveyors will know, under the Prescription Act of 1832 a right to light has to be enjoyed for twenty years without interruption to defined apertures. Since "interruption" in law means one year a right to light can be obtained after nineteen years and one day. A writ to enforce a right of light however, can only be served once the full period of twenty years has elapsed. The Rights of Light Act 1959 overcame the practical difficulty, still seen in the case of some properties, where a vast hoarding was erected in the past to prevent the acquisition of a right of light, by giving servient owners the power to register a notice of "notional obstruction" accompanied by a plan which would effectively replace the need to erect the hoarding. In addition, under the Act, it became no longer necessary to await the expiration of the full twenty years before bringing an action. A notice of registration for enjoyment of light for nineteen years plus a day could be followed by immediate proceedings.

There has never been a right to take action merely for a diminution of light and it must be proved that the reduction in light amounts to a

143

legal nuisance. Accordingly the action rests not upon the degree of light which has been removed but upon the adequacy of the light that remains and expert evidence is normally called upon this particular point. This has long been established under the case of *Colls* v. *Home and Colonial Stores Ltd* (1904) AC 179. The case of *Allen* v. *Greenwood* (1979) 2 WLR 187[4] upset the apple cart of previously conceived ideas. The case concerned the amount of light available to a greenhouse. The plaintiffs sought an injunction to restrain their neighbours from keeping a caravan and a new boarded fence which obstructed their light. They had enjoyed use of the light for at least twenty years as required by Section 3 of the Prescription Act 1832 and so the case, which went to the Court of Appeal, hinged on whether the obstruction of light would be regarded by the Court as an actionable nuisance. The outstanding feature of this case was, of course, that a greenhouse requires an unusually high degree of light.

The Court decided that the plaintiffs were entitled to an injunction. This was tantamount to saying that the right to light was more extensive than had previously been supposed and the case opened the door to the idea of ascertaining the use to which a particular building was put and to saying that if a greater than average amount of light was needed then this was material and also that an abnormal level of light could be acquired by prescription. It was immaterial that the case concerned only a greenhouse and a caravan since the application of the principle is universal. Thus the basis of measurement of the right to light under the Colls case was overruled. The previous level of prescriptive right under the "ordinary notions of mankind" has now been replaced by special circumstances and thus the techniques of specialised architects and surveyors in the field of rights of light have had to be reconsidered and the previous notions of what could or could not be done cast aside. Hence the gloomy faces.

A further illustration may also be useful in relation to the refurbishment of existing leasehold premises. The need for the examination of all legal documents in relation to premises has already been stressed and this will of course extend to leases. These lengthy documents govern what a tenant can do with his property and set out the liabilities of the respective parties. With the type of schemes envisaged in this book most of the leases will probably be of lengthy terms (if not it would be for the architect or surveyor to speak up quickly for it is not unknown for tenants to mistakenly spend large sums on property only to find out too late that the lease is near the end of its life with no prospects of renewal unless a strong

(4) Also reported in the Estates Gazette 13 January 1979 at Page 139.

case can be made out under the Landlord and Tenant Act 1954) and the liability for repairs, more than likely, expressed as entirely the tenants. It is, however, natural for tenants and their professional advisers at times to think of some of the more major items that form part of a refurbishment scheme as being more in the nature of landlords renewals of part of the structure in a form different and better than what it was before. Accordingly it may be thought that the landlord should be expected to pay for such items. Such considerations often arise when tenants wish to carry out fairly extensive works towards the end of a lease and are able to negotiate an early surrender of the old lease and the taking of a new lease to make the work proposed cost effective in terms of security of tenure for a further period of years.

The question of the liability for repairs vis-a-vis tenants is a fairly complicated one and an area which has produced a fair amount of case law mainly because of the different wording used in lease documents. It is the interpretation of words and in particular the meaning of the word "repair" in relation to the length of the lease and the age, character and location of the buildings which has given rise to Court proceedings. Architects and surveyors must be aware of the main principles which have been laid down by the Courts over the years and be prepared to advise their clients accordingly. One such aspect has been before the Courts fairly recently and illustrates the point that what might seem the obvious answer to the lay client may not be the one arrived at by the Courts, concerned as they are with judicial legal precedent, as well as upsetting commonly held notions by the architectural and surveying professions.

The case in question was *Ravenseft Properties Ltd.* v. *Davstone Holdings Ltd*[5] (1980) 1 All ER 929 where stone cladding on a building at Notting Hill Gate, London, was found to be loose and, after discussion between landlord and tenant, it was agreed that Ravenseft would carry out the necessary work and claim from Davstone such of the costs they considered to be the responsibility of Davstone under the terms of the lease. The cause of the failure in the stone cladding was the lack of an expansion joint between the concrete frame and the stonework to allow for differential thermal movement. The workmanship in the tying in of the stone to the remainder of the building was also found to have been inadequate. Ravenseft in disputing their liability to pay for these items of work made two separate points. They said that the damage was caused by an inherent defect in the building and that a repairing covenant could not apply to such a defect and secondly they said that the

(5) Also reported in the Estates Gazette 6 January 1979 at Page 51.

remedial work in question was work carried out to rectify an inherent defect and accordingly responsibility could not be laid at their door. The interesting point from the judgement was that the judge rejected both these lines of argument and decided, going right back to the root of earlier cases, that there was no rule of law to the effect that the remedying of an inherent defect could never be "repair" in the legal sense. He said that "the true test as the cases show, is that it is always a question of degree whether that which the tenant is being asked to do can properly be described as repair, or whether, on the contrary, it would involve giving back to the landlord a wholly different thing from that which he demised". In this particular case concerning a large modern block constructed in the 1950's the judge considered that the cost of the repairs was sufficiently small compared with the total value of the buildings that the lessor would not be said to be getting back at the end of the lease a "wholly" different thing from that which he demised. He did not however go on to suggest at what point the proportion of the cost of repair to the total value of the building the balance would be tilted so that it could be said the landlord would be getting something "wholly" different and accordingly the liability would change. It can be argued that the decision in this case even although it may have been correctly decided on judicial precedent, merely perpetuates wrong headed earlier decisions. It seems certainly perverse, lacking in common sense reasoning and exhibiting the owner bias of most judicial decisions, vis-a-vis the tenant. Why a lessor who builds something wrongly should be entitled to expect a tenant to pay for putting right his mistakes is beyond comprehension and the argument that this should be so because the cost amounts only to a small proportion of the total value is quite illogical. As a House of Lords judgement, however, it remains the law until challenged and perhaps overturned by a decision in a future case based on similar circumstances but where the proportionate principle might not be allowed to cloud the issue.

Of course, where leasehold premises are involved it is vital for the architect or surveyor to read the whole of the lease, not just selected parts, because they usually contain all sorts of restrictions, apart from the liability for repairs already mentioned, on the extent of a tenant's ability to use or alter premises as he may wish. Architects and surveyors need to study all the clauses, since such restrictions are not always in the same place in every lease, at Feasibility Stage so as to be able to advise the client on whether the lessor's consent is necessary or not depending on the circumstances. As with some restrictive covenants on freehold land, it is sometimes difficult for architects and surveyors to believe that "no alterations" in the wording of a lease means in legal terms precisely that; the only exception being where alterations are necessary to meet certain statutory requirements. This is so even though it may be thought, in regard to a particular scheme, that no lessor in his right mind would say "no", since everyone would agree that the proposals will leave the premises in a substantially uplifted state and therefore must be of benefit to the lessor in the long, if not the short, term. What is overlooked is that a lessor, by securing such a clause in the lease, has provided himself with a strong bargaining position for the time when the tenant wishes to carry out alterations. He can, as the price of his agreement, insist on all sorts of possibilities, perhaps a surrender and grant of a new regeared lease, in modern more onerous terms so far as the tenant is concerned, or, alternatively, he may insist on doing the work himself for an increased rent payable by the tenant. On the other hand he may just require a large sum of money by way of a fine or premium sufficient to make the tenant ponder on whether it is worthwhile to proceed. Not many prospective lessees, if well advised, will agree to such a restriction, but even if they are able to extend the wording to "no alterations without licence or consent" and thereby be able to take advantage of Section 19(2) of the Landlord and Tenant Act 1927, which prevents lessors withholding such consent unreasonably when such wording is used, there can still be arguments as to what is reasonable or not. Furthermore the word "improvements" is very much a legal term where it is agreed that the character of the works can justifiably be described thus, or would be so determined by the Court. Should the tenant wish to take advantage of further provisions in the same Act to avoid for ever being charged an increased rent on renewal of his lease or on a rent review an account of his own "improvements" (even apart from the provisions of the Landlord and Tenant Act 1954 as modified by the Law of Property Act 1969) and to claim compensation when he leaves, he has to serve the appropriate notice on the lessor. The landlord's response here in these circumstances may be to exercise the option allowed to him in the Act of carrying out the work himself and charging the tenant a reasonable increase in rent, or such increase as determined by the Court. Architects and Surveyors need to know about this sometimes forgotten Act, its implications when works of alteration are proposed to leasehold premises as well as the background of judicial decisions governing its application.

Before proceeding to a study in the next Chapter of the various types of building contract so as to be able to advise the client in the Feasibility Study on the best type to be used for the proposed project, mention must be made of two other aspects. One of these concerns the rights of adjoining owners in existing structures built upon the boundaries, party walls for example separating buildings, which owing to their character and condition may have an effect on the project. This effect may consist not only of the cost of necessary works but also in relation to the fees which may have to be paid by the client to the professional advisers of adjoining owners. The cost of such works and the amount of the fees may be comparatively small in relation to the overall cost of the project but they need consideration at Feasibility Stage, if only to ensure that there are no fundamental difficulties likely to impede the project if agreement cannot be reached with neighbours. In Inner London and Bristol there are fundamental differences of approach governed by local statutes for dealing with party walls as against the approach for use in the rest of England and Wales and these will be discussed in greater detail in Chapter 9 when the consents which are necessary are considered.

Financial Assistance

The final aspect to be dealt with in this Chapter, while not strictly speaking exercising an element of control over building works, does influence the timing of their commencement and involve further scrutiny of the proposals should the client be able to take advantage of the financial assistance on offer towards the cost of building works. Not all clients are knowledgeable on the extent of grants which are available and even if they have seen advertisements describing what can be obtained they do not usually appreciate that most are discretionary or the conditions which may be laid down in consequence of their receipt. The architect or surveyor needs to include advice in this respect in his Feasibility Report and, of course, the amounts of grant obtainable need to be set off against the likely costs of the proposals being put forward in the Report.

Although the grants system for residential accommodation was first introduced in 1949, it was not until nearly two decades later that the term "Improvement Grant" became familiar to the man in the Street. It was in fact the Housing Act 1969 which introduced a new and more generous grants system than had previously operated that the general public began to sit up and take notice. Following a White Paper "Old Houses into New Homes" in April 1968 and influenced by the rapidly dawning concept that it was better to renovate old houses rather than to knock them down and redevelop, Improvement Grants at last became just that; grants of money from the public purse given to those who intended to refurbish houses for their own occupation with the fewest of conditions attached. This was quite a revolutionary step; previously the idea of disbursement from the state purse to private individuals was regarded, perhaps not unnaturally, with extreme suspicion. The conditions for obtaining such grants were indeed previously so onerous that few people bothered to entangle themselves with all the rules and regulations that then applied.

The Act empowered Improvement Grants to be made through local Councils in one of three ways. The first related to standard grants for the provision of specified amenities to existing dwellings defined in the Act which the Councils were obliged to disburse. The second related to discretionary grants for improvements to single houses or converted property which Councils were empowered to consider and grant money at their discretion only; a fundamental point that is often overlooked. Finally, special grants were to be made available to assist in providing basic amenities in houses in multiple occupation, here again at the discretion of the local authority concerned.

The Housing Act 1969 was, at that time, a major piece of legislation and broke into a good deal of new territory which was, and is, of vital interest to architects and surveyors. Part 1 of the Act which set out a new code for the Grant Aided Improvement and Conversion of Houses in England and Wales was what might be termed the "carrot" section in encouraging improvement and conversion while other "stick" sections were introduced to enable local authorities, by means of increased powers, to require works of repair to be carried out to houses in the private rented sector. Part 2 of the Act dealt with "general improvement areas" relating to the environment rather than individual properties aimed at introducing pedestrian precincts, play spaces and garden areas where such amenities had never previously existed in the close knit terraces of Victorian housing that forms the inner suburbs of all great cities.

A third Part of the Act dealt with the effect of improvements on rents.

The Housing Acts 1974 and 1980 amplified and extended the law relating to Improvement Grants into new areas of need not previously envisaged, such as the special requirements of disabled persons. The precise definitions of what now do or do not rank as "improvements" has been much more closely defined by the Department of the Environment instead of being left entirely to the discretion of any particular local authority. Grants are not normally, now, given for the improvement or conversion of any structure built after the 2nd October 1961.

The old twelve point standard set down in the Housing Act of 1969 with which any building must comply in order to qualify for a Grant remains largely intact although some of the points have been subtly updated to comply with the needs of the present age. Instead of expressions such as "wholesome water" or an "internal water closet if practicable; otherwise a readily accessible water closet" the present standard refers to such matters as electric socket outlets and the thermal insulation of roof spaces.

While it has always been a requirement that houses that are the subject of an Improvement Grant must either be in, or be put in, a reasonable state of repair and be adequate for a certain period of time (now thirty years) the more detailed requirements now known as the "ten point standard" rather than the twelve point standard of the earlier statute are now defined in Circular 160/74 of the Department of the Environment. The ten requirements are as follows:

Each dwelling must be:

1. Substantially free from damp.
2. Have adequate natural lighting and ventilation in each habitable room.
3. Have adequate and safe provision throughout for artificial lighting and have sufficient electric socket outlets for the safe and proper functioning of domestic appliances.
4. Be provided with adequate drainage facilities.
5. Be in a stable constructional condition.
6. Have satisfactory internal arrangements.
7. Have satisfactory facilities for preparing and cooking food.
8. Be provided with adequate facilities for heating.
9. Have proper provision for the storage of refuse and where necessary the storage of fuel.
10. Conform with the specifications applicable to the thermal insulation of roof spaces laid down in Part F of the current Building Regulations.

Improvement Grants are available to freeholders of residential property and leaseholders where the unexpired term has at least five years to run. In addition, regulated tenants in the private sector or "secure" tenants of local authorities, New Town Corporations or Registered Housing Associations can also qualify for a grant as can protected tenants under the Rent (Agriculture) Act 1976. Just as consent is needed from those holding superior interest in the property so freeholders or lessees making application are bound to consult their tenants.

While some rules relating to Improvement Grants can be relaxed at the discretion of the local authorities some cannot. No grant can be obtained by an owner occupier whose house has a rateable value before conversion of £400 or more in Greater London and £225 elsewhere. Where two or more dwellings are to be provided the limits are raised to £600 and £350 respectively.

Local Authorities provide forms of application for Improvement Grants requesting certain basic information which are signed and returned accompanied by working drawings and a detailed specification of work, each item being priced separately and described either as being a repair or replacement on the one hand or an improvement on the other. Local Authority Officers in charge of grant administration frown quite rightly, on Provisional and Prime Cost Sums. Competitive estimates are also normally required.

The Grants Officer normally works out the "eligible expense". While builders costs and profit together with professional fees are allowed, it has always been a source of irritation to the "do it yourself" home owner that his own time cannot be charged up and included in the permitted expenditure. The cost of repairs and replacements cannot normally exceed 50% of the "eligible expense".

The expense limits and percentages have tended to vary according to the locality of the property and whether special circumstances apply; whether for example it is situated in a General Improvement Area.

Applicants often fall into the trap of making application for a grant once the contract has been settled and the work has started on the site, thinking that the result of their application will be a formality. This is far from the case unless perhaps a dangerous structure is involved or some reason for urgent repairs and often an outraged owner will complain loudly about bureaucracy. This is sad since the administration of the Grants Scheme is normally carried out in a practical and sensible manner and the officers dealing with applications are usually experienced and businesslike. A property owner should put himself in the shoes of the officer concerned as, quite obviously, to qualify for a grant from public funds some undertakings must be expected in order to ensure that the money is not wasted or that the occupants of the property are not exploited. Thus evidence of the applicants interest in the property is needed as are details of the present occupants and a certificate of future occupation as well. A time limit which is negotiable is usually set by the local authority for the completion of the works and payment is normally made direct to the builder.

The expression "standard" grant has been replaced, for some reason, by the term "intermediate grant" but similar provisions are still in force in order to enable standard amenities to be provided as of right. These amenities defined in Schedule 6 of the 1974 Act are as follows:

1. A fixed bath or shower.
2. Hot and cold water supply at a fixed bath or shower.

3. A wash hand basin.
4. A hot and cold water supply at a hand basin.
5. A sink.
6. A hot and cold water supply to the sink.
7. A water closet.

An interesting point is that the old requirement for a food store is no longer included in the list of "standard amenities". This illustrates how well the manufacturers of refrigerators have succeeded during the last decade in bringing the price of their products within the reach of practically every householder. The permitted amounts obtainable in respect of each of the above items are specified and defined.

Special grants in respect of houses in multiple occupation remain discretionary but a new departure is that discretionary grants are now obtainable in respect of repairs. "Repairs Grants" as they are called have, of course, to comply with the general rules of Improvement Grants relating to rateable value limits and eligible expense but are designed to bring properties back into the housing stock where very considerable works of repair are needed due perhaps to past neglect or structural faults.

It is always a worthwhile exercise for the architect or surveyor to look into the question as to whether any source for funds exists or not. A number of sources are available for discretionary grants such as where houses are of outstanding architectural or historic interest but in order to obtain Central Government Funds under the terms of the Historic Buildings and Ancient Monuments Act 1953 (as amended by the Civic Amenities Act 1967 and the Town and Country Amenities Act 1974) the building would almost certainly have to be listed as Grade I or Grade II*. Less outstanding buildings may still attract grants from local authority funds however, under the Local Authorities (Historic Buildings) Act 1962. The grants are directed towards the cost of repairs and additional grants may be available from the GLC in the Greater London Council area under the London Government Act 1963.

A number of private sources will consider applications for grants such as the Civic Trust and the Society for the Protection of Ancient Buildings. These are normally however, related to buildings in Conservation Areas. Other grants are available from local authorities that relate to specific problems such as fireplaces under the Clean Air Acts of 1956 and 1968 and the provision of insulation under the Homes Insulation Act 1978 and the Homes Insulation Grants Order 1980.

In addition the architect or surveyor should always remember that even if an Improvement Grant is not being sought the property owner can be very much helped by loans from Banks, Building Societies or Local Authorities under the Housing Acts for acquiring properties in a run down condition and then converting, enlarging, or improving them. The assistance of a valuer approved by the lending institution is obviously vital and the architect or surveyor must take care to comply with the requirements of the particular source of funds providing the backing to his client.

Finally, the most recent sources for assistance relate to those problems that occupy the pages of the daily papers. In the hope of encouraging industrial expansion incentives to businesses to start up or become relocated in development areas are available from the Department of Industry or loans from local authorities are available under The Inner Area Urban Areas Act 1978. This Act was passed in order to help local authorities encourage employment by granting loans for the acquisition of land or works, to establish co-operative or common ownership enterprises and to declare industrial or commercial improvement areas. The Act is aimed at assisting development in the deprived inner areas of cities which contain much wasted land and derelict buildings. Measures have been introduced also to stimulate development in rundown urban areas by means of "Enterprise Zones" and "Urban Development Areas" and, running alongside such measures, assistance is also available under Section 108 of the Housing Act 1980 in respect of the rehabilitation of buildings in such districts.

Chapter 5

Building Contracts in both the Public and Private Sector

Contents

IF Smith asks Brown to repair a window in his house and Brown agrees to do so for a certain sum of money the two parties have set up a binding contract. The intention to create a legal relationship and to arrive at an agreement for consideration are the crucial aspects as to whether a contract exists or not, although a lawyer might cautiously qualify this statement by saying that both parties must have the capacity to legally enter into a contract on the one hand and they must be at one as to the identity of the subject-matter; in other words are Smith and Brown both talking about the same window? There is, in law, however, no general requirement that any contract should be made in writing and signed, except in certain specialised fields, such as the sale of land for example, or where there is no consideration. Obviously, however, few people and indeed no professional architect or surveyor acting for others would rely on an oral agreement and even if he telephoned a builder to, for example, attend at a house to unblock a drain, he would or should, issue a confirmation instruction in writing. It would then be implied that the builder is entitled to payment since, unlike other fields of contract law, it is obvious from the commercial relationship of the parties that consideration must be one of the elements of the bargain.

English contract law depends on the doctrine of offer and acceptance. Both elements are needed before a contract can be said to be binding. In the case of building matters, one party must issue a clear invitation to the other of the terms upon which he will enter into a contract and the other party must then accept. Not unnaturally, some problems have been encountered in the past as to what documents in fact constitute an offer or acceptance. A printed price list for example, has been held not to constitute an offer as contrasted with a written estimate. In the vast majority of simple cases where a householder telephones a builder asking for a quotation to repair, say a gate, the builder then attends and sends an estimate or quotation for the work and the householder then signifies acceptance by one means or another. Whatever the term used, whether it is known as an estimate or promoted to the status of tender, the word used is immaterial to a lawyer since the document in question either does or does not constitute an offer. It must also be emphasised, however, that formal offer and acceptance cannot be subject to variation. In the instance just given, for example, should the householder write to the builder saying that he or she thinks that the estimate is fair but could the builder renew the front boundary fence at the same time that the work to the gate is being carried out, this does not signify acceptance, but is more in the nature of a counter-offer to create a further contract.

Contractors who tender for work, whether invited or otherwise, are making offers and a contract will only come into existence if one of the offers is accepted. The normal provision in any contract documentation therefore that the employer does not bind himself to accept the lowest or any tender, is merely one that re-states the basic position at law.

It is astonishing to the layman, if not perhaps to the lawyer, how many complicated bargains for large sums of money run into trouble since the transaction lacks one or other of the basic essentials of a valid contract. An agreement to carry out building work for a consideration will be seen by the Courts as being perfectly similar in essence to any other type of commercial contract but obviously there are particular problems inherent in building work which do not apply in other fields. It is necessary therefore for the parties to give due forethought to difficult circumstances which may occur since, in the lack of any provision made to cope with these, the contract may founder.

Let us therefore at the outset of this Chapter, briefly examine the building contract that existed between Roland Henry James and Albert Arthur Little for the re-building of a wall. The salient facts have been obligingly supplied by the solicitors to the estate of the late Mr. James who looked out their file dealing with the proceedings at the local County Court. On 10 April 1977, Mr. Roland James, a garage proprietor in a County town, asked Mr. Albert Little, a builder, whom he had known through the local Rotary Club for a number of years, to supply him with an estimate for the re-building of an unusually high garden wall. Mr. James was the owner of a desirable property known as "The Gables" some way from the town centre and he knew Mr. Albert Little by repute as a local jobbing builder who had carried out work for a number of his friends. In the March gales of that same year an elm tree in his garden had fallen and had brought down with it a long section of the brick wall which separated his lawn from the vegetable area at the rear of the plot of land which surrounded his house. The wall, part of a former Georgian structure was a most unusual and attractive feature of the property, greatly admired not only as a feature in itself but for the skill in which Mrs. James had trained plants and fruit trees against it. Although the remains of the Dutch Elm had been taken down and the sections of trunk and branches cut up and removed by a local tree felling firm, the brick wall remained to be re-built and Mr. Little and Mr. James, having met by appointment together surveyed the damage. In view of the acrimony which developed later, it was nevertheless evident that the meeting was a cordial one and Mr. Little provided the following estimate, later produced in Court.

> 16 April 1977
>> To clearing away collapsed brickwork to garden wall. Cleaning mortar from existing bricks where possible, allowing for new bricks as necessary to match existing and re-building wall to previous height .... £1,800.00.
>
> Note: Value added tax will be added to the above account at the current rate.

Mr. James duly received this estimate and being satisfied with it wrote the following letter:

> Albert A. Little Esq.
> Dear Albert,
>> Re: "*The Gables*"
> Many thanks for your estimate which I accept but please get the work done as soon as possible as I have a garden party arranged to which I hope you will come.
>> Regards

It is difficult to know which of the two following incidents had a greater effect upon subsequent events. It was shortly after Mr. Little arrived to commence the work on 29 April of that same year that he sustained his accident. The versions supplied by the parties at the Court Proceedings differed but what is clear is that Mr. Little was wheeling a barrow full of old bricks along a garden path when he tripped and fell. Whether this was due to his own fault or, as he claimed, was due to the fact that the younger son of Mr. James, whom he described as "a nasty little brat" had, in fact, set a trap for him, has always been in doubt. It is evident however, that his enforced rest at home and subsequent loss of income due to his injured ankle embittered him and what Mrs. James was to call "his attempt to blame an innocent child", started the breakdown in the relationship between herself, her husband and the builder. It is also clear that her hostility to Mr. Little was such that it played a large part in her husband's decision to refuse the builder's request to bring in his nephew to deputise for him on the site. This decision further soured relationships.

The second incident occurred shortly after Mr. Little started work on the wall once more and in this case the facts are not lacking. It happened that Mr. Loveday, a surveyor from the Building Inspectors Department of the local Council happened to pass by and, seeing Mr. Little's barrow outside the house called in and was shown through to the garden where he met the builder. In the loud row that followed, it must be remembered that Mr. Loveday was a young man, newly qualified, and that Mr. Little was still suffering from pain as the result of his injury. The argument, heard by the owners of "The Elms" next door starting from such matters as the permitted height of the wall and questions relating to piers and foundations, which later became more personal, need not be referred to here. It is sufficient to say that it reflected no credit on either party.

The final severance of communication between Mr. Little and Mr. James occurred when Mr. Little asked for payment on account of work done. Mr. James retorted angrily that no work of any value had, in fact, been completed. All that had happened was that his vegetable patch had been rendered unusable and his lawn ruined by heaps of bricks and muddy ruts, worsened by the spring rainfall, so that his garden looked like a battlefield and, moreover, what with the row between Mr. Little and the Council, it did not appear likely that he would ever be able to use his garden again. He had already been forced to cancel plans for the party that he had planned and so far as he was concerned Mr. Little would be paid once he had finished the work properly and not before. This was what had been agreed in the first place. Mr. Little, enraged by this reply, said that not only was the delay no fault of his but that he had put in a great deal of work and was due money on account. He said that the heaps of bricks referred to had all been carefully cleaned ready for use in re-building and that this work, dismissed as being of no value by Mr. James, formed a considerable proportion of the cost of his original estimate. He finally, and unwisely, added that so far as the word battlefield was concerned that Mr. James would not recognise one if he saw one as he himself (Mr. Little) had been in the Western Desert in the War while Mr. James had been – and here he used a vulgar expression – sitting at a desk in London. It is perhaps hardly necessary to record that Mr. Little lacked tact. It is accordingly at this point that Mr. Roland James who had, in fact, a distinguished war record, decided to sit tight and defend himself against any claim for payment. Mr. Little instructed his solicitors and, during the months that followed, letters from the lawyers passed backwards and forwards until Court Proceedings were started. It is sad that, due to the untimely death of Mr. Roland James that the Court Proceedings had to be defended by his Executors but the announcement, shortly afterwards, that Mr. Little was unable to meet his financial commitments further complicated events. Mrs. Little, who made no secret of the fact that her husband's problems started with the job at "The Gables" loudly blamed "that family" for not honouring their obligations but it is a fact that some months later, Mr. Little's trustee in bankruptcy quietly dropped the case. The bricks were cleared from the garden of "The Gables" pending the sale of the property and the remains of the high garden wall were finally taken down by the new purchaser to make room for a swimming pool.

The obvious need for a contract between employer and contractor that deals with the particular problems likely to arise in building work, ranging from sub-contracting arrangements, variations, provisions for interim payment and time for completion of the work are, it is hoped, briefly illustrated by the example just given. The solution appears, of course, as all facile solutions do, obvious. Simply draw up a document setting out the terms of agreement between the parties, dealing in particular with those problem areas likely to be encountered and presumably, if both parties have the capacity to enter into a contract and there is nothing illegal about the object of the undertaking, all should be well. The writers can, in their minds eye, see the reaction of the legal profession at the simple and artless point of view. The solicitor open mouthed, the barrister licking his lips in anticipation and the judge with his lips pursed waiting to pronounce. For sadly, as it turns out, attempts by intelligent men to produce contracts drawn up and designed to meet a special set of circumstances have often proved disastrous. Simply clauses on paper, plain as a pikestaff when the draft is being prepared, assume a totally different meaning when things go wrong. The words "it may seem like that on the face of it but it is not what I agreed at all" have been heard by many a weary lawyer and the seductive charms of a simple "do it yourself" form of agreement proposed and drawn up between two experienced businessmen has on numerous occasions lead to frustration and misery and will probably continue to do so upon many occasions in the future. This fact remains a sad one although some consolation, presumably, can be obtained from the fact that even a form of contract prepared by experts in the building field and constantly revised and amended over a period of years can suddenly, and unexpectedly, run into all kinds of trouble, as we shall see. It points to the near impossibility, except in the most simple cases, of a "do it yourself" type of contract proving successful should difficulties arise during its course and there exists a lack of goodwill and commonsense.

It is not, however, simply the inability of ordinary people to envisage problems and to find a form of wording that correctly summarises their joint intentions which provides the main stumbling block. The chief difficulty is that the parties will be unaware that their agreement, to be enforceable, must conform to the general principles of contract law which, as part of the common law of the land, has been set down and re-defined decade after decade so that the whole vast structure, each element of which has been meticulously worked out, stands as a background to each new venture. A particular example of this lies in the doctrine of entirety.

Since consideration forms one of the essential elements of a valid building contract, not only the amount of money to be paid but the time and method of payment goes to the root of the matter. Unlike simple transactions however, where a sum of money is paid upon delivery of a particular article it may not be possible to determine the amount of money that will ultimately be paid since the full extent of the work is unknown. Under such circumstances therefore, the law will require that a precise basis for payment is worked out; not only the intervals at which payments will be made but the method by which the amounts of progress payments are to be ascertained. It cannot therefore be emphasised too strongly that in all the circumstances likely to be encountered in building work, whether fully predictable or totally unknown the essentials of a valid contract must remain intact for the bargain between employer and contractor to be upheld in the Courts. There are however, quite a number of valid types of contract employed to secure the completion of building works known in the building industry and legal profession by specific titles, not all of which may be familiar to the lay person who may use one or other of them at appropriate times without fully realizing the significant differences between them.

The main types of building contract can be summarised as follows:

Lump Sum Contract

In the imaginary case of *Little* v. *James*, described earlier, Counsel for the Defendants would no doubt explain that the matter involved a simple contract, that is to say a contract not under seal and that there was, in this case, a valid offer and acceptance. He would then no doubt have pointed out that the parties had entered into a lump sum or entire contract where the entire fulfilment of the promise by either party is a condition precedent to the right to call for the fulfilment of the promise by the other. The doctrine of the "entire contract" is central to the law of the land but is particularly important in the context of this chapter. It has evolved over a number of years and can be most vividly illustrated by the action brought by the personal representative of a second mate who was due to receive thirty guineas in payment for his services ten days after his ship arrived in Liverpool. The unfortunate second mate however, had died on board the vessel during the voyage and the Court held that neither the agreed sum nor any part of its was due to his estate.[1] The uncompromising nature of the entire contract has since been watered down to some degree by the doctrine of "substantial performance",[2] but nevertheless remains an essential element in English law.

It may seem odd that when a builder quotes a lump sum he may not claim it unless he fulfils every part of the contract as against the case where a builder who agrees to carry out some work but does not specify a particular sum of money might be due for remuneration on a quantum meruit basis. There is however the enormous benefit of certainty in the former case which must not be overlooked. The right to a quantum meruit payment is one thing but to prove the sum that you feel is your due is quite another. The benefits of the lump sum contract are obvious and it is of course true to say that lump sum contracts for all types of building work proceed satisfactorily on every day in the week of every year all over the country and indeed it would be an unimaginable state of affairs if they did not. A defect occurs to a building and the owner of the house, or his wife, thumbing through the yellow pages, asks a local builder to call who, when he arrives and has given an estimate for the necessary work is asked to proceed and where, upon completion, he is handed a cheque with mutual expressions of esteem being given on either side. Some cases, however, end up in Court and although small contracts are just as vulnerable to failure from basic misunderstandings as are larger, more complicated, contracts, nevertheless the problem often lies at the root of the matter in that the essentials of a valid lump sum contract are missing.

The Lump Sum contract is the one that is most fundamental to both English law and to building work as contrasted with contracts employed for engineering works. The benefits of the true lump sum contract are self-evident and the surveyor or architect should always think of this type of contract before others since, assuming patient and painstaking preparatory work this, together with the element of certainty is most likely to contribute to the best result both from the technical and the legal point of view. Adequate preparation is the key to successful building operations and the lump sum fulfils the basis of the entire contract most completely. A contract to carry out well defined work without mention of any price, it having been

(1) *Cutter* v. *Powell* (1795).
(2) *H. Dakin & Co. Ltd.* v. *Lee* (1916) 1 KB 566 and *Hoenig* v. *Isaacs* (1952) 2 All ER 176.

agreed beforehand that the contractor is entitled to payment at reasonable rates, may be an entire contract since the entire fulfilment of the promise to carry out the work is a condition precedent to the right to call for payment but this will not be a lump sum contract where payment of a known sum is conditional upon the whole of the work set out in the contract having been completed. It is this element that is crucial. Provided that this principle is quite clear a true lump sum contract is not invalidated by progress payments being specified during the course of the work.

The lump sum contract can be employed either with or without a bill of quantities but in order that the contractual basis works efficiently, it is vital that the concept of the lump sum or fixed price is adhered to as closely as can be contrived. It is of course impossible, sadly, to achieve a truly fixed price in contracts of any size since variations are bound to occur and inflation will, in any event, see the end of the true concept of the lump sum if the work is likely to take any length of time.

The true essence of the lump sum contract is that the price remains fixed and is unaltered unless there are variations that are agreed by both sides. Bills of quantities or schedules of rates are secondary to the main aim of the contract which is to complete it at a fixed sum and such bills or rates are available only so that the variations ordered by the employer may be subsequently valued or the amounts of interim payments ascertained. The Joint Contracts Tribunal "Standard" Forms (in contrast to others published by the Tribunal), to be discussed later, are suitable for a lump sum contract but, by way of contrast, the Form of Contract issued by the Institution of Civil Engineers is unsuitable for use in connection with a Lump Sum Contract as the whole point of the type of contracting for engineering works is that it depends upon remeasurement and revaluation as a basis for payment for unknown work and is, therefore, different in both form and content to the JCT Standard Form of Contract.

Prime Cost Contracts otherwise known as Cost Plus Percentage or Cost Reimbursement Contracts

Under this type of contract the employer undertakes to pay to the builder the actual cost of his labour and material plus, in addition, an allowance for his overhead charges and a percentage for profit by way of remuneration. It is often said that the Cost Plus form of Contract favours the contractor at the expense of the employer. This comment is to over simplify the situation. There are times when the Cost Plus form of Contract is inescapable due to circumstances and

163

the only way in which a contractor can undertake to carry out certain types of work is in the knowledge that he will be paid whatever happens. Obviously, against the greater incentive to completion provided under the Lump Sum Contract, it can be seen that a building project can degenerate into a slow and inefficient stalemate when the contractor simply delivers the men to the site every morning, the men have the feeling that they are there for ever, and the professional surveyor or architect tears his hair out trying to persuade everyone to get a move on. Such form of contract is often open to the allegation that the contractor will put his least efficient men on the job knowing that he will at least get a reasonable measure of remuneration. Against this, however, it might also be said that no contractor likes to see men on his labour force bogged down for ever with no idea when they can start other work and, while he is being rewarded in a minimal fashion, he is precluded from competing for the greater rewards that will be offered by a more speculative type of contract.

It is, however, possible to ensure that the worst aspects of Prime Cost Contracts are avoided with the use of a fixed fee to the contractor to supply an incentive for speedier work. In order to enable such types of contract to operate efficiently, it is obviously necessary for some reasonably accurate estimate of the amount of work that is to be included under prime cost to be calculated and agreed so that the amount of the fee can be fixed. Sometimes contracts are arranged with a fee which fluctuates in inverse ratio according to whether the final cost is more or less than the agreed estimate of cost.

Another variant is provided by what are known as Target Cost Contracts where the risk element is shared between employer and contractor. Rather better known in civil engineering than building schemes, Target Cost Contracts offer a combination of Prime Cost reimbursement with a shared financial interest in the outcome of the contract. Under such schemes the total value of the contract is calculated in the Bills as a target which is adjusted for permitted fluctuations. The contractor is then reimbursed for his prime costs but, in parallel with this, the profit or loss on the contract is calculated and subsquently shared equally or in whatever proportion is agreed, between employer and contractor.

There are also certain types of "labour-only" or "value cost" contracts which can be arranged and where the contractor simply supplies the necessary labour for a construction scheme, collecting a fee which may be arranged on a fluctuating basis depending on the outcome of the final cost in relation to an agreed initial estimate; the lower the final cost, the higher the fee. Under such arrangements the building owner directly finances the project.

Measurement and Value or "Schedule" Contracts

A Measurement and Valuation Contract is one that provides for the execution of proposed work by agreement but where payment is to be made entirely on the basis of measurement of the work carried out upon an agreed Schedule of Rates or the rates in an approximate Bill of Quantities. This method of contracting is often employed where the extent rather than the nature of the work is difficult to specify beforehand or where a hurried commencement has to be made. A number of permutations and combinations are possible either with a JCT or ICE Contract Form with or without approximate quantities but the essence of such contracts is that a total price is not stated and that the instructions given by the surveyor, architect or engineer in the form of drawings, specifications or site instructions in effect define the contract, the contractor's remuneration merely being ascertained by a method that has been prescribed beforehand.

Such contracts are suited for work of a repetitive nature often minor works of repair and maintenance and make provision for fluctuation factors due to inflation. A period in excess of three years is not normally recommended for such contracts.

THE STANDARD FORMS OF CONTRACT

Introduction

It may seem strange to modern eyes that the whole of the Victorian building boom was achieved without an agreed form of contract for use within the industry but it is a fact that it was only in 1909 that a standard form of building contract was introduced by the Royal Institution of British Architects after discussions with certain interested parties. This set out standard terms to deal with unforeseen problems which might arise during building work which might otherwise frustrate the basic intentions of the parties, namely the employer and the contractor. In 1931, a Joint Contracts Tribunal, which initially consisted of representatives from the Royal Institute of British Architects and the predecessors of the National Federation of Building Trade Employers, was set up to be responsible not only for the publication of a Standard Form of Contract but also its continual revision. In the years which have followed, representatives from other bodies such as The Royal Institution of Chartered Surveyors, delegates from the local Authority Associations, the Scottish Building Contracts Committee, the two main organisations representing specialist sub-contractors and the Association of Consulting Engineers, have joined the Tribunal and two members of the Confederation of British Industry attend meetings as observers. Since 1931, new editions of the contract have been published in 1939, 1950, 1957 and 1963 and amendments and revised clauses to the contract have followed at increasingly frequent intervals. One can, for example, turn to the Joint Contract Tribunal's amendment sheet No. 6 of 1972 which dealt with the revisions to clauses 16, 27 and 30 relating to the retention provisions of the then standard form of building contract. This amendment was an important one as the old "limit of retention fund" was abolished and the expression "percentage of certified value retained" was replaced by the new expression "retention percentage" and detailed provision was made in respect of these new terms. It is accordingly not surprising, since the revised form of building contract of July 1977 was still based on the original 1963 edition, that the need for a re-drafting of the standard form of building contract as a whole was obviously becoming necessary. The new 1980 edition will be discussed in due course as will the variants found to be necessary in latter years mainly due to the enormous volume of increase in the amount of building work required by local authorities who, when in the capacity of employer, use their own particular version of the standard form of contract. The availability of the forms for use in either the private or public sector has again led to further necessary sub-divisions entailing specialised versions of the standard forms where quantities either do or do not form part of the contract and where approximate quantities are employed. The last case is, in fact, a fairly radical departure, as it was not until recently possible to employ a standard form of contract either for local authority or private use with approximate quantities. The forms were traditionally drafted for use either with or without quantities and there was no middle course. It was however, during the last two decades that architects and surveyors began to miss the old RIBA "forms of prime cost contract for use in the repair of war damaged property" which were first issued in 1946. These were still in use long after the War, being last revised in 1956, and were published in green and yellow form providing for a cost plus percentage contract and a cost plus fixed fee contract in the respective cases. Perhaps due to the increasing volume of rehabilitation work, it was felt that a cost plus contract was essential as an alternative to the general obsession with the firmly priced contact which was best applied to new work. The old RIBA standard forms for use in the repair of war damaged property were hardly suitable however, containing much outdated phraseology, for rehabilitation work but then neither were the other JCT forms. There was no adequate way of dealing with the large amount of daywork charges necessary in the repair of old buildings and although the old war damage forms dealt with the financial aspects of such an agreement, they were notably lacking in other necessary provisions which were basic to the contractural requirements of the post-war years. Accordingly, the Joint Contracts Tribunal published "Re-Measurement Contracts" in October 1975 designed for use with approximate quantities and applicable in both the public and private sectors.

With all the care and thought given to re-drafting the contract provisions and the issuing of periodic revisions, it might perhaps be assumed that the terms are so well established and understood that the printed word could be considered virtually sacrosanct and treated as authoritative, not to say with awe, by the legal, architectural and surveying professions. Of course it could be expected that an occasional local difficulty might be presented to the Courts for solution and, of course, it would not be surprising, for example, to learn that a problem as to whether an arbitration award executed under a JCT form for works in Scotland could be successfully challenged in England had finally to go to the House of Lords[3] for a decision.

It may well perhaps come as a surprise however, to learn that far from being regarded as authoritative the JCT forms of contract have attracted bitter criticism, one might almost say hostility from the Courts. In early 1970 two cases in the House of Lords attracted a good deal of publicity. The first concerned the duty or otherwise of an employer to nominate a further sub-contractor if the original sub-contractor nominated in the "RIBA form of contract" dropped out. In this particular case deadlock was reached when the employer failed to nominate another sub-contractor and Lord Reid, giving judgement, said that while he had come to a clear conclusion that there was in the present case a duty (on the employer) to re-nominate, he would add that the relevant provisions of the "RIBA form of contract" were so confused and obscure that no conclusion could be reached upon them without a long and complicated chain of reasoning.

"The RIBA form of conditions sponsored by the Institute was in very common use. It had been amended from time to time. For a long time it had been well known that the question at issue in the present case had given rise to doubt and controversy. It could have been set at rest by a small amendment of these conditions. But the Institute had chosen not to do that, and they had thereby caused the long and expensive litigation in the present case. The Appeal should be dismissed."[4]

In the second case where a point was decided under what was again

(3) *James Miller & Partners Ltd.* v. *Whitworth Street Estates (Manchester) Ltd.* E.G. May 30 1970 Page 1111.
(4) *North West Metropolitan Regional Hospital Board* v. *T. A. Bickerton & Son Ltd.* EG 23 May 1970 Page 973.

described by the Court as the "RIBA contract form" as to whether work completed on time by a firm of sub-contractors but subsequently found to be defective could be treated in the same manner as delayed work so that the sub-contractor was not disadvantaged, further criticism was made in respect of the form of contract then existing. Viscount Dilhorne said that "it was curious that in a form of contract issued by the RIBA and approved by many other bodies, one should find a provision under which a sub-contractor could benefit from his own default. Yet such was the nature of condition 23 (g)." Lord Wilberforce, agreeing, said that the provisions of this condition forced the parties into a paradoxical situation. "The condition had been inserted and drafted without any clear appreciation of its purpose or scope. . . . This type of difficulty was a very grave defect and a serious reflection on the clause. He (his Lordship) could not believe the RIBA would allow it to remain in its present form".[5]

The RIBA, irritated by the comments made in both cases, issued a statement on 20 March that same year. It said "the RIBA can only presume that their Lordship's were not informed that the proper name of this contract is 'the standard form of building contract', which for over sixty years has been a negotiated document and, since 1931, has been produced by the Joint Contracts Tribunal." The statement went on to say that the latest edition, published in 1963 after six years of negotiations, was made between the RIBA, The Royal Institution of Chartered Surveyors, County Councils Association, Association of Municipal Corporations, Urban District Councils Association, Rural District Councils Association, Greater London Council and the National Federation of Building Trades Employers. The statement added that since 1963, membership of the Tribunal has been increased by representatives of the Scottish Building Contract Committee, the Federation of Associations of Specialist sub-contractors and the Committee of Associations of Specialist Engineering Contractors. The RIBA was accordingly now only one body among eleven. The statement ended by rejecting the suggestion that the RIBA should be singled out for personal criticism and added rather acidly that "if the Institute was solely responsible for production of this contract, as had been suggested, it would indeed be an entirely different document". It was because the Institute failed to secure the agreement to certain proposed changes that it found it necessary to publish forms of warranty for the protection of clients in August 1969. Rejection of the personal

(5) *Westminster City Council* v. *J. Jarvis & Sons Ltd. and another.* EG 23 May 1970 Page 974.

criticism however, "should not be read as meaning that the RIBA does not agree that there is obscurity and confusion in the wording in the standard form of building contract". The RIBA, ended the statement, "will take immediate steps to ensure that the justified criticism of the Courts and of other critics are considered by the Joint Contracts Tribunal without delay".

The statement by the RIBA failed to appease its own members. A strong body of members of that Institute had been feeling for quite some time that the Joint Contracts Tribunal was an unsatisfactory vehicle for settling the provisions of a building contract and they passionately wished to form a clean break and go it alone. They felt, not without justification, that the Tribunal as it was constituted had produced the highly unsatisfactory and obscure document that now existed and, more seriously, that there was a definite anti-employer bias, so that any serious revision that would be of real benefit to the architect's client was virtually impossible. A particular example of the frustrations which occurred was in the problem of clause 23 (g) when, in the words of one writer at the time, the RIBA "went down on its knees to the JCT, which wouldn't budge, and so this attempt to deal with a blatant injustice was frustrated, as all others have been, and always will be, in that ludicrous situation in which the contract cannot be altered except with the permission of the party likely to lose by the alteration."[6] The RIBA should, maintained the writer, have resigned on principle rather than have produced Forms of Warranty for the protection of clients. The RIBA members felt frustrated that they were forced to agree with Lord Denning, for example, when he said that clause 4 (2) was rendered meaningless by the exclusions (a) and (b) to clause 12 which became "so nonsensical that it could be ignored altogether". There was further criticism that no definitions were given of such important terms as a PC or Provisional Sum or the words "force majeure" under which a contractor could find excuses for extensions under clause 23 and operate provisions against the employer under clause 26. This was of course the real nub of the argument. A strong feeling among architects and surveyors was that the form was now in such a state that the architect had to request his client to sign a contract that was definitely against his interests. Yet another example occurred in clause 1 of the contract which enabled a contractor to penalise the employer under clause 26 if the architect issued an instruction under clause 2 which caused delay, even if the instruction was given as a result of a breach of contract by the contractor himself! The special meeting of the RIBA on 26 April

(6) Architects Journal 25 April 1973.

1973 ventilated the matter, but the RIBA and RICS are still members of the Joint Contracts Tribunal and the uneasy alliance of the various different members making up the Tribunal continues to the present day.

It would, however, be false to proceed with the idea that all cases before the Courts result in the JCT forms of contract being torn to pieces. The procedure in building contracts and the relationship of the various parties to each other has been formulated and generally well established for many years but such are the complexities of present day building operations that these have to be examined and re-defined at times under different sets of circumstances by the judicature. A further case in the Court of Appeal illustrates this. A claim under an interim certificate drawn under a JCT form of contract and lodged by a sub-contractor against the main contractor, was paid by the building owner to the main contractor, but witheld by him from the sub-contractor, on the grounds of defective work. It was held that a main contractor cannot act in this way and set up an unliquidated claim for defective work as a defence in order to withhold payment under an interim certificate.[7] Another case established the important rule that a final certificate drawn by an architect is binding on the employer and must be honoured notwithstanding the existence of bad workmanship. In the Court of Appeal the contractors had argued that a counter claim for bad work was barred by the final certificate which was "conclusive evidence" that the work had been properly carried out. The employers rejected this argument and demanded arbitration but as they had not requested this before the issue of the final certificate, Lord Denning, the Master of the Rolls ruled that the final certificate was binding. This left the employers with only the one possible source of remedy as an action against the architect should he be found to be negligent (which was not suggested in this case).[8]

Any introduction to the Standard Forms of Contract at present in use must end upon a cautionary note. Later in this volume more will be said on the subject of relating the type of contract form to the size and scale of the work envisaged but at present concern is for the Forms of Contract themselves. While enough has been said, it is hoped, to point to the fact that the forms are hardly regarded as being sacrosanct by Judges and are subject to criticism from all sides there nevertheless must remain with surveyors and architects a feeling, however sub-conscious, that, since the forms are in print, they are inviolate and, once executed, the legal and administrative

(7) *Dawnays Ltd.* v. *F. G. Minter Ltd. and another.* EG 31 July 1971 Page 585.
(8) *P. & M. Kaye Ltd.* v. *Hosier & Dickinson Ltd.* EG 11 March 1972 Page 1327.

side of contract procedure can happily be regarded as having been taken care of once and for all. Worse, the sub-conscious feeling can also exist which suggests that all that is needed is a printed form signed by contractor and employer for everything else to fall miraculously into place. In order to illustrate the dangers of such assumptions before proceeding to the consideration of the forms themselves, two further cases are referred to here. The first, almost by way of a digression concerns what is, or is not, a building contract while the second, an important case to architects and surveyors, shows how venerable assumptions made in connection with the long use of the printed contract forms can be upset.

The first case concerned a firm of developers who proposed to develop a building site. They discussed their plans with contractors who said that they would like to carry out the work and were in a position to provide finance. Once the financier was introduced however, the developers engaged other builders to carry out the work but took advantage of the finance which had been made available by the original contractors. This firm, angry at what had happened, sought a remedy in the courts and produced letters which had passed between the parties but Lord Denning held that as he could find no agreement as to price or any method by which the price for the work was to be calculated, there was no enforceable contract. He said that the question of price was of such fundamental importance in building contracts that there could in fact be no contract unless the price was agreed or there was an agreed method of ascertaining it, not dependent on the negotiations of the two parties themselves.[9] This case is brought forward at this stage to underline finally, before leaving the subject, the fact that the principles of basic contract law are still alive and well and are not matters relegated to dusty legal bookshelves.

The second case relates to the position of the professional surveyor or architect under the terms of a JCT Form of Contract. In the final hearing before the House of Lords, it was decided that a firm of architects was liable in negligence for issuing an interim certificate. Previously it had always been held as an established principle in the surveying and architectural professions that an architect or surveyor was in the position of quasi-arbitrator between the parties to a building contract and that he was therefore entitled to an arbitrator's immunity from actions for negligence. This doctrine, thought till then to be inviolate when the printed contract forms were employed was suddenly exploded. "To my way of

---

(9) *Courtney & Fairbairn Ltd.* v. *Tolaini Brothers (Hotels) Ltd.* EG 19 April 1975 Page 205.

thinking", said Davies LJ in this case[10] "It is . . . a lamentable conclusion that an architect who negligently issues a certificate, interim or final, and thus places his employer in the position of having to pay under it, should be free of all liability. . . ." The main reaction to the outcome of this case at the time among surveyors and architects was the glum feeling that the cards were being stacked more and more heavily against those members of the profession who were foolish enough to supervise buidling work. Apart from the enormous growth of knowledge expected from him and which he is expected to have mastered in the interests of his client, the feeling of the surveyor or architect that the present consumer society was breathing unfairly down his neck and that he was likely to find little justice from the activities of the Monopolies Commission and the Director General of Fair Trading coloured all his thoughts. With clearer hindsight some years after it seems incredible that the earlier doctrine, for which there can be little or no justification, subsisted for as long as it did. The surveyor or architect must therefore always keep himself informed as to changes in the law relating to his profession and bear in mind not only what does or does not constitute a valid building contract but also his own position under whatever type of contract is employed. He should never submit tamely to the provisions of any document however impressive merely because it is in print.

In conclusion it is fair to say that the main criticism against the printed forms of Contract is that both the JCT Form, being a product of the building industry, or the ICE Form, being a product of the civil engineering or construction industry, fail to take into account the needs of the employer or promoter in either case, whose interests, so far as time and money are concerned, are not safeguarded to a sufficiently satisfactory degree. It is, of course, possible for the printed forms to be altered or amended or additional clauses added, but this proceeding is considered to be fraught with danger to even the most experienced. Each form is designed as a piece, clauses interlocking and relying upon each other and referring to additional documents which form part of the contract so that tampering with the text can lead to a whole quagmire of later misunderstandings and confusion. The more human accusation that the printed forms are a load of rubbish and that a building contract depends upon the goodwill of the parties is more understandable but goodwill has a habit of vanishing under the pressure of unforeseen events.

The final fact remains that the standard forms, however imperfect, are the result of deliberations by numbers of experienced people over a long period of time and are constantly amended, partly as the result

(10) *Sutcliffe* v. *Thackrah and others*. EG 6 July 1974 Page 103.

of experience, and partly as the result of criticisms made in the Courts. They are, as such, an aggregation of past experience in building matters and the benefits of this experience remain invaluable. The fact is that they are recognised by surveyors, architects and contractors from long use, and also by sub-contractors whether nominated or not. One can imagine the complications and head scratchings if different contract documents were drawn up anew in each individual case. The final accusation that large construction companies are adept at using the clauses of a JCT Contract to their own advantage, is not really relevant since, presumably, with their own legal staff they would be just as well if not better placed to scrutinise any new or unusual form of contract that might be produced. A generally recognised form of contract, each aspect of which has been tried and tested in the courts, is, it is thought, less likely to give reign to individual enterprise in construing clauses to any particular personal benefit than if the generally used contract forms did not exist. A universally recognised contract form with tried and tested clauses should mean that all parties to the contract, whether with large or small organisations, are put on a more equal footing rather than the reverse. The printed forms of contract are accordingly very necessary not least because of their troubled history.

The JCT Standard Form of Building Contract 1963 – Revised July 1977

There are six variations of the Standard Form of Building Contract 1963, the forms being drafted either with or without quantities for lump sum contracts or with approximate quantities for measurement contracts and for either local authority or private contracts. It is perhaps most convenient to discuss for the purpose of this section the 1963 Standard Form, Private Edition with Quantities before proceeding to deal with the alterations made by the 1980 edition. The form is designed, as mentioned earlier, to provide an Entire Contract on a Lump Sum Basis watered down only to the extent that, since quantities form part of the contract, some variation in the final figure will be allowable ranging, for example, from the correction of certain permitted errors to the final assessment of certain sums regarded as provisional at the outset of the work and for certain increased costs which have occurred since the contract was signed. The form itself is in four parts; the articles of agreement, the conditions, the appendix and the supplemental agreement. The first two form the contract documents, the appendix being subsidiary to the conditions while the supplemental agreement is appended at the end. Although the surveyor or architect may be familiar with completing the obvious gaps provided in the articles and the appendix it is normally assumed that the conditions are inviolate by themselves and it is often overlooked, sometimes with dire results, that a number of alternative and optional clauses are drafted in the conditions that need deletion or amendment. Otherwise however, the conditions should stand intact.

The Articles of Agreement and Attestation

The Articles of Agreement define the parties to the contract, the works, including the site and the date of the agreement itself. The employer's architect is identified and described as "Supervising Officer" if he is unable to use the term "Architect" under the terms of the Architects Registration Acts, 1931–1938. The Contract Drawings are also identified as are the Bills of Quantities and it is recognised that one copy of the latter supplied by the contractor to the employer is referred to as "The Contract Bills" throughout the entire contract.The Contract Bills and Contract Drawings are of course signed by the employer and contractor and it is also desirable practice for the quantity surveyor also to sign the drawings to certify that these relate to the Contract Bills. It is sometimes considered odd that no provision is made in case of the death or failure to act on the part of the architect but here the employer has a clear duty to re-nominate under such circumstances coupled with the right of the contractor to object to the nomination made. Such objection may not, however, be valid in the case of local authority contracts.

Once the contract is executed it appears established law that its terms will act retrospectively to cover actions taken and work carried out prior to its execution provided of course that these relate clearly to the contract itself. Nevertheless the practice of executing the Articles of Agreement at a late stage is obviously a dangerous one, fraught with risk. Broadly, two different sets of circumstances may apply. Firstly no contract may exist since there has been no offer and acceptance while, secondly, a contract may exist since the parties may have agreed a price for certain specified work and a time for completion. Other terms may then be imported by reference, so that where an employer and a contractor agree to be bound by "the appropriate form" this will be sufficient to bind both parties to every clause of the established sub-contract form in common use at the time.[11]

(11) *Modern Building (Wells) Ltd.* v. *Limmer & Trinidad Co. Ltd.* (1975) 234 EG Page 287.

Clause 1 – Contractor's Obligations

The obligations of the contractor are "to carry out and complete the works shown upon the contract drawings and described by or referred to in the Contract Bills . . . using materials and workmanship of the quality and standards therein specified, provided that where and to the extent that approval of the quality of the materials or of the standards of workmanship is a matter for the opinion of the architect, such quality and standards shall be to the reasonable satisfaction of the architect".

When the architect certifies that he is "reasonably satisfied" with the standard of workmanship and materials however, the contractor will remain responsible for latent defects in work that is faulty or has been omitted under the terms of the contract but not for errors in design. What does or does not constitute "reasonable satisfaction" has been the matter of considerable argument both inside and outside the courts. Since each case must depend on its own merits and also, since every set of circumstances differs the Courts in particular have been hesitant in applying rigid rules. In one case in which the Court of Appeal thought that it might be permissible to take the price into account when considering poor quality work carried out to a dwelling house, their Lordships were emphatic in stressing that this particular case turned on its own special facts and that no legal dictum was to be taken as issued on the basis that the architect should automatically take into account the question of price.[12]

Errors or discrepancies between the contract documents which are the contract drawings, bills, articles of agreement and conditions to the contract are at best an embarrassment and at worst a cause for litigation. Under clause 1 machinery is provided for the correction of errors, the onus being placed on the contractor, should he find any discrepancy or divergence, to give notice to the architect in writing. This is vital in order to establish a later claim for extension of time or loss. If the architect is in the difficult situation of stumbling across a discrepancy himself his only straightforward remedy is to issue a variation order under clause 11 of the contract.

Clause 2 – Architect's/Supervising Officer's Instructions

It should always be remembered that the architect is the agent of the employer and he is only authorised to give instructions under a number of specific clauses in the contract relating, for example, to the question of discrepancies, recently discussed, to clauses 4 and 5 on

(12) *Cotton* v. *Wallis*, (1955) 3 All ER 373.

setting out the work, opening up and testing, clause 6, removal of defective work and dismissal of persons employed on the works, clause 11, variations and expenditure of PC sums, clause 15, defects during defects liability period, clause 20, damage by fire, clause 21, postponement of work, and clauses 27 and 28, dealing with PC sums for nominated sub-contractors and suppliers. There are other clauses which give some authority to the architect or surveyor but those referred to above are the main ones.

Since the effect of an architect's instruction is to require the contractor in rather peremptory wording to "forthwith comply" with the requirements, a contractor can be in a genuine dilemma if he suspects that the architect has stepped outside the terms of his authority. Should he fail to comply with the instruction he can be in breach of contract but on the other hand, should the architect have no authority to issue the instruction in the first place, the employer can legitimately withhold payment. The contractor's only remedy under such circumstances is provided in sub-clause (2) of this section which enables him to require the architect to state in writing which specific clause he relies on under the terms of the contract to give him the requisite authority. If the contractor cannot agree, the matter can be referred to immediate arbitration. An interesting point under this section is that once the contractor has put the architect upon enquiry the employer is then bound by the architect's reply, even if it is in error. This of course only means that the employer is bound to pay the contractor. He is not presumably barred from taking subsequent proceedings against the architect.

A fundamental requirement of the contract form is that all architect's instructions are to be in writing. The provisions of sub-clause (3) dealing with oral instructions must at best be rather unsatisfactory. The contractor is, frankly, best advised to await instructions in writing before carrying out the work but he is in a dilemma; there are numerous occasions, such as in shoring up for example, where delay might entail extremely painful consequences to say the least and the architect should be conscious of the contractor's problems and make arrangements to ensure the smooth running of the contract accordingly. This is where the provision of an instruction book for use by those members of the architect's office vested with appropriate authority is an obvious necessity. There is nothing worse than written confirmation dragging too far behind events in a building contract. Contractors, it must be said, are just as likely to be at fault as architects in not wishing to disrupt relationships by pressing for written instructions but sloppy paper-work can lead to problems at a later stage particularly when work is covered up. The provision in the contract form that an architect "may" confirm an oral instruction at the end of the contract due to the fact that the original confirmation in writing was neglected or overlooked is, presumably, inserted to validate late omissions but, from the practical point of view the effect is worthless. Clause 2 highlights as no other clause does, the impossibility of producing printed contract clauses to regulate inefficient contract administration.

Clause 3 – Contract Documents

The procedure for the custody and provision of certain copies of the contract documents is laid out in detail under this clause and should be read in connection with the added terms of JCT Practice Note 7 relating to the provision of extra copies of drawings over and above those referred to. Rather unusually, under sub-clause (8) a complete progression of architect's certificates is set out.

Clause 4 – Statutory Obligations, Notices, Fees and Charges

The contractor accepts a heavy burden under this clause. He is bound to comply with *any* relevant Act of Parliament or statutory instrument which, in this day and age, covers an enormously wide field of knowledge. His duties therefore are by no means merely restricted to serving statutory notices. If he finds any divergence between the numerous statutory requirements and the contract documents or variations issued under clause 11, he is bound to give immediate notice to the architect who will then issue his instructions within seven days. This requirement is obviously mandatory since a requirement under statute is involved and the instruction may involve a variation under clause 11 or even an extension of time under clause 23.

The sub-clauses to this section attempt to deal with difficult situations. Sub-clause 1(d) provides for emergency work to be carried out before instructions are received provided that the contractor is only liable to "supply such limited materials and execute such limited work as are reasonably necessary to secure immediate compliance with the statutory requirements". This work will only qualify for a variation order if the contractor has "forthwith" informed the architect of the steps that have proved necessary. Otherwise however, the contractor is not responsible to the employer if he has carried out the work correctly under the terms of the contract but a breach of statutory requirements is later found. Fees and charges are normally dealt with by way of a provisional sum in the Contract Bills but in the lack of any such sum disbursements will be added to the contract sum. This will exclude value added tax which is dealt with under clause 13a and the

Supplemental Agreement to the contract. Where work is done or materials supplied by a statutory undertaker the charge is to be included under the provisions of clause 4 rather than the provisions of clause 27 or 28 due to the monopolistic nature of the transaction. Extension of time due to the delay of a statutory undertaker is dealt with under clause 23.

Clause 5 – Levels and Setting out of the Works

The contractor must set out the works but he must be given accurate dimensions and drawings to enable him to do so. He is also able to call upon the architect or surveyor to determine any levels required where these are not clear. The architect's or surveyor's duties therefore relate to the supplying of accurate information with any amplification necessary under clause 3(4) but if the plans clearly involve a trespass, the employer will be responsible, as contrasted with the case where a trespass arises due to negligent setting out of the works and where the contractor obviously must assume responsibility.

Clause 6 – Materials, Goods and Workmanship

The contractor is to use materials specified "so far as procurable" and in the event of these not being available must obtain the architect's or surveyor's approval for substitutions. If the contract documents say that the contractor may use the goods of Messrs. Brown "or other approved" goods this does not mean that the contractor is entitled simply to go for the cheapest product in a range of similar materials but must request the architect's or surveyor's authority for any substitution, the architect or surveyor then having a discretionary right to approve any variation.[13]

Obvious but important authority is given under this section for vouchers for materials to be submitted to the architect or surveyor at his request.

Rather curiously, the authority for the architect or surveyor to require the contractor to open up work for inspection and to carry out tests is included under this section. The power can be exercised at any time up and until practical completion and the employer pays for the work unless it is found to be defective or not carried out in accordance with the terms of the contract. This authority should be used sparingly by the architect, surveyor or supervising officer since, if the work is found to be satisfactory once opening up has been carried out this may lead to a claim not just for the extra cost but also for an extension of time under clause 23.

(13) *Leedsford Ltd.* v. *Bradford Corporation* (1956).

178

Sub-clauses (4) and (5) deal with authority to require the removal of work, materials or goods not supplied or carried out in accordance with the terms of the contract and also the right to dismiss any person employed on the works. Most cases of dismissal will presumably involve the transfer of the person concerned to another job although this seems a pity for the new employer. If the person is sacked, however, a problem may occur as to whether the dismissal is "unfair" under present legislation.

It is, perhaps, convenient at this point to mention the question of warranties. The Standard Form makes no reference to warranties but the present position has been well established in the Courts. Unless a particular amendment or exclusion is made to the Standard Form the contractor warrants, or implies, firstly that his workmanship will be of a satisfactory standard, secondly that materials and goods supplied will be free from both patent and latent defects and, thirdly that the goods will be suitable for the purpose for which they are supplied. An employer can generally expect an implied warranty from his contractor when his architect or surveyor or supervising officer specifies building materials in the normal range that are available but instances will arise where an implied warranty will not be expected of the contractor. Such a case arose where a nominated supplier provided goods that later proved to be defective and who had informed the architect categorically that he would not be liable for defects. In this case the House of Lords decided that there was no implied warranty as to the fitness of the goods by the contractor who was helpless in the matter. He had to do what he was told and, in any case, had no remedy.[14]

In another leading case, where a particular type of roofing tile subsequently proved to have latent defects, the House of Lords held that the roofing sub-contractor, who was told which type of tile to use, had no choice, but nevertheless an implied warranty existed unless the supplier of the tiles had specifically excluded liability for patent or latent defects and this exclusion was known to the architect. Since these circumstances were lacking the contractor was found to be responsible for the ultimate cost of putting matters right.[15]

The architect, surveyor or supervising officer should accordingly take pains to see that he does not leave the employer without remedy where defective goods are supplied. If he takes him to a showroom and orders a particular article and then requests that the contractor

(14) *Gloucestershire County Council* v. *Richardson*, (1968) 2 All ER 1181.
(15) *Young & Marten Ltd.* v. *McManus Childs Ltd.*, (1968) 2 All ER 1169.

179

accepts delivery he is well advised to ensure that a warranty as to fitness is not specifically excluded by the supplier in his terms of sale. If so, the contractor, as we have seen, cannot be held responsible under any implied warranty and the cost of remedial work, should the article prove to be defective, may well fall on the employer. This may not, of course, necessarily be so if the defective condition of the article supplied is obvious upon delivery, in the case, for example, of an expensive bath that has an obvious flaw in the finish. The circumstances will apply however, in the case of a bath that appears to be perfectly sound but has some latent defect such as a fracture in the cast iron that only becomes apparent at a much later stage.

Clause 7 – Royalties and Patent Rights

The question of who pays royalties and patent rights depends upon the circumstances. These are most usually paid by the employer since they are likely to arise as the result of instructions given by the architect or surveyor or supervising officer but it is possible that the contractor may use some patent article or process during the course of carrying out the works under the terms of the contract as the result of his own decision to facilitate matters. In such a case the architect will not be involved and the contractor will be expected to pay the necessary royalties.

Clause 8 – Foreman-in-Charge

The present term for the foreman-in-charge tends to be site agent replacing the earlier term of general foreman but, whatever the term used, the contractor must nominate someone who is both competent and who is constantly available. The person nominated is responsible for receiving the architect, surveyor or supervising officer's instructions under the contract and therefore the nomination should be of considerable consequence to the contractor since the machinery of clause 2 is heavily dependent upon the foreman or site agent knowing what is expected of him.

Clause 9 – Access to the Works

Visits to the joiner's shop or metal works of sub-contractors are so often accompanied by suspicious glances that the architect, surveyor or supervising officer has to remind himself that he has the right under the contract to visit the site or other premises where work relating to the contract is being carried out at all reasonable times. This right extends to the premises of all sub-contractors, however remote, whether nominated or not.

Clause 10 – Clerk of Works

The position of the Clerk of Works has been very carefully defined and established over many years. He is simply an inspector and has no authority to give instructions as agent for the architect, surveyor or employer. The contractor is merely obliged to give him every reasonable facility to carry out his duties as inspector but obviously this situation is totally unreal. What happens, supposing the Clerk of Works finds some omission or defect which entails urgent action in the absence of the architect, surveyor or supervising officer? This situation is dealt with under clause 10 in that the Clerk of Works can issue a "direction" to the contractor. The contractor is perfectly entitled to ignore this, even if he does so at his peril, until the direction is converted into a written instruction from the architect or surveyor. This of course presupposes that the direction covers a matter where the architect has authority to act under the terms of the contract and can, in fact, legitimately provide written confirmation. The second requirement however, of clause 10 that written instructions have to be given within "two working days" in order to legitimately convert a "direction" into an instruction can often be impossible to achieve. Mercifully, however, few problems on this score actually arise in practice. If an experienced Clerk of Works finds something wrong and points it out to the contractor, it is obviously in the best interests of everyone concerned to put matters right as speedily as possible. Should on the other hand the Clerk of Works throw his weight about and demand variations not envisaged under the terms of the contract, the contractor can simply ignore what he says.

Clause 11 – Variations, Provisional and Prime Cost Sums

Clause 11 forms the basis of the architect's or surveyor's authority to give instructions regarding variations. Like all other clauses in the contract Form clause 11 cannot be seen in isolation since it must be taken in conjunction with other clauses, an obvious example being clause 2 where instructions are stated to be issued in writing.

The question of what does or does not constitute a variation is defined in sub-clause (2) of clause 11 and is as follows:

"11(2) the term 'variation' as used in these Conditions means the alteration or modification of the design, quality or quantity of the Works as shown upon the Contract Drawings and described by or referred to in the Contract Bills, and includes the addition, omission or substitution of any work, the alteration of the kind or standard of any of the materials or goods to be used in the Works, and the removal from the site of any work materials or goods executed or brought thereon by the

Contractor for the purposes of the Works other than work materials or goods which are not in accordance with this Contract."

Clause 11 does not attempt to define how sizeable or extensive the work covered by a variation order must be before it becomes invalid. Sub-clause 1 states that "no variation shall vitiate the contract" and whether a variation is admissible as such or alters the basis of the contract must remain a matter of fact. This is hardly surprising.

More surprising however, is the fact that while sub-clause (3) enables the architect or surveyor to issue instructions as to the expenditure of prime cost and provisional sums and indeed has a duty to do so (see clauses 27 and 28) there is no definition of either term in the contract Form. One has to have reference to the Standard Method of Measurement for a description of these terms.[16]

> *Provisional Sum* "A sum provided for work or for costs which cannot be entirely foreseen, defined or detailed at the time the tendering documents are issued."
> *Prime Cost Sum* "A sum provided for work or services to be executed by a nominated sub-contractor, a statutory authority, or a public undertaking or for materials or goods to be obtained from a nominated supplier."

Whether instructions to expend provisional sums are issued to the contractor on the one hand or to a nominated specialist or supplier on the other, will determine which sections of the contract document becomes relevant; clause 11 in the case of the contractor and clauses 27 and 28 in the case of the nominated specialist or supplier. The architect, surveyor or supervising officer may wish to make a nomination in respect of the expenditure of the whole or part of a provisional sum and this possibility is foreseen in sub-clause (3) of clause 11 which deals with the substitution of a prime cost sum for all or part of the provisional sum quoted in the contract bills.

Sub-clause (4) deals with the measurement and valuation of both variations under sub-clause (2) and also contractor's work ordered by the architect, surveyor or supervising officer when using instructions on the expenditure of provisional sums. It still appears to be established law under this particular version of the contract Form that while measurement and valuation is the province of the quantity surveyor, the architect, surveyor or supervising officer is not bound to accept his opinion when issuing certificates.[17]

The rules for valuation are listed under paragraphs (a), (b) and (c). These are to be applied one after the other until one particular rule fits the case concerned. The rules are:

(a) The prices in the Contract Bills shall determine the valuation

---

(16) Sixth Edition Rule A7.
(17) *R. B. Burden Ltd.* v. *Swansea Corporation*, (1957) 3 All ER 343.

of work of similar character executed under similar conditions as work priced therein.

(b) The said prices, where work is not of a similar character or executed under similar conditions as aforesaid, shall be the basis of prices for the same so far as may be reasonable, failing which a fair valuation thereof shall be made.

(c) Where work cannot properly be measured and valued the contractor shall unless otherwise agreed, be allowed:

(i) The prime cost of such work calculated in accordance with the "Definition of Prime Cost of Daywork carried out under a Building Contract" issued by the Royal Institution of Chartered Surveyors and the National Federation of Building Trades Employers and current at the date of tender as defined in clause 31 D (6) (a) of these Conditions (or as defined in the Formula Rules where clause 31F of these Conditions applies) together with percentage additions to each section of the prime cost at the rates set out by the Contractor in the Contract Bills, or

(ii) Where the work is within the province of any specialist trade and the said Institution and the appropriate body representing the employers in that trade have agreed and issued a definition of prime cost of daywork, the prime cost of such work calculated in accordance with that definition current at the date of tender as defined in clause 31 D (6) (a) of these Conditions together with percentage additions on the prime cost at the rates set out by the Contractor in the Contract Bills.

Regard must first of all be had to the prices in the Contract Bills. If work is similar the contractor will be landed with the original dispositions of his costs and profits and how he has dealt with the preliminaries whether he likes it or not. He may argue strenuously that work is not of a similar character nor executed under similar conditions in order to shift the emphasis to rule (b). Rule (c) is not as attractive as it sounds. Prime cost is to be ascertained at a time ten days before the date fixed for the receipt of tenders, as in the case of the other rules, but with percentage additions. The rates are those current when daywork is carried out and accordingly fluctuations adjustment under either of the clauses referred to is excluded.

The importance of prompt delivery of records covering work carried out is obvious. The big advantage of having a Clerk of Works is that he can sign sheets as a record and although this is not authoritative, since the quantity surveyor may in any event decide

183

to measure the work and the architect, surveyor or supervising officer has the sole right of certifying payment, nevertheless promptly compiled recorded daywork sheets are, in some types of contract, absolutely vital.

Finally, there is a further rule (d) inserted at the end in order to give authority for applying rule (b) where valuation arises as the result of an omission. Such an omission might have repercussions upon other work carried out and rule (d) is the authority for restoring the balance.

Sub-clauses (5) and (6) give authority for the cost of variations to be included in interim certificates whether expended by way of provisional sums or otherwise and for the architect or surveyor to assess any "direct loss and/or expense" which the contractor has suffered or incurred as a result of variations and the expenditure of provisional sums generally. This duty can only be activated by the contractor making written application as soon as he knows of his loss or increased expenses and is designed to meet a situation where the quantity surveyor's valuation is inadequate. The architect or surveyor will obviously ask for reasons backed up by supporting evidence and he is entitled to override the decision of the quantity surveyor and include an extra sum in the next interim certificate due once he has arrived at his award. Such a situation should only occur under unusual circumstances. The expression "direct loss and/or expense" rules out matters that are too remote from the contract and it is important for a claim to be submitted as soon as the circumstances giving rise to the loss arise.

Clause 12 – Contract Bills

The Contract Bills determine the quality and quantity of the work and should obviously be prepared in accordance with the requirements of the Standard Method of Measurement although it is an odd anomaly that there is no direct reference in the Standard Form to this important document. Presumably, however, the link would be inferred in all cases unless other reference is specifically made. The contractor's opportunity for raising such matters is presumably included under sub-clause 12. If the contract conditions and the contract bills contradict each other the conditions are authoritative and the contractor could ignore the provisions in the bills but would be unwise not to raise the problem at an early stage. Errors in items or omissions from the contract bills are then to be corrected and dealt with as variations under clause 11.

Clause 13 – Contract Sum

This clause underlines the fact that this particular version of the

JCT contract Form is designed for use in the case of a lump-sum contract. The only possible variations in the contract sum are dealt with by the express terms of the contract itself and it is vital therefore that errors in compiling the sum are spotted before article 2 is completed and the contract entered into by both parties.

Clause 13a – Value Added Tax – Supplemental Agreement

The essential part of this clause is that the parties are obliged to enter into a Supplemental Agreement for Value Added Tax. The contract sum is exclusive of VAT but the Contractor is given the right to recover from the Employer any VAT due upon goods or services that he provides. The provisions regarding VAT are complicated and JCT practice note 17 is essential reading.

Clause 14 – Goods and Materials Unfixed or Off Site

Once goods supplied are built into or incorporated in the works and paid for they obviously become the property of the Employer. The situation of goods that are stored for the next phase of construction is more complicated. Generally, while materials brought on to the site by the contractor remain his property, they cannot be removed without the consent of the architect or surveyor. Once they have been paid for under the terms of an interim certificate they then become the property of the employer. There are obvious problems under this clause. It covers unfixed materials and goods delivered to or "placed on or adjacent to the Works" and it must be a question of some difficulty in certain cases to decide as to the true facts. Problems have also been encountered as to the ownership of goods when the contractor goes bankrupt. There is a requirement that to comply with inclusion under this clause the goods must have been adequately protected against weather and "other casualties". The question of fire insurance is dealt with under clause 20.

Sub-clause (2) deals with cases where the architect, surveyor or supervising officer has certified payment for off-site goods and the certificate has been honoured. The goods then become the property of the employer and can only be taken from the off-site premises directly to the works. The contractor remains responsible for protection and insurance.

Unlike the case of fire where the employer may well be responsible, the contractor remains liable for the protection of goods built or fixed into the works which are stolen or destroyed by vandals. In a known case of lead flashings fixed to an estate of houses the contractor had to replace these on six separate occasions at his own expense. Presumably however, the contactor is only responsible for taking all reasonable steps that are practicable under the circumstances and there is a growing practice of making express provision for insurance against theft in the contract documents.

Clause 15 – Practical Completion and Defects Liability

The date for the determination of practical completion is a matter that is left entirely to the architect, surveyor or supervising officer. His certificate then triggers off a whole number of hares ranging from the release of a moiety of the retention percentage, the beginning of the Defects Liability Period, the termination of certain insurance arrangements, the admission of references to arbitration and the termination of liability to liquidated damages on the one hand and the contractor's liability for frost damage on the other. The date also marks the commencement of the period of final measurement and valuation as a prelude to the final certificate.

It is odd that there is no definition of "practical completion" in the contract Form but perhaps such a term is impossible to define. Everyone seems to know what it means, however, and there is good legal authority for saying that practical completion can take place notwithstanding the existence of known latent defects.[18]

A Certificate of Practical Completion is normally issued at the same time as a certificate for the release of one moiety of the retention monies. Subsequently the contractor remains responsible for "defects, shrinkages or other faults". Although this phrase appears to speak volumes it is in fact rather limited in extent. Strict regard is to be had to the contract terms to construe what can be included within the expression "other faults", materials and workmanship not being in accordance with the contract being an obvious example but, due to the Delphic complexity of the words used, the sensible provision that the architect or surveyor must prepare a Schedule of Defects within the Defects Liability Period or, at most, fourteen days thereafter, avoids many problems that might otherwise occur. Since the normal Defectives Liability Period is six months, such a schedule must be prepared and delivered within six months and fourteen days of the Certificate of Practical Completion. The schedule then has the effect of an instruction and must be taken seriously by the contractor who is bound to remedy the defects stated within a reasonable time at his own expense unless otherwise stated.

The preparation of a Schedule of Defects, much beloved of architects, surveyors and supervising officers does not necessarily have to take the form of a single formal schedule. Once the Defects Liability Period commences, he can issue instructions for the con-

(18) *Westminster City Council* v. *J. Jarvis & Sons Ltd.*, (1970) 1 All ER 943.

tractor to remedy any defect but it should always be remembered that his powers end once he has delivered his final schedule or the matter becomes time expired after six months and fourteen days have elapsed. The whole point of the Defects Liability Period is to allow the contractor to put right defects and he should obviously be keen to do so, although not invariably so. In most cases, however, it is obviously preferable to dispose of as many minor defects as possible so that the ultimate schedule is limited to a few items only rather than going on and on for pages and pages.

Once the contractor feels that he has put right all the defects complained of, he is entitled to press for the issue of a "Certificate of Completion of Making Good Defects" as this is a necessary pre-requisite for the release of the second moiety of the retention monies and must be procured before the Final Certificate is due. The issue of the certificate however, does not mean that the architect, surveyor or supervising officer is precluded from pointing out further defects and most experienced contractors will make sure that the time between the issue of the Certificate of Completion of Making Good Defects and the issue of the Final Certificate is kept to a minimum. There is often some "higgling and jiggling" during the Defects Liability Period but usually only ending in an eyeball to eyeball confrontation if the architect, surveyor or supervising officer delays the issue of the Final Certificate when the contractor will flatly refuse to carry out any work and the architect to certify payment. Sometimes the matter is resolved on a "without prejudice" basis. Contractors often complain that the main problems arise from nominated sub-contract work but there the contactor should look after himself and make certain that nothing gets in the way of his own rights and duties under clause 15. He should have entered into the "Green Form" which contains an indemnity in his favour by the nominated sub-contractor against latent defects.

Clause 16 – Partial Possession by Employer

In December 1975 a Sectional Completion Supplement was issued for use in conjunction with the JCT Contract Forms with Quantities where the work was to be carried out and completed by phased sections. The Sectional Completion Supplement together with Practice Note 21 are required reading. This should be emphasised however, that the supplement is for use only where the Employer has expressly wished that the work would be completed in phased sections before the contract is entered into and not subsequently. Should he enter into the normal contract form and then decide during the course of the work that he wishes to take early possession of part only, then clause 16 is designed to deal with this contingency.

187

Should the employer, with the consent of the contractor, take possession of any part of the Works before the date for Practical Completion, this clause 16 automatically comes into effect. The part of the Works of which the employer takes possession is called by the curious name of "The Relevant Part" and within seven days of the employer taking possession the architect or surveyor must certify his estimate of the total value of "The Relevant Part" so that the sub-clauses in clause 16 relating to the question of liquidated damages and retention can take effect. This valuation has no bearing on the final account.

Clause 16 is, in fact, a mini contract dealing with "The Relevant Part" in the manner that the whole contract deals with the main Works. Practical completion of "The Relevant Part" takes effect from the date on which the employer took possession and the Defects Liability Period and other obligations such as clause 15 run from that date. Clause 20 relating to insurance and clause 22 relating to liquidated damages are activated insofar as they are appropriate to "The Relevant Part" and upon practical completion the employer has fourteen days in which to pay the first moiety of the Retention Percentage attributable to "The Relevant Part" only. The Retention Percentage attributable to "The Relevant Part" is in direct proportion to the amount that that part bears to the contract sum. The remaining moiety of the Retention Percentage in respect of "The Relevant Part" is released early upon the same rules as apply in the case of the remainder of the contract.

The provisions of clause 16 are virtually self-contained. As noted earlier they cannot prejudice the issue of the Final Certificate in respect of the whole contract and the clause is mainly to facilitate matters of obvious convenience where an employer is pressed to take over, say, part of a factory once it is ready for occupation. Clause 16 however, cannot be used as a weapon to impose practical completion upon the contractor since this requires his consent and entails a separate contract making use of the Sectional Completion Supplement. In order that section 16 may operate it is necessary that some formal act such as the issue of the architect's or surveyor's certificate is carried out. The fact that the employer merely stores goods on the premises for his own convenience with the tacit acceptance of the contractor does not constitute partial possession.[19]

Clause 17 – Assignment or Sub-Letting

Under clause 17 the employer is not able to assign the contract

[19] *English Industrial Estates Corporation* v. *George Wimpey & Co. Ltd.*, (1972) 71 LGR 127.

188

without the written consent of the contractor. Similarly the contractor cannot assign the contract without the written consent of the employer. The contract form then goes on to make an interesting distinction in the case of sub-letting. As we have seen assignment cannot be undertaken without the consent of the employer while sub-letting cannot be undertaken without the consent of the architect or supervising officer as agent to the employer whose consent in this case cannot be unreasonably withheld. There is a proviso to the effect that any sub-contract entered into must provide for the employment of the sub-contractor under that sub-contract to determine automatically upon the determination of the contractor's employment under the main contract, for any reason.

Clause 18 – Injury to Persons and Property and Employer's Indemnity

A well known clause in the contract establishes that the liability for the injury or death of any person arising out of, in the course of, or caused by the carrying out of the works is a matter for the contractor alone. Indeed the contractor has the duty of indemnifying the employer should any injured person take action against the employer direct. This established pattern could alter however, if injury is partly due to the negligence of an employer's agent or representative.

Clause 19 – Insurance against Injury to Persons and Property

The question of adequate insurance is obviously of the utmost importance in the present day and age and with the high cost of cover and the complexities in this field which now include many statutory requirements, such as the Employer's Liability (Compulsory Insurance) Act 1969. It is obviously prudent for the architect or supervising officer to ensure that advice from reputable insurers and registered brokers is sought early in the proceedings and is available during the period of the contract. The contractor's duty to insure against clause 18 liabilities extends to ensuring that sub-contractors under his wing are themselves adequately insured against such risks. The amount of cover for third party liability in the case of any one claim has to be inserted in the appendix to the contract and it is of course vital from the contractor's point of view that this figure is adequate, as the mere fact that a particular sum is stated does not contain the contractor's libility to the employer within this limit. The level of liability is unrestricted.

The employer is enabled under the terms of the Contract to exercise a reasonable right to inspect insurance documents such as policies and receipts for premiums as a necessary pre-requisite to the power given to him under sub-clause 19 (1) (c) to step in and take out the necessary insurances himself in the contractors default.

Insurance is a rather alarming area for the layman and the gaps that can occur in cover were highlighted by the Gold Case.[20] In this case the employer directly ordered works of piling which were carried out by a sub-contractor of the main contractor. Subsidence occurred causing damage to another building but as there was no evidence of negligence on the part of the sub-contractor the main contractor was therefore not in breach of clause 19 and accordingly no remedy was available to the employer. Reference is now specifically made in the contract form under sub-clause (2) to this area of insurance so that the employer and his agents can, if they think it prudent, insure against other areas of possible claim where the contractor himself would not be liable. Under this sub-clause special provisions are required whereby a provisional sum is inserted in the bills and the insurance is to be in the joint names of the contractor and employer. Furthermore the insurers must be approved by the employer who holds the policy or policies and receipts for the premiums.

The area of risk under sub-clause (2) is, of necessity, limited and here expert and practised help is needed to define what is required so as to obtain a reasonable quotation or quotations.

Clause 19a – Excepted Risks – Nuclear Perils etc.

The contractor is not liable under the JCT Contract Form for loss or injury from nuclear risks and damage caused by sonic and super-sonic aircraft. There is no need for the contractor to cover against such risks and it is up to the employer to take out insurance cover should he think it necessary.

Clause 20 – Insurance of the Works against Fire etc.

The most common arrangements relating to insurance against fire are that the contractor undertakes the risk in the case of new work while the employer assumes the risk in the case of existing buildings. This need not necessarily be so however, and clause 20 (B) covers the case where the employer himself undertakes to insure new buildings under construction. It is therefore important that the matter is considered at an early stage and the alternatives provided under clause 20 carefully read and checked and those that do not apply under the particular circumstances deleted.

In the case of new buildings where the contractor accepts fire and general risks it is normally contemplated that the level of cover

(20) *Gold* v. *Patman and Fotheringham Ltd.*, (1958) 2 All ER 493.

relates to work completed and unfixed materials stored on the site that would ordinarily be covered by an interim certificate for payment. Otherwise the question of risks is a matter for the contractor and it cannot be sufficiently emphasised that such questions should be contemplated at a very early stage prior to the contract. The site may be subject to special perils or be particularly subject to vandalism for example and sub-clause (1) is capable of amendment if necessary.

The full value of work executed and unfixed materials and goods delivered to the site also includes for insurance purposes the cost of professional fees. It should be noted that the percentage should be included in the Appendix to the contract by the employer otherwise he will be unable to recover such costs from the contractor or his insurers.

If clause 20 (A) is invoked, insurances are to be taken out in the joint names of contractor and employer, the employer having the right to approve the insurers and to hold the policies and receipts for premiums. He also has the right to act in default of the contractor and reimburse himself from monies due.

Clause 20 recognises the general business arrangements of contractors to carry policies against continuous risks rather than specific policies for individual contracts and such arrangements are quite in order to satisfy clause 20 (A) provided that certain stipulations set out in the proviso to the clause are obeyed. These are to ensure that the policy covers the "full value" as defined in the contract together with the percentage for fees; that the employer's interest is endorsed on the policy and that the contractor produces documentary evidence that the policy is properly endorsed and valid in all respects.

Clause 20 reiterates that should damage occur the contractor is bound to put matters right and the only payment that he can expect is that available under the insurance. It is of obvious importance, in the interests of all parties however, that adequate insurance cover, taking inflation into account, is arranged in order to allow the contract to be smoothly resumed. It is contemplated under sub-clause (2) that the insurance monies are doled out to the contractor by instalments as certified by the architect or supervising officer less the percentage for professional fees which are due for payment by the employer. The arrangements are broadly those in force under clause 30 relating to Interim Certificates. Insurance monies are generally, in the meantime, paid into a joint account.

Where under clause 20 (B) the employer accepts the risks of Fire and Other Perils, the contractor merely has the duty of giving notice of any loss or damage as soon as it occurs or is known about.

Clause 20 (C) deals with the case of Existing Structures where the employer accepts the fire risk. In this case the contractor has the right to ascertain if adequate insurance is in force but clause 20 (C) is much more difficult to apply than clauses 20 (A) and 20 (B) since the responsibilities and obligations of the two parties are far less clear cut. The fact that the employer makes direct arrangements with his insurance company as an extension of his existing policy is obviously sensible since any other arrangement would be impracticable. Consider for example the case of a hotel where the main reception rooms are being refurbished. However, what does or does not constitute adequate insurance may be seen very differently by employer and contractor and although clause 20 (C) deals with a number of particular circumstances, no contractor, presumably, would wish to see the contract frustrated by inadequate business arrangements relating to insurance even if it is normally blandly stated that since he is not at risk he need not care. The contractor deals with different contracts every day of the week and every week of the year and has experienced insurers to assist him. The employer on the other hand may only assume such an obligation once or twice in a lifetime and may not realise the need for adequate advice. The employer may indeed make superficial enquiries relating to certain risks and, finding that the premiums are prohibitive, settle for lesser or inadequate cover, hoping that all will be well. The architect, surveyor or supervising officer should do all he can to bridge the gap and ensure that the benefit of the contractor's experience is passed to the employer. It is particularly important to arrange for adequate insurance where refurbishment to a building of artistic or historic importance is concerned. The sub-clauses to clause 20 (C) are adequate so far as they go in that they do not prejudice the amount of monies due to the contractor and arrange for a fair basis of determination of the contract in the event of a disaster but adequate insurance arrangements are a pre-requisite to any building operation and are of particular importance in the case of existing structures.

Clause 21 – Possession, Completion and Postponement
There is no machinery in the contract form for the date for possession of the site, inserted in the Appendix, to be altered. "The contract necessarily requires the building owner to give the contractor such possession, occupation or use as is necessary to enable him to perform the contract", said Megarry J. in a case where this point was discussed.[21] Clearly, the contractor is entitled to repudiate the

(21) *London Borough of Houns.ow* v. *Twickenham Garden Developments Ltd.*, (1970) 3 All ER 326.

contract if possession was not granted. The contractor however, presumably in the majority of cases will not wish to loose the work for which he has by now made provision and new terms will be negotiated either specifically quoting a new date for possession or, alternatively, stating a time for completion as being so many weeks from the date when possession is provided. It is obviously necessary to have a clear understanding of what is agreed as the period for carrying out the Works will have been stated in the original invitation to tender and confirmed in the form of tender. It is, in any event, to be hoped that the contractor will be well ahead in his programme of work and forward planning.

In the Twickenham Garden Developments case just referred to, Megarry J took a swipe at the words "regularly and diligently" set down in sub-clause (1). The contractor is obliged to proceed regularly and diligently with the works but, said Megarry J, "these are elusive words on which the dictionaries help little. . . . Such language provides little help on the question of how much activity, progress and so on is to be expected." He then went on to suggest that evidence upon this point as to what was customary would be helpful. The point is important since the contractor's failure to proceed regularly and diligently would entitle the employer to determine the contract under clause 25.

While, as we have seen, the architect or supervising officer has no jurisdiction to alter the date for possession of the site sub-clause (2) enables him to postpone any actual work contemplated provided that the Employer accepts that claims for extension of time and money are the least consequences that might flow from such an order since it is possible that the contractor may take the opportunity of determining the contract under clause 26.

Just as the contractor cannot be required to complete the contract before the date set out in the Appendix to the Contract Form, nor can the employer be required to take earlier possession should the work be completed earlier than expected.

Clause 22 – Damages for Non-Completion

Liquidated Damages, agreed between the parties to the contract at the time that it is drawn up, form the basis for determining in advance the extent of the liability, usually in money form, for some future, specified, breach of the contract. Liquidated damages can be contrasted with unliquidated damages which are ascertained only after the breach of contract has been committed.

The advantage of agreed liquidated damages is that the contractor will know accurately the sum that he will have to pay for each week that he runs over the stated period for carrying out the works.

It is, of course, well established that liquidated damages should, in no way, be used as a weapon by the employer so that, in the case of breach of contract, the contractor is asked to pay a sum that is totally disproportionate to any possible loss incurred. In such a case, the provision will be unenforceable and payment will not be upheld by the Courts.

It is of course obvious, that if no completion date is inserted in the contract, then no liquidated damages can possibly be claimed. Clause 22 is designed for the case where the employer can justly recover liquidated and ascertained damages for failure by the contractor to complete the work by the given date named in the Appendix and to deduct such sums from money that is due to the contractor.

The certificate of the architect, surveyor or supervising officer stating when completion should have reasonably occurred often sets off an interesting chain of circumstances. While such a certificate is not required as a condition precedent to arbitration since, once a dispute arises, either party can refer the matter to arbitration, nevertheless such a certificate often forms the starting gun for such a reference. The contractor may try to claim that the Employer is in some way responsible for failure to achieve the completion date since, should he succeed, this is a valid defence for the recovery of liquidated damages.[22] An interesting situation occurs when the architect, surveyor or supervising officer has issued a certificate under this section and the contractor has already claimed an extension of time under clause 23. There is no need, so far as can be seen, for the architect, surveyor or supervising officer to have decided on the merits of the claim for an extended completion date before issuing his certificate under clause 22 and the matter will be resolved by Arbitration.

Clause 23 – Extension of Time
Under this clause the architect, surveyor or supervising officer is required to make in writing a fair and reasonable extension of time for the completion of the works in certain specified circumstances. The clause has an obvious and important bearing upon the two earlier clauses 21 and 22, obviously affecting as it does, the question of liquidated damages, but the duty of the architect under this clause cuts both ways. If he grants an extension of time the employer's eyebrows may be raised but, should he fail to do so on proper grounds, when the contractor is clearly entitled to an extension, he may imperil the whole basis of his Employer's right to collect liquidated damages.

(22) *Peak Construction (Liverpool) Ltd.* v. *McKinney Foundations Ltd.*, (1976) 1 BLR 111.

As soon as delay is reasonably apparent, the contractor has the duty of writing to the architect or surveyor stating firstly that progress of the work is delayed and secondly giving the cause of the delay. The architect then has the duty of comparing the submission with the paragraphs referred to in clause 23. A refusal to accept the submission may, obviously, give rise to arbitration but if the submission is justified difficulties may still follow. He has firstly to decide if the claim is based on genuine circumstances or if the contractor is merely dragging his feet. He may decide the matter there and then by extending the completion date and giving notice to the contractor or alternatively, may wait to see what happens in the hope that progress may improve. This course of action may be unsatisfactory, however, for a number of reasons although a cause of delay that is of a continuing or intermittent nature may make it impossible for a precise extension of time to be judged. While he should give an extension of time as soon as he reasonably can so that the contractor is not left in doubt as to his programme, he might be quite unable to do so even if this means risking the employer's right to collect liquidated damages. The contract form recognises the difficulty by the words "the architect shall so soon as he is able to estimate the length of the delay beyond the date or time aforesaid and make in writing a fair and reasonable extension of time. . . ." Another difficulty arises from the fact that the architect, surveyor or supervising officer might find himself to be the judge and jury upon his own behaviour. If the reason for the delay is within the control of the architect or surveyor or employer the decision regarding an extension of time should be given at once. Otherwise however, there is no obligation upon the architect, surveyor or supervising officer to decide as to whether or not to make an extension of time up and until the date of completion or even beyond.[23]

The causes of delay are set out as follows:

" (a) By *force majeure,* or
 (b) By reason of any exceptionally inclement weather, or
 (c) By reason of loss or damage occasioned by any one or more of the contingencies referred to in clause 20 (A), (B), or (C) of these Conditions, or
 (d) By reason of civil commotion, local combination of workmen, strike or lock out affecting any of the trades employed upon the Works or any of the trades engaged in the preparation, manufacture or transportation of any of the goods or materials required for the Works, or

(23) *ABC Ltd.* v. *Waltham Holy Cross UDC,* (1952) 2 All ER 452.

(e) By reason of the Architect's instructions issued under clauses 1 (2), 11 (1) or 21 (2) of these Conditions, or

(f) By reason of the Contractor not having received in due time necessary instructions, drawings, details of levels from the Architect for which he specifically applied in writing on a date which having regard to the Date of Completion stated in the appendix to these Conditions or to any extension of time when fixed under this clause or clause 33 (1) (c) of these Conditions was neither unreasonably distant from nor unreasonably close to the date on which it was necessary for him to receive the same, or

(g) By delay on the part of nominated sub-contractors or nominated suppliers which the Contractor has taken all practical steps to avoid or reduce, or

(h) By delay on the part of artists, tradesmen or others engaged by the Employer in executing work not forming part of this Contract, or

(i) By reason of the opening up for inspection of any work covered up or of testing of any of the work, materials or goods in accordance with clause 6 (3) of these Conditions (including making good in consequence of such opening up or testing), unless the inspection or test showed that the work, materials or goods were not in accordance with this Contract, or

(j) (i) By the Contractor's inability for reasons beyond his control and which he could not reasonably have foreseen at the date of this Contract to secure such goods and/or materials as are essential to the proper carrying out of the Works, or

   (ii) By the Contractor's inability for reasons beyond his control and which he could not reasonably have foreseen at the date of this contract to secure such labour as is essential to the proper carrying out of the Works, or

(k) By reason of compliance with the provisions of clause 34 of these Conditions or with the architect's instructions issued thereunder, or

(l) By a local authority or statutory undertaker in carrying out such work in pursuance of its statutory obligations in relation to the Works, or in failing to carry out such work then the Architect shall so soon as he is able to estimate the length of the delay beyond the date or time aforesaid make in writing a fair and reasonable extension of time for completion of the Works. Provided always that the Contractor shall use constantly his best endeavours to prevent delay

196

and shall do all that may reasonably be required to the satisfaction of the Architect to proceed with the Works."

A footnote to this clause requires either or both sub-clauses (j)(i) or (j)(ii) to be deleted if not to apply.

If a cause for delay which is the fault of neither party occurs under (a) – (d), (g), (j) and (l), the employer is not required to pay extra money but must release the Contractor from the consequences of extended time such as liquidated damages. Where matters occur which are the responsibility of the employer or his architect or surveyor however, (e) – (f), (h) and (i) monetary claims may obviously arise under the next clause 24.

"Force majeure" is limited to cover those items not already referred to in the Contract such as war or the outbreak of fire. The meaning of 'exceptionally inclement weather' is a question of fact. The weather must have been so bad when compared with normal records for the locality and have occurred when the outside works were in progress to such an extent that delay was inevitable. This clause does not merely imply that if it rains everyone on the site, whether outside or under cover, has the right to cease work. Similarly under (d) a strike in the manufacturing or road haulage industry may provide grounds for extension of time but not if other similar stock piles of materials are available.

Clause (g) led to the curious decision in the "Jarvis" case.[24] This case concerned the construction of a complex including offices, show rooms and filling station with a multi-storey car park. Peter Lind Ltd were the nominated sub-contractors for the piling work but it was only discovered once the date for completion under the nominated piling sub-contract had been passed that the piles were in fact defective. Jarvis naturally expected to be granted an extension of time but the House of Lords upheld the argument submitted by Westminster Corporation that the sub-contract had been apparently completed and that the sub-contractor, while certainly in breach of contract, was not in breach of contract for delay. The curious rule that emerged therefore is that a contractor cannot claim an extension of time if the sub-contractor completes his own sub-contract work on time but the work is later proved to be defective. However, if the contractor should find out that the work is defective before the date set for termination of the sub-contract then a claim for an extension of time is likely to be upheld. The same rule would presumably apply to nominated or other suppliers. It has been suggested that the judgement in the Jarvis case was influenced

(24) *Westminster Corporation* v. *J. Jarvis & Sons Ltd. & Peter Lind Ltd.*, (1970) 1 All ER 943.

by the very large sum set aside for liquidated damages. Obviously it would have been an odd situation where Westminster Council could have been deprived of liquidated damages due to what was in fact defective work since, if they could not claim it from Jarvis neither could they obtain payment from Lind with whom they had no contractual relationship. Even so, the outcome of the case leaves the determination of sub-clause (g) in the curious position that the word "delay" may turn on whether latent defects happen to be discovered or not.

It is perhaps worth noting that in the case of a JCT Form of Contract to be carried out in phases, delay on the first phase that affects subsequent phases does not automatically imply an extension of the completion date. The express terms in the contract where clear and unambiguous cannot be altered by implication from subsequent events.[25]

Under (i) the architect or supervising officer has the opportunity of giving instructions for work to be opened up for inspection or testing, once covered. Obviously this forms grounds for an extension of time unless of course the work is found to be defective.

Under (j) alternative sub-clauses are provided and Practice Note 2 suggests that the sub-clauses should be deleted either wholly or partly only if it is considered reasonable for contractors to take the risk of either labour or materials, or both, not being available. These sub-clauses are only authority for delay on the ground that shortage of labour and materials could not possibly have been foreseen at the date that the contract was drawn up.

Clause 24 – Loss and Expense Caused by Disturbance of Regular Progress of the Works

A claim by the contractor for loss or expense by disturbance of the regular progress of the works must be made in writing and within reasonable time of the occurrence of delay. The claim then stands or falls on whether the architect, surveyor or supervising officer is of the opinion that loss to the contractor is due to one of the following causes:

"(a) The Contractor not having received in due time necessary instructions, drawings, details or levels from the Architect for which he specifically applied in writing on a date which having regard to the Date for Completion stated in the Appendix to these Conditions or to any extension of time then

---

(25) *Trollope & Colls Ltd.* v. *North-West Metropolitan Hospital Board*, (1973) 2 All ER 260.

fixed under clause 23 or clause 33 (1) (c) of these Conditions was neither unreasonably distant from nor unreasonably close to the date on which it was necessary for him to receive the same; or

(b) The opening up for inspection of any work covered up or the testing of any of the work materials or goods in accordance with clause 6 (3) of these Conditions (including making good in consequence of such opening up or testing), unless the inspection or test showed that the work, materials or goods were not in accordance with this Contract; or

(c) Any discrepancy in or divergence between the Contract Drawings and/or the Contract Bills; or

(d) Delay on the part of artists, tradesmen, or others engaged by the Employer in executing work not forming part of this Contract; or

(e) Architect's instructions issued in regard to the postponement of any work to be executed under the provisions of this Contract; and if the written application is made within a reasonable time of it becoming apparent that the progress of the Works or of any part thereof has been affected as aforesaid, then the Architect shall either himself ascertain or shall instruct the Quantity Surveyor to ascertain the amount of such loss and/or expense. Any amount from time to time so ascertained shall be added to the Contract Sum, and if an Interim Certificate is issued after the date of ascertainment any such amount shall be added to the amount which would otherwise be stated as due in such Certificate."

Under (a) the need for an agreed time schedule or Progress Chart is vital. Such charts are now commonplace but although having no force in the contract would be a necessary preliminary to any claim under this particular section. It is emphasised that this clause covers the reimbursement of the Contractor for loss or expense in the regular progress of the Works that is not covered by any other provision. The distinctions between clause 24 and other clauses in the contract may be a very fine one.

Clause 25 – Determination by Employer

The Employer may under clause 25 (1) determine the Contract under sub-clause (a) if the Contractor without reasonable cause "wholly suspends the carrying out of the Works before completion thereof, or under sub-clause (b) fails to proceed "regularly and diligently" with the Works or refuses under sub-clause (c) or persistently neglects to comply with a written Notice from the architect or surveyor requiring him to remove defective work or improper materials or goods and by such refusal or neglect the Works are materially affected. If he fails to comply with the provisions of clause 17 of the Contract the employer is empowered to determine the contract under sub-clause (d).

The architect or surveyor under this sub-clause is to give notice to the Contractor by registered post or recorded delivery specifying the default and if the Contractor either continues such default for fourteen days after receipt of the notice or "at any time thereafter" repeats such default then the Employer may within ten days "after such continuance or repetition" by notice or registered post or recorded delivery "forthwith determine the employment of the Contractor under this Contract, provided that such notice shall not be given unreasonably or vexatiously".

Clause 25 (1) enables the Employer to do precisely as it says to "determine the employment of the Contractor . . . without prejudice to any other rights or remedies. . . ." In other words the Contractor having been given the sack may still be sued while the employer looks round for another contractor to fill his place.

It is obvious that the architect, surveyor or supervising officer must take prompt action to serve notice in the required form whereupon the Contractor must then dispute it at once or put matters right. Of course, in practice, events are never so clear cut as this section may infer. The worse category is (b) where an inefficient contractor will involve himself and the architect to say nothing of the employer in an intermittent blizzard of miserable problems that are rather outside the bludgeon effect of clause 25.

Clause 25 (2) deals with the bankruptcy of the contractor. Under such circumstances the Contractor's employment under the contract is terminated without any need for notice. The contractor, however, must be adjudicated bankrupt either from the date when a resolution is passed for the voluntary winding-up of a company or the date when the petition of winding-up is presented to the High Court. The contractor however, may be reinstated should the employer and the trustee in bankruptcy or the liquidator mutually so agree.

Sub-clause (3) deals with "corrupt practices" while sub-clause (4) deals with the situation once the contractor's employment has been validly determined under the previous sub-clauses. The employer for example can engage another contractor to carry on with the works, to make claims for any direct loss or damage he has suffered as a result of the determination and to suspend payments of money that would otherwise be due. He may, more validly it is thought, set off sums that he has incurred by way of loss or damage against payments due to the contractor.

Clause 26 – Determination by Contractor

The contractor is entitled under this section to serve notice by registered post or recorded delivery to the Employer or architect determining his employment "forthwith" under the terms of the contract (provided that such notice shall not be given unreasonably or vexatiously) on the following grounds:

(a) The Employer does not pay to the Contractor the amount due on any certificate (otherwise than as a result of the operation of clause 1 (2) (b) of the Supplemental Agreement annexed to these Conditions (the VAT Agreement) within fourteen days from the presentation of that certificate and continues such default for seven days after receipt by registered post or recorded delivery of a notice from the Contractor stating that notice of determination under this Condition will be served if payment is not made within seven days from receipt thereof; or

(b) The Employer interferes with or obstructs the issue of any certificate due under this Contract; or

(c) The carrying out of the whole or substantially the whole of the uncompleted Works (other than the execution of work required under clause 15 of these Conditions) is suspended for a continuous period of the length named in the Appendix to these Conditions by reason of:

    (i) by force majeure, or

   (ii) Loss or damage (unless caused by the negligence of the contractor, his servants or agents or of any sub-contractor, his servants or agents) occasioned by any one or more of the contingencies referred to in clause 20 (A) or clause 20 (B) of these Conditions (if applicable) or

  (iii) Civil commotion, or

  (iv) Architect's instructions issued under clauses 1 (2), 11 (1) or 21 (2) of these Conditions, unless caused by reason of some negligence or default of the Contractor, or

   (v) The Contractor not having received in due time necessary instructions, drawings, details or levels from the Architect for which he specifically applied in writing on a date which having regard to the Date of Completion stated in the Appendix to these Conditions or to any extension of time then fixed under clause 23 or clause 33 (1) (c) of these Conditions was neither unreasonably distant from nor unreasonably close to the date on which it was necessary for him to receive the same, or

(vi) Delay on the part of artists, tradesmen or others engaged by the Employer in executing work not forming part of this Contract, or

(vii) The opening up for inspection of any work covered up or the testing of any of the work materials or goods in accordance with clause 6 (3) of these Conditions (including making good in consequence of such opening up or testing), unless the inspection or test showed that the work materials or goods were not in accordance with this Contract.

(d) The Employer becomes bankrupt or makes a composition or arrangement with his creditors or has a winding up order made or (except for the purposes of reconstruction) a resolution for voluntary winding up passed or a receiver or manager of his business or undertaking is duly appointed, or possession is to be taken by or on behalf of the holders of any debentures secured by a floating charge of any property comprised in or subject to the floating charge,

then the Contractor may thereupon by notice by registered post or recorded delivery to the Employer or architect forthwith determine the employment of the Contractor under this Contract, provided that such notice shall not be given unreasonably or vexatiously.

Clause 26 is a mirror image or role reversal to counterbalance clause 25. The grounds for determination by the Contractor range from late or non-payment subsequent to the issuing of certificates or if the employer "interferes with or obstructs" the architect or supervising officer in his plain duty to issue certificates under the terms of the Contract. If the employer for example attempts to influence the architect as to the amount that he should award or prevent him having access to the site for the delivery of a certificate for example, such harrassment, by no means unknown, enables the contractor to determine the contract.

If the works are suspended for the period named in the Appendix for one of the reasons set out in the sub-paragraphs to clause 26 (usually one month) the contractor may again determine his employment without any further formalities being required. Careful distinction should be made however, between the grounds offered under clause 23 (extension of time) and clause 26. The contractor has the duty of removing his equipment from the site once he has served notice and is entitled to claim payment for work up until the date of determination under specified grounds.

Clause 27 – Nominated Sub-Contractors

A particular problem relating to nominated sub-contractors and prime cost sums (PC sums) was discussed at length in the Bickerton case[26] and the upheaval that followed was directly responsible for the fundamental changes in the JCT Contract Form 1980. The circumstances in this case were that a nominated sub-contractor went into liquidation and failed to complete certain work. The contractor then requested that the architect issue new instructions under JCT clause 11 of the 1963 Contract Form and that he renominate under clause 27 as the original sub-contract had lapsed. In the case the term "prime cost" was defined by Lord Reid as referring to "certain parts of the works reserved for sub-contractors to be nominated by the employer. . . ." It followed from this that the tendering contractor had no concern either with the details of this work or the price to be paid for it. It was the employer who obtained tenders from specialists selected for the prime cost work and then instructed the contractor to enter into a contract with the sub-contractor whom he nominates on terms which he dictates, having settled these terms with the nominated sub-contractor. Lord Reid then went on to say that sums payable in respect of prime cost work were to be expended in favour of nominated sub-contractors and no one else. "I can find nothing anywhere to indicate that the principal contractor can ever have in any event either the right or the duty to do any of the prime cost work himself. . . ."

In the Bickerton case the North West Metropolitan Hospital Board were the employers, T. A. Bickerton were the contractors and Speediwarm were nominated sub-contractors who went into liquidation. Bickerton then stepped in and completed the heating work at a higher price than that agreed with Speediwarm. The Hospital Board then argued that Bickerton were only entitled to be paid the price agreed with the nominated sub-contractors on the grounds that when a sub-contract is terminated it is the right and duty of the main contractor to carry out the prime cost work himself at the original price fixed. They claimed moreover that if the main contractor did not in fact complete the work he would be in breach of contract. Bickerton, however, argued that they were entitled to expect that a further nomination would be made and since it was the employer's default in this that the work had cost more, they were due the extra sums that they had incurred and disbursed. In finding for the contractor the Court established that firstly the architect or surveyor has a duty of renomination under the 1963 Contract Form and secondly that the contractor not only need not, but must not, find a successor; the architect's right of nomination was sacrosanct.

(26) *North-West Metropolitan Hospital Board* v. *T. A. Bickerton Ltd.*, (1970) 1 All ER 1039.

Clause 27 only applies where PC sums are inserted in the Contract Bills or where they arise under specific instructions from the architect or surveyor under clause 11 relating to the expenditure of Provisional Sums.

It states at the outset of clause 27 (a) that "such sums shall be deemed to include two and a half per cent cash discount" in favour of the contractor and it is not presumably possible to make a nomination with a firm who will not accept this arrangement. The Contractor has a right to make reasonable objection to a nomination although if he has merely heard rumours of bad workmanship through the trade it is difficult to see how he can do so.

The clauses that follow in the 1963 version of the JCT Contract Form highlight the problems that have been experienced in the question of nominated sub-contracts. Although the architect or surveyor cannot nominate a sub-contractor who is not willing to enter into the "Green Form" nevertheless the contractor may, with the architect's or surveyor's consent, enter into a sub-contract that differs markedly from the sub-clauses attached to 27 (a). This provides the sort of situation which can often go wrong with the tangle of clauses, none of which are directly related to each other, causing intense problems under the main contract.

Accordingly, the ten paragraphs of sub-clause (a) of clause 27 cannot form part of any sub-contract with the nominated sub-contractor on their own. The provisions of the sub-contract document are obviously crucial. The Form of Tender issued by the Joint Contracts Tribunal in May 1970 simply replaces the Standard Form of Estimate produced by the RIBA and RICS in connection with nominated sub-contract work previously used. This document was, at last, intended to comply with clause 27 of the JCT Contract Form 1963 in a way which enabled the new "Green Form" to be used. It made particular reference to "special attendance" required from the contractor since the Standard Method of Measurement requires a destinction between special and general attendance with close pricing as a more desirable alternative than a provisional Sum. The "Green Form" known more properly as the "sub-contract for use where the sub-contractor is Nominated under the Standard Form of Building Contract issued by the Joint Contracts Tribunal" then came into its own and there was, at last, some relationship between the various documents.

The sub-clauses to 27 (a) specify a number of obvious and not so obvious requirements. They deal with the necessity for the nominated sub-contractor to complete the sub-contract works so as to enable the contractor to discharge his own obligations and to bring the sub-contract works into line with those of the main contract.

Indemnities are required of the nominated sub-contractor against the same liabilities in respect of the sub-contract works as those under the main contract and against claims in respect of negligence, omission or default of the sub-contractor. There is a requirement that the sub-contract works shall be completed within the specified period, that the contractor shall not grant any extension of time without the consent of the architect or surveyor and that the contractor shall inform the architect or surveyor of any representation made by the nominated sub-contractor as to the cause of any delay. There is provision for liquidated damages in respect of the sub-contract work and provision for payment, retention and cash discounts. There is a right for the architect or surveyor and his representatives to have access to the workshops of the nominated sub-contractor and finally a provision that the employment of the nominated sub-contractor is to determine immediately upon the determination of the contractor's employment under the main contract for any reason.

Under clause 27 (b) the architect or surveyor has the duty of giving the contractor a figure of "total value" in respect of the nominated work to be included for payment in an interim certificate. The contractor is then under an obligation to pay this sum to the nominated sub-contractor, less only the retention as allowed for in the sub-contract document, damages for delay in completing the sub-contract works and finally the cash discount of two and a half percent. While this enables the contract to proceed the contractor is nevertheless in the curious position that, since the amount of money to be certified to a nominated sub-contractor is purely at the discretion of the architect or surveyor, the contractor has no say in the matter whatsoever. This apparent system of isolation has little basis in fact. The large majority of nominated sub-contractors rushing from one job to another have one main interest which is to finish the work and not to have to return. They happily arrange with the main contractor that he will make good defects in the sub-contract works and set off the cost against the money that is due.

It is a curious fact that the contractor has fourteen days grace in which to pay over the "total value" under a certificate issued under clause 30 while the employer (assuming that the first class post arrives the following day) has only thirteen days. It is of course universally hoped that the employer will issue his cheque at once and the contractor will then disburse payment once the money has been received. Trouble has been experienced where the date has been altered in the main contract and differs from that inserted in the nominated form of sub-contact. The whole point of cash discount is of course that this is due within the fourteen day period stipulated unless otherwise agreed. Difficulties arising between the main contract Form and the forms for nominated sub-contractors and suppliers have been one of the main problem areas of the 1963 JCT Contract Form and which the Tribunal have sought to correct in the 1980 Edition.

Normally the employer receives the architect's or surveyor's certificate and the contractor receives the duplicate copy but there is provision under sub-clause (c) for the Employer to make direct payments to a nominated sub-contractor if his request to the contractor to furnish to him reasonable proof that all amounts included in previous certificates have been discharged is not met. The architect or surveyor is not obliged to obtain proof but in practice this is the procedure that the quantity surveyor will invariably carry out at each valuation.

Sub-clause (d) refers to the question of delay on the part of a nominated sub-contractor. No extension of time may be granted by the contractor without the consent of the architect or surveyor. It is of obvious importance however, that the proviso to this form is followed in that any representations submitted by the nominated sub-contractor as to the cause of the delay in the sub-contract works must be passed to the architect or surveyor. Otherwise he will be in no position to arrive at a fair decision. Once having considered the grounds the architect or surveyor is then bound to certify the date on which the nominated sub-contract works are to be completed with the certificate being issued to the contractor and a duplicate to the sub-contractor. This is the only certificate not issued to the employer. From it flows the whole question of liquidated damages that will accrue from the sub-contractor but only if, of course, due provision is made in the sub-contract document.

Under sub-clause (e) the architect or surveyor has a dicretionary right to secure final payment to nominated sub-contractors before his Final Certificate to the main contractor is issued. However this can only happen if the sub-contractor has indemnified the contractor against any latent defects in the sub-contract works. The sum to the sub-contractor will include a part of the retention money and make provision for the cash discount. Sub-clause (f) is obviously inserted to stress that there is no legal relationship between nominated sub-contractors and the employer.

Sub-clause (g) attempts to build in a number of safeguards to protect the employer where the contractor expresses a wish to carry out work under Prime Cost sums. The contractor must first be capable of dealing with the work himself and must have recorded in the appendix his wish to do so. The architect or surveyor must be willing to receive tenders from the contractor and obviously, the architect or surveyor and contractor are likely to get together when the contract is being drawn up to agree the appendix items.

Clause 28 – Nominated Suppliers

Clause 28 operates where a Prime Cost Sum occurs in respect of goods and materials to be fixed by the contractor. This must be specified in the Contract Bills or arise as a result of the architect or surveyor's instructions as to the expenditure of provisional sums under clause 11. The only other way in which clause 28 can apply is where a variation is ordered which takes away the normal duties of the contractor to supply goods and materials and substitutes a Prime Cost Sum. Due to the relationship between clauses 27 and 28 it is likely that the conclusions of the "Bickerton" case apply here also.

Prime Cost Sums under clause 28 "shall be deemed to include five per cent cash discount" and necessary expenses such as packaging, delivery and purchase tax can be offset but not trade discount. Any tax or duty which the contractor has to pay in respect of materials or goods are to be refunded to him.

The architect or surveyor has the right under clause 28 to specify a "nominated supplier" and to give instructions as to the expenditure of prime cost sums. Once a nomination is made, the subsequent contract is between the employer and the contractor who then have the right to ensure that the architect makes a nomination from a firm or person who will abide by the sub-clauses of this section. The architect or supervising officer is not necessarily limited to this procedure but must obviously realise the consequences. The relationship of the parties is a delicate one and the architect or supervising officer is well advised to conduct all negotiations through the contractor as otherwise if the contractor is unaware of any criticism made directly to the supplier or of any variation in price or quantity, he will become irritated, understandably, and the use of his experience in assessment and coordination may well be lost. Often problems arise from the fact that a Prime Cost Sum should have been re-designated as a Provisional Sum right at the outset of the contract.

A traditional bone of contention in building work is what happens when goods delivered by a nominated supplier and fixed in place by the contractor subsequently prove to be faulty.

Paragraph (ii) attempts to deal with this situation by stating that a supplier who wishes to be nominated must expect to replace faulty goods or materials and bear "any expenses reasonably incurred by the contractor as a consequence of such defects".

The remaining provisions of clause 28 are intended to protect the contractor over such matters as delivery times, cash discount and like matters. Notwithstanding this the contractor has an obvious duty in protecting himself to ensure that the terms of sale issued by a nominated supplier conform to the small print of clause 28. Should this not be the case he must inform the architect or surveyor at once. This is an area where the contractor must be careful. The 5 per cent cash discount is a very slender reward for all the necessary arranging and the fact that suppliers have to be paid in full under sub-clause (c); often quite large sums have to be paid in advance of any reimbursement being due to the contractor under the next interim certificate. The architect or surveyor on his part has to be careful before he moves outside the provisions of clause 28 (see JCT Practice Note 6 where the 5 per cent discount is varied). An architect or surveyor is well advised to consider another nomination if a quotation is hedged with unusual restrictions or limitations since sub-clause (d) entitles the contractor to point these out to the architect or surveyor who must then take written responsibility for them.

Clause 29 – Artists and Tradesmen

This clause, traditionally designed to cover a sculptor, for example, carving a section of stone fixed by the contractor, has a number of interesting extensions in this day and age but clearly what defines artists and tradesmen must be a matter of fact. A specialist firm applying spatterdash to the face of a building is hardly likely to comply with the definition.

Clause 30 – Certificates and Payments

As noted earlier in this chapter the lump-sum nature of the contract is not invalidated by interim payments being made. Interim certificates issued by the architect or surveyor are normally at monthly intervals before practical completion, unless otherwise stated, and subsequent to the date of practical completion will be issued as and when further amounts become due to the contractor or nominated sub-contractors unless varied by the formula method.

Interim certificates are issued to the contractor and, once these are presented to the employer, payment is due within fourteen days. There is an interesting variation in the local authority version of the JCT Contract Form where the certificate is issued to the employer with a duplicate to the contractor, the period of fourteen days running from the date of issue of the certificate. Assuming that the architect or surveyor applies an appropriate stamp so that the certificate goes off by first class post, and Local Authority employer therefore has only thirteen days in which to find payment.

No interim certificate is final or conclusive and unless the architect or surveyor seriously under-certifies these are rarely the subject of litigation. However, as noted earlier, a case arose on this subject where an architect was found to be liable in negligence for including the value of defective work in an interim certificate. In this case the architect was unfortunate in that the contractor became insolvent and recovery was impossible.[27]

Interim certificates must include the total value of the work properly executed and the total value of the materials and goods delivered to or adjacent to the Works. The sums to be included are accordingly a matter of fact although quite often problems are presented in ascertaining the facts. It should be noted however in a sub-clause that delivery of goods must have taken place up to and including seven days before the date of the certificate. Sub-clauses (ii), (iii) and (iv) are designed to ensure that the goods and materials are delivered in the ordinary course of the contract and that they are adequately protected against weather. These sub-clauses are designed to ensure that the contractor does not send lorry loads of materials at the last minute and dump them in confusion on the site so as to obtain a higher interim payment.

Under clause 30, while it is possible to calculate progress payments at fixed intervals, subject to all the variations anticipated, it is also possible for the parties to agree upon progress payments being made at certain stated intervals such as the completion, for example, of a particular stage of the work.

The problems presented by modern building methods are highlighted in sub-clause (2A) which deals with payment for off-site goods and materials. Payment can be required for pre-fabricated sections or units before delivery to the site and the sub-clause endeavours to deal as best it can with this prickly problem. The materials must be intended for inclusion in the works; much have been completed and set apart and clearly marked at the premises of manufacture. Provision is made as to ownership under this sub-clause and the architect or surveyor is advised to refresh his mind as to the wording should he be under a duty to certify payment prior to delivery.

In normal cases the Retention Percentage is 5% of the Contract Sum unless a lower figure is marked in the Appendix. An interim certificate issued after practical completion will be subject to a deduction of one-half the Retention Percentage held before the practical completion date. The total Retention Percentage is reduced proportionately in the case of partial possession of the site by the employer and early final payment of a nominated sub-contractor.

(27) *Sutcliffe* v. *Thackrah*, (1974) 1 All ER 859.

While the contract Form states that the employer's interest in the amounts retained is to be "fiduciary as trustee" the contractor is well advised in substantial cases to ensure that the Retention is set aside in a separate fund in a joint account as otherwise it is doubtful if he will have any better rights than an ordinary creditor in the event of the employer's bankruptcy. Such a proceeding is merely to protect the contractor. The employer is not obliged to pay interest on the sums dealt with in this manner. The sums set aside should be inviolate unless the employer can correctly claim money to reimburse himself for failure by the contractor to carry out a valid instruction from the architect or surveyor or in certain limited cases such as clause 22 (Liquidated and ascertained damages), clause 15 (Repairing defects), clauses 19 and 20 (Insurance) and clause 27 (direct payments to nominated sub-contractors).

The second moiety of the Retention Percentage is discharged either upon the date of expiry of the Defects Liability Period or the issue of the Certificate of Completion of Making Good Defects whichever is the later.

Sub-clauses (5) to (8) set out the provisions relating to the Final Certificate. Firstly the quantity surveyor must comply with the "Period of Final Measurement and Valuation" normally six months from the day named in the Certificate of Practical Completion unless otherwise stated. By the end of this period the contractor must be supplied with priced Bills of Variation which will form the basis for the adjustment of the Contract Sum. The contractor has a duty to provide all documents necessary particularly those relating to nominated sub-contractors and suppliers. The amounts paid by the contractor including work carried out by him in connection with attendance, for example in connection with prime cost sums or provisional sums and items such as insurance, are necessary for exact calculation of the final amounts due to him or in some cases to the employer.

The Final Certificate must be issued "as soon as practicable" and in any event upon the expiry of a period following on whichever is the later of either the end of the Defects Liability Period or the issue of the Certificate of Completion of Making Good Defects. The Final Certificate must state the total amount paid under interim certificates and the amount of the contract sum as adjusted. The clear balance due either to the contractor or the employer is then a debt upon the expiry of fourteen days from issue.

The conclusive nature of the Final Certificate was underlined in a case relating to defective flooring. A large balance of money due upon interim certificates under a JCT Form of Contract was disputed by the employer on the grounds that flooring was defective.

The contractor re-laid the floor which was then alleged as still being faulty but the employer, instead of referring the dispute to arbitration, sought leave to defend the proceedings on the grounds of defective workmanship. The architect issued the Final Certificate whereupon the employer wished to refer the matter to arbitration. The House of Lords held that since the Final Certificate was "conclusive evidence in any proceedings arising out of this contract" any further legal action including proceedings started long before the certificate was issued, was barred.[28]

The Final Certificate is conclusive evidence that the quality of the materials or standards of workmanship are to the reasonable satisfaction of the architect or surveyor. The only exceptions relate to arbitration where proceedings in this respect have been commenced or in the case of fraud.

Clause 30A Price Code – Disallowance in Prices – Increases in Remuneration
Clause 30B Finance (No. 2) Act 1975 – Statutory Tax Deduction Scheme

Clause 30A is a supplement to the JCT Form rather than a permanent part of it. It has a temporary function and is intended for firm price contracts over £50,000 and fluctuating contracts over £5,000 in contract value. The Price Code was introduced in order to restrict excess remuneration of labour. The Statutory tax deduction Scheme was introduced in order to deal with the problems of tax evasion from the "Lump", the much criticised sub-contracting arrangements. Under clause 30B payments made by contractors to sub-contractors from the 6 April 1977 in what is defined as construction operations are subject to deduction by the payer on account of the payee's tax liability. This particular clause defines the position of the Employer and enables the validity of Tax Certificates to be questioned and makes provision in the event of a contractor's certificate being cancelled or withdrawn during the currency of the Contract. The situation regarding nominated sub-contractors is also covered.

Clause 31 – Fluctuations

There are six major parts to this long section. Clause 31A is the full fluctuations clause where the parties have agreed to allow labour and materials cost and tax fluctuations and parts A, C, D and E are to be used in conjunction with each other. Clause 31F however,

(28) *P. & M. Kaye Ltd.* v. *Hosier & Dickson Ltd.*, (1972) 1 All ER 121.

which again is a full fluctuations clause is only used where the parties have agreed that the contract price shall be adjusted by the NEDO Formula Method under the Formula Rules. Otherwise, parts B, C, D and E of clause 31 can be employed on their own in the case of limited fluctuations.

Part A, dealing with full fluctuations relates to wages and other expenses such as holiday money and employer's liability and third party insurance. The phrase "work people" is defined in connection with wages or emoluments together with insurance, the intention of clause 31 being to provide a basis for permitted increases in the complicated climate of today. The clause covers social security contributions, redundancy fund contributions and the like and defines these according to whether they occur before or after the date of tender for calculation of a net increase. The expression contributions, levies or taxes may cover, for example, contributions to a private pension scheme.

There are additional provisions relating to materials and goods.

Part B of clause 31 is similar to part A but excludes certain aspects relating to wage rates and premiums for third party and employer's liability insurance while including fluctuations in duty or tax on materials or goods. Part C provides for fluctuations where the contractor makes payments indirectly through a sub-contractor while part D deals with procedure and contains a number of miscellaneous clauses. Part E provides for the addition of a percentage stated in the Appendix to the amount paid under the previous sections where certain elements cannot be specified in detail. Part F as mentioned earlier is only used where the parties have agreed that the NEDO Price Adjustment Formula is to be employed.

Clause 32 – Outbreak of Hostilities

Each party has the right to determine the contract upon the outbreak of hostilities.

Clause 33 – War Damage

Under this clause the contract may continue and the contractor obtain an extension of time and payment in respect of war damage or alternatively, notice of determination of the contract can be given.

Clause 34 – Antiquities

Under this clause all "fossils, antiquities and other objects of interest or value" found on the site are the property of the employer.

Paragraphs (a) to (c) under this section form a drill for the contractor so that the antiquities which might be valuable are not disturbed. Power is given for the employer to authorise a third party to examine the objects on the basis that the contractor will not be responsible for his actions. There is also authority for the contractor to be able to claim for loss or expense due to delay or other causes and by reference to clause 23 (k) to be entitled to an extension of time.

Clause 35 – Arbitration

In the event of any dispute or difference between the parties, clause 35 gives authority for arbitration proceedings to decide the matter. Practically any argument under the terms of the contract can be referred to arbitration and a reference can be requested by either party at any time during the progress of the work or after its completion or abandonment. Arbitration proceedings can be commenced by either party within fourteen days from the date of issue of a Final Certificate but the certificate stands as conclusive evidence in all matters except the narrow area to which the arbitration proceedings relate.

Under clause 35 either the employer or the contractor can request in writing that the other party consent that the dispute be submitted to an arbitrator whose name is to be agreed. In the event of no reply being forthcoming, application can be made after fourteen days to the President or Vice-President of the RIBA to appoint an Arbitrator.

Unless both parties agree, arbitration cannot take place until a number of circumstances have occurred. These are either firstly that the Certificate of Practical Completion has been issued under clause 15 or practical completion has been alleged to have occurred by one party. Again arbitration cannot take place until the contractor's employment has been determined under clause 25 or 26 or, alternatively, is alleged to have been determined. Finally, arbitration cannot take place until the works have been abandoned. However, a separate category entirely is provided under sub-clause (2)(B) when both parties may agree that arbitration is to take place without waiting until one or more of the foregoing events has occurred.

There are specific grounds in the event of one or other party being unreasonable where immediate reference to arbitration can take place. These relate to the appointment of another architect or surveyor on the death or incapacity of the existing person or in connection with clause 2 of the contract dealing with architect's or surveyor's instructions. A further ground is for the alleged improper withholding of any certificate or under clauses 32 and 33 (outbreak of hostilities and war damage).

Under section 35 the arbitrator, once invited to decide the matter, in effect assumes the same position as the architect or surveyor and

213

quantity surveyor combined. There are certain limited grounds whereby the appointment of the arbitrator is restricted but other-wise his Award is final and binding on both parties. However, under the provisions of the Arbitration Act 1979 the "case stated" procedure is now defunct and this clause is very much subject to the new provisions of this Act.

Other Editions of the JCT Standard Form of Contract

Prior to 1980 when the JCT Standard Contract Forms were re-drafted, five variants to the Private Edition with Quantities which have just been discussed were necessary due to three main classifica-tions. The first classification refers to the client, whether private or local authority, while the second relates to the basis of payment. The simplest form drafted was on the basis that no Bills of Quantities would be employed, reliance being placed on drawings and specifi-cations alone; the second, as discussed in detail, where quantities form part of the contract. Both of these classifications provide for lump sum contracts while the editions under the third classification both private or local authority with approximate quantities provide for measurement contracts. It is of course a delusion to think of any particular Contract Form in total isolation. Merely to mention the formula rules to the JCT Standard Form of Building Contract is a case in point. The introduction of the formula method of price adjustment has led to a sturdy supplement to the JCT Contract Form which in itself has justified the publication of a useful explanatory book.[29] In addition there are the published fluctuation clauses, which in themselves run to some bulk, and other documents such as the Sectional Completion Supplement and the various practice notes issued by the Joint Contracts Tribunal. These, although obviously not forming any part of the Contract Form, nevertheless carry weight and are indispensible reading for the architect or surveyor in this field.

Brief consideration will be given later to the local authorities version of the most recently published contract Form. It is worth, at this stage, however, discussing the implications of the contract Form where either approximate quantities or no quantities at all are employed.

The private Edition of the JCT Contract Form with Approximate Quantities has a printed note at the outset explaining that the form

---

(29) *Studies in Construction Economy* by P. E. Goodacre M.Sc. A.R.I.C.S.–College of Estate Management.

is for use where the Works have been substantially designed but not completely detailed so that the quantities shown in the Bills are approximate and subject to re-measurement.

While the intention to re-measure is clearly underlined at the outset it is also implied that the drawings and specification are not completed. Unlike the earlier more established Contract Forms with or without quantities the actual status of approximate quantities as contrasted with partly completed drawings and specification is not clear. The preamble to the Articles of Agreement refers to "Drawings and Bills of Approximate Quantities showing and describing, and intending to set out a reasonably accurate forecast of the quantity of work . . ." which suggests that the phrase "substantially designed" referred to in the note is crucial. The form makes no provision for fundamental variations in the work carried out or major departures between the drawings and bills. It is emphasised therefore that the note to the Contract Form and the preamble imply warnings as much as guidance.

The use of the expression "Tender Price" instead of the more usual "Contract Sum" is an obvious need since payment depends on re-measurement, the tender price merely being necessary to form a valid contract. This uncertainty is reflected in the wording where the use of phrases such as "such sum or sums as shall become payable" instead of the time honoured words "contract sum" with the ultimate amount to be paid being defined as "the ascertained final sum".

For obvious reasons the contractor can only report differences in description between the documents as he has no other information upon which to pursue the more elaborate procedures open to him in the other Contract Forms. There are minor changes to clauses 4 (statutory obligations), clause 12 (Contract Bills) which is re-drafted as another clause and the provisions relating to variations, provisional and prime cost sums are amended. The expression "modification of the design" can apply to supplementary drawings under clause 3 (4) but whether these constitute a true supplement and extension of contract or a variation may well be a matter of fact. Complications may mount in the event of a change of design and whether the original or supplementary drawings form part of the contract would have to be clearly stated.

Clause 13 of the Contract Form dealing with Measurement and Valuation offers changes as against the other editions since all work shown on the contract is to be measured and valued and measurement is to follow the principles used in the Contract Bill. Here errors in individual quantities may be one thing, but a fundamental error as to the overall quantity of the work may lead to complications in the value of the preliminary items.

Clause 23; extension of time, is slightly amended by an additional paragraph dealing with the highly probable situation where the quantity of work was not accurately foreseen and extra work is needed. There are some necessary amendments to other clauses, notably clause 26, since obviously the whole purpose of the contract is that the contractor cannot determine under some of the circumstances available to him in other editions.

Clause 30 Certificates and Payments has been altered to comply with the need for the whole of the works to be re-measured to ascertain the final sum.

As to the Private Edition of the JCT Form of Contract without Quantities the specification is specifically named as a contract document and, while a schedule of rates is not actually referred to as a contract document this may become part of the contract nevertheless.

Neither the drawings nor the specification are paramount in the contract documents and if some work is shown in one that is not covered in the other, the contractor can well be in a difficulty. His remedy can only be to seek an architect's or surveyor's instruction under clause 1 (2). Obviously, the specification will be a full version rather than the outline document often drawn up where quantities form part of the contract.

It is possible for a schedule of rates to be presented by the contractor subsequent to the signing of the contract or for this to be formulated and agreed at the tender stage to overcome any later arguments. References to a schedule of rates are dotted about through the contract form, instances being clauses 11 and 12, 30 and 31.

The reference in the Contract Form to the quantity surveyor may seem confusing in a Form designed for use where Quantities do not form part of the contract but the name of the architect or supervising officer is usually inserted at this point.

The fact that the law in Scotland differs fundamentally from English law does not prevent architects and surveyors in Scotland using the standard JCT Forms. However, in conjunction with it a separate document entitled "Building Contract" with the Scottish Supplement to the Schedule of Conditions of the Standard Form of Building Contract published by the various professional bodies in Scotland has to be used. The contract document itself is brief, being in nature rather similar to the JCT Articles of Agreement, allowing for the appropriate insertions to be made and reference to the particular JCT Form that is required. The contract makes it clear that the JCT Form is subject to the Law of Scotland and that the parties so consent.

The first Appendix to the Scottish Supplement is designed to codify the various JCT clauses so that alternatives, amendments and interpretations are all made together so that it is not necessary to amend each set of conditions for every individual contract. Thus the provisions relating to the ownership of off-site materials and goods (clause 14) is deleted due to differences in Scottish Law while clauses 25 and 26 (Determination by employer and contractor) and clauses 27 and 28 (Nominated Sub-Contractors and Nominated Suppliers) are altered so that they comply with the correct Scottish legal expressions. Similar amendment is necessary in the case of clause 30 (Certificates and Payments) due to differences in the Scottish law relating to the ownership of materials and goods. A further clause is necessary to enable a separate direct contract to be formulated between the employer, contractor or sub-contractor so that the items are directly purchased since otherwise they will not pass to him. A building contract is not a contract of sale or purchase under Scottish Law.

Finally, there are points of difference in the arbitration procedure to comply with the Law of Scotland and amendments made to fit in with the long standing Scottish practice of letting a series of contracts for the various trades rather than the sub-contract system more familiar to English readers.

Appendix No. II is similar to the Appendix in the JCT Form and enables information such as contract dates to be filled in while Appendix No. III relates to the provisions for payment of value added tax. Again this section is similar to the supplemental agreement following the JCT Form.

The JCT Form of Prime Cost Contract

Known widely as "The Yellow Form" the correct title of this document is the "Fixed Fee Form of Prime Cost Contract". It consists of an agreement, conditions, attestation, six schedules and an appendix. The Form is intended to be capable of alteration for either private or local authority use and for use in Scotland. The standard Form is designed for use in cases where the nature of the work is uncertain and to provide and regulate payment to the contractor so that he is reimbursed his costs with an appropriate profit margin. There is provision for a fixed fee to the contractor in the second schedule and for his estimate of the prime cost in the third schedule. Obviously, under the very nature of the form of contract where the scope of the work is not known in advance, the contractor may be deluded in his estimate of fixed fee while the employer may be equally deluded in the contractor's estimate of

217

prime cost. The contractor's estimate has little relevance except in calculating interim payments.

The form largely follows the layout of the other standard Forms with some amendments to take account of the obvious difference in the approach to the work. The architect or surveyor for example is enabled to give such instructions as he thinks fit including even postponements or changes in the sequence of working although he may not go back upon the basis of the agreement and change the basic scope of the works as otherwise the contractor may then decide whether or not to withdraw from the contract. Due to the rather delicate nature of the relationship between the parties, an employer, while having the right to instruct others to carry out work in default of the contractor may not reimburse himself for the probable extra costs that would be involved by doing so.

The contract documents are not defined and there are a number of minor variations in the standard clauses mainly relating to the fact that the nature of the work may be largely unknown so that obligations either on the part of the contractor or employer are kept to a minimum. There is no defects liability period as such but responsibility on the part of the contractor may extend to those defects which "at any time appear or are discovered".

Due to the fact that the contract is on a prime cost basis sub-letting might well provide complications due to a different method of payment. The architect or supervising officer's approval is necessary here. There are also differences relating to insurance and completion while the main clauses in the contract governing extension of time, loss and expense caused by disturbance, determination either by the employer or contractor and provisions relating to nominated sub-contractors and suppliers are very similar to those of the other standard Forms. Clause 26 however, governing payment, differs markedly due to the nature of the agreement. Payment is made up from the prime cost of the works defined in the first schedule with nominated items listed in the fourth and fifth schedules and the fixed fee in the second schedule. Clearly the contractor has to provide full details relating to prime cost and it is desirable to specify what is likely to be required in the contract document itself. The method of payment under clause 27 is very similar to clause 30 of the main contract Forms. The purpose of the first schedule to the contract is to specify every type of payment that forms part of the prime cost calculation. The schedule is divided into four separate compartments relating to labour, materials and goods, plant, stores and services and sub-contracted work respectively. Any items not specifically included will be taken to be part of the contractor's fixed fee.

The second schedule to the contract form is merely to record the amount of the fixed fee while the third schedule is the estimated amount of the prime cost. As mentioned earlier, the point of this latter figure is related purely to interim payments but if the figure is widely wrong, complications can follow. This is an obvious difficulty in this type of contract. It is often best to form a smaller initial contract rather than to rush into bigger adventures where matters cannot be forecast with any degree of accuracy. The fourth and fifth schedules deal with work or goods by nominated sub-contractors or suppliers while the sixth schedule deals with items of work to be executed by other persons.

The JCT Standard Form of Nominated Sub-Contract

This document, the correct name of which is "Sub-Contract for use where the Sub-Contractor is Nominated under the Standard Form of Building Contract issued by the Joint Contracts Tribunal". The document is widely known as "The Green Form".

Prior to the introduction of the JCT Contract Form 1980, the Standard Form of Nominated Sub-Contract had been the subject of a number of changes. It was, however, approved by the National Federation of Building Trades Employers, the Federation of Associations of Specialists and Sub-Contractors and the Committee of Associations of Specialist Engineering Contractors although the first two bodies only issued the form under their auspices.

The Standard Form of Nominated Sub-Contract consists of a recital, conditions and appendix with space for signatures or seal. It was intended for use with either the private or local authority editions of the main JCT Form whether with or without quantities or approximate quantities. A Scottish Supplement is also available.

The recital and the appendix to the form are straightforward covering such matters as the completion period, percentage of certified value retained and the limit of retention fund.

The conditions specify firstly that the sub-contractor is deemed to know all about the main contract and its effect on the sub-contract. It is also stated that the work is to the direction of the contractor but to the approval of the architect or surveyor. Other clauses relate to insurance, loss or damage by fire or other causes, variations and completion together with loss and expense from disturbance of the work. There are clauses as might be expected, reflected from the main contract relating to defects and shrinkage, valuation, payment, retention and finance provisions. An unusual point in connection with arbitration is that the sub-contractor can make reference to an arbitrator jointly with the contractor should he feel that his payment is inadequate. A sub-contractor also has the right to suspend work under certain circumstances and to set off payment for sums due. There are also a number of clauses relating to access to the site, sub-letting, the provision of water, workshops and scaffolding together with plant and tools. Items left on the site for example are at the sole risk of the sub-contractor except where negligence can be proved against the main contractor.

Finally, there are provisions relating to determination of the sub-contract by the contractor and provisions relating to the determination of the main contract. The end clause relates to arbitration.

JCT Contract Form 1980

While it is doubtful if the members of the Joint Contracts Tribunal would have expected the publication of the new 1980 Form of Contract to have been received with universal applause they could be forgiven for being taken aback, after so much hard work, by the chilly reception that the new document has received from all sections of the building industry. There is some comfort from the fact that this stems to a great degree from the unfamiliar appearance of the new form and is due also to the fact that it is considerably larger than the 1963 edition. Members of the building industry tend to assume that the larger the document the more complications there are likely to be, with resultant benefits to the larger firms of contractors who have legal departments with the time and skill to operate conditions in their favour. In defence of the Tribunal however, it must be said at once that a good deal of the bulk has been added by necessary changes in the old Contract Form due, for example, to Labour and Materials and Tax Fluctuation Provisions and Value Added Tax. After all, the previous Form was nearly twenty years old and quite apart from the large number of amendments made to the Contract Form since original publication, the requirements of wage-fixing bodies and Customs and Excise, whose intervention now considerably affects the building industry, must now be catered for.

Notwithstanding this, however, a number of more understandable complaints are made against the new Form. The new decimal numbering system is difficult enough to follow but the cross referencing between clause and clause without any reason being given makes the document maddeningly difficult to follow. Everyone misses the familiar indentation in the old form and deplores the chilly appearance of the new one. The main complaint, however, made by lawyers dealing with building matters is that the way in which the form is drafted is perverse. They say that the motivation in the draftsmanship of a large number of clauses appears to be lacking (in other words it is difficult to see what the draftsman was endeavouring to get at as no proposition is stated in broad terms, the new method of cross referencing being preferred). The Form is described by one legal authority has an "awesome document" and it is clear that it will take those experts who deal in building law quite some time to evaluate fully the new Form and to become familiar with it due to the totally different style in which it is drafted. This in itself is a serious disadvantage. The Form should ideally be capable of being studied and understood fairly easily by, say, a non-specialist solicitor or surveyor or a competent builder who has no legal department. If not, then the purpose of the Form has failed. However it is early days yet to take a gloomy view and the building industry is notoriously conservative in its outlook to change. It is certainly not encouraging however, to hear the top legal experts in the country criticise large areas of the Form in varying terms ranging from total mystification (clause 30.4) to incredibly and unnecessarily complex (clauses 30.1 to 30.4). Such authorities do say, rather disarmingly, that much of the mystification may disappear once they become more familiar with the new provisions. Nevertheless it does appear as a gloomy possibility that the new Form has not fully solved the problems of the old, on the one hand, and has introduced further complications on the other.

Apart from changes in the text which are extensive but relatively minor in content and which include a new interpretation and definition clause (1), new contents pages at the beginning of the Form and alternative provisions for fluctuations (clause 37) the basic differences and extensions in the new Form, in contrast with the amended 1963 Edition apart from labour and materials provisions (clause 17), lie in the following areas:

(1) Extension of Time and Liquidated Damages.
(2) Provisions on Payment.
(3) Valuation of Variations and work carried out under Provisional Sums.
(4) Nominated Suppliers and Nominated Sub-Contractors.
(5) Employer's Option – List of Sub-Contractors.
(6) Fluctuations.

Due to the importance of the various changes these will be examined separately. The new Contract and nominated sub-contract documents published by the Tribunal are:

Local Authorities with/with approximate/Quantities.
Private with/with approximate/Quantities.

Local Authorities/Private without Quantities.

Sectional Completion Supplement.

JCT Standard Form of Nominated Sub-Contract Tender and Agreement (Tender NSC/1).

JCT Standard Form of Employer/Nominated Sub-Contractor Agreement (Agreement NSC/2).

Agreement NSC/2 adapted for use where Tender NSC/1 has not been used (Agreement NSC/2a).

JCT Standard Form for Nomination of a Sub-Contractor where Tender NSC/1 has been used (Nomination NSC/3).

JCT Standard Form of Sub-Contract for Sub-Contractors who have tendered on NSC/1 and executed Agreement NSC/2 and been nominated by Nomination NSC/3 (Sub-Contract NSC/4).

Sub-Contract NSC/4 adapted for use where Tender NSC/1 Agreement NSC/2 and Nomination NSC/3 have not been used (Sub-Contract NSC/4a).

In addition, the JCT have now published an edition of the Private Without Quantities 1980 Contract for use where a chartered building surveyor is appointed. The form is contained in a folder which also includes the articles of agreement with modifications to include the designation "chartered building surveyor" and also the contract conditions and appendix.

Extension of Time and Liquidated Damages

A major change in the new contract form is that the Contractor must now give what the JCT Guide to the JCT Form 1980[30] calls "Notice, particulars and estimates of likely delay to completion in respect of any matter which the Contractor has identified as a Relevant Event in his written notice of delay to the progress of the Works and which is causing or is likely to cause delay to completion; and he must ensure that this information is kept reasonably up-to-date."

"The architect is obliged, if reasonably practicable having regard to the sufficiency of the Contractor's particulars and estimates, within 12 weeks of receipt of the Contractor's notice, reasonable particulars and estimates but, in any case, not later than the Completion Date, to give his decision on extension, if any, of the 'Completion Date' (which is now defined as the Date for Completion fixed and stated in the Appendix or any later date fixed and stated – by a decision of the Architect under clause 25 or clause

(30) Published by RIBA Publications Ltd, Finsbury Mission, Moreland St. London EC1V 8VB.

33.1.3). In reaching his decision the Architect must state which of the causes of delay (now called in clause 25.4 "Relevant Events") he has taken into account in reaching his decision; the Architect is permitted after his first decision on extending time to take account of any Variations requiring an omission which have been issued since the date of his last decision on extending the Completion Date. The Architect must give his decision on each notice given by the Contractor not later than the Completion Date then current, but within 12 weeks from the Date of Practical Completion of the Works the Architect must review the progress of the contract and may fix a revised Completion Date; such revised Completion Date can take account of any Relevant Event whether or not notified by the Contractor and can take account of any Variations requiring an omission which have been issued since the date of his last decision on extending the Completion Date. No decision of the Architect under clause 25 can substitute an earlier date for the Date of Completion inserted in the Appendix."

The Relevant Events in clause 25.4 in general repeat, subject to drafting changes, the matters dealt with in the 1963 Edition in clause 23 (a) to (l) but have been varied and increased in number.

The new provisions relating to extension of time are obviously designed to provide a more flexible basis to deal with present day difficulties than were contained in the immediately previous contract form. The positive obligation upon the Contractor to inform the architect or surveyor when he is delayed or anticipates a delay due to any event which might hinder progress is obviously beneficial. Examples would be, for instance, when materials do not arrive on time or where, due to a variation order, the contract requires re-programming. The Contractor must give notice of all delays however they may be caused, specify the circumstances and identify a particular Relevant Event or Events specified under clause 25.4. A copy of his notice must be sent to any nominated sub-contractor who may be involved. The contractor is only obliged to give his own estimate of expected delay but must disentangle and deal separately with each relevant event if there are more than one. The architect or surveyor then has twelve weeks from the submission of adequate particulars, but not earlier than the original date for completion specified in the Appendix (or any subsequent Completion Date) to fix a new Completion Date specifying which Relevant Events he has considered as justifying delay. Under clause 25.3.1 a new innovation in the Employer's favour (and practically the only one according to one eminent legal authority) is that omissions can now be taken into account by the Architect or Surveyor in fixing a revised date or dates.

Clause 25.3.3 allows the architect or surveyor to review his decisions on extensions of time not later twelve weeks after Practical Completion

223

in order to arrive at a final decision. He may review all Relevant Events even those not notified to him by the contractor in order to confirm the Completion Date or alter it to provide for a longer or shorter period. Any nominated sub-contractors affected are notified accordingly.

An exchange of written notices giving specific information is clearly envisaged by this section of the contract. Failure to exchange would presumably have a number of complications not least in the field of liquidated damages. Lack of notice, for example, before final certification by the architect or surveyor may lose the Employer his right to liquidated damages but the position where completion time is extended and the Employer not only claims liquidated damages but also requires substantial variations is likely to be complex to say the least. Irrespective of notice from the Contractor however, the architect or surveyor has the duty to take steps under the contract and it appears that lack of notice from the Contractor will not act as a bar to his claim for an extension of time (clause 25.3.3). Absence of, or alternatively, a defective notice, will only have the effect of postponing the time when the architect or surveyor needs to fix a new Completion Date to 12 weeks after Practical Completion. Apart from the architect's or surveyor's duty of review within 12 weeks after the date of Practical Completion the architect or surveyor has only the duty to respond to the Contractor's notice of Relevant Events giving cause for delay within 12 weeks of such notice or before the existing Completion Date and the preliminary duty in these earlier stages accordingly falls on the Contractor direct. A completion certificate, which is necessary as a condition precedent to liquidated damages, can be issued as soon as the original or any new Completion Date has passed. It should be noted that there is no authority in the Forms for an Employer to order Variations once the Completion Date has passed nor is there any authority for making the failure of the Employer to give possession of the site a ground for extension of time. Unlike the ICE Contract the agreed Completion Date cannot be varied if the Employer refuses to hand over the site (which could lead to a strange situation). The contract might be amended in this connection. It is an odd anomaly that one "Relevant Event" is where the Employer fails to give ingress or egress from the site over other adjoining land which is in his possession but that there is no reference to the Employer's failure to give possession of the actual site where the building work is being carried out.

The JCT Contract Form of 1963 contained rather "hit and miss" provisions relating to liquidated damages which the 1980 version is designed to correct but its provisions depend upon accurate administration. From the practical point of view the architect or surveyor is well advised to act promptly so as to confirm or reject a new Completion Date since if he relies upon the twelve week period allowed he may find himself in some difficulty should other notices from the contractor follow shortly after the first one and the causes of delay become inextricably mixed up with each other. Similarly it is obviously unwise to rely totally upon the provisions of clause 25.3.3. The notification of Nominated Sub-Contractors of every decision taken is also of obvious importance even when these have left the site, due to the possible implications of liquidated damages.

The Relevant Events specified in clause 25.4 are

25.4. 1. Force majeure.
2. Exceptionally adverse weather conditions (formerly inclement).
3. Loss or damage occasioned by one or more of the clause 22 Perils (fire etc.).
4. Civil commotion, strikes etc.
5. Architects instructions relating to discrepancies in or between documents, variations, provisional sums, postponement, antiquities, nominated sub-contractors and suppliers and the opening up for inspection of any work covered up or the testing of any of the work materials or goods unless the inspection or test showed that the work, materials or goods were not in accordance with the contract.
6. Where the contractor has not received in due time necessary instructions, drawings, details or levels.
7. Delay on the part of the nominated sub-contractors or suppliers.
8. Failure in the execution of work contracted to have been carried out by the employer himself or his agents or failure in the supply of materials or goods by the Employer.
9. Statutory powers exercised by the United Kingdom Government which might delay the execution of the Works (i.e. the 3 day week).
10. The inability of the Contractor to obtain labour or materials.
11. Work carried out by Statutory Undertaking or local Authorities or the failure to carry out work.
12. Failure of the Employer to give in due time ingress to or egress from the site of the Works or any part thereof through or over any land, buildings, way or passage

adjoining or connected with the site and in the possession and control of the Employer in accordance with the Contract.

Finally, fluctuations under clauses 38 and 39 can be "frozen" during the period when the Contractor becomes in default over completion provided clause 25 is not amended. There are similar provisions in respect of clause 40.

The right of the Contractor to apply in writing to the Architect claiming re-imbursement for direct loss and/or expense in respect of which he cannot receive payment under any other clause of the contract is contained in Section 26. The architect, having received notice, instructs the Quantity Surveyor to ascertain the amount of such loss or expense upon reasonable particulars being provided by the Contractor. Factors entitling the Contractor to reimbursement are:

26.2. 1. Drawings not having been received in due time.
2. Opening up for inspection and testing of work, materials or goods where it was found that these were in conformity with the contract.
3. Discrepancies in and between the Contract Drawings and the Bills.
4. Failure on the part of the Employer to carry out work or supply goods as contracted by him.
5. Postponement of work.
6. Employers failure to grant access over land in his possession and control as agreed in the Contract.
7. Work in respect of variations and provisional sums.

The requirement however under clause 26.3 that the Architect is to state specific periods of extended time for each of the above events if this should be necessary to ascertain the direct loss or expense introduces a complication into an otherwise relatively straightforward clause.

Liquidated Damages

The JCT Guide to the Standard Form of Building Contract 1980 refers to the provisions on Liquidated Damages formerly in clause 22 of the 1963 Edition which now appear in clause 24 of the 1980 Edition. The main changes, the guide indicates are:

"1. The certificate of the Architect that the Contractor failed to complete the Works by the completion date remains a condition precedent to the right of the Employer to liquidated damages; but this certificate is now only a confirmatory certificate of the completion date fixed after the Architect has considered all applications for extension of time under clause 25 and carried out the review in the 12 weeks after Practical Completion.

2. Payment of liquidated damages is no longer obligatory when the Architect issues his certificate; the Employer has a discretion as to whether or not, having received the certificate from the Architect, he wishes to require the Contractor to pay or allow liquidated damages.

3. The Employer must give notice before the issue of the Final Certificate of his intention to exercise his discretion to claim or deduct liquidated damages."

The term "liquidated damages" appears in building contract terms to have attracted the same unfortunate connotation as the word "premium" in residential landlord and tenant matters. The suggestion as in the past, and now even more so, lies heavily in the air that to deduct liquidated damages is somehow not quite cricket. The new contract form, while not stating this in so many words, lays heavy emphasis on the fact that the employer "may deduct", the inference being that if he does so, he is really beyond the pale. In fact the whole question of liquidated damages serves to illustrate the delicate balance of the parties to the contract irrespective of the legalities. An employer, if he has any sense, will use liquidated damages with care as an ultimate sanction and is unlikely to do so unless on very sure ground or unless goodwill is entirely lost. He is hardly likely to require them if his own position, when extras are balanced against omissions, is unfavourable. The new Form accordingly offers no real change except a change of emphasis but a dangerous situation from the Employer's point of view could occur. Clause 24.2.1 lays down that subject to the issue of a certificate, the contractor shall, as the Employer may require in writing, not later than the date of the final certificate, pay or allow liquidated damages. The danger is that if the Contractor is late and a certificate is issued, the Employer, wishing to preserve relations and not put the Contractor into financial difficulties, does not claim liquidated damages and the final certificate is then issued. The Contractor challenges the certificate within fourteen days as he has a right to do and brings in every aspect of claim that he himself can think of. The Employer is then effectively barred from counter-claiming liquidated damages. The unfortunate effect of such a situation might well be that the Employer would be advised to sue his Architect or surveyor for the amount of the liquidated damages that are lost to him. It is not clear if a statement reserving the right to counter-claim for liquidated damages in the earlier notice would reserve the Employer's right to a subsequent claim or not.

The old 1963 Contract arrangement whereby the architect or surveyor must issue a certificate under clause 22 before liquidated damages can be recovered is still retained but the rules relating to the certificate under the new clause 24.1 are altered. There is still the right, given grudgingly, that liquidated damages may be deducted but if the architect or surveyor in his final appreciation of the circumstances relating to time within the twelve weeks after practical completion grants an extension then the liquidated damages have to be repaid without interest. Clause 24.2.1 is the authority for requiring that subject to the issue of a Certificate under clause 24.1 the Contractor shall, as the Employer may require in writing, not later than the date of the final Certificate, pay or allow liquidated damages.

Provisions on Payment

A revised clause 30 appears in the JCT Contract 1980 which replaces the provisions of the earlier clause 30 relating to payments in the 1963 Edition. Under this new clause Interim Certificates are to be drawn by the architect in favour of the Employer with a copy to the Contractor based upon interim valuations made, if the architect so requires, by the quantity surveyor. The Interim Certificates are to be drawn at monthly intervals (unless a different period is provided for in the Appendix) and payment is to be made within 14 days of the date of the issue of a Certificate. The monthly Certificates are to be issued during the period specified in the Appendix "up to and including the end of the period during which the Certificate of Practical Completion is issued. Thereafter as the occasion arises and in particular after the expiration of the Defects Liability Period named in the Appendix or upon the issue of the Certificate of Completion of Making Good Defects (whichever is the later)." Final payment to all nominated sub-contractors is made by means of an Interim Certificate drawn not less than 28 days before the issue of the Final Certificate.

The main change however, is described in the JCT Guide to the 1980 Contract Edition as follows:

"The amounts which are to be included in Interim Certificates are to be divided into two groups; the first setting out those amounts from which Retention can be deducted; the second setting out those amounts which the Employer is required to pay without deduction of Retention. The rules on retention have been altered so that it is no longer necessary for

228

the Architect to issue Certificates especially for the release of Retention when Practical Completion takes place or when the Employer takes partial possession or when defects have been made good. The Retention deducted in each Interim Certificate is now calculated at the full percentage on the total value of work which has not yet reached Practical Completion and on the value of all unfixed materials and goods; at half that percentage on the total value of work which has reached Practical Completion but for which a Certificate of Completion of Making Good Defects has not been issued; and at Nil percent on work on which such a Certificate has been issued.

The new rules ensure that an appropriate release of Retention is made (because a smaller deduction is made from cumulative value) when the Employer takes possession of a part of the Works before Practical Completion of the whole of the Works or when a Nominated Sub-Contractor's Work is subject to the provisions on early final payment or when Practical Completion of the whole of the Works takes place and when defects are made good in the whole or any part of the Works. The standard Retention Percentage remains at 5% but with a revised footnote advising that where the Contract Sum exceeds half a million pounds the Retention Percentage should be 3%".

Amounts subject to retention and not subject to retention and deductions not subject to retention are set out in clauses 30.2.1 to 30.2.3. Under clause 30.3 the value of off-site materials may be included at the Architect's discretion.

The old requirement that Retention money in the hands of the Employer is to be regarded as trust money has now been extended with certain rules relating to the trustee obligations of the Employer. In the Private Editions of the contract form the Employer has to place the Retention in a separate trust account if so requested by the Contractor or any nominated Sub-Contractor. No such requirement is necessary in the Local Authority's Edition.

The Employer is still entitled to deduct certain amounts from monies otherwise certified as due to the Contractor, such as liquidated damages or the cost of rectifying defects consequent upon failure by the Contractor to comply with the Architect's instructions, but he is no longer authorised to have recourse to Retention for these amounts. His right to deduct from monies due entitles him to take monies included in a Certificate, including any released Retention, notwithstanding the fiduciary nature of his interest in the Retention. It should be noted that the Employer cannot deduct from Retention until it is released by inclusion in a Certificate. Because of the fiduciary nature of Retention, however, the Quantity Surveyor is obliged to provide an analysis of the Retention into divisions relating to that carried out by the Contractor and that attributable to each nominated Sub-Contractor. A new provision requires the

Employer to inform the Contractor of the reasons for any deduction and where the deduction is from Retention the Employer must state the amount he has deducted from the Contractor's share of the Retention or from any Nominated Sub-Contractor's share of the Retention. This information is needed by the Contractor who is in his turn a trustee of the Retention for each Nominated Sub-Contractor. Where the deduction is due to some act or default of a Nominated Sub-Contractor the Contractor is empowered by Sub-Contract NSC/4 or NSC/4A to recover it from the Nominated Sub-Contractor.

Provision, as we have seen, is made for an Interim Certificate to be issued 28 days before the Final Certificate which will set out the amounts finally due in respect of all Nominated Sub-Contract Work. The Final Certificate will then only deal with any amount due to the Contractor from the Employer or from the Contractor to the Employer.

The replacement of the old certificates procedure to release Retention monies in favour of a more automatic procedure to release half at Practical Completion and the second half upon Completion of making good defects has a good deal to commend it as has the requirement upon the Architect to issue a statement with each Interim Certificate as to the amount of the Retention money that is being withheld and how much this relates to the Contractor's own work and how much is in respect of Nominated Sub-Contractor's work. A particular point to note is that a large number of payments are not now to be the subject of Retention at all, including fees or charges, remedial work, opening up, royalties, insurance premiums, loss or expense claims, fluctuations, nominated sub-contractor's final payments and nominated Sub-Contractor's loss and expense claims plus two and a half percent (clause 30.2.2). There are some fairly detailed complexities regarding the question of Retention and Nominated Sub-Contractors. The Employer is now bound to pay a Nominated Sub-Contractor direct if he is not paid by the Contractor although the Employer need not pay more than is due from him to the Contractor. Nominated Sub-Contractor's Retentions cannot be used to pay direct. The architect under the provisions of clause 30 can be put into a delicate if not to say difficult position. The Nominated Sub-Contractor can suspend work if not paid direct by the Employer (21.8.1.2) but the architect may well be bewildered by a dispute to which he is not a party and the architect might be in equal difficulties whether he either authorises or does not authorise direct payment as he is then open to an action from either side.

The new provisions relating to Nominated Sub-Contractors have yet to be experienced. All Nominated Sub-Contractors are now to have a special Final Certificate 28 days before the Contractor's Final Certificate (clause 30.7) and the Nominated Sub-Contractor must now be paid in full and the Retention released to him 12 months after he completes, notwithstanding that he may still be responsible for making good defects under the main contract maintenance period. There is little incentive for a Nominated Sub-Contractor to return to the site since the Employer is now bound to disburse the money in the manner referred to and the ultimate remedy for both Employer and Contractor is Arbitration with all the burden of proof upon them.

The final conclusion under this section is that the rules relating to Retention monies which have been carefully and painstakingly worked out may be perfectly sound so far as large contracts and fully capable and solvent contractors and Nominated Sub-Contractors are concerned but in smaller cases there is a strong risk element of matters going badly wrong. The requirement under clause 30.5 that private Employers are to pay sums into a special bank account as trustees is subject to the requirement of 30.1.1.2 that deduction from the Retention is not possible except as provided for under the terms of the contract and a private Employer cannot use the funds that he or she has deposited in a bank to remedy defective work before the Final Certificate and accordingly, if another Contractor is employed to make good defects in default of the original contractor, other money will have to be found. There are additional complexities regarding the use of the Retention where a number of Nominated Sub-Contractors are concerned, for example it is not clear whether the Employer can use the whole of the Retention monies including the Retention of Nominated Sub-Contractors to deduct monies due to him from the Contractor but no doubt in the future, particularly in larger contracts, experience will produce a generally accepted consensus of what is intended under the contract form but the main problems remain with the smaller cases where the financial status of the parties is more fragile.

Variations

The definition of "Variation" has been extended from that previously contained in clause 11 of the old 1963 Contract Form. There are now essentially two kinds of variations. The first relates to alterations in the work; "alteration or modification of design, quality or quantity" while the second now includes the "addition to, alteration of, or omission of any obligations or restrictions imposed by the Employer in the Contract Bills in regard to access to the site or use of any specific parts of the site, limitations of working space, limitations of working hours and the execution or completion of work in any specific order." The Contractor is entitled to raise an immediate objection to compliance with a variation instruction· provided that this is reasonable and any dispute is then subject to immediate arbitration (clause 4.1.1). It is worth noting incidentally that all instructions by the Architect under clause 4.3.1 must be in writing. The definition of "variation" is specifically not to include the nomination of a sub-contractor to carry out measured works to be executed by the Contractor which has been priced by the Contractor in the Contract Bills.

Clause 13.5 deals with the valuation of variations. The method of valuing additional or substituted work still depends on whether or not the work is of similar character to work set out in the Contract Bills, and is executed under similar conditions, and work is always to be valued by measurement where possible. For work that is similar in character but is executed under different conditions or involves a significant change in quantity the rates in the Bills can be adjusted to allow for these new factors but work that is not similar to that in the Bills is measured at fair rates and prices.

Clause 13 however, is notable for another introduction into the variation amendments. This relates to the position of the quantity surveyor. The clause is significant for the fact that the Contract Bills may now specify obligations and restrictions mutually agreed between the Employer and the Contractor as long as these do not, obviously, conflict with the conditions in the printed contract form. Previously the Bills were restricted to defining the quantity and quality of the work that was the subject matter of the contract. Furthermore, unless the Employer and the Contractor agree other-wise, all variations and work under provisional sums must be valued by the quantity surveyor. In the case of work carried out by nominated sub-contractors the terms of the sub-contract will rule the method of measurement while if the Contractor carries out work previously intended for a nominated sub-contractor, the terms of his original tender will rule the method of measurement. It should be stressed, that while the architect must issue instructions for the expenditure of provisional sums which normally creates a nomina-tion, an instruction to a specific sub-sub-contractor or supplier need not do so.

The provisions of the 1963 Contract Form clause 11 are thus unchanged in regard to work which cannot be valued by measurement since provisions for the use of day work are included as before but under clause 13.5.4 of the 1980 Edition there is a new reference to providing information regarding plant employed on the site. Finally, clause 13.5 excludes any element of what is usually termed "disturbance cost" arising out of compliance with instructions requiring a variation or on the expenditure of provisional sums. A new clause 26 replaces the old clause 24 of the 1963 Edition and provides a new ground for ascertainment.

The extension of the list of items to be regarded as variations are intended to take into account modern conditions which are more and more commonplace and to provide a more flexible solution to matters which might otherwise frustrate the contract. It is an odd anomaly however, as mentioned earlier, that where an Employer refuses access to the site this cannot be dealt with under clause 13. The rules for valuing variations are basically as previously existed but allowance must now be made for percentage or lump-sum adjustments and for any time-related preliminary items. It should be emphasised that the power to change the batting order, so to speak, in the sequence of work, including such matters as restrictions as to access or use of the site, working space and working hours can be exercised only if these were originally stipulated in the Bills. The right of the Contractor to object and the early arbitration provisions are a necessary adjunct to these changes.

Nominated Sub-Contractors and Suppliers

If Part I of the 1980 Contract Form has attracted criticism this has been mild compared to the reaction, varying from downright hostility to wails of despair, that have been attracted by Part II. This is sad as the provisions relating to Nominated Sub-Contractors (clause 35) and Nominated Suppliers (clause 36) have been worked out in great detail and have exercised a great deal of time and thought on the part of the tribunal to overcome obvious problems from the previous contract form; the main example being those arising in the Bickerton case.[31] Nomination has always been a hybrid activity in the field of building contracts. The whole essence of the law in this field is that a contract is an agreement that is freely entered into by the parties in the absence of any force but the whole point of nomination by the Employer is of course that the Contractor has to accept a Nominated Sub-Contractor and is deprived of any arrangements he would have preferred to make on his own account. The battle over the ethics of nomination have raged throughout the building industry for years. It appears however, that the contents of the Simon Report which came out heavily in favour of direct contract and sub-contract relationships were counteracted

---

(31) *Bickerton* v. *North West Metropolitan Hospital Board*, (1970.) 1 WLR 607.

by pressures to allow the Employer to appoint specialists of his choice. A strong body of opinion within the industry asks what is wrong with that? The only response can be that arguments between Contractors and Nominated Contractors are legendary for their ferocity and for sheer non-cooperation and bloody mindedness cannot be beaten. The Contractor who is forced to accept a Nominated Sub-Contractor may "go through the motions" feeling responsible in contract terms only. A contractor who selects his own Sub-Contractor to carry out work feels a sense of moral as well as financial responsibility that is lacking where a Sub-Contractor is nominated. It is for this reason that problems will continue in the field of nomination that can never be solved by any contract form however carefully thought out its provisions may be.

With this anomaly in contract law it is hardly surprising that the Courts tend to lean over to favour a Contractor's complaint where, in the feeling of the Court, nomination was forced upon him. There have been some cases where an Employer has been left high and dry, his only remedy being a claim in tort. The modern trend where the Employer tends to nominate Sub-Contractors more and more and have direct dialogue with them, with the consequent shrinkage of the direct area of control exercised by the Main Contractor, the more the basic provisions of Contract Law are weakened with glum results to the employer himself in the long term.

In the absence of good will, it can readily be seen that difficulties between Contractors and Nominated Sub-Contractors can flare up where chinks appear in the contract armour. Simple delay in nomination may justify a claim by the Contractor ("I could have got this work done by a Sub-Contractor of my own long ago"). There is also the traditional difficulty in concluding a Nominated Sub-Contract. There are problems over negotiations for the payment arising from delay, liability for defects of work and materials and quarrels over who is responsible for a fault in design. Problems have arisen over inconsistencies between the contract and the Nominated Sub-Contract and an Employer has been taken aback in cases where the benefit of a guarantee by a Nominated Sub-Contractor works to the benefit of the Contractor only, leaving the employer with little or any benefit and where repudiation by a Nominated Sub-Contractor leaves him helpless.

The complicated provisions of the new JCT Contract Form 1980 are designed, obviously, to overcome past problems. The contents of Part II are however, basic to the whole contract form but the drafting together with the cross-referencing of clauses is so bewildering that much time is needed simply to start to understand the new provisions. An example is clause 30 which deals with the inclusion of amounts in respect of Nominated Sub-Contract work in Interim Certificates and in the new penultimate certificate for final payment in respect of Nominated Sub-Contractors.

Under clause 35 Nominated Sub-Contractors are now defined, says the JCT Guide,

"as persons whose final selection and approval for the supply and fixing of any materials or goods or the execution of any work has been reserved to the Architect. Such reservation to the Architect can be effected **either** by the use of a prime cost sum **or** by the naming of a sole Sub-Contractor in the contract documents so that the Contractor is therefore bound to enter into a sub-contract with that person."

The main alteration under Part II is that

"where the Architect is going to nominate, then **the basic method by which such nomination is made** is by use of the new JCT Standard Form of Nominated Sub-Contract Tender and Agreement (Tender NSC/1) which involves the Employer and Nominated Sub-Contractor in entering into the JCT Standard Form of Employer/Nominated Sub-Contractor Agreement (Agreement NSC/2). If for any proposed nomination the Architect does not intend to use Tender NSC/1 and Agreement NSC/2, then this must be specifically stated in the Contract Bills or Specification or in the instruction requiring a Variation or on the expenditure of a provisional sum which requires work to be done by a Nominated Sub-Contractor . . .. Where Tender NSC/1 and Agreement NSC/2 are to be used, the Architect will obtain a Tender (NSC/1) completed, so far as possible at that stage, on behalf of the Employer and the proposed Sub-Contractor; the Architect then issues a **preliminary Notice of Nomination** to the Contractor enclosing Tender NSC/1 and the Contractor must thereupon seek to agree with the proposed Sub-Contractor any remaining details of the Sub-Contractor's tender (see Tender NSC/1 Schedule 2) in regard to such matters as programming, site arrangements and so forth. If during these discussions any problems arise which would prevent the nomination instruction being issued, the Contractor must immediately request the Architect for further instructions. When Tender NSC/1 is completed and signed by the Contractor and proposed Sub-Contractor it must be returned to the Architect who then issues his instruction nominating the proposed Sub-Contractor on the Nomination Instruction Form (nomination NSC/3). The Contractor and the proposed Sub-Contractor are then bound to a Sub-Contract in accordance with the terms of Tender NSC/1, one of which is that the Contractor and Sub-Contractor will comply with the General Conditions of Sub-Contract in the Tribunal's new Standard Form of Sub-Contract for Sub-Contractors who have tendered on Tender NSC/1 and executed Agreement NSC/2 (Sub-Contract NSC/4)."

The alternative method of nomination to the basic method is that

"where the contract documents, or the Architect in an instruction requiring a Variation or the expenditure of a provisional sum, specifically states that

235

NSC/1 and NSC/2 are not to be used then the Architect issues a nomination (but not on Nomination Form NSC/3) and upon the issue of such instruction the Contractor and proposed Sub-Contractor must enter into an adapted version of Sub-Contract NSC/4 namely Sub-Contract NSC/4A. Sub-Contract NSC/4A differs from Sub-Contract NSC/4 mainly in that it has to contain, in entries in the Appendix, the various matters of which, under the basic method, would have been set out in Tender NSC/1.

"Where the above alternative method of nomination is used, the Employer and the Sub-Contractor are to enter into an adapted version of the Agreement NSC/2, i.e. Agreement NSC/2A unless the Employer has, in his invitation to Tender for the nominated Sub-Contract work, stated that he will not be using Agreement NSC/2A and the proposed Sub-Contractor by tendering on that basis has so agreed. The right of the Contractor to make reasonable objection to a proposed Nominated Sub-Contractor is preserved but the last date by which such reasonable objection can be made has been adapted to meet the two methods of nomination referred to above."

Agreement NSC/2 and NSC/2A place on the Sub-Contractor a responsibility for the design of Sub-Contract works including the selection of materials and goods with the Employer direct, but only to the extent that the Sub-Contractor has designed these works and/or selected goods and materials therefor. The Contractor is expressly relieved of responsibility for the design of the Sub-Contract Works.

The essence of Agreements NSC/2 and NSC/2A is to place a direct relationship of responsibility between the Employer and the nominated Sub-Contractor for the design of the work and materials and goods for which the Sub-Contractor is solely liable. The Contractor is correspondingly relieved of responsibility. As an extension of this the Architect has a duty to establish that sums set out in interim certificates (other than the first) and the final certificate have, in fact, been paid over by the Contractor to the nominated Sub-Contractor otherwise he has a further duty to so certify and pay the respective amounts direct to the Nominated Sub-Contractor concerned by way of a deduction from the amounts due to the main contractor. Under Agreements NSC/2 and NSC/2A the nominated Sub-Contractor has, in fact, a right to enforce direct payment by the Employer.

Agreements NSC/2 and NSC/2A also provide for early final payment of Nominated Sub-Contractors with a corresponding right for the Employer to proceed against a Nominated Sub-Contractor for failure to remedy defects between early final payment and the issue of the final certificate. The main Contractor remains basically responsible for the whole of the works however and in view of this the Employer now has a duty to re-nominate in the event of failure of the Nominated Sub-Contractor and meet any difference in cost between the original sub-contract price and the new sub-contract price.

The whole process of nomination as it was understood before 1980 has been drastically altered and is now very much more complex. Under the new "basic method" the Architect sends NSC/1, a five page document, with two Appendices and two Schedules to a proposed Sub-Contractor giving information under fourteen heads (Schedule 1 to NSC/1). Details of fluctuations are to form Appendix either A or B but not both. The proposed sub-contractor then completes and signs Tender NSC/1 and returns it to the Architect spurred on by the hope that, if acceptable it is then signed by the Architect on behalf of the Employer. The proposed Sub-Contractor and the Employer then execute Agreement NSC/2 which creates a number of rights and duties between the parties. This in itself is useless however without the desired objective which is for the Architect to issue Nomination NSC/3 as soon as possible, since if, between the date of NSC/2 and NSC/3 the Architect requires design work of a nominated Sub-Contractor this may result in an extra payment. At the same time as executing Agreement NSC/2 therefore, the Architect issues his preliminary Notice of Nomination which he sends together with Tender NSC/1 to the Main Contractor. The Main Contractor and the proposed Sub-Contractor must then try to agree all remaining terms of the sub-contract tender.

The completion of Schedule 2 to NSC/1 containing details of the sub-contract programme, including preliminary work, time for performance and completion date may not be an easy matter and it may be imagined that the Architect will be well pleased to receive back Tender NSC/1 signed by the Contractor so that he can then issue his formal nomination instructions NSC/3. The main contractor and the Sub-Contractor finally complete Sub-Contract NSC/4.

This structure of Tender, Agreement and Nomination Forms is designed to preserve the need for the Sub-Contractor's Tender to be made to the employer while at the same time preserving the right of negotiation between the Main Contractor and the Sub-Contractor. The Contractor has, of course, the right to object to the nomination but not, obviously, after he has returned Tender NSC/1 to the Architect. Although complex, opinion generally accepts that the basic method is the best way, under sound practice, of dealing with nominated Sub-Contract work. The documents are a considerable improvement over what went before, NSC/4 replacing the old green form and the former grey form; the old Employer/Sub-Contractor warranty having been incorporated in NSC/2, and in cases where the Sub-Contract work is particularly important due perhaps to its size or complexity, including a large element of design, the "basic method" is obviously then to be preferred. The method is also most suitable when a nomination of a sub-contractor has to be made well before a main Contractor is appointed.

What then of the "alternative method"? One has perhaps only to contemplate the probable reaction and comments by a local heating engineer or electrician likely to be engaged in work to a small house refurbishment should NSC/1 thud through his letter box. But the alternative method, although seductively shorter, has flaws. Sub-Contract NSC/4A is not like NSC/4 in that it has to "go firm" on matters negotiated under NSC/1 so that the lack of agreement on a number of vital matters may result in a failure in nomination, so that the process of nomination has to start all over again. However, the obvious savings of time and energy point to the alternative method in smaller cases but the architect or surveyor may wish to present the proposed nominee with the alternatives whereupon it will be difficult for him to be too awkward when the problems in the "alternative method" bob to the surface.

Criticism of the "alternative method", however, does not mean that the "basic method" will survive triumphantly. The complexity of the procedures rather takes for granted the facilities of the largest firms for immediate evaluation of proposals from both technical and legal points of view.

The basic procedure under 35.6, i.e. the use of Tender NSC/1 and Agreement NSC/2 is the brainchild of the Tribunal producing the 1980 Form and has been elaborately and painstakingly worked out. Forethought has been given to the procedure if negotiation breaks down, although it is not so clear what happens if negotiations are delayed, since problems over agreement of the many terms are endemic in negotiations of this sort and can never be solved by Forms, however carefully drafted. Clause 35.8 is an example of a problem where, if the Contractor is unable within ten working days from receipt of the preliminary Notice of Nomination to reach agreement with the proposed Sub-Contractor, the Contractor "shall continue to comply with clause 35.7 but inform the Architect in writing of the reasons for the inability to reach such agreement"; and the Architect shall "issue such instructions as may be necessary". It is difficult to see what instructions the Architect can usefully issue under such circumstances but the clause is there nevertheless.

It appears vital that the basic or alternative procedures for nomination of a Sub-Contractor are considered and that one or other is followed in its entirety so that there is no risk of a muddle. The alternative scheme would not operate satisfactorily unless the procedures under the first scheme are discarded but under the alternative procedure 35.11 and 35.12 the Contractor is required to "proceed so as to conclude a Sub-Contract" but the results of non-compliance are by no means clear.

One of the difficulties with the 1963 Contract Form which was subject to much criticism was that there was no machinery to ensure that Sub-Contracts bore a family resemblance to the main Contract. The 1980 version goes a long way to meet the previous difficulties but it is essential that the new procedure is followed to the letter. The repercussions from the Bickerton case appear in clause 35.24 dealing with re-nomination. Whereas under Bickerton however, where the principle was that the Nominated Sub-Contractor must have dropped out, that is to say have been repudiated, re-nomination now takes effect by default under one of the express clauses of the Sub-Contract documents. The grounds include failure to proceed in accordance with the agreed programme or reasonably in accordance with the progress of the Main Contract works but, obviously, a question of degree is concerned here and the failure must be reasonably fundamental. Nevertheless this sets up a situation where the architect may find himself in a difficult position. The clause as drafted suits the Contractor since previously, delay could hardly be classed as repudiation. On paper the Contractor merely has to show difficulties following from delay but in an acrimonious situation where the two sides have never got on with each other from the start it may be very difficult to sort out the wheat from the chaff. The Contractor cannot determine the Nominated Sub-Contractor's employment under clause 29 of NSC/4, 4A, without an instruction from the Architect but conversely the Architect cannot take action in the matter until notified by the Contractor. What happens for example if the Contractor tells the Nominated Sub-Contractor that he is not ready for him to arrive on the 4 July, the date stipulated but that he must come on the 14th and the Nominated Sub-Contractor then never arrives at all?

The procedure whereby the Employer pays the Sub-Contractor direct if the main Contractor defaults is complex and the implications of a mistake are worrying. Advice should be sought under such circumstances from specialist lawyers.

Nominated Suppliers

The provisions relating to Nominated Suppliers have been revised and are set out in clause 36. The main changes are that Nominated Suppliers have now been defined as such. A supplier is nominated or deemed to be nominated if (1) a prime cost sum is included in the Contract Bills or in an instruction as to expenditure of a provisional sum and the Supplier is named in the Bills or instruction or subsequently named by the architect or (2) in an instruction as to expenditure of a provisional sum or in a variation instruction the architect specifies materials or goods which can only be purchased from one supplier. Whenever the nomination of a supplier arises from the expenditure of a provisional sum or from a variation, the clause requires that the materials or goods be made the subject of a prime cost sum. It should be noted that a Supplier who is named in the Contract Bills is not a Nominated Supplier unless there is also a prime cost sum in the Bills.

Clause 36 appears to deal fully with the question of Nominated Suppliers including the architect's requirement to issue instructions as well as the ascertainment of those costs which are to be set against a prime cost sum for Nominated Suppliers. The sale contract provisions, which have been altered, require particular attention to be paid to obligations regarding quality and standard of materials or goods.

The enlarged definition of Nominated Supplier is interesting. Fundamental to the definition is the existence of a prime cost sum. This is the distinctive characteristic of a Nominated Supplier since otherwise if his name is merely specified in the Bills he is an ordinary supplier of materials at a specified cost. The point of a Nominated Supplier is presumably that the architect retains control over price.

A number of aspects relating to Nominated Suppliers do not appear to follow logically the steps relating to Nominated Sub-Contractors and peter out. Re-Nomination for example does not appear to be dealt with and there is no warranty by a Nominated Supplier.

Employer's Option – List of Sub-Contractors

In order to provide an alternative and to take the heat out of the strong provisions for nominating Sub-Contractors allowance is made in the new Standard Form for an alternative system to be adopted. This contains a code so that Employers can outline certain work for pricing in full by the Contractor but which the Employer requires to be executed by a Sub-Contractor selected by the Main Contractor from a list provided by the Employer. Clause 19 provides that where the Employer has given a list of not less than three Sub-Contractors who are able to carry out the work priced by the Contractor in the Main Contract Documents and, provided that the Contractor is entirely free to select which Sub-Contractor on the list he wishes to engage, then the Sub-Contractor selected is not regarded as nominated but comes within a new definition of "Domestic Sub-Contractors".

Once again like so many clauses in the 1980 Edition of the Contract an element of goodwill would appear to be vital since a Contractor if he wishes can circumvent the Employer. Firstly he has the right to add a name to the list at any time unless there is reasonable objection to this and in any event he has the whip hand in that he can shake off any undesirable Sub-Contractors by offering too low a price. It is difficult to see how the Employer can overcome the strength of the Contractor's position in this respect.

Fluctuations

Limited conventional fluctuations under clause 31B of the 1963 Edition (Contribution Levy and Tax) are now revised under a new clause 38. Full conventional fluctuations however (labour, materials, contribution levy and tax) under old clause 31A are now much expanded and enlarged under the new clause 39. New items include increases due to the operation of a bonus incentive arrangement and the expansion of the clause to embrace a much wider range of operatives both on and off the site and site staff now designated as "craftsmen". There is provision for electricity and fuels as optional extras and a more generous range of travelling expenses. Full formula fluctuations formerly under old clause 31F are now restated under new clause 40.

Standard Form of Nominated Sub-Contract NSC/4

The original provisions of the 1963 Edition of the main JCT Contract Form and the Green Form have been completely revised in the new Sub-Contract Form NSC/4. Obviously, a number of the main alterations reflect changes in the JCT Standard Form of Contract 1980 but the benefit of NSC/4 can be instanced for example in the case of contract variations. Under clause 10.3 the definition of a variation is widened to include the alteration of information provided in tender NSC/1 as to site conditions, working hours and the carrying out and completion of work in a stated sequence. The right of either the main contractor or sub-contractor to make reasonable objection and for the right of immediate arbitration is a considerable step forward over the provisions of the Green Form in settling awkward disputes. The rules for valuing variations have been amplified and expanded.

One of the main changes over the 1963 Edition and the Green Form is in respect of extensions of time. Under clause 9.4 the architect must decide upon the grant of an extension of time within twelve weeks of receiving adequate notice and particulars from the main contractor and this period could be shorter if the stipulated date for completion of the sub-contract works expires before this

241

time. Formerly, although there was a rather loose obligation on the architect there was no time limit. Under clause 9.4.4 the reference in the Green Form to delays in progress has been expanded to include the words "commencement, progress or completion" of the works thus ending arguments over problems causing delay at the outset of the sub-contract period. A new provision is also, of course, that a previously granted extension of time may later be reduced if circumstances warrant. Under clause 9.5.1 the "relevant events" providing grounds for extensions of time are expanded.

The provisions on payment in sub-contract document NSC/4 have been revised and made more precise. The sums in monthly valuations are to be set out more fully while the main contractor is now bound to pay his nominated sub-contractors within seventeen days of the date of issue of a particular architect's certificate unlike the rather woolly provision made in the Green Form. The rules relating to retention money have been largely overhauled and clarified, retention monies having Trust Fund status in a manner that follows the provisions of the JCT Contract Form 1980. The rules relating to the deduction of amounts previously certified are again tightened so that failure of the main contractor to make a particular payment will not prejudice the right of the sub-contractor to claim such payment under subsequent certificates. There are variations in the provisions relating to cash discount under clause 8.6 while under clause 8.7 the mandatory provisions for direct payment to the sub-contractor under certain circumstances are new as are the provisions under clause 8.8 for suspension of the sub-contract works. A further provision under clause 8.9 relates to the final account in respect of the sub-contract works since payment upon early completion is now mandatory.

There are fundamental changes under clause 9 relating to commencement and completion of the sub-contract works framed to clear up the muddled situation under the provisions of the Green Form. The incorporation of the agreed programme for the works set out in Tender NSC/1 including the period of preparation for contract documentation in the sub-contract NSC/4 shows the benefits of the new structure while the provisions for notice of delay under clause 9.3 are far more detailed than before. The sub-contract document also deals with fluctuations (clause 11), determination and bankruptcy (clause 12), and arbitration (clause 13) in much greater detail.

With regard to the question of nominated suppliers, much greater recognition is given under NSC/4 to the status of a supplier under the terms of the sub-contract document. Where the name of a supplier is stated and restricts, limits or excludes his liability in the contract of sale, then copies of such limitations must be sent to the main contractor who refers a copy to the architect. The architect and main contractor may either jointly approve the restrictions stated but if they do not, the relationship between the sub-contractor and the supplier fails.

In order for a supplier to become nominated, the materials and goods to be delivered must be the subject of a prime cost sum. Where a variation order specifies materials or goods for which the supplier is a "sole source of supply" the supply must be the subject of a prime cost sum so that the supplier then becomes "nominated".

The conditions which form a part of the contract of sale with a nominated supplier are contained in clause 36 of the Main Form and specify warranties and limitations.

JCT Contract Form 1980 Local Authorities Edition

The Local Authorities Edition of the Standard Form of Building Contract 1980 is precisely similar to the Private Edition except for those necessary alterations that have had to be made to render it suitable for local authority use. Accordingly, the definition of the term "the Architect" under article 3A can either mean a person entitled to use the name "Architect" in accordance with the Architects' Registration Acts 1931 to 1969 or an alternative is presented under article 3B where officials of the Local Authority, not being registered Architects are able to adopt the term "the Supervising Officer" and, upon inserting their names, are then known by this term throughout the remainder of the document. On page 9 of the contract form a blank page is provided for attestation so that the correct formalities relating to local authority work can be included. Under article 19A which does not appear in the Private Edition and which is headed "Fair Wages" a number of clauses are inserted relating to Rates of Wages, hours and conditions of labour and the right to belong to a Trade Union. Under article 19A.3 there is provision for appeal upon any of the aspects of the contract provision relating to Fair Wages being in dispute.

A rather interesting addition occurs under article 27.3 which again does not appear in the Private Edition and which deals with corruption. Under this article, if the Contractor offers, gives or agrees to give any person a gift or "consideration of any kind" as an inducement or reward for doing or forbearing to do some action or for showing favour to any person in such a way as to commit an offence under the Prevention of Corruption Acts 1889 to 1916 or shall have given any fee or reward, the receipt of which is an offence under section 117 of the Local Government Act 1972, the Employer shall then be entitled to determine the employment of the Contractor.

Under article 28.1 dealing with the Determination of the Contract by the Contractor the clauses set out in the Private Edition are repeated word for word but clause 28.1.4 is excluded. This deals with the circumstances where an Employer under the Private Edition becomes bankrupt; a situation that presumably cannot occur under local government work although one begins to wonder, bearing in mind modern conditions, whether it might not have been wiser to retain this particular provision in case it might be needed in the future!

The Ice Contract Form (5th Edition) 1973

It is not envisaged that the ICE Contract Form which is used by engineers in construction contracts will be employed for projects within the scope of this volume but reference is being made to it for two reasons. The first is that construction contracts specifically designed for civil engineering work impinge far more than they used to do upon building work so that some recognition of the ICE Form of Contract is desirable but secondly, and it is hoped rather more interestingly, to point a contrast between the way in which surveyors and architects on the one hand and engineers upon the other manage building and construction contracts respectively and how the contract forms are drafted with each particular case in mind and how they are surprisingly totally different in substance.

The main difference between building and civil engineering contracts is that, in the latter case, unforeseen site conditions are fundamental not only to the project but to the whole form and shape of the contract so that clause 12 which deals with unforeseen site conditions has no counterpart in the JCT Contract Form where such conditions are marginal and are simply dealt with by way of variation.

Where unforeseen site conditions are calmly expected by engineers under construction contracts as contrasted with surveyors and architects under building contracts where it is hoped that unforeseen conditions will not occur, a much stronger site representation and authority for dealing with all unknown conditions, and a fair and prompt method of paying the Contractor, are necessary for the effective running of the Contract. These conditions are recognised in the ICE Contract Form firstly in the importance given to the special position of the site or resident engineer and secondly in the provision made for periodic payments to the Contractor. Nowhere in the scope of this book has the essential basis of the law that a builder is only entitled to expect payment once he has substantially completed the work, been altered to a greater extent than under the ICE Contract Form where provision for periodic payment is deliberately made.

As in the case of an architect or surveyor under the JCT Form of Contract a consulting engineer is not a party to the ICE Contract which is executed between the client and the Contractor. His own agreement will be likely to be one or other of the Conditions of Engagement produced by the Association of Consulting Engineers and it may be a surprise to know of the number and variations of conditions available. The types of engagement vary from those covering report and advisory work to the design and supervision of construction and separate forms are naturally available for civil, mechanical and electrical projects as against structural engineering work. Other forms show the impact of modern technology upon building work as well as construction contracts since separate forms are available for the design and supervision of structural engineering works in buildings where an architect or surveyor is appointed or for the design and supervision of mechanical engineering systems in buildings and other projects or for structural engineering services in connection with industrialised building systems.

Whatever the particular nature of the engineering consultant's agreement he will have a central role under the ICE Contract Form since a large number of the conditions refer to him directly. The more obvious examples being clause 12 where he has to decide about adverse physical conditions, clause 16 relating to the efficiency of the Contractor's employees, clause 37 relating to site access and clause 39 where he has the duty of deciding about improper work. Under clause 48 the engineer has the basic duty of certifying completion.

Nowhere, however, is the power of the consultant engineer set out more clearly than under clause 51 which relates to variations. Under this clause the engineer has the mandatory power to order variations that are necessary, in his opinion, for the completion of the work and the discretionary duty of ordering variations that are desirable for the "satisfactory completion and functioning of the works". The distinction is an interesting one. The Engineer's Agreement is with his client but where the ICE Contract Form states under clause 51 (1) that the "engineer shall order . . ." or "shall have power to order . . ." it is obvious that by experience it has been found that consultant engineers can either act directly or be called upon to act by the Contractor under a wide variety of circumstances ranging from decisions such as extensions of time (clause 44), instructions such as the suspension of works (clause 40)

245

to approvals and consents such as Sunday work (clause 45) and the receipt of Notices and Certification (clause 48).

In general terms the duty of the consultant engineer does not differ from that of the architect or surveyor in that he has to exercise the standard of care to be expected in a reasonably competent engineer engaged in the type of work in question. Like an architect or surveyor under the JCT Form of Contract he has the same duty of performing his dual function to represent his Employer on the one hand and to hold a fair balance between the Employer and the Contractor on the other. It nevertheless however, seems certain that the case of *Sutcliffe* v. *Thackrah* (1974) would apply to consulting engineers just as it does to architects and surveyors under the various forms of Contract in that the role of quasi arbitrator is a myth.

The provisions of clause 51 under the ICE Contract Form envisage variations only, rather than new work, but the whole basis of this form of contract is that little limitation is imposed upon the consultant engineer and the Contract Form is designed to give him the widest possible powers to deal with unknown circumstances.

It follows therefore that the provisions for the valuation of variations, once ordered, and the method and machinery for resolving disputes must be precise and clause 52 of the ICE Contract Form is complex. Generally speaking, where work is of a similar character and executed under similar conditions to work priced in the Bills of Quantities, similar prices to those in the Bills are to be adopted. If the work is not similar in both the stated respects the prices in the Bills are to be used as a basis for valuation insofar as this is reasonable and thirdly where it is not reasonable to rely upon the Contract rates a fair valuation is to be made. Further work therefore, however extensive, of a similar character to that already carried out will attract the normal Contract rates but it is open either to the Contractor or the engineer to serve upon the other a Notice indicating that he considers the Contract rate unreasonable or inapplicable and to demand a change. In order for the Notice to be valid it must be served before the extra work is started or as soon as is practicable under the circumstances.

A final "safety net" provision under clause 51 is that the engineer has power to order that additional or substituted work be carried out on a day-work basis. This order overrules other provisions for the valuation of extra work under the section and this clause is no doubt introduced on the basis that, should all else fail, the Contractor is sufficiently protected by day-work and the employer, at least, can rely on a traditional method of payment. There is provision for the Contractor to claim extra remuneration but the whole basis of the clause, interesting to architects and surveyors, is the meticulous need for Notices to be served when unusual circumstances occur. Failure to provide a Notice by, say, the Contractor, will not, obviously, mean that he is entitled to no extra payment at all but he has prejudiced his case by depriving the engineer of his right to investigate the claim on the spot. Late submission of a claim entitles the engineer to say "Why wasn't I told at the time? . . .".

The conditions in the ICE Form of Contract which relate to extensions of time are similar in essence, although not in content, to the JCT Contract Form involving the usual battle with an eye to liquidated damages at a later stage. Where a Contractor is entitled to extra time however, this does not of itself, provide any right to extra payment. An admitted right to extra time prevents the Contractor being in breach of contract only and, therefore, relieves him from liability to liquidated damages and while in practice the granting of extra time leads to extra payment this is not necessarily so unless the Contractor can produce some clause in the Contract as his authority.

The ICE Form of Contract is not suitable for a Lump Sum or Fixed Price Contract as it is in all its essentials a measurement and valuation contract, envisaging that the Contractor is only paid for work actually completed. This is recognised by clause 60 which specifies in detail the method of payment which puts the onus upon the Contractor for the detailed submission of monthly statements. The Engineer must then issue his certificate within 28 days less the retention and percentage amounts specified in the Contract. The Employer on his part is entitled to deduct reasonable items of counter-claim. Finally, the Engineer issues his completion certificate upon "substantial" completion this date having considerable importance from the point of view of liquidated damages on the one hand and as the commencement for the maintenance period on the other.

Provisions relating to Sub-Contractors whether domestic or nominated and those relating to Provisional and Prime Cost Sums are familiar to architects and surveyors used to the older JCT form of building contract with the important distinction that where design work is the subject of a Nominated Sub-Contract the liability of the Contractor is correspondingly reduced from the design point of view, provided that the responsibilities of the parties are clearly stated. It would appear that a "Nominated Sub-Contractor" includes what an architect or surveyor would call a "Nominated Supplier" (clause 58) but otherwise the provisions are familiar in that the Contractor may object to the nomination of a Sub-Contractor upon reasonable grounds and if this submission is accepted by the engineer he may take one or other of the alternative courses of action open to him under the Contract. What happens if the engineer does not accept the Contractor's submission is not provided for in the Contract. Early arbitration is not possible and the consequences of the inevitable delay are likely to be laid at the door of the party who ultimately proves to be in the wrong.

The general principle that a Main Contractor is liable to the employer for bad work carried out by Sub-Contractors even when these are nominated is varied under the ICE Conditions. In the event of a breach by a Sub-Contractor which leads to a breach under the Main Contract by the Contractor the Employer is only able to enforce his loss against the Contractor to the extent that the Contractor is able to recover from the Sub-Contractor. At least however, the ICE Contract Form is not so vulnerable to criticism under the Bickerton case, described earlier, as the JCT Contract Form was on that occasion regarding re-nomination of a Sub-Contractor, since this is provided for under clause 59B. Under clause 59C an Employer may make direct payment to a Nominated Sub-Contractor but only under certain conditions where the sum has already been certified and where the Contractor has no grounds for withholding payment.

The arbitration provisions of the ICE Contract Form, under clause 66, contain rights of appeal to the High Court on any point of law under the terms of the Arbitration Act of 1979. The dispute has to be referred first to the engineer when it is important to require his decision under clause 66 as otherwise, in the absence of that decision, there can be no right to arbitration. An interesting provision is that interim arbitration is allowable under certain set circumstances such as adverse physical conditions (clause 12) the withholding by the engineer of a certificate or part or whole of the retention money or under clause 63 in the case of forfeiture.

When arbitration is pending the Contractor is required under the ICE Contract Form to proceed with the work but an oddity exists that the Employer, if he is dissatisfied with the decision of the engineer, can still set off sums of money certified by the engineer in his payments to the Contractor.

The powers of the Arbitrator are wide. He is given full power to open up, review and revise any decision, opinion, instruction, certificate or valuation of the engineer and arbitration forms a particularly strong protection to the Contractor under the particular terms of the ICE Contract Form.

The JCT Form of Agreement for Minor Building Works 1980

The 1980 Edition of the JCT Form of Agreement for Minor Building

Works replaces the 1968 Edition and its subsequent revisions. It commences with a new head note as follows:

> "This Form of Agreement and Conditions is designed for use where minor building works are to be carried out for an agreed lump sum and where an Architect/Supervising Officer has been appointed on behalf of the Employer. The Form is not for use for works for which bills of quantities have been prepared, or where the Employer wishes to nominate Sub-Contractors or Suppliers, or where the duration is such that full labour and materials fluctuations provisions are required; nor for works of a complex nature or which involve complex services or require more than a short period of time for their execution."

As the head note points out the Minor Works Form of Contract is capable of dealing with the simplest types of project only. There are no adequate provisions for financial problems if the lump sum basis of the contract is frustrated by unforeseen circumstances particularly as quantities either approximate or otherwise do not form part of the contract and, in particular, the form is not recommended for use when the Employer wishes to nominate Sub-Contractors or Suppliers. The duration of the works is expected to be short as labour and materials fluctuations provisions are not envisaged. Nor are works of a complex nature contemplated. There are no clauses to deal with the appointment of a Clerk of Works, for example, or for arranging sectional completion if desired. The form is therefore designed to cater only for those very simple cases where a Lump Sum Contract is still appropriate but where very straightforward work is expected to be carried out by a single contractor in a short space of time.

The Form of Agreement for Minor Building Works should be read in conjunction with the supplementary memorandum published by the Joint Contracts Tribunal which is in two parts; Part A dealing with contribution, levy and tax changes and Part B dealing with value added tax. In addition a practice note M1 is published as a supplement by the Tribunal explaining changes that have occurred since the 1968 Edition, last revised in February 1977, and which the new edition supersedes.

A manual for use with the JCT Minor Works Form has been published by the Royal Institution of Chartered Surveyors which will be of value to all intending users.

The first change in the new document over the previous Edition is in the drafting of the Recitals. This change is designed to provide greater flexibility and coordination so as to include what are now described as "the Contract Documents". Rather surprising and at first sight an anomaly is the fourth Recital which deals with the appointment of a quantity surveyor. Since the head note says that the Form is not for use with works for which bills of quantity have been prepared, this clause assumes that the quantity surveyor is appointed at the outset simply in connection with the Schedule of Rates referred to in the second Recital and to act as general adviser in monetary disputes.

The Contract Form certainly has the benefit of being brief although, like its larger brothers, it has been swollen to some extent with provisions relating to tax. The list of contents is new as is the decimal numbering system which gives an air of unfamiliarity in direct comparison with the earlier Edition. One further change has been made in the articles, as under article 4 dealing with arbitration, the President of the RIBA or RICS has been substituted for the President of the Chartered Institute of Arbitrators to decide upon an appropriate appointment.

The new clause 1 of the Form of Agreement deals in fuller terms with the Contractor's obligation and the duties of the architect or surveyor. The works are now to be carried out in accordance with the Contract Documents using materials and workmanship of the quality and standards "therein specified" but there is provision made where there are no guide lines for quality and standards to be to the "reasonable satisfaction" of the Architect or Surveyor. The various duties of the Architect or Surveyor himself have been usefully extracted and codified on page 5 of the Manual for use with the JCT Agreement for Minor Building Works published by the RICS.

Clause 2 sets out the provisions relating to commencement and completion, to extension of the contract period, damages for non-completion, the completion date and defects liability. The amount of liquidated damages has to be inserted into the text and, as the RICS Manual correctly says, this should reflect the Employer's estimated actual loss, and not contain any enhancement value. Under clause 2.5 a three months defects liability period is specified but it is contemplated that this could be altered if required since space is allowed for an amendment.

Clause 3 of the Agreement Form deals with control of the works. Under clause 3.1 there is a new prohibition against assignment of the contract by either the Employer or the Contractor without written consent. The provision against Sub-Contracting is similar to previously but an amplified version of the original clause 4 contains the provision that the architect or surveyor may require the exclusion from the Works of any person employed thereon. The RICS Manual explains that the reason for the term "exclude" is that to dismiss any person may contravene the Employment Protection Act.

Under clause 3.5 oral instructions from the Architect or Surveyor must be confirmed in writing within two days which makes one wonder what happens if instructions are issued late on Friday. Presumably this means two working days although it does not say so. If within seven days after receipt of the written notice the Contractor does not comply with the contents then the Employer may employ and pay other persons to carry out the work. This is a new provision and should, it is thought, only be exercised with extreme care. Whatever the Contract Form may lay down, the Courts in particular, dislike this sort of clause and it may well be that the Contractor might have a perfectly valid excuse for non-compliance.

The provisions under clauses 3.6 and 3.7 relating to variations and provisional sums reproduce clauses from the earlier edition but reference to prime cost sums has been entirely omitted in view of the decision that the Form should not provide for nomination of Sub-Contractors and Suppliers.

Clause 4 relates to payment. Clause 4.1 deals with the correction of inconsistencies but recognises that every correction may not provide a variation but only the correction of an inconsistency which results in a change. Where the correction is not a change there is no variation. This illustrates, however, the need to classify the documents in order of importance so that two inconsistent documents can be amended by agreement.

Under clause 4.2 "interim payments" are now known as "progress payments". There is now provision for the deduction of a retention percentage on progress payments. A five per cent retention is specified but a space is left beside it in case any alteration is agreed between the parties. Progress payments are now to include "the value of any materials and goods which have been reasonably and properly brought upon the site for the purpose of the Works and which are adequately stored and protected against the weather and other casualties . . ."

Under clause 4.3 the architect or surveyor "shall within fourteen days after the date of practical completion certified under clause 2 hereof certify payment to the Contractor . . ." The period was ten days under the earlier Agreement. The percentage of retention to be kept back by the Employer during the defects liability period is reduced at this stage.

Under clause 4.4 the Contractor is now "obliged" to supply the necessary documentation for the final account to be drawn up. This is certainly of value so far as some builders are concerned who are notorious for not producing correct information to back up total amounts.

Under clause 4.6 a new and uncompromising definition of the term "fixed price" is included.

Under clause 5 headed "Statutory Obligations" the Contractor is obliged to notify the architect or surveyor of any differences which he finds between the statutory requirements which he is obliged to obey and the work that he has agreed to carry out. If he does so and the architect or surveyor fails to respond, the Contractor would not then be liable to the employer for the cost of non-compliance.

The remaining sub-clauses under clause 5 relating to statutory obligations deal with tax and fair wages with the exception of sub-clause 5.5 which deals with the prevention of corruption. This should be deleted in the case of private contracts as it is intended only for use on local authority contracts.

The clauses under clause 6 relating to injury, damage and insurance have been considerably expanded. It should be noted, however, that the provisions are simple and certain cases would undoubtedly require supplementary cover as a wise precaution. Briefly, the contractor is responsible for indemnifying the Employer for loss or damage to real or personal property arising out of the execution of the works and, only if the employer is a local authority, to insure against loss and damage by fire, lightning, explosion and other comprehensive risks. It is interesting to find that a percentage addition is included for professional fees. The Contractor then has the duty of replacing the work or materials damaged. Under clause 6.3B, as an alternative, the employer is responsible for the insurance of the works including existing structures and all unfixed materials and goods as regards loss or damage by fire, lightning, explosion and comprehensive risks. Obviously, either clause 6.3A or 6.3B is to be deleted as agreed. Clause 6.4 provides that evidence of insurance is to be produced by either Contractor or employer as applicable.

Clause 7 of the Contract Form deals with determination of the contract. In the event of the employer validly determining the employment of the Contractor, "the Contractor shall immediately give up possession of the site of the Works and the Employer shall not be bound to make any further payment to the Contractor until after completion of the Works". The grounds under which the Contractor may determine the works have been amplified to include not just failure by the Employer to make a progress payment, to obstruct the work or to become bankrupt, but also the occasion when he suspends the carrying out of works for a continuous period of at least one month. It should be noted, however, that the Contractor is bound to specify the terms of the Employer's default by registered post or recorded delivery and can only take action seven days after the notice is likely to have been received. The Employer is then liable to pay to the Contractor not only "such sum as shall be fair and reasonable for the value of work begun and executed, materials on site . . ." but the removal of all temporary buildings, plant, tools and equipment.

A separate Scottish Building Contract for Minor Building Work is published by the Scottish Building Contract Committee.

The Government GC/Works/1 Form of Contract

The form in general use by government departments and for government corporations differs from the JCT Contract Forms for private or local authority use. The very origin of the form is quite different as the government form originates from an Inter-Departmental Committee representing the Ministries involved with construction who consult with the employers federations in the construction industry. The responsibility for the form primarily rests with the Property Services Agency of the Department of the Environment.

Form GC/Works/1 is normally regarded as having the best elements of both the JCT Contract Form and the ICE Contract Form and certainly "The Authority" (a much more impressive term than "the employer") has much more scope to direct and decide matters than his private sector counterpart. A number of distinct areas are removed from arbitration and the decision of the Authority is to be binding and conclusive in a way that does not apply in the private version of the JCT Contract Form.

The position of the architect, surveyor or other supervising officer under the JCT Contract Form is replaced by the term "The Superintending Officer". Differences obviously flow from the fact that he or she will often be an employee of the Authority and not an independent professional person, although the Form GC/Works/1 is used even when an independent consultant is employed to design and supervise the building works.

The contract itself is formed by the Tender with abstract of particulars and a letter of acceptance which takes the place of the appendix to the JCT Contract Form. The case of a contract under seal does not apply.

While a number of clauses are similar to those in the JCT Contract Form, a number are quite different. These lie mainly in the field of insurance against injury to persons and property and the fact that the contractor cannot determine the contract as he can do under the JCT Contract Form. Other differences lie in the way that fluctuations in cost are dealt with and the lack of any provision relating to war damage.

The contract documents comprise the definitions, specifications, bills of quantities and drawings and, rather unusually, the Authority's schedule of rates and the Contractor's schedule of rates. A notable feature is that the specification becomes a contract document. The contract sum is defined as "the sum accepted, or the sum calculated in accordance with the prices accepted". This suggests that a lump sum contract whether or not related to quantities is envisaged or, at least, a set of prices from which the contract sum can be calculated. Prime cost contracts are obviously excluded. The contract form is therefore suitable for use with or without quantities or with approximate quantities or for use in conjunction with a schedule of rates either for measurement of work as it is carried out, or to assist with costing variations in the case of a lump sum contract without quantities. Finally, when only drawings and specification are employed, in the case of a lump sum contract without quantities, a schedule of rates compiled from the tender document may be supplied by the contractor in order to give authority for the calculation of variations. The fact that both the Authority and the contractor submit a schedule of rates is the unusual feature and which schedule takes precedence is determined by circumstances.

Under the Government Contract the contractor has to give notices and pay all fees and indemnify the authority but there is no provision for the sums due to be added to the contract sum. The Contractor must accordingly make provision for them when he submits his tender. Another provision relates to the status of the Superintending Officer. Under the terms of this contract the decision of the Officer appointed is final and conclusive. His duties are defined and enable him to give far more direct instructions than are contemplated in the JCT Form of Contract. Oral instructions are to be confirmed in writing by the Superintending officer rather than confirmed by the contractor as in the JCT Form.

A marked departure concerns the appointment of a Clerk of Works. Here the Superintending Officer can delegate powers to the Clerk including the power of giving instructions which is a far cry from the JCT Contract Form. A further condition is that the contractor is bound to conform to the rules and regulations of the particular establishment within which the works may be situated.

The contractor does not have the latitude over the commencement and progress of the works set out in the JCT Form of Contract. Commencement is by notice so that the contractor may have little time in which to make his arrangements but on the other hand the date for completion cannot be altered unless the Superintending Officer so agrees. This is an instance of the wide ranging nature of his powers.

Condition 9 of the Contract Form deals with the question of the valuation of the Superintending Officer's instructions. This broadly covers the ground of clause 11 of the JCT Form and admits the same alternatives of measurement or day work. Under sub-clause (3) of Condition 9 there is a distinct variation from JCT Clause 11 in that the quantity surveyor has the right to pronounce upon the value of work that has been covered up before he has had a chance to see it. His decision cannot be questioned in these circumstances.

Apart from Condition 53 which deals with the expenses of prolongation and disruption of the contract the question of added expense is dealt with under Condition 9 (2). Under this particular Contract Form the provisions of Condition 7 relating to confirmation of instructions together with the duty of the contractor to provide information and documents as quickly as possible are strictly enforced. The Contractor does not have the duty of making a claim as is required under the JCT Form. Valuation by reference to rates is covered under Conditions 9 and 10 which relate with Condition 5 – Schedules of Rates, Condition 24 – Procedural Matters relating to Day Work and Condition 37 where the contractor has a duty to supply information and assist the quantity surveyor.

Condition 16 deals with the appointment of a resident engineer or clerk of works with the sensible extension of the provisions of the JCT Contract Form where the engineer or clerk merely has the status of "inspector" in that under clause 16 the Superintending Officer can delegate further powers to him, such as the power to condemn work and to give necessary instructions. The contractor of course must be notified of the full extent of the powers of the engineer or clerk and in the absence of such notification may refuse to carry out certain instructions.

A useful illustration of the increased powers of the Superintending Officer as against those set out in the JCT Form is contained under Condition 23 where he has total power to order the suspension of work that is at risk, due to frost for example. The contractor will only be reimbursed for added expense if he can show that he has followed the provisions of the specification or alternatively that the specification is silent on this aspect of the work. Condition 28 provides yet another interesting illustration of the increased powers of the Superintending Officer over and above those contained in the JCT Contract Form. The works are to be to the satisfaction of the Superintending Officer and are to be delivered up by the completion date except where this is modified by extensions of time granted under Condition 1 of the contract. There is a relationship with JCT Clause 23 in that delays due to circumstances wholly beyond the control of the contractor are grounds for increased expense but no extension of time is granted if the contractor is negligent and, in this connection, he is expected to foresee difficult circumstances and cope with them. It is significant that there is no mention of shortages of labour or materials or delay due to problems with sub-contractors in this connection although grounds for extension are as under the JCT Conditions, Acts of Default by the Authority and adverse weather conditions. The question of Partial Possession under Condition 28A is similar to the provisions of the JCT Contract Form leaving aside the question of insurance. A certificate of satisfaction has to be forthcoming from the Superintending Officer however, whose decision under this clause is to be final and binding. Unlike the JCT Contract Form the question of phasing can occur under Condition 28 as this is envisaged by agreement between the parties in the contract document. An unusual provision however, certainly when contrasted with the JCT Contract Form, is that the Superintending Officer can require the Contractor to give possession even if this is against the Contractor's wishes. Admittedly such requirement could lead to a claim for extra payment but this again highlights the drafting of the Government Contract Form in the interests of the Authority. The provisions of Condition 27 relating to assignment or transfer of the contract and the provisions of Condition 29 relating to liquidated damages have both been sharpened when contrasted with the JCT Contract Form.

Condition 30 relating to sub-letting contains certain individual conditions but there is no reference to nomination, although this is referred to under Condition 31 – Sub-Contractors and Suppliers and is defined in Condition 40.

Condition 38 covers Prime Cost items and provides that the Superintending Officer may nominate or select Sub-Contractors or suppliers as he wishes. He may for example review the competitive tenders obtained by the Contractor and make his own final choice. The amount of discount is restricted to what is obtainable and in any event is not to exceed $2\frac{1}{2}\%$. The sub-clauses to this section regulate the contract very strictly in relation to Prime Cost items. The Authority reserves the right to order and pay for such items direct which could well bring into argument the question of cash discount. Furthermore, an amendment, no doubt as a result of the Bickerton case, places the responsibility upon the contractor for carrying out work where a sub-contract is ended. If he cannot find another sub-contractor to carry out the work he must complete it himself in the knowledge that he will not be entitled to any extra payment than that arranged under the terms of the original sub-contract. Even if he finds another sub-contractor he must pay him in full and bear the reserve (retention) on the main contract sum or sums. There is no mention of damages. On the other hand under Condition 39, dealing with provisional sums and provisional quantities, alternatives are provided which are settled by measurement under the main contract terms.

Conditions 40, 41 and 42 deal with the question of advances, payments and certificates. Under Condition 30 the reserve (retention) upon work in progress is 3% while materials on site are subject to a reserve level of 10% and there is no provision at all for materials off-site as provided for in the case of the JCT Contract Form.

Advances on account are dealt with at monthly intervals upon the Contractor's valuation. On larger contracts in excess of £100,000 further interim advances upon approximate estimates might be granted but there is no remedy by the contractor for an Authority's delay in making payments. The Superintending Officer may decide to allow additional sums or savings and the value of old materials may be deducted from advances as may sums included in previous advances due to the contractor's default in paying sub-contractors and suppliers. The inclusion of suppliers in this connection does not necessarily entail nomination. Again, reserve is not mentioned and there is no duty upon the Contractor to make payment until he himself has been paid. Nominated suppliers have the same right as nominated sub-contractors regarding direct payments in the case of default.

Upon completion the final sum is estimated, taking progress payments into account, and the balance is paid with the exception of half the reserve. There is no provision for further advances as in the JCT Contract document. The release of the second half of the reserve is presumably held until the final sum is agreed. Payments from this sum are at the discretion of the Authority. Payment of the final balance is made upon the appropriate sum being agreed. This is not linked to the making good of defects as in the case of the JCT Contract Form but if settlement occurs within the maintenance period, the reserve is withheld and only the further balance due over and above this sum becomes payable straight away. The balance of reserve is released upon the making good of defects. The Contractor has the right of arbitration should the final account, prepared by the quantity surveyor, not be agreed.

Certification under Condition 42 is very similar to the machinery under the JCT Form of Contract but while an interim certificate is not "conclusive evidence" over quality or amount the Contractor cannot dispute an interim certificate although he has full rights over the amount of the final certificate.

Under Condition 44 the Authority has the right to determine the contract at any time and for any reason. It should be noted that this clause does not refer to default by the contractor which is covered under Condition 45 but is designed to cover extraordinary conditions due to major upsets on policy for example. There are numerous sub-clauses covering various items mainly relating to payment to the Contractor, removal of plant from the site and provisions relating to the determination of sub-contracts. A hardship claim, not subject to arbitration, might be admitted.

Conditions 45 and 46 deal with the determination of the contract due to the default or failure of the contractor. These provisions follow the clauses of the JCT Form of Contract but while there is no automatic determination in the event of insolvency, an added cause of determination is a breach of security under an earlier condition. In the event of determination the Authority may recoup any loss by selling plant which it has acquired under the provisions of Condition 3 while liquidated damages are the specific amounts recoverable as against the loss or damage clause under the JCT Form.

Condition 47 which relates to injury to persons and loss of property is specially drafted having regard to the particular position of the Crown in relation to its servants. The contractor generally is to indemnify the Crown and its servants against all types of claims and is liable where he is neglectful or neglect can be proved against persons for whom he is responsible. There is a difference in this obligation to that under the JCT Contract Form.

There is a particular provision under Condition 48 that the Authority will indemnify the contractor against claims for damage to highways or bridges by "extraordinary traffic" used in the operation of the works provided that the contractor takes all reasonable steps to prevent damage.

Condition 50 is designed to ensure that the contractor does not have the exclusive right to possession of the site during the execution of the works. Section 53 covers disturbance generally due to this cause which must be unexpected to qualify for payment for matters not specified in the original contract documents. Condition 53 covers prolongation and disruption expenses generally and includes those costs not otherwise provided for or reasonably contemplated by the Contract covering instructions of the Superintending Officer, damage to the works under Condition 26, work by contractors under Condition 50 and delay in the Superintending Officer providing design information. Claims can also be submitted in the event of delay by the Authority in making nominations or taking direct steps on the question of PC sums but before payment can be made to the contractor three conditions must be fulfilled. They are as follows:

Firstly the instructions of the Superintending Officer must be in writing. Secondly the contractor has to give all information or take such steps as are required by the Superintending Officer or the Authority and thirdly he has to give immediate advance notice of any likely claim and provide the necessary documentation shortly afterwards.

Condition 61 deals with the question of arbitration. The arbitrator can be agreed between the parties or appointed by the appropriate professional body but arbitration normally takes place subsequent to completion unless otherwise agreed. It should however, be noted that, since a number of matters subject to arbitration in the JCT Contract Form are dealt with under the Government Contract by the direct decision of the Authority or the Superintending Officer the grounds possible for cover by arbitration are rather shrunken in consequence. Arbitration therefore cannot take place on the right of the contractor to remove plant or materials from the site, the total power of the Superintending Officer to give instructions and the amount provided for in interim certificates. Finally questions as to whether payment can be withheld due to the contractor's default in paying sub-contractors or the question of hardship payments are also excluded from the area of arbitration.

In conclusion, the majority of items in the Government Contract Form follow those of the JCT Contract Form although with different wording such as the variation in price provisions under various sections which are similar to the JCT fluctuation clauses. There are some differences which do not parallel the JCT Contract Form in certain matters such as market fluctuations over labour costs, the Authority's right to examine supplier's accounts with a view to reducing excessive claims, but the most important provision is that the decision of the Authority is to be final and binding.

Variation of price specified in the separate Formula Price Adjustment Document can be incorporated in the contract and is similar to the JCT Formula Provisions. The GC/Works/1 Contract operates on the basis of being exclusive of Value Added Tax except as agreed under Condition 139A. Tax is reimbursed in interim and final payments and while it is the responsibility of the Authority to calculate the amount of tax due, the contractor has the duty of providing the necessary information so that the sums can be calculated.

Chapter 6
The Report on Feasibility

CONTENTS

IT is now time for the architect or surveyor to gather together the threads of the work that he has completed to date in order to present his Feasibility Report to the client. Since the "client" might be a private individual, a company, trustees, a Council Committee or one or more administrators in charge of a particular project, of which the architect or surveyor's scheme may form only part, the items of information which will be regarded as essential and the order of priority will differ enormously according to the type of project and the client concerned. In some cases, the architect or surveyor will have worked in virtual isolation, having little or no need to refer back to the client since settling the original brief so that the Feasibility Report that the client receives will be opened with anticipation and read, it is hoped, with concentration and interest. In other cases the feasibility report may be nothing more than a concise summary of steps taken in the preparation towards fulfilment of a project which are already very well known to the client. The document may indeed be little more than the latest edition to an already thick file of papers and while, in this case, the client may read the report with interest his anticpation when he opens it may be rather less acute.

Even where the client is a single individual, a householder who wishes to improve, convert or extend his house, the scope and therefore the contents of the Feasibility Report may differ widely. For example an architect or surveyor may be asked to report on the feasibility of altering or extending an urban dwelling house to cater for the needs of a growing family of the owner and his wife. On a case in point the alternatives were either to re-convert the interior of the structure or build an addition either at roof level or as an adjunct to the existing back addition. A further requirement however, might be that the cost of the work having regard to fees and incidental expenses taken together with the existing amount of the mortage on the property should not exceed the market value of the property, once converted. Obviously therefore, this example introduces at once a new personality on the scene; the consultant valuer. The Feasibility Report in this case was relatively short, the part of the document that was obviously read with most interest being the final conclusion giving recommendations as to which of the options were possible within the parameters laid down.

In another case where the improvement and a certain amount of discreet conversion of a derelict listed building did not involve any extension, the Feasibility Report concentrated on structure, the

262

alternative ways in which period construction and detailing could be replaced or alternatives found and, in particular, the sources available for financial help which could be approached. Again, where a doctor who owns a large Victorian property and, with the help of his wife, who is a state registered nurse, intends to convert it in order to provide a nursing home for the elderly, with a modern annexe, the financial aspect of the scheme will be of obvious fundamental importance. But so equally will other factors; a copy of the drawing submitted for outline planning consent may well be included as an appendix to the Report while the need for the various detailed consents that will be necessary under the Building Regulations and other statutes, the question of means of escape in case of fire being an obvious example, will be considered in some detail. The sketch plans are likely to be studied with care and the architect or surveyor is wise to back up any recommendations with quotations from an authoritative source such as "Housing Standards for the Elderly" published by HMSO as justification for his layout scheme. Equally important however, and matters that he is likely to be questioned about even at this preliminary stage will concern health and hygiene, comfort and safety. The points that may well be put to him are freedom from damp, sanitary and other fittings, heating, insulation and ventilation and in particular provisions relating to safety and the special needs of the elderly in this connection. The client's wife will be particularly interested in matters of convenience ranging from the control of services to refuse disposal and car parking facilities. The doctor, while leaving the discussion of such important matters to his capable wife, will display a strong interest in the architect or surveyor's capability of reducing running and maintenance costs in the future. What type of fuel is planned for the boiler, whether internal fixtures and fittings can be maintained at reasonable cost, and whether the expenditure needed upon external and internal maintenance can be reduced to a minimum level. In this type of Feasibility Study and Report there is a good case for attaching a number of appendices either provided by the architect or surveyor or by knowledgeable consultants in the field. The doctor and his wife in such a case will be concerned to see how the architect or surveyor, along with consultants, has satisfied the terms of the brief thrashed out for such a comparatively unfamiliar type of project.

The Director of a small company who wishes to convert a building to office or factory use will expect a Feasibility Report to concentrate upon the particular circumstances of the case having regard to his own requirements. This may not be quite the same in the case of a large international company which intends simultaneously to provide warehouse accommodation with five more retail outlets as the Feasibility Study is likely to be much more far ranging and take in the opinions of many more advisers and consultants than the architect or surveyor would normally encounter. Indeed such a company may issue fairly rigid requirements as to what is expected in the report itself. In either case however, the question of time is likely to be an all important one and the Feasibility Report will be received with less than satisfaction if it does not give full consideration in all its aspects to this vital factor.

Trustees or Committees enabled under various powers to spend money on behalf of other people are obviously interested in all aspects of the project that forms the subject of the Feasibility Report but they have a particular concern over one main aspect; the budgeting and control of finance. It might be said that this should be so in all feasibility studies particularly since this aspect of building work lies at the heart of this book. Those who are responsible for spending money entrusted to them by other people are normally working under a heavy burden of financial responsibility whether imposed by contract in the private sector or by Statute in the public sector. The type of contract to be employed and the whole range of financial checks to be set up firstly to ensure that the right amount of money is available at the right time and secondly to deal with variations or unexpected occurrencies in a prescribed manner is vital to their whole function and the architect or surveyor is well advised to establish a good business relationship with the banker or solicitor who is responsible under the terms of a family trust or the hard working manager of a Pension Fund who may have many other matters on his mind as well as the particular project with which the architect or surveyor may be concerned. An insight into the ability for financial planning in other matters displayed by the professional accountant involved in Trust or Fund work often tends to make the architect or surveyor rather ashamed of his own, by contrast, rather elementary approach to such matters. Familiarity in these circumstances leads to respect.

In the various branches of the Public Sector, or where public control is exercised, the architect or surveyor is likely to encounter his opposite number, so to speak, which can be quite an unnerving experience. To meet another surveyor or architect who has a detailed, not to say encyclopaedic, knowledge of financial rules and specialist regulations, be they technical or administrative, can be a humbling experience. Similarly, the architect or surveyor who hands over his carefully prepared Feasibility Study to a chartered surveyor, say, in charge of a Housing Association may, when he sees his precious document placed on a pile with a number of others, walk away feeling somewhat diminished in consequence.

In the field of Feasibility Studies and Reports, healthy argument flourishes and will no doubt continue to flourish as to the question of presentation. A good modern type for the text, a good looking durable cover for the report with the name of the firm attractively presented and appendix sketch plans and photographs, together with other documents in a jacket pocket competently prepared, printed and folded would appear to be the minimum requirement, but opinions vary. One Feasibility Report seen in what might be described as rather "William Morris" circumstances was certainly unusual as it was written in dark ink on paper of unusual hue and contained, in an appendix folder, samples of the actual materials proposed, ranging from linen and wall papers to samples of wood for finishings. There were a number of sketches drawn roughly but very attractively and to a high quality and many more sketch interiors and perspectives than is normally the case. The Feasibility Report suited its purpose admirably in the circumstances of the particular project. The fact, however, that one winces to imagine the impact of such a report upon a Pension Fund manager does not in any way diminish the validity of such a report but merely highlights the enormous difficulty of laying down any hard and fast rules for the presentation of the results of a Feasibility Study to different people under different circumstances. There is, however, in nearly every case an element of "selling" a scheme so that presentation and clarity are all important.

Enough has been said, it is hoped, to establish the fundamental fact that knowledge of the client's stated requirements is not enough to write a convincing and effective Feasibility Report. The architect or surveyor does well to remember that all clients, without exception, are subject to restraints, checks and balances and the Feasibility Report that is passed through a series of Directors of a company and receives unanimous approval may succeed due to the fact that the architect or surveyor has taken pains to discuss individual problems with each head of department just as another feasibility report might succeed where the surveyor or architect has taken the trouble of informing himself as to certain procedures, previously unknown, of a particular Trustee Company or Government Department. A mark of failure against a Feasibility Report is where substantial questions are referred back to the architect or surveyor for urgent clarification or supplementary information. By the words "success" or "failure" the writers do not mean that the scheme itself is necessarily invalid but that its justification or feasibility has been badly or only partially presented. Referal back under such circumstances is a mark of failure within the context of this Chapter.

The type of drawings to be submitted with a Feasibility Report are often a matter of some argument in larger firms. For smaller projects there is the freehand/sketch school of thought which others abhor, saying that if God gave set squares to architects and surveyors why should they not be used? Whatever the viewpoint taken, however, the sketches or drawings should be brought up to the same commensurate level as the report. This is to say that the drawings, while well presented, should not be too detailed but merely express the outline ideas of the designer at the feasibility stage. Large drawings with too much detail are positively dangerous as the client may fix on some pet feature at an early stage and be disappointed when it does not reappear in the final plans. Over elaboration in this sense can be counter-productive.

It is now necesary to turn to that fundamental aspect of building work referred to earlier in the previous chapter; the type of building contract to be selected. Advice in this connection must be given to the client in the Feasibility Report and it is essential to explore the options to the architect or surveyor according to the type of project.

The building industry has received a bad press lately. Not only from the national papers castigating building failures but for informed and authoritative professional sources. The building industry in the United Kingdom has been compared very unfavourably with the building industry in the United States where productivity has not only been said to be consistently higher but where buildings are produced more quickly even though there is a higher rate of fatalities on building sites. "In the United States responsibilities and risks for the various parts of the design and construction process are more clearly defined and the client has a major role deciding what sort of building he wants and how much he is going to pay. There is a strong incentive upon him from the nature of the contractural arrangements not to have any changes of mind. In the United Kingdom however, the building industry is slower, less productive and since responsibilities are far from clearly defined, compromises and extra costs are inevitable. While the system that has evolved in the United Kingdom can, by the nature of its flexibility, cope with the client who cannot make up his mind it tends to produce buildings that are far too costly." These comments come from a recent study carried out by the Building Research Establishment in this country.[1] The four main areas where the

---

(1) Comparative Studies of the Construction Industries in Great Britain and North America: A Review. BRE CP 5/81.

performance of the building industry in the UK shows up badly against that of the US are firstly that the contractual responsibilities for design, control of costs and construction are much simpler in that country leading to fewer coordination problems and clearer accountability and secondly that their documentation for a construction project at tender stage is simpler than that in current UK practice. Bills of Quantities are rarely used and US contractors take much more responsibility for detailed design. Thirdly, designers in the United States pay much more attention to the availability of materials and components and the sequence of trade following trade on the site. Lastly, the client in the United States is able to exercise more control over time and cost than is common in the UK. Late variations in design are much more actively discouraged than in this country.

In a report by the Bow Group, a chartered surveyor says that there is evidence to show that the UK Construction Industry is significantly slower than that of most other industralised nations.[2] In the United States, to quote from the report, contractors are brought in at the design stage because of the value of their experience not only in construction methods but in costing and the importance of time. The JCT Form of Contract is criticised and the system where Bills of Quantities are employed, while making it easy for the client to make alterations, leads to extra costs. The delay and disruption that occurs as the result of variations leads to an inflated final account for which the client may be unprepared. The vast bureaucratic system of regulations comes under attack as does the established form of scale fees, and the lack of standardisation of components and materials in the building industry. More "design and build" contracts are advocated to overcome the deficiencies in the present system.

The criticisms made in both papers are authoritative and cannot be ignored or dismissed. Concern has been expressed by project managers and others that the increase in costs under the established British system are more and more difficult to justify to the executives of commercial firms who have had experience of building operations in the United States or in other European countries. A good deal of criticism and, in some eminent legal circles, downright hostility, is directed towards the types of building contract in general use in this country. The main argument centres around the status of the quantity surveyor, whose inoffensive appearance belies the deep anguish and turmoils that he produces in others. The reasons for this are not hard to find.

The compilation of quantities as a means of assessing the value of building work dates back to mediaeval times and possibly long before.

(2) Environment in the Eighties, Bow Group 240 High Holborn, London, WC1.

It is tempting, indeed, to fancy that stone age man, in attempting to decide whether to build a dwelling for a neighbour against the proferred payment of, say an Ox, would list the labour and the materials such as the various tree trunks and armfuls of thatch that he would require in order to decide whether the project was worthwhile or not. An early Bill of Quantities in fact. The importance of quantities rose to a peak in the Victorian building boom but the quantity surveyor was then engaged to assist the contractor in compiling an estimate for submission to the employer. The notion that Bills of Quantities become central to a contract so that it is in fact the main document upon which amounts of payment depend, is relatively new. So is the status of the independent consultant quantity surveyor which stems, in part at any rate, from the efforts of the Quantity Surveying Division of the RICS which, with the undoubted success of the techniques evolved for measurement and the approval accorded to members for their balanced judgement has secured a well merited place in the building industry for its members. This represents a substantial scale of achievement. The Quantity Surveying Division of the RICS has no direct parallel either abroad or in the engineering industry. It is related purely to building work.

In any achievement however, there is always some alloy. It was always traditional at law that there were, broadly speaking, two main types of building contract. The first was the "lump sum" contract where the contractor was bound to a fixed price, or a "Schedule" contract where the work was started without any contract sum being specified, the contractor merely issuing a Schedule of Rates for labour and materials in the expectation of being reimbursed at agreed intervals according to the amount of work actually completed. It is true that, in the case of a Lump Sum Contract, Schedules of Rates could also be included but these had a subsidiary function only in that their inclusion was in order to assist in measuring and costing variations and they had no other direct bearing upon the contract sum. These two methods from the legal point of view were perfectly understandable and straightforward and either would be employed according to the circumstances involved. Bills of Quantities did not form part of the contract and that was that. Since 1939 however, the modern type of English building contract has become accepted where "quantities form part" in such a way that the Bill of Quantities itself becomes of central importance, going far beyond the mere measurement of variations or assisting in calculating interim payments. Under modern conditions the ultimate contract sum can be subject to final re-measurement, firstly in respect of work previously unknown where the figures guessed at are replaced with the amount of actual work carried out such as, for example, in the case of foundations or secondly where errors in taking-off measurements from plans are put right by substituting the correct figures. It is claimed in some circles that this right of re-measurement destroys the root of the contract where the employer is led to believe that the contractor has undertaken to carry out work for a specific sum.

Most of the criticism surrounds the "preliminaries" to the contract. It is said, and with reason, that the Standard Method of Measurement does not lay down firm guidelines to counteract the situation where the contractor can write-in sizeable and unspecified amounts into the Preliminaries Bill so as to ensure that he is able to claim a sizeable sum as the first interim payment to start him off on the right road financially speaking. The fact that such figures are also used as a lever to negotiate substantial sums on a claim due to delay, for which the Employer is totally unprepared, attracts bitter resentment which is not soothed by the quantity surveyor's rejoinder that the position is fair to both sides. Admittedly part of the resentment surrounding the quantity surveyor arises from the fact that, should he make mistakes in taking-off so that the contractor is then entitled to press a claim for extra payment the Employer is generally denied the opportunity of claiming reimbursement of this extra expense from his quantity surveyor on the grounds that he has, after all, suffered no actual loss. He has merely been led into believing that he can get something done for less than its true cost. The quantity surveyor's reply that over measurement can result in a credit being given to the Employer is usually received with a cynical smile. There is a strong feeling that the emergence of the quantity surveyor has been of greater benefit to the contractor than to the Employer. While this allegation is angrily denied by quantity surveyors, it must be admitted that the current provisions of the Standard Method of Measurement, in going a very long way to achieve uniformity in tendering procedures have, nevertheless, become highly complex. Critics say that the detailed way in which items of work are measured are so complicated that this in itself opens the door to variations since, even if the measurements themselves are correct, the manner in which they are translated into the Bills of Quantities may be wrong, thus leading to argument which, it is said, benefits the contractor rather than the employer. Whether this is true or not, it is certainly a fact that the provisions of the Standard Method of Measurement are now extremely complex and, while well established for traditional methods of construction such as stonework or bricklaying do not adapt so easily to modern pre-fabricated or similar forms of construction. Quantity surveyor's dispute this but the point is often made. The building industry in this connection is often compared unfavourably with the engineering industry in this country due to the fact that for engineering works there is no separate profession which has a vested interest in the preparation of Bills of Quantities and therefore the Standard Method of Measurement employed for engineering work is, it is said, simpler and more elastic.

The main criticism levelled against the Standard Method of Measurement is that it does not provide a clear-cut basis for re-measuring any ultimate disparities in quantities. It is said that there is no really clear scheme which defines the exact items of expenditure which are to be included in the Preliminaries and not in the later unit rates of construction. The practice of the contractor to allocate overheads and other items of expenditure in any manner that he wishes as between the Preliminaries on the one hand and the later Bills which contain the unit construction rates on the other muddies the pool so that subsequent claims for extra payment are difficult to resist. Furthermore it is said that the benefits claimed on behalf of Bills of Quantities that they reduce the cost of tendering and that they provide a precise and therefore fair method of comparing tenders and providing payments are watered down, so far as the Employer is concerned, by the fact that the larger contracting firms in the United Kingdom now have highly skilled departments of quantity surveyors, well used to looking after the interests of their firm in every particular.

It would be interesting for an onlooker to have full experience of observing how a successful contracting firm makes up a tender. It would seem that this is often done on two separate levels; the first by making a Prime Cost Estimate of the cost of the project on the one hand, while secondly re-measuring and pricing the detailed items in the Bill, firstly as a cross-check and secondly to detect any errors. It is alleged that, if any substantial variations are found, a type of "Gamesmanship" ensures whereby the contractor fixed his rates in such a manner that subsequent re-measurement will rebound to his benefit. It is said that, if such meticulous checking is carried out in the second place why, therefore, are Bills of Quantities prepared by a quantity surveyor necessary in the first place?

The purpose of relaying criticisms made against quantity surveyors is not to encourage sniggers from architects or surveyors who, heaven knows, have their own problems, but to acquaint them with the feelings which may be latent, even if not actually expressed, in the client. Quantity Surveyors are well able to look after themselves so far as their own profession is concerned and can, with every justification, point to the muddles that are made where they are employed too late or not at all. It is considered that in spite of undoubted faults and problems the relationship of the Employer, architect or surveyor, quantity surveyor and contractor will probably endure. Its particular strength, in spite of what is said to the contrary, can be seen when applied to the medium range of building contracts envisaged by this volume. If that were not the case this book would be a short one indeed. Comparisons with building contracts in the United States should be noted but are to a large extent misleading. Neither the employer nor the contractor here is generally in a position to take risks of the entrepreneural kind in connection with the type of building work envisaged by this book and the flexible nature of the British type of contract has a great deal to offer in this particular context and becomes a virtue rather than, as suggested earlier, a failing. Nevertheless, and it is necessary to return to this point with monotonous and no doubt dreary insistence, in all contracts accurate and painstaking preliminary work is absolutely vital. In this connection, engrossed, as he may well be, in the preparation of the sketch layouts and in making enquiries of various authorities, sub-contractors and suppliers, the architect or surveyor must remember to give early warning to the quantity surveyor who, it is hoped, will assist him in the Feasibility Study. Clients are often reluctant to pay fees for professional work in connection with a project that might prove abortive but many architects or surveyors have regretted that they did not taken an early opportunity of insisting that a quantity surveyor be instructed to offer guidance not only on the early feasibility of a scheme but also later on the costing as the design drawings are produced. Many an architect or surveyor has subsequently had cause to bless the dogmatic way in which the quantity surveyor has presented unpleasant aspects of financing to the client. The quantity surveyor is used to this. He fully expects the wails of despair which greet his announcement of the costs of unexpected or overlooked items and he is unmoved when his estimate of contingency sums is criticised as being far too large. Although, under recommended practice, the quantity surveyor, while being nominated or approved by the architect or surveyor is appointed and paid direct by the client, his emotional involvement with a particular scheme is mercifully rather less and it would tend to take the realistic view that a few tears now are worth a great deal later on. His main concern is with the purse strings and he will do all that he can to see that he does not land himself and others in a position of misery at a later stage. This he will do by erring on the pessimistic side on costs at the Feasibility stage.

271

The choice of the method of Contracting

There has, lately, been a good deal of restiveness at the "us and them" relationship; "the professionals" on the one hand and "contractors" on the other. There are many who say that this system is outmoded. It is said to be rather like the situation in the old Spanish Navy where there was a gulf between the gentleman who commanded the ship and the officers who were responsible for sailing her. The traditional relationship has in fact received most criticism at the top end of the scale, financially speaking, where contracts for vast factories or industrial schemes containing an enormous amount of mechanical equipment are concerned. Why, it is argued, should the larger contracting firms, who have all the expertise and experience necessary, not organise the project for the client from start to finish for a specified fee? This argument changes the traditional relationship so that the main contractor now acts directly for the client on a fee basis to either carry out or participate in the design, programme the work and see the job on the site through to completion, employing subcontractors selected by competition. While certain preliminaries such as site preparation and security are arranged by the main contractor and certain other expenses are paid at prime cost the main renumeration lies in the percentage fee negotiated with the client. Such an arrangement known as "management contracting" is largely an American import and has been used with success in a number of vast projects in this country.

Management contracting has emerged as an alternative to the existing system of running contracts and where, due to the enormous size of the projects concerned, unified and disciplined management is vital having regard to the costs involved and the obvious importance of time. It is claimed that the expertise of the management contractor is particularly effective in organising competitive sub-contract work in view of its detailed complexity on the one hand and the need for standardised components on the other and where, due to the sheer size of the project, vast savings in costs can be made.

The successful schemes turned out in this country by management contracting have, it is fair to say, employed a large number of the most able and experienced men in the building industry. It is perhaps not unfair to say that such men would ensure the success of any scheme. If management contracting however, is to grow one must look firstly furthermore down the scale and here a cloud of uncertainty begins to develop. Since the firms engaged in this work positively discourage selection on the basis of competition to find the lowest management fee saying, with some justice, that selection of the firm concerned should involve their experience in similar projects, the nature of their management structure and the promise shown by the way in which they propose to deal with the day to day running of the project the client is put into the immediate difficulty of attempting to make assessments of different proposals in an area where he may well be unfamiliar. Management contractors say that the financial benefits lie principally in the main contractors ability to secure good bargains with competing sub-contractors and suppliers and while this is admitted as being the substantial benefit of such schemes, the difficulty of assessing this capability will increase with the growing number of firms who offer such services. While the top contracting firms are able to offer the best conditions for professional, managerial and clerical staff other smaller firms cannot compete so efficiently in this direction and, since management contracting depends in the final analysis upon able and experienced men of complete integrity, as indeed do all building operations, the selection of the appropriate firm for a particular scheme is vital. The conflicts endemic in building work cannot be brushed under the carpet. Awkward decisions of price versus quality will still have to be made in relation to sub-contractors, for example, and savings in costs balanced against the quality of the building in the interests of the client. Should an inefficient firm be selected with many staff changes, leading to a resultant muddle, it might be difficult for the client to know where the blame lies and to pin down liability. There is even now a good natured argument amongst the top contracting firms as to whether the management contractor should remain strictly "professional" or whether he may carry out some of the building work and go so far as to compete with other tenderers. The risk, as seen, is that firms increasingly will venture into this business who will lack the professional expertise and experience by which, in the final analysis, the firm will be judged. It is fair to say that at present we have seen the best of management contracting in this country where large and complex schemes in excess of costs at the time of writing in the region of one and a half to two million pounds have been involved and where the employers have total control and sufficient flexibility to keep options open that will be to their ultimate benefit and are themselves fully understanding and knowledgeable in their own right.

It is claimed with some force by the advocates of management contracting that full control of the time to be taken by the project and consequent costs can be maintained by those best used to dealing with the day to day problems concerned while maximum competition is engendered between sub-contractors to the ultimate benefit of the employer. It would seem however, that the main benefit of this type of arrangement is the early involvement of the contractor with the interests of the client so that he is, in effect, in the position of an additional adviser at a very early stage of the design process. Much depends of course upon how the budget package is defined but at least the contractor is involved at an early stage in the specification needed for the contractual documentation and the methods by which costs and changes will be monitored. In a number of cases the design element proceeds to a point where cost plans are produced and approvals obtained. Bills of Quantities are then prepared for the section of the work that is already designed and construction then starts. It is claimed that the directly employed operatives get the project off to a good start, and this, combined with the sub-contracting arrangements coupled with the control of prices for preliminaries leads to great savings not only in labour and materials but also in time. The fact that at the design stage the project strategy is known and that planning, programming and estimating can proceed together in one operation using the resources of the construction technology available in the management contracting firm together with the advantages of its research and development department are other benefits claimed. Finally the system of "parcelling" or placing contracts with sub-contractors is said to provide total flexibility since decisions can be made at once in the light of what is needed at the same time that control of site conditions and finance are retained.

While the lofty heights of management contracting are beyond the scope of this volume, the advantages claimed for the system are extremely interesting as they do highlight specific problems with the traditional arrangement of architect or surveyor acting for the employer and preparing project documentation and contracts to be entered into by the employer and contractor. It is claimed that management contracting removes the traditional "adversary" relationship between architect or surveyor acting on behalf of the employer and the contractor but this comment in itself ignores the virtues of the traditional system where everyone has a role to play which is thoroughly understood by both the Courts and the public at large. The next point; that in the traditional system the contractor is introduced at too late a stage to make full use of his expertise in planning and programming is a very valid one. It serves to highlight one of the main weaknesses in the traditional system in that the professional architect or surveyor concerned soldiers on with all the preparations in virtual isolation. He is without the benefit of being able to confer with the contractor who will ultimately carry out the work and whose knowledge of the commercial side of building, ranging from the availability of labour and materials to costs generally and the time involved in certain types of operation would otherwise have been invaluable to him.

Once the suggestion is made that the professional in charge of the project is separated by the nature of his activities from the commercial world it is but a short step to allege also that he is therefore incapable of exercising sufficient control on the site. The impression that the professional architect or surveyor is a dreamy academic, far removed from the horny handed sons of toil who occupy the site hut, is a total myth but an enduring one at that. The cry is repeatedly made "why can we not have a businessman – someone used to the commercial world of finance and management – in short a project manager?" Those however, who shout most loudly for the appointment of a project manager are often those least able to define the precise qualifications that are needed. In any event, to lay all the blame for the less attractive features of building in the 1970's at the door of the professional architect or surveyor, while something of a popular sport, is ill-considered as previously discussed. If the site office is in a muddle from the point of view of organisation and the site itself an untidy mess, the growth of the sub-contract labour system has a good deal to answer for, as this makes supervision difficult and, in some extreme cases, virtually impossible. This fact was recognised by the Banwell Committee[3] who took the basic viewpoint that the increasing complexity of sub-contract arrangements were harmful to the industry. The Committee recommended that a return should be made to the old established system whereby the main contractor was responsible for engaging all types of labour and was also responsible for their actions. The contrary view is that the system of sub-contract labour is here to stay, that it is unrealistic not to recognise this fact, and that the contractual relationships between the parties should be made more flexible in order to take into account this undoubted trend. This has led to the suggestion that, since site supervision is extremely difficult under the present system, the architect's or surveyor's constructional responsibilities as set out in the RIBA Architect's Appointment and the RICS Conditions should be expanded to provide a bridge across the current contractual gulf and thus make available to the industry as a whole in a positive way, the best input of brain power and training presently available to it.[4] This in turn raises the question of who should be in control of the project. The suggestion that the architect

---

(3) The Planning and Management of Contracts for Building and Civil Engineering Work. (The Banwell Report.)
(4) Architects Journal 7 May 1980.

or surveyor may be a good designer but is lacking in skills relating to modern business administration is an old one and is often totally untrue but, with the growth of complex projects, not necessarily in terms of size but in the sophistication of the constructional process relating to substructure and services for example, the question of who should control the project is of considerable importance. The report from the National Economic Development Office "The Public Client and the Construction Industries" (The Wood Report) recommends that a single person should be nominated to provide a single interface between client, designer and contractor and it recommends that on large or complex projects the client should appoint a Project Manager to act on his behalf with the responsibility for the management and co-ordination of the relationship between client, design team and contractor. The report says that while a sound knowledge of design procedures, construction economics and method are needed, the background and training of a Project Manager are of less importance than his management expertise, decision making ability and leadership qualities. In the NEDO Report "The Professions in the Construction Industries" fresh approach to organisation brought about by more complex projects is recommended with greater integration between design and construction to speed project completion, growth in size and work load and the increasing demand for total packages. From these factors, says the report, the demand for the role of Project Management has grown. The NEDO Report "Construction for Industrial Recovery" suggests that one participant from the industry should take full responsibility for a project thus ensuring co-ordination between design, construction and the various participants. The desire for overall control is foremost in the three reports but the Wood Report went further, recommending that there are advantages in the co-ordination of the design team being regarded as a separate function.

The burning question of who should be in control of building or constructional projects is a difficult one. It is easy to say that a Project Manager should be selected according to his particular abilities having regard to the size and nature of the project but when the Wood Report says that, while a sound knowledge of design procedures, construction economics and method are needed, the background and training of a Project Manager are of less importance than his management expertise, decision making ability and leadership qualities, it is saying a good deal. It is saying in effect that the candidates not only have to have academic training in construction and business management but must also have the ability to control and criticise the designers while having the drive and ability of the true entrepreneur to get things done. This is indeed a lot to ask of one man. It is hardly surprising that "the function of Project Management suffers considerably from problems of definition and different terms are used with the same meaning in different parts of the industry. Regrettably, the converse is also true and other terms including that of 'Project Manager' itself, have various meanings."[5]

A report by a Research Group of the Central London Branch of the RICS on the subject of Project Management[6] commenced a carefully worded if lengthy definition as follows:

"The overall objective of Project Management is to establish the management and control of a project from inception to completion within the parameters of the client's brief . . ."

This wording has been largely followed by the Institute of Building in their paper on the subject, referred to earlier, in their brave attempt to narrow the welter of conflicting views as to understanding of what Project Management actually means. Their definition is as follows:

"The overall planning, control and co-ordination of a project from inception to completion aimed at meeting a client's requirements and ensuring completion on time, within cost and to required quality standards."

Obviously, the success or failure of Project Management depends absolutely on the qualities of the individual Project Manager concerned. The system has the advantage that the interests of his client are paramount to the Project Manager whose services, should he be one of the able and gifted men who undertake this work on a regular basis, are worth their weight in gold. As will be appreciated however, Project Management uses and relies on the traditional contract system and a poor manager unused to the intricacies of the system as it operates in the traditional form, could prove to be a disaster.

What are, arguably, seen as faults in the traditional system of running contracts have led to further pressures for "package deals". The Employer to whom time is vital may well be advised whether rightly or wrongfully that the existing contract procedures will not give him a guaranteed completion date on the one hand and, due to the late appearance of the contractor upon the scene will lead to antagonism and muddle. Such arguments form the reasons behind

(5) Chartered Surveyor April 1977 Pages 290–292.
(6) Project Management in Building published by the Institute of Building (Occasional Paper No. 20).

the appearance of the new Design and Build Contract published by the Joint Contracts Tribunal. Under this scheme the building surveyor or architect changes his responsibility from acting on behalf of the client to being responsible to the contractor alone for designing and inspecting the works during progress. Whether the disappearance of the architect or surveyor as agent for the Employer is desirable or not is a much debated point but critics of the present system where the quantity surveyor is central to the building team find it difficult to restrain their pleasure that he is restored to a more subordinate capacity in Design and Build arrangements.

Under the JCT Design and Build Contract Form it is envisaged that the contractor/developer's architect or surveyor will prepare drawings based on "the employer's requirements" with supporting specification to enable the contractor to submit his proposals which will become the basis of the contract. Payment can be requested either at the periodic intervals customary under the traditional methods or alternatively, provided for at specified stages when certain elements of the construction are completed, for example foundations, frame, main walls and roof coverings. There are three alternative clauses dealing with fluctuations but these cease to be paid for subsequent to the named completion date in order to ensure that the contractor will not profit by delay.

Those in favour of the new Design and Build Contract Form claim that it is as near the traditional basis of the Lump Sum Contract as is possible in this day and age, can be employed speedily and is geared towards an effective completion date.

Those less certain of the benefits of the new Design and Build Contract Form argue, on the other hand, that it is basically inflexible, geared to achieve a single aim at a given time and that everything else is subordinated to this. Bricks and mortar, it is said, come first and quality of design is the sacrificial offering. The main argument about this type of Contract however, is that the offers to the Employer are extremely expensive to prepare and that comparison of the bids received is extremely difficult even to those with experience in this field. It is odd that those who watch with glee the quantity surveyor reduced to a subordinate capacity are silent when these disadvantages are discussed.

We now come to the traditional arrangement where an architect or surveyor is in control of the project and employs one or other of the types of building contract discussed in Chapter 5. Of all these types the most traditional of all is, of course, the Lump Sum Contract, much criticised but enduring because of its undoubted virtues. The disadvantages have been stressed often enough; the long period of preparation that is necessary before construction commences, since, to be effective, a Lump Sum Contract depends upon accurate documentation, and the fact that the contractor appears late on the scene with, probably, no opportunity for collaboration or even consultation in the creation of the scheme. This leads, it is said, to his interest being largely a financial one without any real enthusiasm for the project. His main energies are thus, it is said, directed to uncovering inconsistencies or omissions in the contract documents so that these can be used for his own gain, the relationship between himself, the Employer and thus the architect or surveyor therefore being antagonistic from the day on which the contract is signed. Whether these allegations are true or not and it is conceded that they could well be true in certain cases, the picture presented is a warped one since the advantages of the traditional method, rarely stated, are undoubted. The first is that, whatever the critics say, a lump sum price and a binding completion date are of inestimable value as any architect or surveyor who has run into difficulties over other types of contract can testify. Moreover the contractual arrangements are flexible enough to permit changes which are often inevitable, certainly in the typical job envisaged by this book though not so inevitable in entirely new work provided all decisions are taken in advance. Finally, however, and most importantly, the relationship of the parties is clearly understood, all having a shared interest in completing the contract within the time determined and, as nearly as humanly possible, to the price agreed. A Lump Sum Contract should, in the view of the authors be the one generally adopted in connection with the more substantial private or public sector contracts preferably with competitive tenders unless there are obvious reasons for a contrary view to prevail. Criticisms of this type of contract often melt away in practice. Many builders are used to working frequently with a particular architect or surveyor and the supposedly "antagonistic" relationship may well be, in fact, a friendly if businesslike one. If the architect or surveyor feels that he is unable to control the contractor's requests for extras it means either that the preliminary work has not been carried out with meticulous thoroughness on the one hand or that his client has entered into the wrong type of contract on the other.

In many cases, of course, competitive tenders are not necessary. A negotiated tender with a particular contractor may be entered into in certain circumstances where, say, a builder who has just completed work satisfactorily under tender, is asked to carry out certain very similar work on the same site or nearby. There are, however, obvious problems in departing too far from the market place. The dangers of this method of procedure without tenders are highlighted by the rules of certain public authorities which require that a contractor, before selection, must have won some recent contract by open competition.

The question of when to suggest to the Employer that a quantity surveyor is employed in connection with Lump Sum Contracts depends upon the size, nature and possibly the complexity of the works. Certainly a quantity surveyor should be employed in all contracts over £100,000 in value at the time of writing in 1982. In larger schemes the presence of the quantity surveyor is of great comfort to the architect or surveyor. He not only secures a fair basis for the selection of the winning tender, for dealing with price variations and provides valuations for interim and final certificates but provides projected forecasts of expenditure at regular periods which are of enormous value to the Employer and his advisers. The question of cash flow is often treated as a secondary matter and it is little wonder that some schemes run into financial difficulty. The feeling that once the client has swallowed a fixed estimate of cost that is the end of the matter is a short sighted point of view to say the least. However, it is against the background of the Lump Sum Contract that financial arrangements can be most easily judged and made.

Cost Reimbursement Contracts

There will obviously be cases where some aspects of the work are not capable of accurate definition or where the nature and extent of the work might change once a start has been made, either by the direct orders of the Employer on the one hand, or unforseen circumstances found upon the site upon the other. The fact that a lady client has not finally decided on a kitchen layout in a contract for the full refurbishment of her Georgian house is no reason to abandon the concept of a Lump Sum Contract but where there is no effective way in which a lump sum contract can be formulated as there is insufficient information available, the idea of such a contract must, of course, be dropped in favour of another type of contract. The instance most often given is where the extent of work to eradicate dry rot in a listed building is unknown and there are likely to be many on the spot decisions to be made as the removal of panelling and other items of joinery discloses fresh horrors underneath. This may be so if that is basically the only work being carried out but dry rot in part of a house subject to a full refurbishment programme is quite a different matter and there is no reason why a Lump Sum Contract should not be employed in those circumstances.

The architect or surveyor can often persuade both himself and his client that, since it is not possible to estimate the cost of the work with any accuracy, a cost reimbursement contract should be entered into. This decision, often made as the easy way out, may be cursed at a later stage. If there is no need for haste and often there is not, a Lump Sum Contract should be abandoned only after a struggle to achieve one has been lost.

Cost Reimbursement Contracts, if inevitable, at least have the virtue of certainty in one sense in that the Employer actually pays for the labour costs involved in the contract plus materials and a fixed profit element. Such contracts, however, are vulnerable to the criticism that payment is due to the contractor for all the hours that an inefficient or slack employee works, even the time spent in putting right his own mistakes. It is doubtful if a fixed or fluctuating fee is sufficient in most cases to act as an incentive to overcome the problems of this type of contract while "Target" cost or "Value" cost contracts require a considerable degree of experience and foreknowledge to make them work effectively.

Schedule Contracts, in which the quantity surveyor prepares approximate quantities against which the contractor enters the appropriate rates or schedules prepared and priced by the quantity surveyor as a basis for a quotation by the contractor either by a single sum or by separate figures against each item, have been much in use for local authority work in recent years mainly on mainte- nance contracts and on large housing rehabilitation schemes and are coming into fashion for private sector residential and commercial work. The Property Services Agency of the Department of the Environment have used schedule contracts fairly widely in housing rehabilitation work using their own schedule of rates as a yardstick. The fact that work carried out is subject to re-measurement of work completed on the site as against that contemplated in a set of plans, for example, removes the allegation that the Employer is paying a man for putting right his own mistakes but the presence of the quantity surveyor does not help to any great degree in a forecast of cost. He has no crystal ball and can only introduce "spot" figures where the nature and extent of the work cannot be accurately specified.

The industrialist or the managing director of a chain of retail shops who suddenly has to face the need for a new warehouse or the Director of a large store who decides to refurbish a particular department during the six weeks when business is slackest may know exactly what he wants. If he is from Europe or America he is very likely to have a disciplined approach to construction, more so than his British counterpart, in that he will appreciate that varia- tions due to changes of mind once construction starts can be very costly. Such excellent candidates for Lump Sum Contracts may only be prevented from being entirely suitable by the factor of time. Time, that is, for the effective preparation of documents. It is therefore necessary, but in some cases difficult, to make clear to the British Employer that the mere existence of an approximate quotation with the safeguard of final re-measurement will not necessarily result in the final contract sum bearing any resemblance to that postulated. It will do so only if exceptional forbearance is brought to bear not to alter the scheme in any respect once it has commenced. Even if there are no major variations, increases in costs due to inflation or labour rates and increases in the cost of materials and specialist goods and equipment are bound to lead to some increase as are unforeseen extra items of work on the site as against those itemised in the contract documents. The same criticism can of course be made under a Lump Sum Contract but the variation in projected and final figures is not likely to occur in anything like the same degree due to the much greater time given to the work of preparation. Furthermore the client can be shielded against the shock of most increases from whatever course if the quantity surveyor is encouraged to provide forecast completion derived from the successful tender figure by the use of inflation factors and the provision of sensible sums by way of contingencies. It has been known for a measurement contract with approximate quantities in respect of the refurbishment of a City shop in London to result in a cost of double that planned.

When the value of the proposed work is likely to be below £50,000 at the time of writing in 1982 the architect or surveyor should consider whether the use of the JCT Form of Agreement for Minor Building Works should be preferred to the JCT Standard Form of Contract without Quantities. Since a recent survey showed that three quarters of all contracts placed by members of the RIBA in a particular year were below the figure of £50,000 the correct contract form to employ assumes considerable importance coupled with the fact that in the experience of most practitioners "the smaller the value of the contract the more likely it is to go wrong". In taking a brief further look at the JCT Agreement for Minor Building Works it is worth repeating the head note.

This Form of Agreement and Conditions is designed for use where minor building works are to be carried out for a lump sum and where an Architect/Supervising Officer has been appointed on behalf of the Employer. The form is not for use for works for which bills of quantities have been prepared or where the Employer wishes to nominate sub-contractors or suppliers, or where the duration is such that full labour and materials fluctuations provisions are required; nor for works of a complex nature or which involve complex services or require more than a short period of time for their execution.

282

It is obvious, since the head note gives more cause for alarm than encouragement, that the Minor Works Form of Agreement is contemplated for use in projects where few complications are envisaged, either technical or legal, and where variations are likely to be minimal. Projects for which this type of contract can be employed should be relatively straightforward and simple, involving few trades where the period for the works is not likely to run foul of the lack of provision for fluctuations. The rudimentary provisions for extension of time due to whatever reason and the lack of any provision to assist the contractor to recover loss and expense which he may incur during the course of the works will run the architect or surveyor into difficulties if complications occur or the time scale is too long. In particular however, the lack of any means for nomination of sub-contractors or suppliers can be a serious disadvantage. It goes without saying that specifications and drawings to say nothing of Schedules of Rates should be prepared with painstaking accuracy before the work commences. In particular, the preliminary clauses in the specification should be complete, thorough and drafted without ambiguity perhaps based on the clauses of the National Building Specification, Small Jobs Version or other authoritative examples.

The main problem with any form of building work is to attempt to foresee the problems that are likely to occur. This is difficult enough at the best of times and, with all the effort and will in the world, unexpected difficulties are bound to crop up. Where the Minor Works Form of Agreement is used however, it is more than ever necessary to devote thought to likely problems. The RIBA Practice Note; "Choosing a Contract for Jobs without Quantities" has this to say:

> "The complexity of the works should be assessed in operational and programme terms – what is the likelihood of delays, disruptions, claims for extensions of time? The Minor Works Form does not contain detailed provisions for these matters. The absence of full labour, materials and labour fluctuations provisions means that the Minor Works Form should not normally be used for contract periods in excess of twelve months."

The big difficulty, however, with the Minor Works Form, is that no provision is made for the nomination of sub-contractors and suppliers against PC sums. This presents certain problems which can never be overcome to an entirely satisfactory degree since the powers of the surveyor or architect to control the selection of specialist contractors are limited. The RIBA Practice Note lists the following possibilities:

1. By exercising the power of consent under clause 3.2 relating to

283

the employment of 'domestic' sub-contractors; a power which in fact is very limited in practice.

2. Naming (as distinct from nominating) "approved" sub-contractors and supplying a list. Under the Minor Works Form there is no lower limit on the number of firms to be listed. Details of the work will have to be finalised early enough for them to be appropriately described in the contract documents.

3. Making the specialist work the subject of a separate contract direct with the employer. Obviously, the specialist work must be capable of clear definition and almost be a separate activity as it is difficult to see how such a system could work in the case of a sub-contract for concrete for example.

4. Issuing instructions under clause 3.7 for the expenditure of a provisional sum requiring the acceptance of a tender from a particular sub-contractor or supplier. There is no specific provision in the Form for Prime Cost Sums, but that does not amount to a prohibition of their use. However, there is no definition of what is meant by provisional sums.

The RIBA Practice Note of August 1980 adds, quite rightly, under this alternative, that the absence of detailed provisions relating to nominated sub-contractors and suppliers means that provisional sums should be used for nominations only where there is known to be a very low probability of dispute between the main contractor and the nominee. Care should be taken to ensure that the tenderers, discounts and programme are agreed by the parties in advance.

It is universally agreed both by the Building Surveyors Division of the RICS and by the RIBA that the Standard Form of Building Contract without Quantities is too large for relatively minor works and makes too many provisions for possible complications so that, regretfully, it cannot be used on small jobs. The chief danger, however much this is denied in certain quarters, is that excessive documentation unrelated to the size of the contract can inflate tenders. It is also certainly true that excessive documentation involves, at least, a waste of every one's time. It is clear that in due course of time a form of contract will be produced that stands half way between the Minor Works Form on the one hand and the Standard Form without Quantities on the other but until this appears a decision will have to be made as to which form of contract is least subject to the disadvantages outlined. It should also be said that the type of work envisaged is the primary factor rather than its likely cost. The figure of £50,000 as a rough rule of thumb was given earlier below which the use of the Minor Works Form should be considered but it might be preferable to employ the Minor Works Form in the case of the re-painting contract for a small industrial estate where the value exceeds this sum and to employ the Standard form without Quantities where, for example, a small house is to be refurbished with the provision of new bathroom and kitchen facilities, central heating and up-to-date services but the total cost is below £50,000.

Again, the traditional documentation involving specification, plans, schedule of rates or quantities may prove rather inflexible for small or medium sized projects. A most interesting booklet "Tendering and Contract Procedures for Small and Medium Sized Projects" has been published by the Building Surveyors Division of the Royal Institution of Chartered Surveyors. In this booklet an alternative approach is recommended to overcome the disadvantages of the existing methods of procedure in smaller contracts and where a hybrid document is carefully worked out being basically a specification but which includes simplified quantities for certain indefinable items. The object of these quantities is to reduce ambiguity and uncertainty so that tenderers compete on the fairest basis and the maximum information is available at the onset of the building works. The decision as to whether quantities should be given for any particular item obviously depends upon the individual circumstances but the provision of certain quantities in the right hand margin of the specification, other items being left blank, is obviously useful as this avoids a duplicated effort of measurement by the various contractors tendering for the works and also provides a much fairer basis upon which competitive tenders can be based by removing any doubt about the amount of work to be included. Ingenious recommendations for the use of a Schedule of Rates in the form of a small Bill of Quantities or a Priced and Totalled Contingencies Bill to overcome the problem of large amounts of day work against contingency sums are included in this booklet as is a method to avoid the troublesome nomination of sub-contractors and suppliers by specifying work on a performance basis and giving a list of firms that would be acceptable. Suggestions relating to design liability and performance bonuses for early completion are also put forward and this interesting booklet should be procured by all who are engaged in building work.

It is useful perhaps for the architect or surveyor to put himself in the position of the contractor. The contractor is obviously in business and thinks firstly of the income to sustain his men and overheads. Beyond this however, according to his nature his view of speculation may vary widely. Some builders will like to take a punting chance in the hope of gaining an attractive profit while others will see any form of speculation as highly dangerous and will mark up prices heavily against such contingencies. Building is all about risk and this is why the architect or surveyor may find that his own view of future risk in building operations may differ widely from that of the contractor. It may accordingly, in the case of minor works for example, where the time to be taken by the contract is expected to be short, be an idea to ask the contractor for two prices; one where provision for fluctuations is provided and one where it is not. The resulting figures might be a complete surprise.

Finally, in conclusion to this part of the chapter, it should always be remembered that the mere size of the project does not necessarily prescribe the type of contract to be employed although, obviously, this is a matter to be taken into account. The type of work and whether this is capable of accurate definition or not, the basis of payment that is envisaged, the speed of commencement and the time scale for the completion of the project as a whole are equally important aspects. The element of time and the location of the project may not be matters which alter the nature of the contract documents since a contract for the repair of some shops in Sydenham may not be too dissimilar from one relating to a factory in Farnham. On the other hand the amount of specialised work and the type of control that the employer, guided by his architect or surveyor, wishes to exercise over the work may run to the very root of the contract arrangements.

It must be admitted that the published contract Forms certainly have their faults. It was said, not so long ago by a leading legal authority in building matters that an architect who advised his client to use the then current 1963 version of the JCT Contract Private Edition with Quantities, without amendment, was guilty of negligence.[7] It is certainly true, as we have seen, that the Forms have been and probably always will be subject to strong criticism and no doubt the JCT Contract Form 1980 will prove to be no exception to this rule. Having said this however, the temptation to amend printed contract Forms or adopt some hybrid form of contract that supposedly embodies all the virtues of the various established methods but has none of their faults should be resisted. A number of disasters have resulted from brave ideas of this sort. The current Standard Forms, however difficult to understand, are the products of the whole industry whether building or engineering and have been, notwithstanding all their faults, prepared by bodies representing each side of the industry. A particular printed contract

(7) Hudsons Building Law, 10th Edition, p. 146.

Form is not drawn up by one interested party so that it brings down upon its head the protective terms of the Unfair Contract Terms Act 1977 but is representative of all parties. Furthermore these representatives continually sit together and decide upon necessary amendments as a continuing process. The whole reason for the emergence of the JCT Contract Form 1980 was to deal with basic defects in the 1963 Edition relating to sub-contract work and fluctuations at completion to name two items only. At the time of writing, in 1982, many firms are hoarding JCT 1963 Contract Forms and, much to the disgust of the Joint Contracts Tribunal, the RIBA have printed a further 50,000 copies of the old Form. The reasons against using the old Forms will appear more and more obvious as time goes by.

In conclusion, Letters of Intent are, in the view of the authors to be regarded with extreme suspicion. It is tempting to provide a Letter of Intent saying that the provisions of such and such a printed contract Form in common use will be adopted mutually but when one thinks how much time is needed for careful selection and amendment of the contract Forms for any particular case, it will be easily understood that problems can arise if the various alternatives are not in fact accurately defined. Letters of Intent are nowadays commonly used in order, it is said, to avoid delays on the site. If a particular item is known to involve a very long time for delivery, a Letter of Intent can be drawn up to ensure that an early order is placed. Ordering of certain types of material by the Employer may be necessary even during the design stage before the main contractor is selected but difficulties nevertheless often follow.

In addition to discussing the types of building contract which are available and where possible providing a recommendation the architect or surveyor will, in his Feasibility Report, also discuss the question of appointing suitable consulting engineers and, where applicable, the appointment of nominated sub-contractors. In the first case a consulting engineer may have already been instructed by the client upon the recommendation of the architect or surveyor to advise on feasibility but, if not, the question of an appropriate appointment, where applicable, should be discussed in the Feasibility Report. It is highly desirable to raise the question of all such appointments at a very early stage in the proceedings since, while the architect or surveyor might feel that the appointment of an independent consulting engineer is an obvious step to take, since his advice will be impartial, nevertheless the client might have other ideas. It is an unhappy fact that a resentment to pay additional fees is extremely hard to overcome and arguments that a consultant can be cost effective since he will more than recoup the amount of his charges in savings made in the costs of the contract often fall upon deaf ears. The client will point to those steelwork firms that claim to save consultants costs by providing a package service which offers design as well as supply. The architect or surveyor, preferring the more flexible alternatives offered by an independent consultant will tell the client that commercial firms offering design capability are more likely to be costly in the end as the design services have inevitably to be paid for but the ground may be cut away from under his feet if the client should reply that he knows a friend in such a firm personally who assures him that the rates for pricing steelwork remain the same whether an outside consultant's design is used or whether calculations for the scheme are made by the firm's design department. Moreover, the client might add, he is reliably informed that the firm concerned is expert in its particular field and have more than adequate indemnity to face any problems that might occur. All that the architect or surveyor can do under such circumstances is to point out that the opportunity for testing the market by alternative quotations will be lost but, if the client is prepared to accept this, then so be it.

Nominations for sub-contractors are likely to be very rare at so early a stage as the Feasibility Report but circumstances may well arise where the expertise of a particular firm is considered to be of great advantage and where vital time may be saved by submitting a name for nomination at an early stage. Before taking such a step however, the architect or surveyor should be certain of his ground. If the firm concerned, however enterprising in their own sphere, have a bad record for co-operating with other firms, the situation might be fraught with risk as well known general contractors selected to tender for the contract at a subsequent stage may refuse to accept the nomination.

Finally, in the submission of the Feasibility Report, the question of fees, costs and expenses should be set out in detail. The architect or surveyor may well also separately take the opportunity of submitting his account in accordance with the agreed terms.

It is also desirable for the architect or surveyor to forward a further copy of his particular Conditions of Engagement with the Feasibility Report and state what fee he will charge. It is also necessary to stress the apportionment of fees between stages of the service. Until recently, both the RIBA and RICS made similar provision in this respect as follows:

Work Stage	Proportion of Fee	Cumulative Total
C. Upon completion of Inception, Feasibility Studies and Outline Proposals.	15%	15%
D. Upon completion of Scheme Design.	20%	35%
E.F.G. Upon completion of Detailed Design, Production Drawings, Specification and Bills of Quantities.	40%	75%
H. Upon completion of Tender action to completion	25%	100%

With the introduction of the new booklet published by the RIBA in 1982 entitled 'Architect's Appointment' dealing with architects' services, conditions of appointment and recommended fees and expenses the apportionment is amended as follows:

Work Stage	Proportion of Fee	Cumulative Total
C. Upon completion of Inception, Feasibility Studies and Outline Proposals.	15%	15%
D. Upon completion of Scheme Design.	20%	35%
E. Upon completion of Detail Design.	20%	55%
F.G. Upon completion of Production Information and Bills of Quantities.	20%	75%
H.J.K.L. Upon completion of Tender action, Project Planning, Operations on Site and Completion.	25%	100%

It can accordingly be seen that the former group comprising services E.F. and G. and amounting to 40% of the total has now been separated so as to provide two distinct sections.

Obviously, consultants' fees, value added tax and incidental expenses will be itemised as forecast in the future and attention to meticulous detail is amply repaid since costs will be much easier to claim in the future if they are correctly detailed at the outset of the matter. Nothing irritates a business client more than to find that an early list of projected costs is wildly wrong. It is excellent practice to combine a timetable for the works with the cost requirements for payment to

289

the contractor and all fees and expenses so that the client can see at a balance how the project will have to be financed from design to completion and therefore be able to make appropriate arrangements.

The period of waiting between the submission of the Feasibility Report and instructions to proceed with the scheme will vary widely. At one end of the scale the building surveyor or architect in private practice may only have to wait a matter of days before he receives instructions while, at the other end of the scale, the surveyor or architect in public service may expect to wait a considerable period of time for instructions to proceed with the scheme that is complicated both in the nature of the work involved and in the financing. It is hoped however, that whatever the circumstances, the surveyor or architect will try to give himself as much forward notice as possible as to whether he is likely to obtain instructions or not. This type of suggestion always receives a weary groan from hard pressed professionals who say, with some justice, that they have enough trouble trying to keep up with work actually before them without telephone calls that are likely to introduce tiresome questions over a scheme that might well not proceed. The client, of course, whether in the public or private sector, assumes that the surveyor or architect sits in his office sharpening his pencil, brushing up on his technical publications, and only interrupts his stream of instructions to his loyal staff to lay in sufficient drawing paper and blank contract and party wall forms in order to enjoy a brisk jog round the office building so that he will be instantly fit and ready for the call once it comes. The fact that this is hardly the case is beside the point as the client or clients, even when told that a period of notice will be needed, will make the unfortunate assumption, if matters do not proceed with due speed once instructions are given, that the surveyor or architect is not interested in his, or her, or their particular scheme.

It is accordingly, at this point, that the surveyor or architect has a last opportunity to look at his own organisation in order to determine whether or not he or she is able to deal with the work should it be offered. It is very easy to say that the same experienced professional architect or surveyor who prepared the Feasibility Study should then prepare the Contract Documents and supervise the scheme from drawing board to completion, but this may be impossible. For one thing, the man or woman concerned may no longer be with the organisation, having left in the hope of bettering his or her career or, on the other hand be simply too busy to take on further work which then has to be handed to someone else. This is just as true of the small private practice firm as the large Government Department. In the former case the erratic circumstances of today mean that the partners of small firms have to take on whatever comes their way so that it is difficult for them to drop everything and concentrate on a new commission. By the same token, Government Departments suffer from the same unreliability of work flow which, coupled with cuts in staff, make it very difficult to concentrate adequately on each scheme right from the outset. How often has one heard the cry "I had earmarked this scheme particularly for him and now he is leaving . . ." There is no sadder cry in any professional office.

Although it is difficult to achieve, the success of the scheme will ultimately depend to a large degree upon dedicated continuity of work from as small a group of people as is practicable having regard to the size of the project. This demands skill in organisation in any of the large central or local government offices or the big surveying and architectural firms in private practice. Sensible dispositions are, however, often blown off course and it is obvious that a project where a succession of people replace each other, each having had a go in turn, can result in a glorious muddle. Adequate organisation is, however, equally necessary in small practices. The larger organisations do at least have the benefit of being able to allocate men or women of the right grade to deal with every aspect of the contract and subsequent work but in the small office where, say, a single draughtsman struggles to cope with urgent demands for detailed drawings relating to several contracts and then leaves the firm in frustration, the results can be dire. So many different skills are needed to run a small architect's or surveyor's practice that the sudden absence of the capable lady that runs the outer office due to unexpected bereavement or the absence of the partner's hardworking and trusted secretary can cause real problems.

Part 3
Project Documentation

Part 3

Project Description

Chapter 7
Surveys and Drawings

CONTENTS

Introduction

THE initial investigation will have provided the client with all the information necessary to reach a decision on whether to commit further funds to the building project he has in mind. The practical physical constraints of the site and existing buildings will have been considered, the legal restraints exemplified in the Building Regulations, other national Acts and all local regulations will have been investigated and the financial implications given due weight. The client will have been told whether his proposals are feasible or not and, if they are, the total estimated order of cost for putting them into effect, together with the timing of the payments which will arise under the recommended form of contract.

To arrive at the total estimated order of cost, the architect or surveyor will need to have considered the type of contract appropriate to the proposals and whether it will be necessary to engage the services of specialist engineering consultants or whether nominated specialist contractors are to be used. If the type and size of the project warrants, the possibility of using a quantity surveyor will have been considered, statutory fees will have been included and the extra work and fees involved in survey work and negotiations with adjoining owners covered, including the fees of other professional advisers acting for neighbours. It will be clear therefore that the total estimated order of cost includes not just the cost of the proposed works and the architect or surveyor's fee as a percentage of that cost but also all other work and fees likely to be incurred as well. At this time the client will be informed that if he decides to proceed with the next stage comprising the preparation of all the information necessary to obtain a firm price for the physical works and all formal consents (approximately the stages E, F, G and H of both the RIBA Plan of Work for Basic Services in the Architects Appointment 1982 and the RICS Conditions of Engagement) the liability for professional fees will be heavy. It is at this stage that the bulk of the architect or surveyor's work, together with that of any other professional advisers, is done and appropriately the bulk of the fees become due. For his budgeting the client will, of course, need to know what these costs are likely to be and they will need to be separately identified within the total estimated order of expense. Armed with this information it is now up to the client to decide whether to proceed to the next stage and, by doing so, commit that separately identified sum of money to the project.

296

If, and when, the decision is taken to proceed, the architect or surveyor will already know the extent and nature of the project documentation which it will be necessary for him, and perhaps others, to prepare. Advice on this aspect will already have been given in the Feasibility Study. Naturally the scope of the documentation will vary just as widely as the different nature and size of projects. The documentation might range from a brief specification of works covering repairs required to a run down property, with perhaps a few replacements for defective items, to a large sheaf of drawings, bulky Bills of Quantities, lengthy and detailed consents obtained under various regulations, numerous agreements with drawings attached, made with neighbours, all relating to a major refurbishment and extension of a property or group of properties. Notwithstanding the possibility of these wide variations the basic purpose remains the same in that the documents will be used by:

(1) Contractors who, coupled with instructions to visit the premises in question, will be asked to prepare estimates either competitive or otherwise from the information supplied in the documents and the measurements which they will be required to take on site.

(2) Quantity surveyors who, again coupled with a visit to the site will be asked to prepare Bills of Quantities setting out the amount of materials and labour required to complete the project. The Bills will be for subsequent submission to contractors along with any drawings prepared by the architect or the surveyor in order, again, to obtain negotiated or competitive tenders.

(3) Local and perhaps Central Government Officials administering the Acts and Regulations controlling building operations and any system of grants that may be appropriate to the project in order to provide formal consents.

(4) Possibly other surveyors representing owners of superior interests in the property or neighbours likely to be affected by the works, again, in order to be able to provide the necessary approvals.

The above are typical of the range of people who will use the documents in the stage of the building process about to be undertaken. At the conclusion of this new stage about to begin, the client will be presented with the competitive tenders or a negotiated tender and the formal consents and he will then have the opportunity of deciding whether to proceed to have the works carried out or, if circumstances have changed, abandoning the project and settling the outstanding liabilities which, as previously mentioned, are likely to consist mainly of fees to professional advisers. On the other hand, although it is unlikely to be forgotten, it is worth stressing that the documentation will also need to be produced with the two final stages of the project well in mind, the carrying out of the actual work on site and the final approval and certification that the project is complete including settlement of the account. As will be seen, however, if the work on documentation at this stage is tackled in a thorough and proper manner there should be no, or at most few, difficulties, about the use of the same documents for subsequent stages.

Good project documentation will assist, in a considerable way, in overcoming some of the principal complaints from clients which arise in relation to building works. They can, of course, do nothing to overcome lack of knowledge or poor judgement on the part of the architect or surveyor. Good drawings of bad details for example are of no assistance in the long run. Indeed they are more than counter productive since a bad drawing might have caused queries to be raised and as a result made the architect or surveyor think again. Similarly, the clear unambiguous specification of poor materials and inferior standards of workmanship will bring no credit when the subsequent weakness of the materials becomes all too clear. On the other hand, good clear drawings of well thought out details will further the interests of the project coupled with clear precise specification details of appropriate materials and workmanship. Two of the most common complaints by clients relate, firstly, to final accounts being far in excess of the amounts they had been led to expect and, secondly, to that of undue delays arising during the course of the works. Both of these complaints can very often be attributed to poor documentation of even well thought out schemes if sufficient attention is not paid to completeness, precision and the solving of all problems at this stage, together with the proper recording in clear and unambiguous terms of all the decisions taken. Items missed out will be an obvious source of extra costs but no less so are changes of decision during the course of the works which, beside adding to costs, cause delays in completion.

It is generally thought that contractors derive benefit from poor documentation in that, more often than not, a greater profit can be obtained from extras than from a contract sum produced by a competitive tender. This is probably so in the short term but such a viewpoint overlooks the aspect of reputation and the satisfaction a contractor will derive from a job where what is required can be clearly ascertained right from the beginning. The actual work can then be carried out smoothly from start to finish and the account settled without long acrimonius arguments. In the main, contractors are far happier to be working on this basis and certainly the medium sized firms operating in a particular locality rely heavily on the fact that their name is likely to be mentioned in glowing terms if a few contracts in succession can be completed in this fashion. Unfortunately for such firms the contrary situation equally applies in that reputations suffer when budgets are substantially exceeded and delays occur, even though the reasons may be entirely beyond the control of the contractor. Work completed satisfactorily to a good standard, not only within the budget but to time, is the ideal to be achieved and, if attained, reflects on contractors to their benefit as well as on the architects or surveyors concerned. If the ideal is not always achieved and this shortcoming can be attributed to poor documentation it will be found that contractors very quickly learn to appreciate the true situation, often at the estimating stage. They will rapidly associate failures of this nature with a particular architect or surveyor who would not be flattered if he could hear the comments in a contractor's office on the receipt of his request for an estimate; "another smudgy (or 'pretty-pretty' as the case may be) set of drawings and an unreadable specification from old so and so. Say we are too busy at the moment to tender." That would be the response (although the adjectives used would probably be stronger) from the reputable contractor who values his good name over the years more than mere short term profit. The more unscrupulous contractor will look upon such documents with positive glee and the likelihood of very fat profits to be made at someone else's expense. Some architects or surveyors who find it difficult to persuade contractors to tender for the work which they have in hand could perhaps ponder on the reasons why this should be so. One reason might be little more than an inadequate presentation of their ideas on paper both graphically and textually.

In this part of the book the various aspects of Project Documentation will be considered. Ways and methods commonly adopted and which seem likely to produce unsatisfactory results when later stages of the project are put in hand will be criticised and methods more conducive to ultimate success highlighted.

The broad scope of possible requirements for documentation have already been mentioned. For the typical job envisaged by this book both drawings and a specification are required and form part of the contract. With neighbours also affected there will be Awards and special drawings for attachment. Obviously none of these documents are prepared in isolation and neither precedes the other. The development of both drawings and specification should be concurrent but it remains a practical consideration that where drawings are involved these tend to be somewhat in advance of the specification during the production process and, for this reason alone, drawings and related survey aspects form the subject of this Chapter. This, however, is not to overlook the fact that the specification is probably the most important of all the documents the architect or surveyor will produce and also the most demanding since its quality, more than anything else, makes or mars the project. The specification is also, of course, a document which can stand on its own and indeed is all that is required for some types of contract, unlike drawings which cannot stand alone, and invariably require to be accompanied by a specification.

While the documents required for the typical job envisaged in this book will form the thread of subject matter to be considered, the documentation for both smaller jobs and for larger jobs involving Bills of Quantities and numerous consultants will also be discussed.

Confirmation by the client of his approval to sketch plans and a Feasibility Study together with approximate estimates will be coupled with his authority to proceed with the next stage of obtaining formal approvals on a detailed scheme from the appropriate authorities and obtaining competitive tenders from contractors.

It is the architect or surveyor's responsibility to decide the best way to describe the works proposed in a clear and straightforward manner so that the ultimate aims are achieved with no misunderstandings arising from inadequate documentation. Unlike new work there are occasions when comparatively simple jobs of repair and maintenance can be described merely by words, a specification in effect, of a length appropriate to the task. More often, however, the work involves some element of alteration and it is usual in these circumstances for a combination of words and illustration to be used. Normally these are developed in conjunction so as to avoid burdening one with material more appropriate to the other. The specification and drawings are therefore the documents with which we are mainly concerned and are usually sufficient in themselves for the vast majority of the typical jobs envisaged by this book. A vast scheme for an enormous building or comparatively repetitive treatment to a range of smaller buildings brings the need for a Bill of Quantities in which case the specification may be amalgamated into the Bill and not be treated at all as a separate document. It remains however, the architect or surveyor's responsibility to supply the quantity surveyor with the necessary material for incorporation in the Bill. All three types of documents will be discussed in this and the following chapter.

If, as in most cases, drawings are to be involved then, at this stage, a decision needs to be taken as to whether the information on the existing building on which, to date, sketch designs and the Feasibility Study has been based is sufficiently complete and accurate to form the basis for detailed work. Although, as discussed in Chapter 3, a structural survey may have been a requisite before the preliminary report and approximate costs could be made it is unlikely that detailed plans would have been prepared especially for the purpose. More likely thumbnail sketches based on approximate measurements would have been used unless the architect or surveyor himself had previously dealt with the building or had been supplied by the client with drawings prepared by others. Even then, at the time of writing, many old plans, however well they may have been prepared, may have to be rejected because they will be in Imperial not Metric scales and therefore inappropriate to present day building work.

If thumbnail sketches only are now available then there is little doubt of what is required; a full measured survey and drawings. Similarly if the architect or surveyor had been using plans prepared by himself on a previous occasion he will know whether these will be sufficient for the purpose in most instances. In certain other cases there will be a little doubt perhaps on the suitability of existing plans. This might arise in a large organisation where the architect's or surveyor's knowledge may not be personal in regard to the provenance of old plans. If he is not personally sure then he should err on the side of safety and arrange for new plans to be prepared since the ultimate responsibility will be his if it be shown later that the old plans were inaccurate.

In other cases difficulties may arise which are imposed by others. Sometimes the client will foist on the architect or surveyor a set of plans in his possession and insist upon their use so as to save him the expense of a new survey. Here the dilemma of the architect or surveyor whether to accept the plans or not should be solved at the outset, since cases are known when, to please a client or more likely under pressure of events, a scheme is based on inaccurate drawings supplied by the client. The position of the architect or surveyor could, under such circumstances, be disastrous. His authority with the contractor will be undermined and, even if a solution is found, the situation will lead to giggles in the site hut while the errors in the drawings, particularly if major, will be shown to all and sundry. Nor can the architect or surveyor blame the client. That worthy may well have forgotten that he supplied the drawings in the first place and be genuinely taken aback when the architect or surveyor seeks to lay blame at his door. He will respond indignantly that the plans were only supplied to help the architect or surveyor and if he had known that accurate plans were so vital he would certainly have paid for them. He had thought, he will say, that the plans were accurate and had assumed, in any case, that the architect or surveyor would check them carefully. He is now amazed to hear that the architect or surveyor has not done so. Indeed something similar is the likely attitude of clients if the architect or surveyor demurs to the slightest extent at the suggestion that old drawings be used. As a result the architect or surveyor is then left with a heap of old drawings and the charge of checking them for accuracy.

Checking the accuracy of old drawings is easier said than done since shape as well as linear measurement is involved. Two paradoxes often arise in this connection; firstly, the neatest, smartest drawings are often the most inaccurate; secondly, sample checks always tend to be taken where measurements "happen" to be correct, seldom where they are wrong. This means that major errors are left to be discovered the hard way later. Sample checks are no real proof of accuracy at all and it is really necessary to take as many measurements to check a drawing as it is to carry out the survey in the first place. With this dilemma, the architect or surveyor presented with old plans may well wish to agree a fee with his client for verifying the plans' accuracy, probably on an hourly basis having explained the likely total order of cost. Of course if the plans are shown to be wrong then the client will be faced with a further fee for the survey and drawings which he would have had to pay had there been no drawings in existence in the first place. With this knowledge in advance of the work of checking being commenced, it is thought that most clients would see the sense and economy of discounting any old plans in existence and going straight to a new survey for the purpose of the job in hand and to obtain a new set of drawings. Some clients are obdurate, however, and have to learn the hard way. The cost of new drawings can only be marginally more to the client than proving an old set of plans to be accurate and could entail much less than the final cost of exposing errors in old plans and then still having to pay for new survey work.

Perhaps the basic need for a new survey and drawings of existing work should have seemed obvious from the very first but it remains quite astonishing how many schemes go wrong due to inadequacies in the basic drawings with all sorts of claims arising from the contractor which in most cases can be laid fair and squarely at the architect or surveyor's door. Often the stumbling block at first confirmation of instructions to proceed lies in the cost of a new survey since the temptation is very strong to make use of existing plans and make the false economy of saving the admittedly fairly high expense of such work to say nothing of the time to be saved. As we can see, the architect or surveyor's reputation is very early on put to the test of overcoming this hurdle and there can be very few cases where it is satisfactory to proceed without the basic essential of a new provenly accurate survey and set of drawings of existing conditions. With this in mind, as we have discussed in Chapter 2, it is not something that should be forgotten when the first mention of fees crop up in discussion with the client. There is no use in saying that the fees for the repairs and alterations are so much per cent of the cost of the work when, as soon as the Feasibility Study and approximate costs are accepted, the client is faced with approving a fee for a survey, the size of which he may not previously have suspected or have even known about. Both the Architects Appointment and the RICS Conditions of Engagement and plan of work make the separate nature of this fee clear but the client's attention needs to be drawn to it, certainly at an early stage, if not at the very outset of a job.

Of course, if the architect or surveyor already has some plans of existing work, it may well be that the client has already paid for these on a previous occasion of other work being carried out and all will be well. At times, however, there may be cases where the plans have been paid for by someone else, most likely a previous owner also a client of the architect or surveyor. While there is no doubt that the copyright of design work remains with the architect or surveyor it must not be forgotten that the ownership of such plans as these lies with the person who paid for them. The architect or surveyor has no right to make these freely available to another client supposing, for example, he has not parted with the negatives. The correct procedure here is for the two clients, or new and old client as the case may be, to be put in touch and once they have agreed, hopefully, on a suitable payment to be made from new client to old, work may proceed on the basis of re-use of the architect or surveyor's previously prepared plans.

The survey of existing buildings and the subsequent drawing up of the survey information requires knowledge, skill and a degree of experience. While it is useful training and fairly common practice to entrust such work to comparative youngsters in the office it is not wise to do so unless the architect or surveyor is absolutely sure of the persons reliability and degree of skill. Surveys left to the office junior are likely to be wrong, be very counter productive in the long run and may lead to endless exasperation, quite apart from the risk of an action of negligence against the architect or surveyor.

A little thought by the architect or surveyor before the survey is commenced as to what drawings will be required can save wasted time and effort. Invariably some areas require to be measured in greater detail than others. There is no point, for example, in measuring architraves which can barely be plotted at 1:100 all over the building if, in the vast majority of rooms, such detail remains undisturbed. On the other hand there is no point in merely taking basic measurements in rooms if details at 1:20 are to be drawn for an improved kitchen or bathroom. Every detail needs to be precisely measured in these circumstances not only in plan but usually also in elevation so that all four walls can be detailed.

The measuring up at this stage may also be combined with opening up the structure as much as is necessary or possible to draw accurate details of the construction of floors, partitions etc. The aim will be to obtain every item of information necessary to draw and specify the repairs and alterations leaving nothing to chance that can be anticipated or basing the proposals on assumptions that are unreasonably wide. For example, if partitions have to be re-built, it may be necessary to dig trial holes to ascertain the depth required for new foundations. Again, if a wall is to be raised, now is the time to ascertain the adequacy of the existing foundations and whether it will be necessary for them to be underpinned. The architect or surveyor should not forget that, as the scheme is being formulated, his thoughts will be turning to the effect on adjoining owners and whether party wall notices will be necessary two months in advance of the works commencing. Now will be the time for making arrangements for access to adjoining properties so that the thickness and details of party walls and chimney breasts, for example, can be obtained not only to complete the survey of the existing premises but also so that special drawings for attachment to the party wall Award or agreements can easily be prepared at the appropriate time if these are necessary. Also in the case of any extension work that may be proposed it will be necessary to obtain access to adjoining premises so that the outline of shape and height of buildings and the position of windows can be plotted in relation to the proposed work. This will enable the architect or surveyor to check whether there is any danger of an infringement to a neighbour's right to light as the drawing work proceeds.

It is a disturbing fact how often this aspect of party walls and possible infringement is overlooked at the time of the survey. A whole scheme is often prepared and tenders obtained on the basis of assumptions of party wall thicknesses and with no notification given to adjoining owners. This is probably because the stage of detailed scheme and tenders seems a logical one to deal with in isolation.

Nothing further, it is thought, need be done until the client accepts a tender and gives instructions that the works should proceed. After all, he might still decide the whole idea is too costly and that will be the end of the matter. The client wishes to go ahead but is then told about the need for notices and an agreement with adjoining owners (at an extra fee of course, not only to the client's surveyor but to the adjoining owner's surveyor as well in most cases) and there is a mad rush to comply with the statutory requirements in London and Bristol and the Law of Property Act 1925 elsewhere. If the contractor is ready to start work almost as soon as his tender is accepted (and it will readily be apparent that a contractor with perhaps some spare "capacity" and able to start almost at once will often be the one who puts in the keenest price) immediate delay will arise as a result. The client, it can be imagined, will not be pleased if the architect or surveyor has not taken steps well in advance to warn him of this need to approach adjoining owners and to obtain the necessary instructions to do so. It should be obvious, of course, that proposals to adjoining owners cannot be made in precise terms if proper details of the intervening features have not been obtained in advance. The time to obtain these details is at the survey stage so that the proposals can be developed with the detailed scheme and adjoining owners formally notified as soon as the scheme is fully prepared and at the same time as application is made to obtain other formal approvals e.g. town planning, Building Regulations or By-Law, lessor's consent.

Once the client's authority to approach adjoining owners has been obtained, a certain amount of tact may be necessary. A long standing owner may know his neighbours well, in which case a phone call or a chat over the garden fence will clear the way for the architect or surveyor to make an appointment for access. On the other hand a new owner may not have the remotest idea who his neighbours will be. In this case the architect or surveyor's initial approach may be vital to future relations. A courteous personal call by the architect or surveyor rather than by a junior member of staff is by far the best of all possible means and far preferable to a stiff formal letter to "The Owner". The call will usually elicit not only names and likely times of possible attendance for survey work but also the neighbours attitude to the possibility of works next door. After all he will probably be just as curious to know who his new neighbours are going to be and what they have in mind and may even be a little apprehensive. It is at times like these that the architect or surveyor can go a long way towards establishing a good relationship between neighbours by a courteous explanation in simple terms of what is in mind, how this will affect the neighbour and how his interests will be protected at all times. All that is required at this stage is access for a survey adjacent to the party wall but the architect or surveyor will wish to follow any initial visit with a polite confirming letter, again signed personally, suggesting suitable times for his staff to call and inviting personal contact with the architect or surveyor either by phone or letter should any difficulties arise or should there be any doubts in the neighbour's mind. If the architect or surveyor bungles his approach and antagonises the neighbours, the price may well be delay at a later stage for his client, since there is no right of access to adjoining premises for survey purposes. If a scheme is based on assumptions the opportunity to verify those assumptions will not arise until much later after the service of notices, when delaying tactics may well be adopted by neighbours and their surveyors acting entirely within their rights but angling for a "sweetener" to help them along the way to giving an early answer. Clients who have to make such payments do not like having a pistol held against their heads in this way and the architect or surveyor could find himself between the devil and the deep blue sea.

It is convenient to mention here briefly what is required in the survey of party walls. In plan, details are required of the wall itself from both sides, at each floor level, particularly of all chimney breasts and any changes in thickness. The thickness and construction of all features abutting the party wall are also required. It is best to extend the detail adjacent to the party wall for a distance of about 1.5m on the adjoining owner's side since it may be necessary to assess the buttressing capabilities of such features. Some complicated measuring may be necessary around the ends of the wall along front and rear elevations and through windows to establish the true thickness of the wall. In older construction, surprising dimensions will sometimes be found bearing little seeming relation to brick thicknesses. This may be due to the presence of two external walls with a small gap between, the earlier wall perhaps being out of plumb when the second wall was built. Alternatively, if only one common wall exists, the construction may well be of brick bats with substantial making out of uneven areas by the use of many layers of lime mortar. Plan details should extend through any loft space and include a plan at roof level. Sufficient measurements should be taken to enable an elevation of the wall to be drawn from both sides and, of course, for drawings in section, care should be taken to relate floor levels on both sides as well as noting whether floors on the neighbours side actually derive support from the dividing wall.

On arrival at the site to carry out the survey of the existing building it is as well to follow the old adage, useful for all surveys, that "time spent on reconnaissance is seldom wasted". A walk around the property with a view to getting a general feel of the place and planning the programme of work will save time in the long run particularly if the property is fairly large. It is not within the scope of this book to describe in detail how to carry out surveys of buildings. This should be part of the skills deployed by every surveyor and architect. Notwithstanding, the stressing of a few points which seem to pose problems fairly frequently will not come amiss:

(a) It is important to sketch approximately to scale and pacing is quite adequate for the approximate sizes of rooms on the sketch paid. Divide large floors up into sections, preferably structural units, using major partitions as the boundaries, but not forgetting to complete detail thoroughly at the edge of a sheet so that none is missed. In this connection the use of faintly printed squared paper provides a useful discipline to maintain the approximate scale. A large clip-board and suitable paper are essential. A small lined pad for example is useless.

(b) Accuracy is vital. Running dimensions are preferable to individual measurements as small amounts of rounding off soon build up to quite a few centimetres of error. Both sides of any projection should be measured; one should not assume that both sides are the same as changes in wall thickness can be missed entirely if this is done. Diagonal ties must always be taken in all rooms. It is impossible to tell whether a building has been built with corners forming true 90° angles just by looking at it and it should be clear that just because two sides, or even four sides, of a room have the same overall measurement it does not mean that the walls are at right angles to each other. A glance at the large scale Ordnance Survey sheets will show that many buildings in City centres were built far from square on cramped sites. Strange as it may seem, however, it is not only those built in the older towns which are out of square. Many that may have been intended to be built square on comparatively open sites turn out to have odd angles between walls possibly because of the setting out errors by the original builder.

(c) Obviously the degree of detail to be taken for subsequent showing on the plans will depend on the scope of the work but it may well be necessary to measure the position of every floor joist and, if a roof conversion is involved, every roof timber.

(d) Consistency is important. Plans should always be thought of as horizontal sections through the building, which is indeed what they are. As it is sensible to show the position of windows in a room, it follows that this section is usually taken more than just a few centimetres above floor level. Provided one is consistent it does not really matter whether the section is taken 1.0 metre or 1.5 metres above floor level but the usual convention is 1.0 metre. It follows that when a room is being measured in an attic which has sloping walls, the same convention should be followed and other salient features such as the skirting line and the junction of the sloping walls with the ceiling can be shown by a dotted or broken line. Plans at this level can with considerable advantage be extended to show the line of any parapet wall and perhaps parapet gutter.

(e) In the case of sections it is necessary to take special care on measuring the thickness of floors. It is usual to measure floor thicknesses overall in staircase wells but it may on accasions, be necessary to take up floorboards. It is also important to remember that floor thicknesses can vary in different parts of a large building and it must not be assumed they are the same throughout. Sometimes there are voids between floors, perhaps constructed to take a water cistern. It is useful to draw a section in each room with details of the heights and projections of skirtings, dado rails, picture rails and cornices. Heights in rooms with elaborate cornices can be measured along the edge of an opened door. Although it is preferable, where pitched roofs are found, to take sufficient measurements in the roof space to draw the roof without measuring angles, a check is possible by using the arms of a folding rule to take the angle between rafters and ceiling joists and to transfer this on to a piece of paper. Alternatively a carpenter's rule with angles marked on the centre joint can be used.

(f) With elevations, it is necessary to secure a datum line, usually a pronounced brick course, for example at the top of a plinth, and measure up from that line. If the property is built on a steep slope it may be better to take the line of a band course or other feature, say at first floor level, and measure up and down from that. If it is necessary to use different datum lines on different elevations, it is important to relate one to another. If counting brick courses to measure heights it is important not to forget to check in a few places the height of, say, four courses and use the average as the measure; it is also important not to make assumptions as to heights. Mention might also be made of new developments which can be used for the preparation of elevational drawings. The method which has been in use for some years of preparing maps from aerial photographs has now been used successfully by a number of specialist survey firms to produce accurate detailed elevations to scales as large as 1:50. The process works on the principle of stereoscopic images in that photographs of the same detail are taken from different points and the images projected, with various corrections applied, on to a drawing table. The process has proved particularly valuable as a cheaper method of producing elevational drawings in congested City areas than ordinary measuring, even from a mechanical gantry, and also for work on historical buildings where it is obviously cheaper to photograph than to measure every individual stone.

(g) Whether it is necessary to carry out a survey of the site upon which the building stands will depend very much on circumstances. The total renewal of the underground drainage system might be one example, and it is usually a necessity when an extension is to be constructed. Often, however, an extract from the Ordnance Sheet is suitable for site identification purposes, although in this case the architect or surveyor should not forget to give suitable copyright acknowledgement and pay the appropriate fee. At other times an enlarged extract from the ordnance sheet say to 1:500 scale with added detail might suffice in lieu of a survey, provided this added detail is properly tied in. Proper tying also applies of course to external detail at ground level added to the ground floor plan in most instances, for example drainage inspection chambers.

It is essential to plot survey notes as soon as possible after taking the measurements while they are still clear in the mind. It is also preferable for the person who did the measuring to do the plotting. In theory it should, of course, be possible for somebody quite strange to the job weeks later to pick up the notes and plot everything satisfactorily, but however well the building has been sketched and however well taken and clearly shown the measurements may be, it is still easier and invariably quicker for them to be plotted as soon as possible. In order to achieve this aim it is a good idea to divide the work into alternative sessions of measuring and plotting rather than to do all the measuring for say plans, sections and elevations in one attempt. By this means should, by chance, any measurements have been forgotten in the early stages they can be picked up without of necessity having to make a special trip to the site since there will still be other measuring to do as well as the taking of those notes that have been forgotten.

At the conclusion of this section on survey measuring it is relevant to point out that the aim is to produce a drawing that cannot be proved wrong; it cannot be proved wrong because it has been prepared on the basis that sufficient measurements have been taken not only to plot irregular or out of square figures but also to "prove" that those figures are of the correct shape as drawn and cannot be otherwise. That is the whole art of land surveying and surveying for measured drawings of buildings yet it is extraordinary how often the principle is forgotten. So many surveys are plottable but not provable. Taking too many measurements is far preferable than taking too few but a complexity of haphazard measurements is not the answer since these will, at best, confuse and, at worst, be counter productive. The practice of taking measurements and showing them clearly on the plan, whether along walls, or as ties, with the commencing and ending obvious to the draughtsman, and all wall thicknesses and angles that can confuse clearly noted, is an art only acquired with practice.

The conclusion of the survey brings us to the point of plotting the measurements to produce the drawings of the building as it exists before works are begun. These drawings of the building as existing will form the basis of the working drawings for the scheme and accordingly it is appropriate at this stage to consider some of the physical aspects and desirable attributes in the production of the working drawings in architect's and surveyor's offices. It should be self evident that such drawings should:

(a) provide an accurate record of the proposals.
(b) show the proposals in a clear and easily understood manner.
(c) show everything in sufficient detail for the purpose of completing every part of the contract without undue repetition.
(d) provide information as it is required and so that it can easily be found.
(e) be economical to produce.

It should also be apparent that the prime purpose is communication to the user be he client, regulating authority, consultant, quantity surveyor, contractor, sub-contractors, foreman, clerk of works and building operatives. If the drawing is not clear to this multitude of people, all with varying degrees of knowledge and ability in the field of building then it will have totally failed in its objective. Yet how often are one or more of the following seen in day to day work:

(a) Drawings so cramped on a sheet that it is impossible to distinguish where one begins and another ends.
(b) Drawings with lettering so stylised as to be unreadable.
(c) Drawings with conflicting information as between each other within the same set.

(d) Drawings that are impressive at first sight but do not show any of the crucial details.

(e) Drawings which somehow become smudgy at an important point.

(f) Drawings consisting of a mass of uncontrasted lines where it is impossible to distinguish the purpose of one line as against another.

(g) Drawings where the background is so dark that it is difficult to distinguish anything.

When presented with examples such as those described above the recipient could be forgiven for considering that technique for technique's sake has become paramount, the draughtsman having taken an ego trip and totally forgotten the purpose of communication or even perhaps that economy has been taken to extremes. It is not often that these two traits are combined but if they are, the results can be dire and it is not surprising that mistakes due to a misunderstanding of the intentions are all too common. The reactions of the recipients to such drawings deserve a thought and they can be forgiven for thinking that if clarity cannot be found in the work of the architect or surveyor how then can expertise and precision be expected? Clarity to provide ease of communication must obviously be paramount yet clarity can easily be influenced by a number of factors such as:

(1) The materials used in the production of drawings.

(2) The techniques of or adopted by the draughtsman.

(3) The organisation within each drawing and within a series of drawings.

(4) The processes used to reproduce the drawings.

One of the foremost influences on the way working drawings are produced relates to the need to supply so many copies to all sorts of different people. To satisfy the insatiable demand for copies the architect or surveyor needs to have available a quick, simple and cheap system of copying either within his own organisation or readily available from a local supplier. The reproduction of the drawings is often thought of as the last stage in the process of producing working drawings but in many ways it is the over-riding influence on the way they are produced from the very beginning.

At one time it was necessary to copy all drawings by hand either by pricking through salient points from one opaque sheet to another or later with the use of tracing paper. It was not until the 1840's that a process became available to reproduce a copy direct by contact from a translucent original. The ferroprussiate process produced copies on opaque paper or cloth with white lines on a blue background to form the "blueprint", which is now rarely seen. The process produced copies by bringing the original and the prepared paper or cloth into contact and exposing both to an arc light followed by developing the prepared paper in water. An adaption of the process to overcome some of the distortion problems inherent in the system used a ferroprussiate paper to deposit an image on a gelatine bed which could be inked and from which good quality prints could be rolled off on to a good quality paper, for example a heavy cartridge paper suitable for hand colouring. This true-to-scale process had the advantage that deletions were possible during the printing process and that different coloured lines on the same drawing could be employed using separate original overlays. The process is now obsolete being fairly expensive and suitable mainly for presentation work but in the later years of the 19th century and the early part of the 20th century it was still much cheaper than reproduction by photographic processes which, besides being costly, were also cumbersome.

While the cheap blueprint was undoubtedly better than hand copying it was not ideal for clarity and a need for a cheap copying process to produce a print with a black line on a white background other than the costly true-to-scale process remained. This came about in the 1920's with the development of the Diazo process. This produces the "Dyeline" prints (or "whiteprints" as they are known in the USA in contrast to "blueprints") not yet superseded to this day for the reproduction of working drawings. Good prints can be produced on paper, cloth or film, with dense black or other colour lines on a white or clear background provided, as with the ferro-prussiate process, the lines on the original are light fast. If lines are not dense then it is possible to have a darkish grey line on a light grey background but obviously clarity suffers as a result and it is possible to incur criticism on this score, as already mentioned. However, with the Diazo process it is still necessary for the original drawing to be on translucent material since it is placed in contact with the print material and both are exposed to intense light before the print paper or other material is developed either with liquid ammonia, ammonia vapour or heat. Over a period of time the coating on the print material discolours on exposure to light but this is not too damaging a factor in the context of working drawings since their required life is really only the duration of the works plus perhaps the defects liability period and some time to settle the account. For record purposes, of course, the architect or surveyor retains the "negative" as it is popularly known, although this should more properly be called the "master positive". Distortion, as with the blueprint produced by the ferroprussiate process, is inherent in the system, but despite this the Diazo process is the cheapest, quickest and most satisfactory way of reproducing working drawings of any size at the present time. The distortion factor however, in both these processes is no doubt the origin of the admonition often seen "Do not scale from this Drawing" rather than any admission by the architect or surveyor that his work might be wrong! In relation to work on existing buildings however, there are other equally cogent reasons for this wording to appear on every drawing, an aspect which will be discussed later.

Other processes are, of course, available such as contact copying and optical copying by photographic means but the former is slower and much more expensive than the Diazo process while the latter is even more expensive for prints at the size of the original drawing. Where copying by photographic means comes into its own is where reductions or enlargements of the original are required or it is decided to microfilm originals for storage and record purposes. Contact copying can however, help out on those occasions where it is necessary to copy an opaque original or a double sided original and particularly where there is poor contrast on the original document.

Mention must, of course, be made of xerography which may yet one day change the way of preparing working drawings. Although electrostatic copiers capable of coping with A1 size sheets have been demonstrated they are by no means in general use and do not yet appear likely to supersede the Diazo process for reproducing working drawings because of the expense of the equipment. So far the practical economic limit seems to be A3 size but, of course, should there be a breakthrough in design or manufacturing processes, or some other method of copying be evolved and become all pervading, then there may well be sound economic reasons for changing drawing methods and materials to suit. Notwithstanding its failure to take over in the drawings field xerography has swept the board on the clerical side and schedules at A4 and A3 size and small drawings at these sizes can all quickly and economically be reproduced by this method which copes with either opaque or translucent originals.

We have therefore at the present time to prepare the larger drawings on a translucent material otherwise copying will be slow, expensive and uneconomic. Of the three translucent materials available tracing cloth because of its expense, its dimensional instability and the need for preparation before use has almost entirely fallen out of favour. The choice now lies between tracing paper and film and while there are advantages and disadvantages with each the disadvantages of film are gradually being overcome so that it seems likely that this will eventually entirely supersede tracing paper.

Natural tracing paper (as distinct from the expensive prepared tracing paper made from pure cotton rags and subsequently treated with oil, resin or wax) is rendered translucent in manufacture and comes in a range of weights from 63 to 112 grammes per square metre and in smooth and matt finishes. The thinner paper is really too flimsy while the thickest is something of an unnecessary luxury. Best for general drawing office use, if this is the preferred medium, is the 90 gramme material with a smooth surface since the matt tends to wear down pencil points too quickly and to cause undue smudging. The main advantages of tracing paper over drafting film are its cheapness, its universal availability, the fact that no special pencils, pens or ink are necessary and also that ink dries more rapidly on tracing paper than on film since there is a certain amount of penetration. Against these advantages are the instability if the humidity level changes unduly and the difficulty of erasure when ink is used. This latter point can be alleviated by the use of the new vinyl erasures containing tiny bubbles of a chemical solvent which dissolves the ink without damaging the surface.

Earlier drafting films of acetate were prepared by roughening the surface either mechanically or by chemical means but this type has largely been superseded by films coated with a lacquer or similar material. For drafting purposes this can be applied on one side only the reverse side being left smooth and glossy but able to accept printing inks should pre-printing be required. Cellulose acetate film had the disadvantage of a low melting point and could not be used with forms of reproduction equipment producing a high temperature. Although being extremely translucent and providing a high degree of contrast it also tended to tear easily if the edge was nicked and to become brittle with age. The polyester based materials now in use have overcome these problems and are stable, durable and suitable for long term storage. The main advantages of drafting film over tracing paper are its dimensional stability, its durability, easy erasure of pencil and ink work, provided the right materials have been used, and the possibility of producing fine prints utilising the high contrast available between ink or pencil and its background. To get the best out of the material it is necessary to use the special pencil leads (waterproof or non-waterproof plastic), pens with hardened tips which will withstand wear, the correct inks both etching and non-etching and the special plastic erasers. Against these advantages are the additional cost of the film and special materials over tracing paper and ordinary pencils, pens and inks, the propensity for static electrical charges to build up, causing dust to adhere and printing problems, and the length of time ink takes to dry on film since film does not absorb ink. Some films are now treated to overcome the problems of static electrical build up.

To some extent it is still a matter of personal preference whether to use tracing paper or film. However, developments by the manufacturers of drawing office equipment, another great influence on practice nowadays, tend increasingly along the lines of overcoming the difficulties with film. Tracing paper has been with us for many years and such scope as there has been for improvement in both the paper and the materials used on it has long been exhausted. Film has the two pronounced advantages over tracing paper in its dimensional stability and durability but on the other hand ink takes longer to dry out on it and it is a good bit more expensive. To overcome this problem the drawing office equipment suppliers have sought economies in methods of producing drawings so as to bring the cost of using film overall within the same range as that of using paper. For example some pencils, although not so far to an extent sufficiently sharp for plotting, no longer need sharpening; micro leads in a special clutch holder can provide pencil points sufficiently sharp for this purpose but tubular leads can provide lines of uniform thickness according to size for general drawing. This is fine for tracing paper, if of polymer, but pencil on tracing paper does not really produce prints of the best quality; these are often smudgy and not ideally contrasted. Polymer leads are even more prone to smudging on film but the development of plastic leads which can be either just smearproof or both smearproof and waterproof has overcome this problem on film. The normal practice of plotting a measured survey on opaque paper with a graphite pencil and then copying in ink on tracing paper or film with the disadvantage, in the first case, of possible distortion and in the second case of the bore of waiting for the ink to dry, can be overcome by a direct plot on film with waterproof plastic pencil in grades appropriate for the work as a finished job. This cuts out the entire process of tracing where, however carefully done, slight errors are introduced and man hours unnecessarily spent. If on the other hand personal preferences insist on the use of tracing paper it is possible to obtain immediately a Diazo print on film by dry processes which would overcome all but the initial distortions arising in the tracing paper and this degree of accuracy is generally considered acceptable in the field of working drawings related to buildings.

Whatever material is used it is worthwhile to have paper or film cut to size and pre-printed with margin, title panel and folding guidelines. The bore of cutting from a roll of paper or film and drawing common features each time for a new drawing is thus avoided and time saved. To avoid using another sheet of paper a draughtsman is often tempted to clutter the sheet he is working on at the time and pre-printing helps to overcome this problem. Although there is no reason why all the "A" series of international sheet sizes should not be pre-printed, it is probably better to limit the number of different sizes to those which suit the architect or surveyor's working preferences best. It is irritating for a set of drawings to comprise a whole range of different sizes and therefore better that the temptation to compile such a set does not exist. It is handy to have small sheets of the same size as the larger sheets of correspondence paper so that A4 is a suitable size for the smallest sheet but beyond this it is probably best to limit the range to another two sizes at most. The A1 size equivalent to the drawings prepared in former days on double elephant sized boards is really essential leaving the choice for the third size to either A3 or A2 with the latter being the strongest contender for preference. The A2 size is equivalent to the old Imperial sheet so that with the A4 sheet of about foolscap size completing the trio, quite a broad range of sizes is provided. It is hardly every likely that the A0 sheet size will be required and if so, the occasions would only be for the very largest of jobs or surveys.

Pre-printing should certainly incorporate a margin which is where most of the wear caused by handling takes place and which also allows for the frequent smaller mis-alignment errors in printing to be of no consequence. Marks to guide folding should also be incorporated. It is also sensible to fold plans down to A4 size overall but to leave within that overall size a margin on the left hand side. Posting of plans is thus facilitated but more importantly drawings can be filed along with the letters which accompanied them but also so that they can still be unfolded and be completely visible without dismembering the file. When drawings are subject to much revision it can become very confusing, however well each revision is described on the title panel, to readily identify what was or was not on a particular drawing enclosed with a letter. Attaching the plan to the filed copy of the letter obviates this difficulty and is far less likely to result in loss of the particular drawing than would be the case should the drawing be tucked away in the pocket of the file in a separate folder. In the case of one drawing or group of drawings being sent out identically with a number of different letters then an annotation on the drawing included with a copy of the first letter in time should suffice.

Title panels on drawings tend to follow the preferences of individual architects and surveyors but there are obviously certain basic features which should be common to all. Among these should be:

(1) The architect's or surveyor's name, address and telephone number.
(2) Address of the property.
(3) Title of the project (e.g. alterations, improvements, conversion etc.).
(4) Title of the drawing (in specific rather than general terms).
(5) Drawing number with date (possibly a basic number with a suffix if one of a series).
(6) Revision number with date.
(7) Draughtsman's name or initials.
(8) Checker's name or initials.
(9) Scale, or scales if more than one.

Other possible items in the title panel depending on preference and size of practice may include client's name, project number, partner in charge or project architect or surveyor. Notwithstanding the inclusion of all these items the title panel, which should always be placed at the bottom right hand corner of the drawing so that it is always totally visible when the drawing is folded, should be extended on the larger drawings, either horizontally or vertically but preferably vertically, to include panels for a key to symbols, any special notes and the details of revisions usually taken in that order reading upwards. On the larger sheets and with the more complicated jobs this usually takes up the whole of the first vertical fold, i.e. a little less than A4 width times the total depth or height of the drawing. Clearly for the smaller size of the A4 sheet the panel needs sensible adaption otherwise there will be no room for the drawing!

We have looked at two of the items on the list which have a major influence on the clarity and suitability of drawings for their prime purpose of communication, namely the reproduction processes and the materials used by the draughtsman both to draw on and with which to draw. Another important influence is the draughtsman's own technique.

A draughtsman's basic technique and style tends to be formed when young during his training under the influence of his teachers, the practice current at the time and from model examples in text books. Depending on his adaptability it may change during his lifetime under the now quite considerable influences extended, as we have seen, by the drawing office equipment manufacturers. The growing influence of these has been matched over the years by the decline in the amount of time spent on training in draughting skills and the amount of time devoted to practice by the draughtsman to developing a good technique. This has resulted in a fairly mechanical style being presented with less concentration on the labour consuming frills adopted in the past as an aid to clarity. The growth of employment opportunities has also meant that there is no longer a pool of able drawing office staff content to pen away for a pittance. The older tools were time consuming and demanded some skill in their use; the new tools designed to spur things along may sometimes be quite expensive initially but still have their advantages and disadvantages. For example the old ruling pen with its need for regular wiping of the blades and frequent replenishment of the ink supply and occasional resharpening has been displaced by the technical pen with its almost continual flow from a reservoir of ink. Skilled use of the ruling pen produced a superb job but even in fairly unskilled hands use of a technical pen is much quicker and it is usually easier to maintain a more even thickness of line. Against this however, is the fact that the thinner inks now in common use with technical pens are less dense and the line produced tends to fade in the middle. Even where added care is taken to draw all lines at a fairly slow and even pace there is a tendency for the ink to thicken at each extremity. On the other hand the work produced with such pens is usually perfectly satisfactory for the purpose.

Even before the days of British Standards, conventions existed in the production of working drawings which most practices followed so that the wilder fancies of individual style and technique could be controlled and generation gaps between staff employed could be bridged. It was also of course, in everyones interest that the contractors, certainly those in a particular area, were not presented with widely differing types of drawing and symbols on the drawings of one practice meaning something totally different from those on the drawings of another. Even so all drawings for safety's sake were, or should have been, provided with their own individual key to symbols and any colouring used.

Current practice is exemplified by "Recommendations for Building Drawing Office Practice" BS 1192: 1969, the second re-written and updated version of a standard first published in 1944. Although open to criticism in detail, it represents the joint endeavours of a committee drawn from twenty different organisations and it seems a pity that it should be found necessary, as now proposed, to undertake a further revision so soon. However, many other British Standards have been published or revised since 1969, for example those relating to services, engineering, electrical work and fire protection systems in buildings, while PD 6479 "Recommendations for Symbols and other graphic conventions for Building Production Drawings" was published in 1976. These all contain different symbols from those which appear in the 1969 edition of the British Standard. The proposal for the new edition of BS 1192 is that it should be an inter-disciplinary standard in a number of separate parts and also incorporate such international standards as are appropriate. Parts will probably cover architectural practice, structural work and civil engineering work and there may also be a part specifically dealing with symbols which will, in effect, be a revised edition of PD 6479. The first of the new parts is expected to be published towards the end of 1983.

Whilst it is true that many of the symbols recommended for use in the current edition of BS 1192 will undoubtedly need to be changed much of the material in regard to the general principles of drawing office practice will probably be carried forward into the new edition; this is rightly so, as there can be little of such advice that can be thought outdated and in need of revision in such a short period of time. We have mentioned already some of the recommendations in the British Standard without actually indicating the source, for example on the sizes of paper and film, title panels on drawings, and folding of sheets and it would be as well to highlight a few other recommendations as distinct aids to clarity. It would be true to say that any architect or surveyor who followed the advice given in the 1969 edition of BS 1192 would produce good working drawings and the same comment will no doubt apply to any architect or surveyor who closely follows the advice given in the forthcoming edition. However, there is a great deal of advice that is quite properly orientated towards architectural practice for new work rather than towards works of repair and alteration to older buildings though the Standard admittedly by no means neglects this field. It is just that the choice of subject covered and advice given in part is rather broad and needs to be pinpointed for our-particular purpose.

We have already mentioned that lines on drawings need to be dense and firm for reproduction. They should also be in varying thicknesses to provide not only good contrast to the backing but also contrast between themselves. The British Standard makes this point and recommends that no more than three differing thicknesses on a drawing should be used in the ratio of 1:2:4. This is sound advice certainly, but the example drawings shown in the Standard employing this ratio are not too good and could be much clearer if provided with contrasted lines at an increased ratio to far better effect. The thinnest line should obviously be used for dimensions, indicator lines for notes and hatching and can afford to be less than the 0.2mm recommended which is really too thick for this purpose. A line for these purposes should appear to be as fine as practicable. Provided drawings are not to be microfilmed, a line nearer 0.1mm is satisfactory and can be reproduced without difficulty by most printers on the Diazo process. Provided arrowheads for dimensions and as pointers are clearly visible it does not really matter if a small part of such lines break up on printing. These lines should appear thread like. Most of the actual detail drawing will of course be carried out with the line of medium thickness and this could well be about three times the thickness of the thinnest line. The British Standard is quiet on the point as to whether lines should be crossed at corners and other intersections, as was the common practice a few years ago. Since none of the drawings in the standard show such crossings it must be presumed that the practice is no longer in favour. Notwithstanding, the practice does have certain advantages not to be too readily dismissed. For example it is easier and quicker to draw using crossings than it is to endeavour to stop precisely at the point of intersection, particularly when ink is being used. More often a gap occurs as a result of trying to do this. Also the crossing, particularly when shown on vertical or horizontal sections, when thickening up is also used subsequently, enables the junction to be precisely pinpointed. It is also easy, at the same time as drawing the actual detail, to extend the crossing out beyond the detail itself with the same stroke of the pen or pencil so that it becomes a stop for a dimension line. This again is quicker and more accurate than going round the drawing again and adding such "stops" with the same thin line as the dimension line itself.

Finally the thickening up of sections, both vertical and horizontal should be done quite boldly and continue the 1:3 ratio suggested previously. This work should however, be seen as a "thickening" process and detail should not be drawn with a thick line initially otherwise it will be found that accuracy will suffer considerably. With series 1 technical pens, dependent on the type of drawing of course, the following nibs might well be used; 0.13mm, 0.35mm and 1.0mm, while with series 2 the sizes could be 0.15mm, 0.4mm and 1.2mm.

Colouring on plans used to be a useful way of very readily differentiating new work from old. It is, however, obviously expensive on labour and can introduce inaccuracies, as anyone who has coloured a dozen plans all the same will testify. It is much too expensive to do nowadays and resort must be had to the use of conventional signs and hatching to differentiate between new and old, a task that needs some care if it is to be done effectively. For large areas dry transfer sheets of hatching can be used preprinted in the appropriate BS symbols.

As already indicated there is now a difference between the symbols used in BS 1192: 1969 and some subsequent British Standards. The surveyor himself should be consistent and use those in BS 1192: 1969 for the present, but specialist consultants may of course be tempted to use those appropriate to their own discipline on their drawings. Because of this there is a need at present to insist on all drawings being provided with a key, which is preferable, or a reference to where the symbols can be seen, which is much less satisfactory. The need for a key may lapse later when the new edition of the Standard is published and when a simple note of reference to it coupled with the date of revision and the part number may suffice. The arrival of this situation will depend however, on a fairly universal acceptance by architects, surveyors and contractors to the contents of the new edition.

A good symbol and conventional sign for use on a working drawing should be simple and quick to produce, distinctive, and, if possible, convey something of the character of the material or item depicted. The main purpose is to convey the maximum amount of information with the minimum of effort. The representation of materials should always be accompanied by a descriptive note stating the type and thickness of material. Hatching etc. should always be adapted to the scale of the drawing. Nothing looks worse than hatching too closely and inaccurately drawn and yet, obviously, if hatching is too widely spaced, its meaning may fail to register. Some of the drawn examples in BS 1192: 1969 are prone to these failings. There is a happy medium which looks just "right" and shows off the skill of the draughtsman to full advantage. It is also a good indicator that even in this mechanical age a good eye for style can still register.

Lettering forms an integral part of every architect's or surveyor's working drawings. It is no exaggeration to say that many drawings are rendered, quite useless by incomprehensible or near incomprehensible lettering. A spidery scrawl purporting to be linked lower case lettering is usually the worst offender often produced quite apparently, at great speed and without the aid of guide lines. Since, as already noted, clarity and communication must be the principal objective the draughtsman might just as well have sat at home and twiddled his thumbs. A little practice should provide all draughtsmen with a reasonable hand for lettering provided one or two basic points are given due attention. These can be summarised as follows:

(a) Keep to upper case letters only and do not link.
(b) Generally keep letter sizes uniform throughout, apart from titles.
(c) Use guidelines or a template.
(d) Keep uprights "upright" or if the draughtsman finds this impossible at least all at the same degree of slope but certainly not backwards. In any event all horizontals should be kept horizontal and not waver up and down.

(e) It is better to exaggerate the "roundness" of a letter such as "C", "O", "Q" etc. rather than "pinch" them. Space between words should be equivalent to the space taken by the letter "O" with the space between sentences twice this amount.

(f) Take extra care with forming numerals. Whereas individual letters are usually read as part of words each figure counts as a significant unit. Although it is not likely that fractions will be used now with metrication, if they are used then it is wise to keep the top and bottom numbers exactly the same size as the main numerals and separate them with a diagonal line.

(g) On a drawing, collect together notes of a general character, otherwise put notes as near as possible to the detail being annotated but not so close as to be confusing. It is best that lines connecting a note with its appropriate detail should be at an angle rather than horizontal or vertical so as to avoid confusion with any detail line.

(h) Obviously the size of lettering can, to some extent, be a matter of choice related to the scale and size of the drawing. However, as a guide a lower limit of 1.75mm is thought suitable for most purposes including the possibility of subsequent microfilming. Titles can be 5.0 to 8.0mm. There is a tendency for the inexperienced to do lettering at too large a size and this is a danger to avoid.

BS 1192: 1969 suggests that underlining should be avoided but another and preferred viewpoint is that underlining is essential to give titles due prominence on a sheet which has more than one detail. Similarly punctuation marks form an essential aid to communication and the advice in the Standard that they should be left out unless absolutely essential to the sense is more likely to cause misunderstanding than their use would be. The idea that full stops, commas etc. within a panel of lettering or the underlining of titles would cause confusion does not really hold water.

Although it might be said that anyone who cannot, even with practice, produce a reasonable hand at lettering would be better off in another profession (for the benefit of those architects or surveyors remaining rather than their individual benefit) there are artificial aids for lettering drawings other than by hand which are available. Stencils, for example, are certainly better than the worst hand lettering but are still fairly poor in appearance and time consuming in use; their use is probably best restricted to titles. Dry transfer lettering is too slow, cumbersome and expensive for general notes though it too can profitably be used for titles, particularly on panels for pre-printed sheets and presentation purposes. It needs the application of a fixative, of course, when used otherwise there is considerable danger of it peeling off. Smaller drawings can be taken off the board and notes typed on but the normal correspondence type faces are really too large and a smaller face needs selection which usually means that a special typewriter has to be kept in the office solely for the purpose. If the draughtsman cannot do the typing himself, it usually means that a print has to be provided with the notes in longhand draft for the typist to copy both as to wording and position. Corrections on the typed work are, of course, very difficult to make without ghosting on both tracing paper and film and it can be seen that the process is probably more time consuming than hand lettering. Another method of utilising the typewriter, however, is with transparent adhesive sheets. The draughtsman supplies the typist with the information which is typed in panels on the dry transfer film, cut up and then stuck by the draughtsman on the drawing. Obviously drawings of any size can be lettered in this way and the problem of correcting errors is not so acute as it is probably quicker and easier to re-type correctly the whole note again rather than to erase the odd letter or word.

Sensible decisions taken at the time the survey is commenced will govern the scale used in the plotting and the layout of the drawings now to be produced. We have already mentioned the need to decide upon the degree of detail necessary in the measuring on the actual survey depending on the scope of the proposed work. Such decisions will now be reflected in the plotting and fair drawing of the survey of the existing building. For example, a decision that all detail needs to be measured to a fine degree will result in plotting complete floor plans to 1:20 on separate sheets probably because there are to be alterations in practically every room. On the other hand the taking of broad overall dimensions with detailed measuring confined perhaps to a couple of rooms where new kitchen fittings or bathroom alterations are to be installed will produce general layout drawings to a scale of 1:100 with only the rooms in question to a scale of 1:20. The advent of metrication in the building industry has not altered the view that the halfway house scale of 1:50, in the same way as the old 1:48 quarter inch to the foot scale, seems curiously useless. It is not really possible to show any more detail at 1:50 than it is at 1:100 and to be worthwhile for the extra detail it is necessary to move up to 1:20, equivalent to the old half inch to one foot, when it is possible to show not only plaster thicknesses but tiling thickness as well. It follows therefore that if substantial works are to be carried out which affect most rooms then it is worthwhile to draw floor plans on separate sheets at 1:20 scale and if it should be necessary to prepare a general layout drawing at 1:100 to do this by means of a compilation of separate photographic reductions from the 1:20 plans. Care is needed, moreover, if this is to be done to ensure that any lettering applied or fine detail drawn at the larger scale will still be legible. Some blurring of plaster thickness drawn at 1:20 may not matter too much but otherwise it may be better to letter the reduction separately from the larger scale plan.

Various alternative scales are suggested in BS 1192: 1969 for building drawings of various types. It must be acknowledged however, that the more scales there are present in a set of working drawings the more likelihood there is of mistakes arising. In our view there should be no need to add to the range of 1:100, 1:20, 1:5 and perhaps full size drawings if required. These correspond to $\frac{1}{8}''$: and $\frac{1}{2}''$ scale drawings, quarter full size and full size details familiar to all members of the building profession long before the change to metrication. There seem to be no good reasons for using any other scales except in the most exceptional circumstances. Unfamiliar scales certainly can lead to confusion among the diverse members of the building team.

It should be the rule rather than the exception to maintain a set of drawings of the building as it exists rather than to have such drawings muddied by the addition of alterations. This is quite possible these days without having to trace or re-draw in laborious fashion since it is possible to prepare further negatives or positives on film from either tracing paper drawings or film. The drawings of the existing building can then be retained intact and further prints taken if necessary both for record purposes and also for the "before" situation when required by approving authorities in order to give consent for the proposed works together with the many other parties involved in the project who will need such drawings e.g. consultants, nominated sub-contractors and perhaps quantity surveyor. It undoubtedly pays at this stage to take just that little bit of extra care to provide a degree of "solidity" to the drawing even if it does mean that more time has to be spent on the drawing of the existing building before further negatives are prepared. For example inking in walls solid black or thickening up the line will make the drawings of floor plans and sections that much clearer and enable a satisfactory distinction to be made between existing and altered detail on the working drawings. It goes without saying that on balance the preference must be for ink on film or perhaps still tracing paper so as to achieve the utmost clarity at this stage, although as we have seen special plastic pencils on film can now achieve to all practical purposes just as good results.

The floor plans, sections and elevations of the existing building reproduced as master positives, preferably on film, now form the basic skeleton for the first group of working drawings.

BS 1192: 1969 recommends that working drawings be prepared following a simple classification of types rather than in a sequence of vague unrelated sheets. Although this may not be considered essential where work to a single small building is being contemplated, it is very important for schemes involving a number of buildings or a very large single building. The classification system advocated is little more than a scheme which involves moving on from the general to the particular but it has the element of logicality and on a big scheme should lead to a set of drawings being prepared complete in itself for both the quantity surveyor and the contractor and in a form easily recognisable and which can easily be used on site. Once again clarity in communication will be seen as the prime motive.

The first classification group provides for "location" drawings. In work to existing buildings these comprise the drawings to be developed from the measured survey, thus floor plans, sections and elevations of the existing building to show the position occupied by, or to identify, the various spaces in the building and to show the general construction, a site plan to show the position of the building on the site, together with drainage and other service runs, and a block plan to show the site in relation to other buildings and features in the locality. These drawings show where items fit in a building, where the building "fits" on the site and where the site "fits" into the surrounding locality. Obviously the limitations of scale particularly if a large job is involved suggest that such drawings should not be cluttered with too much detail or information which can better be found either in the specification or in a second group of drawings prepared to a larger scale, the "assembly" drawings. Notwithstanding, location drawings need to be fairly liberally supplied with the appropriate references to indicate where the additional information can be found.

"Assembly" drawings show how the various elements or parts of a building are fitted together, particularly the junctions between the various elements themselves i.e. how a new window or door is fitted into a wall, the connection between wall and roof construction or wall and floor. It may be that there is scope here for the use of standard or typical details favoured by the architect or surveyor and utilised over a number of different jobs because they have been proved to be successful. Sometimes isometrics are useful at this stage for improving clarity. While assembly drawings will be provided with all the information necessary for the contractor to form the necessary junctions and assemble the various elements it is quite likely that

325

there will also be brief references to the final classification group of drawings known as "component" drawings.

Component drawings will show the shape, dimensions and the details for fitting together an item to be made either in the contractors shop (not necessarily the main contractor) or on site and to be fitted into a building. For a major component e.g. a purpose made window or door, this may be drawn at 1:5 in metric terms or a quarter full size in Imperial terms. Minor components might consist of concrete cills or timber architraves drawn to full size. There might also be a component range drawing showing a series of one type of component e.g. doors or windows, giving overall sizes as well as identifying type with position. All component drawings are likely to have a fairly full range of specification notes and may well be complete in themselves requiring just the necessity for a note of reference to appear in the specification. Again the surveyor may be finding a place for a number of components standardised in the office.

Clearly an extensive range of drawings should have some form of referencing system preferably one that is recognised throughout the whole of the construction industry. Such a system is available in the form of the CI/SfB coding (this being the application of the international SfB classification system in Britain). This enables information contained in different types of documents such as drawings, specifications, bills of quantities, texts, books and trade literature to be co-ordinated and correlated for the maximum benefit of the user. Although all five tables in the CI/SfB matrix are used in library classification for books, trade literature etc. covering physical environment (0), Elements (1), Construction (2), Materials (3) and Activities (4) and details of all five can be found in the information sheet produced by the SfB Agency UK (available from RIBA Publications Ltd., 66 Portland Place, London W1N 4AD), only Table 1 is required for referencing drawings as reproduced on Page 328. This table provides a numerical code for the various parts of a building. With a prefix of "L" for location drawings, "A" for Assembly drawings and "C" for Component drawings, a simple classification system can be developed. Thus A (21) 03 would be the third Assembly Drawing dealing with external walls or C (76) 02 might be the second component drawing dealing with storage units e.g. cupboards or shelf units. There can be problems in the classification of Assembly Drawings where two elements form a junction in a building. In these cases the predominant element provides the code or, if they are both of equal predominance, then the element having the highest number in the Table can be used. Obviously such a reference system on a medium sized contract can be carried to ludicrous extremes and care may need to be taken not to allow this to happen. Simplicity should be the key and a breakdown of main elements into too many sub-divisions should not be necessary on works to existing buildings.

On large contracts it is advisable to keep a "drawings register" which might well be started at the beginning of the drawing stage as a programme of work. Similarly a "drawing circulation sheet" provides an essential reference to ensure that all who should have drawings do in fact receive them. Copies of the circulation sheet should be sent to all concerned at regular intervals so that consultants and nominated specialist sub-contractors can check that they have all the drawings they need. As the work develops consultants and sub-contractors drawings can be added to the sheet. It is easy for example for the heating engineer's drawing to be received by the architect or surveyor, examined and then put aside because of the pressure of other matters. If the circulation sheet, when distributed, shows that it has been received the structural engineer may then jog the architect or surveyor into ensuring that it is despatched as appropriate so that, for example, the structural engineer himself can see where pipe runs penetrate floor slabs.

It has already been said that sets of master positives should be made from the drawings of the measured survey for use by consultants and sub-contractors. This is much better than sending out prints from which others may well trace inaccurately or scale from, again perhaps inaccurately, to make up their own details at quite a different scale to the confusion of all. The same applies, of course, to working drawings as they are developed. It is much better that consultants and sub-contractors use these as necessary instead of preparing their own drawings. The architect or surveyor should take a firm hand as a co-ordinator of all consultants and specialist sub-contractors work and insist on their use of his own allocated drawing numbers and that they follow such timetable for the production of drawings as has been agreed. In this connection the imposition of arbitrary timetables by the architect or surveyor is worse than useless. Timetables must be realistic despite the pressures that will exist to finish all the drawings so that the next stage can be reached in the project. Pressures from clients should be resisted to the full. There will, however, be severe pressure at times to cut corners and leave a detail to be solved at a later date. It is always best and cheapest in the long run to produce information at the proper time and the working drawing stage is the time to solve all remaining problems. The surveyor and his staff should be able to draw everything that is required in the way of the works and there should be no ducking of the problems posed by difficult spots of detailing. For this reason all fittings should have been selected by

Table 1
Elements

(--) Sites, projects, building systems

Substructure

(1-) Ground, substructure
(10)
(11) Ground
(12)
(13) Floor beds
(14)-(15)
(16) Retaining walls, foundations
(17) Pile foundations
(18) Other substructure elements
(19) Parts of elements (11) to (18)
Cost summary

Structure

(2-) Primary elements, carcass
(20)
(21) Walls, external walls
(22) Internal walls, partitions
(23) Floors, galleries
(24) Stairs, ramps
(25)-(26)
(27) Roofs
(28) Building frames, other primary elements
(29) Parts of elements (21) to (28)
Cost summary

(3-) Secondary elements, completion
if described separately from (2-)
(30)
(31) Secondary elements to external walls; external doors, windows
(32)*Secondary elements to internal walls; internal doors
(33) Secondary elements to floors
(34) Secondary elements to stairs
(35) Suspended ceilings
(36)
(37) Secondary elements to roofs; rooflights, etc

Use for doors generally if required

(38) Other secondary elements
(39) Parts of elements (31) to (38)
Cost summary

(4-) Finishes
if described separately
(40)
(41) Wall finishes, external
(42) Wall finishes, internal
(43) Floor finishes
(44) Stair finishes
(45) Ceiling finishes
(46)
(47) Roof finishes
(48) Other finishes to structure
(49) Parts of elements (41) to (48)
Cost of summary

Services

(5-) Services, mainly piped and ducted
(50)-(51)
(52) Waste disposal, drainage
(53) Liquids supply
(54) Gases supply
(55) Space cooling
(56) Space heating
(57) Air conditioning, ventilation
(58) Other piped, ducted services
(59) Parts of elements (51) to (58)
Cost of summary

(6-) Services, mainly electrical
(60)
(61) Electrical supply
(62) Power
(63) Lighting
(64) Communications
(65)
(66) Transport
(67)
(68) Security, control, other services
(69) Parts of elements (61) to (68)
Cost summary

328

Fittings

(7–) Fittings
(70)
(71) Circulation fittings
(72) Rest, work fittings
(73) Culinary fittings
(74) Sanitary, hygiene fittings
(75) Cleaning, maintenance fittings
(76) Storage, screening fittings
(77) Special activity fittings
(78) Other fittings
(79) Parts of elements (71) to (78)
Cost summary

(8–)*Loose furniture, equipment
(80)
(81) Circulation loose equipment

Use only (7–) if preferred

(82) Rest, work loose equipment
(83) Culinary loose equipment
(84) Sanitary, hygiene loose
equipment
(85) Cleaning, maintenance loose
equipment
(86) Storage, screening loose
equipment
(87) Special activity loose equipment
(88) Other loose equipment
(89) Parts of elements (81) to (88)
Cost summary

External, other elements

(9–) External, other elements
(90) External works
(98) Other elements
(99) Parts of elements
Cost summary

the client where the question of choice is involved. It is only by a rigid adoption of this policy that subsequent calculations for Bills of Quantities or estimating can be carried out with any degree of reliability and the works on site once started can proceed with a degree of coherence and, hopefully, expedition. Details not solved and fittings not selected at this stage can later be the cause of delays and changes in plan perhaps causing the undoing of work already carried out in accordance with the drawings or the amendment of details already considered settled. Whatever the consequences they may well be laid at the feet of the architect or surveyor since, apart from any aspect of indecision by the professional adviser, it is more or less certain that the client would have been quite happy to have chosen his fittings early on if he had been told of the possible consequences of not doing so and most of all of the additional expense by way of extras which could be incurred as a result of non-selection.

Consultants and specialist sub-contractors will eventually be sending drawings "for approval" to the architect or surveyor. This is one of the architect or surveyor's tasks not always given the degree of care and attention which it warrants. As part of the architect or surveyor's overall control, it is his responsibility to co-ordinate and integrate and to see that others do what he requires and not what those others may wish to do themselves perhaps, for example, "because it is easier that way". The architect or surveyor must therefore make sure that he understands not only the drawings and details sent in by consultants and specialist sub-contractors but also that he gives careful thought to all the consequences of the details shown, not only in regard to those aspects of the works over which he has a direct design interest but also in relation to the work of all the other consultants and sub-contractors as well. If he does not understand the details shown he should ask questions and continue to do so until he gets all the answers or explanations he needs.

Consultants and specialist contractors generally have a confident air acquired over years of dealing with the same sort of problems in a fairly limited field but also with a high degree of expertise which, of course, is why they are so useful and why they are brought in by architects and surveyors in general practice. They can however, exhibit an element of intolerance and impatience with lesser mortals and the architect or surveyor should guard against being put off or being hesitant on raising queries. Everyone can make mistakes or find themselves working under a misapprehension about what is required and the architect or surveyor is the last person who should be shy at seeking all the answers. It may be that on a particularly tricky point in the design a number of drawings will have to be considered in relation to each other all at the same time. This can be an exhausting and time consuming exercise which temptation may suggest should be cut short in the face of other pressing matters and approval given on the principle that "it will all probably be all right". In fact the perverse nature of building operations in these instances usually means that it will be far from right.

At some point during the course of the works one sub-contractor or another will be found doing something which spoils or interferes with the work of others or threatens to spoil the whole concept of the proposals. On challenged to take down what has been done already and do it differently the sub-contractors answer may be "but the architect or surveyor approved the drawing". If this is indeed the case (and it generally will be because no sub-contractor with any business sense will put work in hand without obtaining the architect or surveyor's prior approval), an acrimonious argument can develop as to who will pay the extra cost involved for altering the work. The architect or surveyor may, if he is lucky, be able to argue convincingly that the work should never have been proposed in that particular fashion in the first place or, alternatively, that the sub-contractors or consultants drawing was not clear on the point. As a result he may be able to persuade the sub-contractor to foot the bill but here it must be said that the prospect of future work coming from the client or the architect or surveyor may well colour the sub-contractor's decision rather than any sense of generosity to the client or his professional adviser. If there is a substantial sum involved even this consideration may not be enough and the sub-contractor may take a firm stand on principle and not be shaken. It is unlikely in these circumstances that the client's indulgence will stretch to meeting the extra charge when the architect or surveyor comes to explain the presence of the item of extra cost on the final account. There is certainly no reason why he should, since he employed his architect or surveyor to supervise the whole operation and to avoid such unfortunate occurrences.

Obviously in giving approval to plans the architect or surveyor cannot be expected to provide total exoneration to work which is a specialists province, otherwise there would hardly be any point in having specialists at all. The surveyor can only be expected to give approval to the general arrangement shown and this should be made quite clear in the signing of the plans both on the copy retained by the surveyor and on the copy returned to the sub-contractor. Professional consultants are, of course, usually far more aware of this aspect and may often ask for approval in this form only. It is hoped however, that the importance of this approval to general arrangements has been sufficiently stressed and that the architect or surveyor will not fall into the trap of treating the task lightly. No approval of any nature should be given until everything is clearly as the architect or surveyor would wish to have it.

At the appropriate times other drawings, apart from those for use by consultants and sub-contractors, will be required and will need to be prepared by the architect or surveyor. Drawings for obtaining, for example, all the formal approvals required for the works will need to be prepared and despatched. The method of working described in this chapter should, it is considered, provide for these to be made ready with little or no disruption to the programme of work because "special" drawings as such should not be necessary. Keeping a set of plans etc. of the building in negative form as it existed before the works commenced has already been mentioned and this set will take care of the "before" situation. The working drawings are probably the best drawings to send along with the "before" drawings and the written application. It is sometimes said that the working drawings show too much detail, far in excess of that required by the planning officers, building regulation officers and district surveyors in order to give their approval. This may be so, but it could also be said to be far better to have too much information in these circumstances than too little. Any disadvantage is outweighed by the advantage of only having one set of working drawings in a complete form suitable for all purposes rather than sets in various degrees of "completeness" i.e. almost in outline for planning requirements and merely "anno-tated" with a little more detail for building regulation approval. The danger here is that ideas do sometimes change even with the best will in the world as the drawing work proceeds. If, for example, sets at an early stage are sent in for approval, an approval may be obtained for something that is subsequently abandoned. This may not matter but far more dangerous is the omission at the time the application is made of some important part of the design which crops up later as the drawings proceed to completion. The new detail goes forward into the contract and later it may be found that the contractor is actually carrying out work for which no approval has been given at all. This would be an unforgivable situation for any architect or surveyor to fall into, one that would harm his reputation considerably in the area in which he practices as well as causing damage to his pocket if, as a result, there is delay in completion of the works and claims for extras become involved while late approval is hurriedly obtained. Again such aspects are just those for which an architect or surveyor is employed so as to keep his client clear of such difficulties and a failure to do so can be of substantial financial consequence. There should, of course, be a continuing dialogue between surveyor and controlling authority up to the time when applications are duly submitted. By this means the obtaining of approval becomes a mere formality since the architect or surveyor will know that all problems have been thrashed out and solved before the submission as will the Planning Officer, Building Regulation Officer or District Surveyor. Many of the delays attributed to the building control system stem in fact from neglect of this simple process which is even more necessary in relation to works on existing buildings than it is for new works. Current regulations may need tempering with common sense when old buildings are being adapted to new uses and it may be necessary to involve the waiver procedure. Early discussion at a draft stage with the drawings will reveal whether such difficulties are capable of resolution under the regulations or whether it will be necessary to apply for a waiver to overcome the difficulty. Once again the architect or surveyor should really know before submitting such an application that its success is assured. If success is not assured then clearly a delay could be involved and such a problem would need exploration with the client since other alternative solutions may be available which would still meet with both the client's and the authority's approval and thereby avoid delay.

An exception to the use of working drawings for submissions might be made in the issue of an application for planning approval on a particularly sensitive issue of alterations or extension to existing buildings. A special drawing to show the proposals to their best effect might well make all the difference between approval and refusal when presented to a lay committee of the local authority (such committees not always following the advice of the Council's permanent officers). There may be a case in such instances for the preparation of a special coloured sketch or isometric drawing more easily understood and appreciated by a lay committee than working drawings which the non-professional sometimes has difficulty following.

While a sight of Location and Assembly Drawings would probably be appreciated by most surveyors acting for adjoining owners, even although they may not be entitled to see them, the architect or surveyor acting for the building owner should consider the despatch of such drawings an essential part of his programme. By this means he will ensure that nothing comes as a surprise to the neighbours. It is essential to face the possibility of objections before works begin rather than later when delay to the contractor may arise and cause the client more expense, and which may eventually perhaps be passed on to the architect or surveyor. On the other hand when it comes to dealing with Party Wall Awards and Agreements it is better practice to attach specially prepared drawings strictly related to the works covered by the Awards or Agreements, so that these documents in themselves are easy to follow, particularly so far as the contractor is concerned. In these circumstances the contractor has to bear in mind that he has to satisfy two surveyors, not just one. Large unwieldy working drawings covering much work unrelated to the Award are not appropriate for attachment to such documents and the extra effort required to produce the special drawings is well worthwhile.

Chapter 8
Specifications

CONTENTS

OF all the documents which architects and surveyors prepare in relation to building works the specification is the most crucial and fundamental to the project. A specification can be described as a representation in words prepared by the client's architect, surveyor or engineer of his requirements for building works, both as to the extent and quality, and the condition under which those works are to be carried out.

Over the years specifications have acquired a traditional form and the general practice for works of repair and alteration is for the specification to be set out in three distinct sections. These are:

The General Preliminaries and Conditions of Contract

The items in this section set out the conditions under which the building works are to be performed. In many cases it will be stated that the contractor will be expected to enter into a particular form of printed contract, for example the Joint Contract Tribunal Form of Contract in its current edition with or without quantities and whether for private use or local authority use. The completing words or figures for any blank spaces which have to be filled in on a standard printed form would be set out in the specification and any alternatives suitably identified. Printed contract forms have been dealt with in Part 2 of this book along with the general principles of all types of contracts applicable to building works. If a published printed form is not to be used then all the conditions appropriate to the proposed job have to be considered and set out in detail. Many practices or organisations which do not use a printed form of contract for smaller jobs develop their own set of contract conditions and preliminaries and maintain duplicated or photo-copied sheets to be amended or adapted to suit particular circumstances.

Materials and Workmanship

This section sets out the quality of the proposed work by describing in detail the materials to be used, the bricks, cement, plaster etc. and the workmanship required to put them together to complete the job, for example the proportions of materials in mortar, its mixing and use in bonding brickwork.

The Works

This section describes the works to be carried out using the materials and workmanship laid down in detail in the previous section. For example there may be different places where new brickwork is to be "built" or new floor tiles to be "laid" and it is convenient in this section merely to specify "Build new wall with . . ." or "lay floor tiles" without on each separate occasion needing to set out in detail types of bricks, mortar, pointing etc. or types of tiles and how they are to be laid. Usually, of course, in this part of the specification there is opportunity to cross reference to drawings.

Although all parts of the specification are of equal importance and have, of necessity, to be complete, not all of the sections seem to provide the same degree of difficulty in preparation. The implications of the decision to use a particular form of building contract have already been discussed in Part 2 of the book and need not be repeated here although other aspects of preliminaries, such as access for the works, protection for existing features, hoardings, screens, provisional sums and contingencies will need some attention. Similarly, not a great deal need be said here about the third section dealing with the works as this will be unique to the particular job. Much of this chapter will, however, be concerned with the section covering materials and workmanship since it is this part which provides the "bulk" in most specifications. Much of the material contained in this section of a specification is usually common to many other specifications but it is here that considerable problems often arise, not so much as to what to put in, but what to leave out and also very much in relation to the appropriateness of the contents to the project in hand.

The specification should be complete in itself but, as already discussed, where it is more convenient to represent the clients proposals by way of drawings than these must be referred to in the specification with precision so that both can be read in conjunction. It may be that on a very large job relating to a single building, repetitive work to a number of buildings, or on entirely new work of sufficient size, the specification will be but a stage towards satisfying the recommendations of the National Federation of Building Trades Employers. These provide that for the avoidance of much time and the unnecessary duplication of effort by contractors, the services of a quantity surveyor will be engaged at the clients expense to measure from the drawings (or sometimes at an existing building) the amount of materials and workmanship required according to the specification and any supplemental drawings and to describe that work by way of the standard and the conditions embodied in the specification. At the time of writing (1982), it is recommended that a quantity surveyor be employed where the cost of the proposed work is likely to exceed £100,000.

As discussed at the beginning of Part 3, Chapter 7, works of pure repair can probably be described by way of a specification only even though they may be in respect of a large building and may cost a substantial sum of money to complete. Whereas it is fairly common for a specification to exist on its own this is unlikely to be the case with drawings. It is comparatively rare for a drawing to be provided with sufficient notes for it to exist on its own in the form of a combined drawing and specification and highly unikely for it to have the information in regard to contract terms e.g. the possibility of any retention period and other preliminaries such as suitable access or protection for existing occupants, necessary for it to comprise the entire contract documentation. It would be impracticable for such notes to be complete and even a fully annotated drawing would, in such circumstances, almost certainly need to be accompanied by a letter giving the remaining information necessary for a contractor to put a price on the work proposed.

A specification, therefore, is very fundamental to the work of surveyors dealing with building repairs at all levels and much more so than in the case of architects concentrating in the main on new works. With architects, as we shall see, the tendency has been to hand the responsibility to a quantity surveyor whenever possible who, in turn, is left to obtain any information not shown on the drawings from the architect by way of sending him a series of information question sheets. To avoid these sheets reaching ludicrous proportions and to speed things along the quantity surveyor often makes assumptions as to the architect's requirements. This can be a satisfactory arrangement if the two professionals and their staffs frequently work together and have found by experience that they have an identity of mind but, obviously, the arrangement can have its dangers. Wrong assumptions can be made by the quantity surveyor necessitating changes when the contract is under way and possibly involving extra charges being passed on to the client. In these circumstances the contractor rightly gets the impression that the architect does not really know what is included in the specifying sections of the Bill in the first place and tends, therefore, to treat the contents in a somewhat cavalier fashion. If architects' "specifications" are thought of in this way surveyors should not feel too smug as contractors, in the main, think no more highly of specifications prepared by surveyors. It will perhaps come as something of a surprise to surveyors to hear that their specifications are often thought of as verbose, pompous, obscure, inadequate, sometimes grossly unfair and frequently wildly out of date. Many of the disputes on interpretation which arise during the course of a contract and at the final account stage can be attributed to inadequacies in the specification. This was never the case to anything like the same extent as it has been in the decades following the Second World War. Some thought needs to be given, therefore, to how this situation has arisen before proceeding to consider the ways and means of specifications writing and whether the traditional methods and the traditional type of specification can be improved.

Whereas architects and surveyors happily embark upon the preparation of drawings and quantity surveyors approach the preparation of Bills of Quantities with a degee of enthusiasm which the rest of us find puzzling, very few view the prospect of writing a specification with other than abhorence. Those who have been involved with a project the size of which justifies the preparation of Bills of Quantities will have, perhaps, experienced the sense of relief on realizing that a specification in the strict sense is not a requirement if the JCT Form of Contract is to be used; the specification in these circumstances is not a contract document. Previous to 1939 both specification and Bills were contract documents but owing to the large number of disputes which had arisen through inconsistencies between the two, it was decided in the 1939 Revision of the Contract Form to dispense with the former. It had been the intention that the surveyor or architect should continue to prepare the specification and that the quantity surveyor would prepare his Bills of Quantities from the drawings and the specification and it would be he who would iron out any inconsistencies by reference back to the surveyor or architect. It did not, however, quite work out the way intended and, ever since, most surveyors and architects have happily abrogated their responsibility to specify when circumstances have permitted them to do so and have often allowed the siren voice of the quantity surveyor to whisper in their ears "leave it to me" even although at the back of their minds there may have been a suspicion that this was not a wholly wise thing to do. To a great extent the position of the quantity surveyor has become more prominent in the building team as a result; this was particularly so on larger jobs, where once the standard or quality of the proposed building had been decided upon he would be left to take the decisions on materials and to describe the workmanship required. Surveyors and architects have been happy to let quantity surveyors do this, feeling that such detail is more appropriately left to a profession noted for its precise and organised way of working and its close attention to detail.

Despite much exhortation that both surveyors and architects should take more interest and care over specification writing since it really is a most fundamental facet of the design and building process worthy of close study, most of us tend to remain unconvinced and, to many, specification writing comes as a grinding chore. It is the very immensity of the task that is often so daunting. Wherever one turns, enormity is apparent. An old office specification for even a comparatively medium size job lands with a resounding thump on the desk. What is even more depressing is that other firms or organisations' specifications look even bigger and more comprehensive. If one turns to written advice the stress is always on size and completeness with the admonition to make sure that "nothing is left out". The quantity surveyor writer of one book on practice states that his "Type" or "Sample" specification, from which others are built up, runs to 1820 clauses covering 990 foolscap pages. The invaluable publication "Specification" (Architectural Press Ltd) which fifteen years ago appeared in two volumes amounting to about 1,000 pages, excluding the advertisements now runs to five volumes. The National Building Specification comprises four volumes in its main form of over 1,000 pages while the Small Works Version consists of 220 pages in a single volume.

Every experienced architect or surveyor will have known times when having slogged away at a specification for ages and having taken particular pains to include everything, even down to the kitchen sink and its accessories, he is faced later with a contractor enquiring as to what is to be done at a particular point and the realisation dawns that he would not have asked had the appropriate direction already been included in the specification. Another extra on the contract sum looms ahead with a risk of displeasure from the client. Generally if such an incident happens only once or twice on a contract the architect or surveyor can count himself lucky or perhaps he is very well experienced indeed. An omission of this nature relating to an item entirely missed out or one which arises in consequence of other work which was not foreseen is different from another type of omission which might arise during the progress of the works. With a repair and part renewal contract on a house the architect or surveyor might see the new sanitary fittings which he has specified being installed and in process of connection to the old pipes with plastic pipes although all the existing plumbing in the house is in copper. On being challenged for not using copper pipes, the contractor may well reply that since there was no mention of using copper pipes in the specification and that it would obviously cost more to use them he has chosen plastic. Similarly on seeing a bricklayer raking out joints preparatory to repointing, the architect or surveyor might say to him that the depth is insufficient. If the specification does not give the depth of raking out which the architect or surveyor requires, the bricklayer could say that his depth of raking out was the way it was always done according to his experience and if the architect or surveyor wanted a greater depth then someone would have to pay extra for it. Both architect and surveyor might, in these circumstances, order a greater depth of raking out and advise the client to refuse to pay the extra. However, this might not be acceptable to the contractor and if a number of such disputes had arisen on the contract and relations had reached such a low ebb that the contractor had come to believe that he had no likelihood of further work from either the architect or the surveyor or the client he might well sue for the extra if payment was not forthcoming. Short of surrendering or compromising with the clients agreement the architect or the surveyor might find himself in Court arguing, at an obvious disadvantage, before a Judge inexperienced in building matters, what the custom of the trade really is and probably not coming out of it very well. Whatever the outcome, it will probably not have escaped the client's notice that all the fuss could have been avoided if the architect or surveyor had been more precise and set out exactly what was required. If the decision should go against the client then it is highly probable he might threaten to deduct the extra cost from the fees due to his professional adviser.

These are but two small examples of what can happen so easily at any time but perhaps more so now than in the past. In times when, operating in a particular area, an architect or a surveyor could build up a relationship with a number of builders all of comparable size and capabilities, there would be a mutual understanding of the standard of materials and workmanship which the architect or surveyor could expect. The building firms would be based on a steady workforce, in the main the operatives serving an apprenticeship and reasonably happy to have a job, so that supervision in many instances would be a mere formality. The staff would know what was expected of them in nearly all building operations, could be left to get on with the job and while generally knowing when to call for help, advice and a decision from higher authority would also take a pride in solving the smaller problems, which inevitably arise, without reference to a supervisor, architect or surveyor. In these circumstances much could be left on trust and a specification could be less full of minutae. If the specification said "rake out and repoint" a depth of 19mm, at least, would be assumed by all as reasonable for the raking out so as to give an adequate key for the new work. In the case of the pipes already mentioned, if copper was not assumed to be required (and this would be most likely in the circumstances of copper pipes already being present) the point would be cleared at the estimating stage and an extra would not be thought of as something to be seized upon to boost the account at the end of the contract.

Of course, a complete item totally forgotten by the architect or surveyor in his specification might also be overlooked by the contractor's estimator and lead to an eventual extra to be settled on a mutually satisfactory basis for those immediately concerned, if not for the client. Sometimes, however, an item arising in consequence of another, again forgotten by the architect or surveyor, will be noticed by the contractor at the estimating stage. If estimating in competition, the contractor may not wish to put himself at a disadvantage viz-a-viz other contractors by including the cost in his tender without mention, but will generally make a point of noting it separately, either as being included in the estimate and quoting the amount involved, or setting it out quite apart altogether. The contractors interest is maintaining a reputation for good work with clients and their professional advisers in a particular area, in order to secure further possible contracts, meant that the contractor would often complete the architect and surveyor's work for him by including in estimates items missed out from the specification; at this stage of the building process, to some extent, baling them out. Such cosy relationships are nowadays comparatively rare but brief reflection will show that they are not really ideal or indeed very businesslike. In a way the contractor, perhaps even quite innocently, is progressing subtly towards a position where the architect or surveyor will almost be relying upon the contractor to correct his mistakes for him. It is obvious that such a situation could lead to abuse and a failure by the architects and surveyors to protect their client's interests to the fullest extent in all respects.

Nowadays many contractors will price a specification exactly as it is written. If little is said about standards of materials and workmanship it will be taken that the minimum will do and the cost of the work estimated accordingly. It should also not be forgotten that the scope for extras may well play a considerable part in the contractor's desire to secure the contract. A loosely phrased sloppy contract specification can be mined for extras to very considerable additional profit and this may be more attractive to some contractors than a detailed and "tight" specification giving no such opportunities. As mentioned earlier in this Chapter it has often been said that contractors make their main profit on extras and there is nothing like a sloppy specification to produce a substantial list of additional works not covered by the estimate. In addition, of course, the architect or surveyor will be faced with the unenviable task at the end of the day of explaining to his client why so many extras had arisen and why the estimate had been exceeded to such an extent. There might also arise the question of whether the architect or surveyor had the client's authority to order all the additional work assuming he had done so without reference to the client. It may in these circumstances boil down to an argument as to what constitutes an "appreciable increase in costs" or what are "major changes in constructional matters relating to . . . costs" or "material alterations or additions" necessitating the knowledge and consent of the client unless such authorisation had previously been given in specific terms in advance, (see paragraphs 1.3.2 and 1.3.3 of the General Conditions of Engagement issued by the RICS and paragraphs 3.3 and 3.4 of the Architect's Appointment 1982 issued by the RIBA). Again there can be an argument on the precise meaning of "constructional reasons" necessitating alterations which can be made before the client is notified. In many cases these alterations are not genuinely constructional but arise out of errors on the drawings or in the specification.

Some clients have been known to adopt the attitude on extras of "you ordered it, you pay for it" on the principle that once they accept an estimate they cannot be expected to pay more. Although this attitude may seem unreasonable to architects and surveyors in the often difficult circumstances of repairs and alterations to existing buildings it is, in fact, a completely sensible and indeed logical attitude for the client to adopt. His resources may well be limited and if by chance some unavoidable and totally unexpected extra becomes necessary he is fully entitled to early advice. He may have no choice but to authorise the additional work but, if advised, and his authority is sought at the appropriate time, he will be given the opportunity to decide whether he needs to cut out a "frill" perhaps elsewhere to balance the extra cost and keep within his budget. It is easy for architects and surveyors to allow and authorise a number of what seem at the time fairly small extras without client's approval on the basis that these are within their authority (see paragraphs 3.3 and 3.4 of Part 3 of the RIBA Architects Appointment and paragraph 1.3.2 of the RICS General Conditions). At the end, on the settlement stage of the final account, it is found that these "small" extras have built up to a substantial sum; far larger than anticipated. It is in the nature of building works for this to happen and therefore dangerous for the architect or surveyor to initiate extra works without having been certain that he has his client's total approval. It is an unwelcome but salutory experience for an architect or a surveyor who has had to order additional works so that the whole job can be completed satisfactorily but does so without the client's authority and so as to overcome his own errors of omission, to be left holding the bill. There can be little sympathy for the architect or surveyor in these circumstances as also in the case of either architect or surveyor who thinks he knows best what his client requires and proceeds to order, at whim, costly and elaborate extra works because he arrogantly assumes that client will cheerfully pay up when the bill comes in.

There can be no doubt now that the surveyor and architect are responsible for setting the standard of materials and workmanship necessary to fulfil the client's requirements. There can be no delegation of this responsibility in the normal course of events except with the express approval of the client. There had been some doubt in recent years on this, particularly in connection with new work where a quantity surveyor was employed and this led to the need to make an amendment in 1976 to the 1963 Edition of the Joint Contract Tribunal Form of Contract. The revision made it quite clear that the contractor was obliged to complete the works using materials and workmanship of the quality and standard "specified" in the contract document, and this was irrespective of whether the version with or without quantities was used. To be able to fulfil his obligations under the contract it is clear, therefore, that the contractor needs these standards to be laid down and if they are set out insufficiently the contractor may be able quite reasonably to get away with standards somewhat lower than both the client and the surveyor or architect originally had in mind.

The foregoing all seems to suggest that nowadays an enormous specification covering every conceivable item of material and entering into exhaustive detail on every aspect of workmanship, however basic, is required. When one thinks of the shoddy building materials which always seem to be available and the standard of work proffered by some operatives at the present time it is not really difficult to come to that conclusion. However, sheer bulk without regard to content is not everything and even what seems, on the face of it, to be the fullest of specifications can often be held in a fair degree of contempt by contractors as a few examples will show.

On occasions, it will be found that a bulky specification is not in fact of a length appropriate to a complete description of the works, but long simply because it has been padded out with long unwieldy paragraphs of well-nigh incomprehensible English. This may arise because of misplaced endeavour to describe works already shown on drawings instead of making simple reference to the drawings themselves. In this event the damage may not be too great but, more often, the flaw arises from trying to describe constructional details or works of a complicated nature in words instead of by drawings. In this case different interpretations may be put on the words by different contractor's estimators so that in fact, at the tendering stage, the estimates submitted may not be truly comparable even although the contractors will have each genuinely thought they were reflecting the requirements correctly. When it comes to carrying out the works the architect or surveyor will begin to realise that what is being built is not entirely in line with what he had in mind although he may be found to admit that the contractors interpretation of the words is just as equally valid as his own. Substantial arguments could arise, probably involving extra costs to the client, the ultimate responsibility for which must really lie with the surveyor or architect for failing to express himself clearly. Most people will have come across situations similar to this where it seems perfectly clear to the writer what is meant. To some extent the writer becomes blinkered and refuses to accept the possibility of alternative interpretations so that the more he re-reads a paragraph the more convinced he becomes that it is capable of one interpretation only. The value of check reading becomes self-evident in such circumstances.

Of course, it could be said that if architects and surveyors concerned themselves far more in eliminating all possibility of having more than one interpretation put to any paragraph or clause, specifications would eventually become similar to legal documents, such as leases or even Acts of Parliament. Lawyers and Parliamentary draftsmen are well versed in this problem but unfortunately their efforts to overcome their own particular difficulties do in fact entail the documents which they produce being virtually incomprehensible to all except other lawyers and draftsmen. Such a situation is always good for the employment prospects of lawyers but a lesson needs to be learnt here in that specifications are not, in the normal course of events, written to be read by other surveyors and architects but by contractors' staff at all levels. It is perhaps going to extremes to insist that the quality of the writing should be pitched at the most basic level but it is an undoubted fact that most building operatives are happier working from a drawing than from a specification. Generally, of course, a foreman or a supervisor will be present who is more versed at interpreting the written word but it is undoubtedly a desirable attribute in the surveyor or architect to know when it is more appropriate to provide a drawing rather than a written description and to be able to strike the correct balance between the two.

Some architects and surveyors of experience have been known to suggest that a specification couched in long official and important sounding phrases carries more weight and authority and will be held in greater respect by the contractor. However a specification which sets out to be "official" is more likely to contain ambiguities and give rise to contractor's claims than one which is written with clarity in mind from the start. This aspect will be discussed again later in this chapter but it is sufficient at this stage to say that no merit can be seen in this suggestion whatsoever. Simple clear directions on the contractor's liabilities and on what the contractor is to do is what is required.

If an architect or surveyor knows exactly what he requires in regard to materials and workmanship it will be easier for him to follow the maxim to be clear and direct in specification writing. If, however, the architect or surveyor is a little unsure of what precisely is wanted either through indecision or, in the less experienced, lack of knowledge, there may be a tendency for this lack of uncertainty to be reflected in the writing. The inexperienced will often cloak their ignorance in obscurity and undue length and in the case of specification writing will hope that the contractor, out of the jumble presented, will select the right solution. On the occasional clause or paragraph such a gamble may pay off but a whole specification prepared on this basis is likely to lead to substantial difficulties. Not only will the estimates obtained be likely to show wide variations (generally a good warning signal of trouble ahead) but if the works are put in hand on the basis of accepting one of the lower tenders much difficulty in "supervising" the works will be experienced. In the end, the client may well find that his architect or surveyor will have lost the element of control, in the worst cases perhaps even all control of the works in progress. At the final account stage the bill presented will bear no resemblance to the original accepted quotation and, furthermore, there may be little scope or opportunity to argue about it.

Contractors will recognise the long ambiguous specification prepared by the inexperienced architect or surveyor lacking in knowledge rather quicker, probably, than the same type of specification prepared by the knowledgable but verbose architect or surveyor. More than likely the former will be accompanied by the bland drawings containing sectional details which seem to be always taken where no particular difficulties occur. The latter will be accompanied more likely by sheets of drawings comprising a veritable jungle of detail uncoordinated and in no particular order as discussed in the previous chapter. The contractor with the sharper eye for business will pounce on the former and consider it a likely source of extra gain and he may well succeed in achieving the same end with the latter, although probably with much more of a tussle with the architect or surveyor concerned. Even so a risk of extras for reasons of failure in this respect is not one which the prudent architect or surveyor should take when, with care, it can be avoided.

Until one considers in detail how most traditional specifications are written it can be surprising to find so often in the longer specifications a considerable number of irrelevancies. In the preliminaries, requirements perhaps for hoarding, lighting and protection totally unrelated to the works in hand and in the materials and workmanship sections untold details not in the least related to the works required may be found. How the contractor views specifications full of irrelevant material is perhaps a matter of degree. If prepared by an individual architect or surveyor in private practice he will guess that old specifications are being copied without a great deal of thought being given to whether clauses are appropriate or not. A few such clauses in an otherwise good specification will be overlooked but if there are many then there is a danger that the contractor will take the view that if one particular clause does not apply perhaps quite a few of the others do not either. If challenged he will be quite entitled to point this out and the architect or surveyor will begin to have an uneasy feeling that the contractor may well have a point of view, probably with real justifcation. On the other hand, the contractor will be familiar with those organisations which perhaps having been caught in the past for leaving out some item or other, understandably decide to put in everything conceivably possible, and many others besides, just to be on the safe side. Contractors are perhaps resigned to this method of preparing a specification and to the extra work it gives to each of them to wade through copious pages to select relevant items. For a large authority with much work in hand it is in the contractor's interest to co-operate. Notwithstanding, the inclusion of everything, including the kitchen sink, can take on ludicrous proportions when applied indiscriminately to small, medium and large jobs with no distinction between them and makes the organisation and it's architects and surveyors, look silly and lacking in that confidence necessary to make the appropriate judgements as to what should be included and what should be left out. Furthermore, it is illuminating to find that such organisations continue to get caught out just as frequently as others in cases which can be attributed to just that lack of detailed thought which should be given to every job. Many jobs are similar but all are unique and most have a few features quite different from other jobs. An "umbrella" specification inhibits just that extra thought necessary to cover the individual aspects. The contractor may identify missing items at the estimating stage but he is just as likely not to say anything at the time and will await the award of the contract and the commencement of work before indicating what they are and collecting the extra on completion. Some offices and organisations even try to cover this eventuality by inserting "escape" clauses designed to ensure that the contractor should accept the responsibility for anything left out of the specification. Wording such as "the contractor is to include for any item not specifically mentioned herein necessary to complete the work" are grossly unfair, highly unpopular with contractors, of doubtful legal validity and really of dubious benefit. Contractors are unlikely to submit competitive tenders on such a basis since it puts them in a position of submission at the whim of the architect or surveyor. If tested in the courts it is probable that the clauses would be seen to be what they are; merely a device to shift the architect or surveyor's job on to the contractor and to make him accept a responsibility for what is not his in the least.

Surveyors and architects who do not keep themselves reasonably up to date can be prone to write specifications, sometimes quite lengthy, with numerous clauses, admittedly quite relevant to the works, but couched in terms redolent of past eras and utilising materials long since unavailable. Contractors readily identify such specifications and when it comes to carrying out the works can easily demonstrate that certain materials are now difficult to obtain are on long order or are not available. The contractor, however, will arrive at the conclusion, very probably correctly, that the architect or surveyor is not really quite up to the job and may take a calculated risk in saying that other materials specified are no longer available, irrespective of whether they are or are not, for the architect or surveyor not to know any better. By adopting this approach early on in the contract and, should it be successful, continuing with the same tactic the contractor may be able to save himself much time and money by passing off inferior materials and thereby increase his profit. This could be another instance where the architect or surveyor could find control of the works rapidly slipping from his grasp. By the nature of things, the newer materials replacing those no longer available introduce the more "advanced" methods now used in lieu of out-dated practices with the result that the variations both in the materials and workmanship produce so many extras that the final account may become a positive nightmare to settle. This situation needs to be differentiated from those cases where the architect or surveyor quite deliberately specifies materials or even a way of working which has fallen out of common use simply because he believes them to be superior to current practice. This can be quite a common necessity in dealing with existing buildings, particularly older dwellings, but in these circumstances the surveyor will need to know in advance that the materials he is specifying really are available and, when he makes requirements for a standard of workmanship, that there are operatives capable of achieving that standard. In the case of materials it is probably a fairly easy matter to check where they are obtainable and to forestall the contractors anticipated grumble by giving the name and address of one or, preferably, more than one supplier. The requirement for a standard of workmanship is a little different in that it may be necessary either to ensure in advance that all the contractors invited to tender are able to carry out the work to the appropriate standard or alternatively that there is a sub-contractor, or again preferably more than

348

one who is able to do so. In the latter case obviously the sub-contractors should be named if they are all considered to be of equal capability or perhaps, in some circumstances, a single firm should be selected and nominated for the work.

At the beginning of this part of the book it has been mentioned that one of the objectives of this particular stage in the building process is the need to arrive at a firm price for the proposed works, subject, as we shall see later, to certain inevitable caveats in regard to the inflationary aspects of increases in the costs of wages and materials. The feasibility study will have produced approximate estimates but now, with a fully documented scheme, it should be possible for a contractor to produce a detailed figure for the work. Sometimes, however, circumstances, such as indecision or pressure for speed from the client being obvious examples, prevent the scheme being developed to its fullest extent. In other circumstances an architect or surveyor may not be able to decide what to specify as he has been dilatory or has not researched the requirements of a particular aspect of current legislation, either national or local. In yet other cases he may deliberately leave certain matters involving decisions by the client to a much later stage when the works are in progress. What is at risk here are not items which the architect or surveyor has forgotten, since the number of these in any job will vary according to the particular architect's or surveyors experience and application, but known items which have not been decided upon in detail.

The usual way of providing for items not fully decided upon is by the inclusion of provisional sums in the specification. For example a specification might include a clause thus "provide the provisional sum of £300 for eradication of dry rot in the kitchen floor" or another "provide the provisional sum of £500 for works as required by the Fire Officer to improve the means of escape provisions to the property". For items left for the client selection until later it is usual to include Prime Cost (PC) sums for example "provide the PC sum of £600 for the supply and delivery of kitchen units to the client's selection." We shall see later that the contract preliminaries need to define and prescribe how these sums are to be treated in the build up of the contract figure but at this stage we are merely concerned with the desirability of their inclusion in the specification. Furthermore, towards the end of the specification, it is usual to find that the surveyor or architect has included a clause to the following effect: "Provide the sum of £500 for contingencies to be used only as directed by the surveyor and to be deducted in full or in part from the contract sum if not required."

It must be accepted that on a scheme of repairs and alterations to existing buildings of any size it is impossible to provide for every eventuality in advance. However disparaging clients may be about the inclusion of a contingency sum it is common and accepted practice for such a sum to be included in a specification and for it to be carried forward into the contract figure. Provided it is of a reasonable amount it would be right for any architect or surveyor to resist its exclusion from the contract sum even although many clients suggest that its inclusion should not be necessary if the architect or surveyor is doing his job properly. The question always arises as to what is a reasonable amount as well as to the type of occurrence whereby the contingency sum becomes expendable. To a great extent this figure will already have been settled at the feasibility study stage since a suitable figure should have been included at that time to give an overall impression of the likely order of cost. However, as the scheme is developed it may be that the approximate costs have to be revised either upward or downward as appropriate and, accordingly, the contingency sum should be varied accordingly to 10% of the estimated approximate cost, this percentage being considered by most practitioners as reasonable. As to occurrences justifying its use, it is of course not included to be used to pay for the architect or surveyor's mistakes, but to meet the cost of genuinely unforseeable items. There will of course, be cases where the contingency sum varies from the strict 10% stated. Some architects and surveyors do this deliberately in order to give no indication to the tendering contractors as to the contract sum envisaged.

What of provisional and prime cost sums? It must be admitted that in the case of the latter it is often extremely difficult to persuade a client, or in many cases his wife, to decide at an early stage as to the fittings which are required. It is often unreasonable to expect them to do so since many clients feel that they will have a better idea when the works are under way and they can judge the standard and quality needed. Many lay clients are incapable of envisaging matters that the architect or surveyor takes for granted. Perhaps however, this is a reflection on the architect or surveyor rather than the client, but the advice must be that every effort should be made to obtain client's selection before tendering stage, so that the project documentation can be fully prepared reflecting all the client's requirements. So often selection during the course of the works not only far exceeds the PC sums allowed, but also has further consequences necessitating alterations to the architect's or surveyor's preconceived details and thus involving variations on the contract sum and extra charges.

As to provisional sums the aim must be to eliminate these altogether in theory. By the time tendering stage is reached the surveyor or architect should have solved all problems in relation to the works. For example all exposure works should have been carried out so that the extent of work previously hidden can be fully ascertained. The requirements of all authorities should have been researched and incorporated in the scheme so that at the tendering stage the only unquantifiable items to be included in the estimate will be the contingency sum and as few as possible PC items on which it has proved impossible for understandable reasons to obtain the clients decision. Having said that it must be acknowledged that there are bound to be occasions when a client, for example, is in occupation at the stage of project documentation and tendering and will not be put to the inconvenience of exposure works. If this is the case, the architect or surveyor has no alternative but to include a provisional sum to cover not only the exposure works but also the repairs to hidden parts. In these circumstances it is essential that great care is taken in pitching the sum to be included in the contract at a level appropriate to the likely costs. This is, of course, stating the obvious, but is in practice easier said than done and it is in the nature of building works that invariably the sums included are far too small resulting in substantial extras being added to the contract sum at the end of the day. This can have serious consequences to a client working to a tight budget and therefore it is highly adviseable, indeed essential, to discuss the possible outcome of a decision to defer exposure works until the contract is under way and discuss fully the possibility of extra sums being necessary at the end of the day.

It has been stressed repeatedly that the tendering should produce as accurate an estimate of the total cost of the project as it is possible to achieve. This can never be done as previously discussed, however, if the project documentation is incomplete or not fully developed. It is quite possible to prepare a specification which is full of provisional sums, contains many PC items and culminates in a substantial contigency sum. The outcome might consist of tenders which are no more than half way between the approximate costs incorporated in the feasibility study and what could have been, in different circumstances, an accurate reflection of contractors considered estimates for the work. It will then become more a matter of luck whether at the end of the contract the final account is anywhere near the estimate figure as embodied in the contract sum. It is far more likely, however, that there will be a wild discrepancy between the two and by the nature of building works it will not be likely that this will end in the clients favour. At the very least the architect or surveyor may find himself in difficulties explaining the differences and, if he has not carefully monitored progress during the contract, could conceivably find himself in considerable difficulties over the bills for extras. It is generally inattention to detail, lack of care or eagerness on the architect's or surveyor's part to get on to another job which results in specifications of this nature which always present problems with very dissatisfied clients at the end of the contract. It is not, however, quite on the same level as the deplorable practice of a few architects or surveyors dealing with householders of fairly limited means who deliberately put in low approximate estimates, obtain tenders which are not greatly above those approximate figures but know full well that the final account will be far in excess of the original figures. This practice, related as it is to the architect's or surveyors desire to obtain and retain the job to keep himself busy and in a position to earn fees is, of course, far worse but the two are not dissimilar in outcome since both produce clients with a very jaundiced view of the building professions. In the one case it is sharp practice on the architect or surveyor's part, in the other incompetence, but both have led to the client being faced with far higher bills than he had a right to expect if the architect or surveyor had been acting in a truly professional and competent manner on his behalf. Of course, a client caught once in this way or the more knowledgeable client may well, on the next occasion, take the precaution of running through the specification with a fine tooth comb and extract a total of the provisional and prime cost sums together with the contingency sum for comparison with the total tender figures. If the proportion is unduly high the architect or surveyor may find himself in the awkward position of having to justify the situation and perhaps arguing for the retention of some, if not all, of the items in the contract sum. Professional or Institutional clients do this as a matter of routine. By this means a client can expose the rather cynical practice of some architects and surveyors in boosting the contingency sum to cover, hopefully all eventualities, beyond the normal 10% by distributing, at suitable intervals throughout the specification, further "contingency sums" disguised as provisional sums in the high hope that the client will not notice. The shrewd client will spot just such a practice and the offending architect or surveyor may find that the client will take the perfectly correct attitude and say that he will accept a tender but on the basis that certain clauses are deleted from the contract specification and the contract sum reduced accordingly.

So far in this chapter the less desirable features that can creep into some specifications have been mentioned and the consequences that can follow during the course of the contract, and more particularly at the final account stage, have been discussed. With these examples as a cautionary tale, it is now possible for formulate a list of the essential attributes in a specification so that the long term aim of producing a sound job to the satisfaction of the client both from the aethestic point of view and that of his pocket and which will also bring credit on the architect or surveyor can be achieved. A consideration can then be made of some of the methods available by which these attributes can be provided, some which seem to be better than others and also some of the sources to which a surveyor or architect may turn for assistance towards achieving these aims.

As discussed, difficulties will arise if a specification is deficient in one or other of the following characteristics:

(a) It should be complete. By this is meant that it should be sufficiently complete for the proposed works. There are degrees of "completeness" and there may be cases where a specification will be sufficiently (as we shall see) complete for its purpose wihout necessarily including every nut and bolt.

(b) It must be readily understood. By this is meant that it should be capable of being understood not only by other surveyors or architects and the hierarchy of building firms of some size but also by the average building operative and even by a lay person with a smattering of knowledge of building operations.

(c) It must be wholly relevant to the works. It should not contain items which are inapplicable merely as an insurance against eventualities.

(d) It must be up-to-date and apt for the works proposed. By this is meant that it should not be counched in out-of-date terms utilising materials which cannot be obtained or methods of workmanship which are unattainable.

(e) From the specification the contractors tendering should be able to produce an accurate estimate of the cost of the proposed work. For this the specification should contain as few provisional and prime cost sums as possible and those which are included together with any contingency sum should be realistically assessed before inclusion.

There is no point in denying that to write a presentable complete and authoritative specification to incorporate the above characteristics, sound knowledge, skill and, above all, a degree of stamina are required. Not many architects or surveyors have the tenacity to build up a specification for a job of any size from first principles without consulting other aids to specification writing for ready made clauses. Possibly a newly qualified surveyor or architect might be in a better position to do this than a slightly more mature practitioner since the newcomer will not have had the chance to forget so many of the essential details of materials and workmanship that are necessary for incorporation in most specifications. The reverse, however, may also be true if the newly qualified practitioner has only had drawing board experience. These details will be found in the up-to-date British Standards and Codes of Practice together with other documented advice for example Agrément Certificates and the codes of trade organisations such as the Timber Research and Development Association and the Copper Development Association along with other authoritative advice culled from textbooks, papers etc. It is the very plethora of documents coupled with their size that causes the problems because there can be no short cuts. It is absolutely essential to read them all from cover to cover as so many contain alternatives which require consideration and selection of the appropriate guidance or advice both as to materials and workmanship. The possession of a catalogue list of Standards and Codes on its own is no earthly use as it is essential to be familiar with the detailed contents of each. The sheer effort involved in doing this is prodigious and it is very easy along the way to lose the thread of the researches and to become side tracked into interesting by-ways which may have nothing to do with the job in hand. The result is often that sections are left out entirely or, in other cases, items are not followed through to their logical conclusion.

It would be no bad thing, however, if every architect or surveyor at some time in his professional career, preferably in the early stages, had to prepare a specification in just the same way described above. It would never be found less than an illuminating experience. In the case of the over confident it would serve to temper some of that excess exuberance and might engender a modicum of humility. In the case of those who are terrified of the prospect, then once the task was under way a certain confidence might develop as the realisation dawned that perhaps the experience was not quite as bad as had been expected. Assuming that a satisfactory conclusion was eventually reached then a warm glow of a job successfully completed would be justified. While the next specification might not be tackled with enthusiasm it would not hold the same degree of terror.

The difficulty with writing a specification from first principles is always to know if a document satisfactory for its purpose has been produced. There is nothing like a real job to stimulate the mind in preference to the coldness of an exercise yet it would be distinctly unfair to the client, not to say unwise, from the architect's or surveyor's point of view, to proceed and utilise a specification prepared as an exercise for the purpose of obtaining estimates and putting works in hand. A further check would be absolutely essential even after the architect or surveyor has read the document through and through on completion. The necessity for this further check rather pre-supposes that the architect or surveyor is a member of a larger organisation and not working solely on his own account. If the latter were the case then working from first principles would be too risky a method to adopt for writing a specification for a real job and could not be recommended. Other methods would have to be adopted in these circumstances whereas, with more experienced colleagues or superiors to rely on for checking, a satisfactory document could be produced with every confidence that the client's best interests were protected. It is very probable that, in the process of checking, it will be found that quite a substantial dialogue will develop between the writer and checker, the extent depending on how well the architect or surveyor has done his task. If the specification prepared from first principles is a good one it is highly likely that the checker will learn something himself from the exercise which probably only goes to show that there is more than one way of writing a satisfactory specification. The checker will of course pay special attention to completeness and any sections of doubtful interpretation in the phraseology but can also examine the specification without preconceived ideas, not only to see that the client's interests are protected in full but also from the viewpoint of understanding by the contractor's estimator and the contractor's foreman for the later time when the job will be carried out on site.

The natural inclination for anyone who has had to prepare a specification from first principles is to make sure that the considerable effort involved is not wasted and that as much mileage as possible can be derived from it in the future. Thus, when the next job comes along the earlier specification will form the basis for the new and to this will probably be added any experience deduced from using the earlier specification to obtain estimates, for supervising the work and for settling the final account. So experience is built up and perhaps, it could be said, that if the experience on each subsequent job is continually monitored and fed back to be reflected in the documentation all should be well. This should be a far cry from merely adding further "safety" clauses. Perhaps it is, in some practices, but it does not always seem to work that way for various reasons except perhaps for really exceptionally single minded architects or surveyors. One reason is that when an architect or surveyor is working on his own on various jobs of differing types (and this can happen in a large practice or large organisation as well as in a small one or with an architect or surveyor working on his own account) it is usually the most recent specification, or perhaps the last two or three, which are consulted and earlier experience tends to be overlooked as time goes on or becomes so spread over earlier documents and files as to be too diluted and difficult to recover for use when required. This is, of course, the chief failing of relying on any old specification to build up a specification for a new job which is, in fact, the way most newcomers joining an office have to approach the task. It is highly unlikely that an office would be prepared to allow the time for newly joining member to prepare a specification from first principles. Much more likely the newcomer will be handed an old specification with the injunction to "follow it" because that is how the practice or organisation likes to see it done. If the newcomer is lucky and the old specification happens to be of a job of a distinctly similar character and of very recent origin and furthermore prepared by someone who, if not an expert, is at least up-to-date and reasonably competent, then the old specification will be very useful. More often, however, it will be for an entirely different type of job, may be of venerable age having been in turn prepared perhaps from even older specifications and will almost surely contain items inappropriate to the new job while omitting others definitely required. The danger is that the newly arrived architect or surveyor will be overwhelmed by the contents of the old specification and incapable of thinking clearly on the requirements for the new job. The result may well be a specification along the lines of some of those described earlier in this chapter with the consequential distressing and confusing figures on tendering coupled with inability to establish control on supervising the job resulting in a final account bearing little resemblance to the accepted estimate.

Another way of preserving the fruits of the considerable labour involved in writing a specification from first principles would be to keep the basic form and add and subtract from it as experience grows and develops. The result is a "Type" or "Office" specification covering all sorts of different circumstances and for differing types of buildings and forms of construction to which the architect or surveyor turns for the "bones" of a specification for a new job, extracting from it what is needed and adding to it as required. This is indeed the system adopted by many practices and organisations who purport to maintain a "type" specification built up over the years and to which has been contributed the benefit and experience gained by all the members working in the practice or organisation over a period of time. Of course, there are two ways in which a Type specification can be used, one good and one bad. As already mentioned earlier on in this Chapter, there are those organisations which, having perhaps been caught out on occasions, work on the principle of including everything and leave the contractor to ignore those items not pertinent to the job. It is to be hoped that the disadvantages of this way of operating have been sufficiently stressed as it most certainly does not seem to lead to the all embracing insurance which it is intended to provide. Another way in which the Type specification can be used is much better in that in preparing the new specification the surveyor draws on the clauses which are appropriate, rejects or excludes those which are not, and adds new clauses which may be unique for the new job in hand. This sounds ideal, of course, and indeed if everything is managed as it should be in practice, this can be as good as system as the best of the other methods. The trouble lies in the time and effort necessary to keep a Type specification in a satisfactory condition to provide a sound basic source for the future. In the smaller practices the pressure of work tends to mean that the feedback of information is somewhat lacking or at best desultory, the implications of the feedback, such as it is, on sections already included in the Type specification seldom being considered as fully as they might be, and the necessary review of material every few years to update or weed out obsolete information being inclined to be overlooked. It is possible for the same faults to arise in the Type or Office specification of the larger practices but generally the resources of larger organisations are able to release one member of the organisation to be responsible for the maintenance of the material. Provided this person is sufficiently interested in the subject to carry it out with a degree of enthusiasm, diligence and competence, is likely to remain with the organisation for a considerable length of time, so that he thereby becomes really involved in the task, coupled with the fact that he is also a strong personality able to extract, challenge and discuss the feedback information from other members of the staff (who would generally far rather be dealing with current problems than raking over the past) all should be well. The trouble is that there are few such people available in the first place and fewer still prepared to undertake such an unrewarding task for a considerable number of years, involving as it does a certain element of self sacrifice. Those that do take on the job can tend, in the larger organisations, to be administratively minded and, if they take to the work, can become increasingly divorced from the practicalities of building to the extent that the remainder of the staff can become lax in supplying feedback information. The result is that gradually the Type specification becomes to be treated with less than the proper degree of respect. Often it is found that the Type specification has fallen a long way behind current practice and it may be necessary to make a completely fresh start.

If a newcomer to a job is not given an old office specification to work from (or rejects the idea of working from one), has no access to Type or Office specification yet also has no time to prepare his own specification from first principles then he must turn to other source material and consideration must now be given to those other sources which are available.

There are text books, of course, but it has been said with a degree of truth that there are no satisfactory treatises on the subject of specification writing. The truth lies in the fact that it is probably impossible to write such a treatise because of the wide variations in the general or specific requirements for specifications. Most of the books available provide the broad advice and indeed, it must be admitted, many of same general conclusions as set out in this Chapter. The sample specifications provided in the books, however, tend to be limited to a particular job and therefore fall into the same category as the "old office" specification. Most of them also tend to have fallen into a state of being considerably out of date and smack of practice going back some years. The lack of recent sound text book advice on the subject of specification writing may be due to the difficulties presented but may also reflect the general lack of interest in the subject over the last couple of decades in the architectural and surveying professions, a lack which can now be seen to have had disastrous consequences. One text book couples some sound general advice together with an extensive check list. This is designed to bring to mind varying aspects of typical jobs and thereby jog the memory of the architect and surveyor. With the aid of the check list, it is said, the architect or surveyor should be able to build up a specification without missing salient points, but he would still need to turn to much the same source material as he would do if he was building up the specification from first principles. The clauses would still need to be built up sentence by sentence. Check lists are undoubtedly useful in many respects and if an architect or surveyor does indeed find them of help then there is every reason for fully comprehensive lists to be kept for the purpose.

An invaluable publication which at the time of writing is in its 79th Edition is "Specification" published by the Architectural Press Ltd., 9 Queen Anne's Gate, London SW1H 9BY. This consists of 1,200 pages of technical text, standard specification clauses and product information plus much advertisement material and at even £45.00 represents a good array of very useful information unobtainable elsewhere in a single publication. In former days when the costs involved in publication and printing seemed to be much less, Specification used to be published annually but now the publishers make a critical assessment of changes in regulations, standards and products before deciding whether it is worthwhile to prepare a new edition. Publication is therefore intermittent but when it does take place the opportunity is realised to update most of the sections and each new edition usually contains some brand new sections or entirely re-written sections from the previous edition. Referencing is generally fairly straightforward as there is a comprehensive subject index and there is a quick reference system in regard to data on products and services through a directory of manufacturers and trade names with addresses and telephone numbers.

It can well be imagined that the non-standard and individual approach to specification writing, which has always existed in the past, produces a wide diversity of finished product within a broad generally agreed framework. As we have seen, this situation has been somewhat aggravated over the past couple of decades by the introduction of many new building products and the substantial changes which have taken place in building techniques. At the same time a considerable expansion in the volume of building work has taken place to make up not only for the losses incurred during the Second World War but also for the general stagnation in many types of vital development which had occurred in the period between the two World Wars. The pressures arising have meant that not all practitioners have been able to keep abreast and many poor specifications have been produced as a result. Although the buildings covered by these documents were eventually completed, no doubt the cost in delays and disruption to previously arranged plans of work, necessitated by changes in design as work proceeded, was very high and, in the main, it was the client who had to pay. Even apart from the aspect of building failures and poor detailing, criticism of the industry grew in intensity and most of the delays and extra costs were attributed to a lack of clear decision taking by the clients themselves and changes of mind during the course of the works. The contracting side of the industry rightly pointed out those schemes which were well thought out and well documented to begin with and where the initial intentions remained unvaried through to completion and cited these as being the most successful. Both contractors and the clients therefore tended to turn on the professionals; contractors felt that they were getting blamed for a state of affairs brought about more by a lack of clear direction than anything else, the clients felt that they had been badly let down by their advisers on the basis that they should have been told the consequences of their indecision and changes of mind. The upshot was the financing of a feasiblity study by the Economic Development Council for Building in 1968 to ascertain whether it was possible to develop a national specification. The Council considered that the general standard of building specification was in urgent need of improvement and concluded that the widespread use of a national library of specification clauses would substantially increase the productivity of professionals and builders alike. In consequence the first edition of the National Building Specification was published in 1973 by NBS Services, Mansion House Chambers, The Close,

Newcastle upon Tyne, NE1 3RC on behalf of National Building Specification Ltd. a wholly owned subsidiary of the RIBA.

The National Building Specification is a highly rationalised, well researched specification text with accompanying guidance notes facilitating the production of specifications to a sound modern standard with preambles to bills of quantities. There are two versions, the Full Version and a Small Jobs Version. Since first publication in 1973 major changes in technical content, arrangement and presentation have been made.

At the time of writing the National Building Specification is available as a subscription service to practices and organisations at a charge depending on the number of technical personnel in the group. As an indication of cost for a practice with between one and four architects or surveyors, the current charge for the first year is £120.00 with an annual renewal subscription of £85.00. The first years' payment for a practice or organisation with 100 or more technical staff rises to £420 with a renewal annual subscription of £290 and there are various bands in between. Educational establishments, public libraries and contractors are charged at the lowest rate.

Subscribers receive the text in loose leaf form in a set of six binders and the text is accompanied with guidance notes and is kept up to date and expanded by quarterly issues of revised and new sections. The subscription service includes both Full Version and the Small Jobs Version which can be used by itself or intermixed, section by section, with the Full Version according to the needs of a particular job. The Small Jobs Version is a selection of basic clauses and guidance notes from the NBS Full Version Text and is about one third the size, being updated at the same time as the Full Version. Both can be obtained either in CI/SfB or the Standard Method of Measurement order and subscribers choose which version they prefer. Extra copies in the sets of binders are supplied to subscribers for use in their offices for an initial charge of £75.00 with a renewal subscription of £30.00.

Quite separately, the Small Jobs Version, as described above, is available as a book with no updating service. The current 1980 Edition in either CI/SfB or SMM order is available looseleaf in a single binder based on the latest subscription service text and the 1980 JCT Form of Contract at £35.00.

Exceptionally useful additional services are also available from NBS Services including mark-up copies of both the Full Version and the Small Jobs Version. These contain the NBS clauses only, without the guidance notes, and are suitable for the preparation of draft specifications for typing. The mark-up copies available to subscribers are priced at £15.00 for the Full Version and £7.50 for the Small Jobs Version, the latter also being available to non-subscribers at £10.00 per copy. A mixture of the subscription service Full Version and Small Jobs Version excluding sections not relevant to a particular job can be obtained to special order at 3.5 pence per page at the time of writing.

Mark-up copies prepared as a proof for typing can, of course, be typed in the office, proof read and corrected as necessary. NBS Services, however, offer a sophisticated typing service to relieve offices of this chore which includes a certain amount of limited checking of content other than technical. The checking ensures that all clauses are either deleted or retained, i.e. all alternatives on offer have been selected, all insert facilities are complete and handwriting is legible. Any queries are cleared by telephone and at the same time critical dates settled, the order (SfB or SMM) confirmed, extra title pages or contents pages discussed and type of paper selected. The typing is produced from a central memory store of standard clauses with the specifier's inserts and additions typed in. A top copy and a carbon copy are produced together with a temporary magnetic memory tape holding the edited job specification text. Using the carbon copy the specification is proof read and any corrections made. The top copy and the original draft are then returned to the specifier ready for photo-copying. Alternatively even that task and the collating of the sheets can be carried out by NBS Services. The temporary magnetic memory tape is retained by NBS Services for one month as a precaution against the top copy being lost or damaged in tansit or in the specifier's office. The service is said to be less expensive than conventional typing, proof reading and correcting due to the use of the memory bank and word processors.

A two stage service can also be provided in that changes can easily be made if required with the automatic word processing if pages are returned. A facility also exists for larger practices, which might have particularly strong views on certain additional clauses, who wish to include details of certain proprietary products for fairly routine use and who might wish to ensure that official office policy on specifications is fully implemented at all times for the production of standard office specifications based on NBS and for these to be held on permanent magnetic tape separately from the NBS master memory. This might be extremely useful for a practice which deals only with a particular type of job since the office standard specification can be quickly produced and tailored to the actual requirements.

Additionally, specifications can be typed on A3 paper and photographically reduced to A4 reducing the bulk by about 25%. A slimmer document is produced as a result and photocopying costs are reduced. For large jobs and where many copies are required pages can be printed and all specifications, however, produced, can be bound.

The National Building Specification is a library of clauses from which a selection is made to produce a job specification. It is not a standard specification since all clauses are optional. The specifier is free to choose and to modify them to suit the particular needs of each job. The text is designed to allow easy deletion and alteration of clauses and the addition of supplementary information and additional clauses. Within each section materials clauses are kept separate from workmanship clauses and the guidance notes are provided alongside for ease of reference to help the specifier. The clauses are written in a precise imperative style described by some as "the new staccato" and which may come as something of a shock to those used to writing lengthy specification clauses. NBS Services make no apologies for this saying that the English language has been "regimented" so that it ceases to be gracious and flowing and becomes merely a means by which information can be transmitted with economy and precision. This is maintained as being necessary so that the NBS can be more comprehensive than traditional specifications but without becoming unduly cumbersome. Since it is anticipated that users will wish to insert their own clauses some trouble has been taken to rationalise the method adopted for presenting the NBS clauses so that additional clauses can be written in the same style. The saving of words is achieved by leaving out technical content which is covered elsewhere, technical content which is not necessary and words and phrases which are grammatically not necessary. An example in relation to coarse aggregate for concrete will suffice to show the difference. Traditionally this might appear as:

> Coarse aggregate shall be clean natural gravel or crushed stone complying with BS 882 and shall be free from chalk, clay, organic or other deleterious matter. The particles shall be well and evenly graded to conform to the limits given in Table 1 of BS 882 for the maximum size aggregate appropriate to the concrete mix. Different gradings shall be stored separately.

In the National Building Specification this would be reduced to:

> Coarse aggregate: to BS 882, gradings to Table 1, store different gradings separately.

A sound point is made that although the specification has to be read through as a whole at various stages of the building process it serves as a source of reference for much of the time. Each clause is therefore provided with a key word as an aid to scanning so that the contents of a page can be examined at a glance. The key words can be of different kinds provided they are informative in the context of the clauses. Products and materials are relatively straightforward e.g.

Coarse aggregates:
Bricks:
Concrete tiles:

Others can relate to parts of a building such as:

Jambs:
Soffits:
Reveals:

Or perhaps a general subject or process for example:

Bonding:
Laying:
Mixing:

Or for that matter conditions of work:

Cold weather:
Strong sunshine:
Fog:

Materials which are sometimes referred to in NBS as products or components may be specified by reference to a British Standard or by means of the makers name e.g.

Clay floor tiles: to BS 1234.
Size ....
Finish ....
Colour ....
Manufacturer and reference ....

This could be completed thus:

Clay floor tiles: to BS 1234.
Size: 150 × 150 × 15mm.
Finish: Diagonal ribbed.
Colour: Peat.
Manufacturer and reference: Smith Tile Company Ribtile 103.

Materials are classified in groups related to the "form", bricks, pipes, sheets etc. following generally the category of the CI/SfB Table 2 division. Workmanship clauses in each work section are grouped in sub-sections such as "preparation of base", "laying", "protection", etc. At the beginning of some sections there are "schedules" which define types of work by cross referencing to individual materials and workmanship clauses. Brickwork is an example where the required brick, block, bond, mortar, etc. which are all separately specified may be set out as a "type" of brickwork for example "Facing brickwork above dpc" or "Manhole brickwork".

Cross referencing to and from drawings, bills of quantities and schedules of work to the job specifications can be kept simple by using only the work section codes, for example ceramic wall tiling is S33, or schedule references such as F11/2 for facing brickwork. Cross referencing to individual clauses should not be made because each work section should be read as a whole.

As the drawings for the scheme are developed it is recommended that the specification is developed at the same time in the following general stages:

1. Select relevant work section from the CI/SfB Table 2.
2. Select materials clauses required, inserting additional information where necessary and checking that the sizes, colours, strengths etc. chosen under a British Standard Specification or from a chosen manufacturers are available, all in accordance with the guidance notes.
3. Delete those materials clauses not required.
4. Write new materials clauses in the same style where NBS does not provide for the particular item required and code in the same manner from Table 2.
5. Select the workmanship clauses applicable ensuring that those clauses relating to the selected materials are retained.
6. Delete clauses not required including any conflicting alternative clauses.

The range of clauses is wide and great care should be taken to include only those required for the particular job. Only those clauses which the specifier is prepared to enforce should be included. As discussed previously, there is always a danger for the inexperienced when using old specifications, type specifications or in this case the NBS standard clauses of including too much just to be on the safe side. Although this is an error on the right side it is still one to be avoided since the inclusion of superfluous items tend to undermine the authority of the remainder.

The National Building Specification represents a radical departure from earlier practice and introduces an entirely new feature to the building scene the like of which has not previously been available. It has clearly been well researched and rationally thought out and deserves support. It may certainly help to improve the comprehensiveness and clarity of specifications used in support of drawings and measured items in bills of quantities. However, as with all job specifications the final outcome rests on the expertise of the specifier even more so than on the quality of the library of clauses. The more expert the user the more skill will be brought to bear so that only those sections relevant will be included, the appropriate alternatives are correctly decided upon the blank spaces properly completed and new clauses added complete in themselves and tailored to suit the style of NBS.

Obviously NBS has been developed with architects principally in mind and indeed a rebate on the premiums to ABS Insurance Agency for indemnity insurance is available to architects who use the current NBS Subscription Service. Obviously also the greatest benefit from NBS will be derived from its use on the largest of projects for new buildings. Yet with the Small Jobs Version and the appreciation that anything that purports to be comprehensive must clearly contain much that may not be required on a particular job (for example on roof coverings it is unlikely that any job will use more than say two out of the dozen covered in detail) the NBS must provide more rather than less assistance to the preparation of an appropriate job specification than would be the case if the surveyor or architect were operating without it. There may well be very small jobs where its use may be too cumbersome and seem like taking a sledgehammer to crack a nut, in which case the architector or surveyor will probably prepare a specification from first principles. Even then there can be very few jobs where there is so little description of materials and workmanship that a reference to some document or other is not necessary, in which case a reference to the NBS text would probably be better than to any other in the first instance. Certainly, in the case of the typical job envisaged in this book, involving not only repairs and alterations within an existing structure but with, in effect, a completely new building added on, however small in scale, NBS should prove an ideal aid to the production of the job specification. Whatever method of help or standard is adopted, the specification for such a typical job will inevitably be large. Similarly NBS would be of help for all larger jobs and particularly for those where a quantity surveyor is brought in who is sympathetic to the idea of NBS. Where on a smaller job its use proves to be too cumbersome it could still serve as a useful checklist in the same way as an office standard specification might do in similar circumstances if it too proved to be too large for the particular job.

One of the great advantages of NBS over what might appear at first sight the similar production of an office standard specification is that the updating to keep it abreast with current British Standards and Codes of Practice etc, is done centrally, so that one of the main difficulties in maintaining an office standard specification is overcome. It is not necessary for staff time within the practice or organisation to be devoted to the collection of feedback information and updating which tends in most practices to be thrust into the background when there are more interesting and profitable things to do. This aspect of continuous development and improvement is of vital importance yet, as we have seen, there is still scope within the NBS system for individual preferences to be taken into account and for special items to be included.

Of course, up to now, all the sources which have been considered have provided material for what might be called the common ground of the specification, the preliminaries, giving the conditions under which the contract is to be carried out and the materials and workmanship, which will determine the quality of the final product. These, as we have said, are in fact common to most specifications and subject only to comparatively limited variation commensurate usually with the size of the job. This does not of course apply to the final section of the specification coming under the heading of "The Works". This section consists of a description of the actual work to be carried out, in effect an inventory of things to be done, unique to that particular job, certainly in so far as the position in a particular building is concerned, if not in terms of the precise operation. Here the architect or surveyor is entirely on his own, but it is obvious that the production of this section will have regard to, and will certainly be influenced by, the way in which the earlier parts of the specification have been prepared. It is important to bear in mind, however, in alteration and repair work in particular, to keep "The Works" section entirely separate from the earlier sections since it is preferable for the contractor to be able to measure and price from this section, collecting together in one item or under one heading all the particular trades to complete a particular operation. Specifications where the works and the materials and workmanship are inexorably mixed can be very confusing indeed and cause untold difficulty to both the contractors estimator and operative alike. This can happen if trade order is used and the works of that particular trade follow on the materials and workmanship clauses. This is fine for new works, since it more or less follows the order that trades appear on the site. It may also be quite satisfactory to divide a specification into two separate parts where, as we have in the typical job envisaged in this book, there is a new extension, virtually a new building in its own right, so that the new work is kept clear of the repairs and alterations and trade order used for that part. For repairs and alterations however, it is far better to put items in a recognisable order of for example roofs, elevations, in turn followed by the interior, room by room around the building preferably clockwise and to conclude with the services and external work adjacent to the building, fencing etc.

Clearly a surveyor or architect who has been building up his own specification from first principles will carry over the same style into his description of the works. Pomposity, prolixity and a tendency to ambiguity may be hard to avoid if that is the writer's way with words and has already been exemplified in the earlier parts of the specification. However, the need for straightforward plain English has already been stressed and this applies equally to the description of the works. In the case of the use of an old office specification, hopefully for a similar type of job of fairly recent origin, no doubt the surveyor or architect will tend to follow a similar style as that used in the old document and may even copy clauses direct. Many of the operations carried out in repair and alteration work, for example renewing defective fittings, filling in old openings or cutting new openings in walls are of an identical or very similar kind in one job after another. It is very often just the position in the building that is unique to a particular job with such commonly occurring items.

A standard office specification may, of course, be extended to include a number of commonly required operations clauses. For example the work involved in taking out old fireplaces and blocking up the openings is an often found item in housing improvement work. The work is probably the same whatever room and perhaps even in whatever building on a large scheme. A standard clause may help to ensure that, for example at the lowest level, the ventilator to the existing flue is not forgotten or the new skirting across the opening. Such common items can be set out in a section at the beginning of the description of the works and where occurring in the building be referenced back to the appropriate clause for example:

FIRST FLOOR
NORTH WEST ROOMS
Take out existing fireplace and block up opening as clause:

For users of the National Building Specification NBS Services recommend that the description of works, which they refer to as the Schedule of Works, should obviously be complete but should also be as concise as possible and contain:

(a) The minimum number of words to identify clearly each kind of work. Cross references to the materials and workmanship section are most useful as appropriate.

367

(b) Any additional information not given in the earlier sections of the specification or shown on the drawings.

Typical examples quoted are thus:

ROOM 11
Remove fireplace and hearth. Block up in half brick thick common brickwork F11/2; 255 × 150mm clayware airbrick; plaster P31/1 with 225 × 150mm plaster louvred ventilator; make good to timber floor; new skirting H25/2, profile to match existing.
Block up openings to Rooms 10 and 12 in half brick thick common brickwork F11/2; plaster P31/1 both sides.

It is appropriate to conclude this part of the chapter covering the traditional form of specification for repairs and alterations with a reminder on a points which can become overlooked in the General Preliminaries and Conditions of Contract if a standard printed form of contract is not being used.

As discussed earlier, it is important to exclude as many provisional sums and prime cost items as possible. However, it is inevitable that some will be required and therefore it is important that their meaning should be defined and the contractor instructed as to how they are to be treated in his estimate. It is customary for the former to be treated as complete and to which no additional sums need be added while the latter is only a basic cost to which the contractor must add his costs for taking delivery, fixing costs, overheads and profit on a supply item and for taking delivery, attendance upon cutting away and making good for sub-contracting items. In addition the contractor will need to be directed to include in his estimate the cash discounts allowable under PC sums to nominated sub-contractors, usually $2\frac{1}{2}\%$, or nominated suppliers usually 5% or if GC/Wks/1, the Government contract, is followed again $2\frac{1}{2}\%$.

Items often overlooked are the charges which may be raised by statutory undertakers and local authorities for work which they may need to carry out. For example the supply undertakings for gas, electricity and water may need to bring new mains in from the street and make the appropriate connections to the installations in the building or, as in sometimes the case, to supply pipes near the boundary of the site. It is usual either for the architect or surveyor to obtain or to make an estimate of these costs and to include them as provisional sums in the specification, to which the contractor needs to be instructed whether to add for attendance and any discounts allowable.

A vital aspect in any contract dealing with repairs and alterations to an existing building is insurance and it is necessary to set out the appropriate responsibilities of client and contractor in the preliminaries of the specification so that the contractor can provide for his liabilities in this respect within the estimate. The need to ensure that the respective liabilities are undertaken and appropriate cover maintained during the dangerous period while works are in progress is mentioned in Chapter 11, as it will be one of the vital contract requirements for the architect or surveyor to be satisfied upon before work starts on site.

There can be very few contracts that proceed to conclusion without additional works or variations to the works being required. It is, of course, the ideal to obtain estimates and clients approval to any additional expenditure so that when such charges appear on the account, no eyebrows need be raised. Since this is not always possible, however, it is as well to provide in the specification (and accordingly in the contract if no standard form is being used) for a method of determining daywork charges to provide for labour and material costs with appropriate additions for overheads and profit. The RICS and the National Federation of Building Trades Employers jointly publish a booklet entitled "Definition of Prime Cost of Daywork carried out under a Building Contract" for the convenience of those who choose to use it. A further booklet "A Definition of Prime Cost of Building Works of Jobbing or Maintenance Character" is also published for use where such work is carried out as a main or a separate contract, not incidental to or under a building contract, so that circumstances will dictate which definition should be proposed, bearing in mind that the contractor may counter propose something quite different even apart from different profit rates to those set out by the architect or surveyor.

All estimates for alterations and repairs to existing buildings are generally given by contractors exclusive of VAT. The fact that VAT is charged on works of repair and renewal and not on new construction, remains a substantial base of contention in the construction industry but there has been no success to date for efforts to change the way the tax is applied. Works of improvement not involving repair to an existing building are not usually considered to be subject to VAT and Customs and Excise issue guidance on typical projects considered to be within the exclusion category and works which are not. It has needed success in the courts to persuade Customs and Excise to change their advice in certain circumstances to the benefit of the building owner. For example, underpinning was counted as a repair liable to VAT until a Court of Appeal decision held that the provision of foundations in a different form was new work and accordingly not subject to VAT. At the time of writing however there are proposals to bring within the orbit of VAT a whole range of "improvements" formerly considered exempt from VAT. Obviously at the current rate of 15%, whether or not works are liable to VAT is an important aspect and it is useful to require the contractor in the specification to provide separately in his estimate for the repair works and his further estimate of the VAT liability in accordance with the requirements at the time the estimate is prepared so that proper advice can be given to the client when tenders are received. Obviously the architect or surveyor needs to know the appropriate requirements of the law on VAT in relation to building works and to keep abreast of changes.

Performance specifications

The type of specification which has been discussed up to now in this chapter is a prescriptive specification, in that the architect or surveyor instructs the contractor what is to be done in an imperative manner. To prepare the specification in this form clearly involves the selection of materials and components by the architect or surveyor of a type, in his view, best suited to fulfil the client's requirements. It is the rapid changes in building materials, products and components over the last twenty to thirty years which has made this selection process increasingly difficult. Weighing one product against another has become very burdensome.

Increasingly over this period the information produced by the British Standards Institution and the Agrément Board have helped to ease the task in many respects. The selection of a product complying with an appropriate British Standard or one accompanied by an Agrément Certificate will be an insurance of a certain standard of performance which may well satisfy the client's requirements. The use by many manufacturers of the CfB format for trade literature has also meant that the performance of new products is set out in a logical form enabling very often one new product to be compared with another. The testing, which in other times the architect or surveyor may have asked to be demonstrated to him by the maker or which he might even have done himself, has been done for him.

Although the number of Standards and Certificates has grown substantially, the number is still relatively small compared with the vast range of materials, and components available. Moreover the process of setting standards, testing and obtaining Certificates is time consuming. It has sometimes been said that by the time representatives of the users have met, deliberated in committee, prepared various drafts, agreed on a final draft for publication and

370

the Standard has been printed, so many years have elapsed that the building industry has moved on to some other phase and the standard is already obsolete. The big manufacturers in particular are inclined to say that their own research and testing programmes coupled with their own market research do all that the British Standards Institution and the Agrément Board do, only better. There was a tendency in the late 1960's and the early 1970's, when technology was to be the white hope for the future, to believe this and to discount Standards and Certificates as being rather outmoded. The more adventurous and reckless specified the very latest of everything relying on some of the most outrageous claims of manufacturers and their advertisers on the quality of their products. The consequences are all too apparent in many cases with vast bills arising on remedial measures and, in the more extreme cases, in demolition. Others devised a different method so as to take advantage of what they believed to be all the skills and research carried out by the big manufacturers and suppliers and the growing emergence of specialist sub-contractors, yet also to absolve themselves from the actual responsibility of making the selection of products and components.

The method evolved was in itself derived from the procedures adopted for developing British Standards and consisted of merely setting out the requirements which had to be fulfilled for the various materials, components or elements of construction and leaving the actual selection to the specialist contractor or the manufacturer or supplier of components. This schedule of requirements is known as a "performance specification".

It is possible to conceive the idea of a performance specification being prepared for a whole building say, for example, a range of semi-permanent structures. Client and architect or surveyor would get together and decide on what was required, a document would be prepared and issued to selected manufacturers who in turn would submit estimates, details and illustrations of what could be provided to meet the requirements. The architect or surveyor would check the details submitted to see that there were no obvious errors in complying with the issued requirements and would no doubt advise on which of the manufacturers shoud be selected as being the most likely to produce the best solution and the client could make perhaps the final decision based on appearance. Part of the performance specification would, of course, need to provide for procedures for acceptance of the work on completion, testing of equipment, acceptance trials (perhaps along the lines of the way ships are commissioned and accepted by their owners) the rectification of faults, guarantees and perhaps also maintenance over a period.

To some extent this is an enlargement of a process already fairly common in the provision of mechanical and electrical engineering services in large buildings. Instead of the architect or surveyor selecting and nominating a specialist sub-contractor to advise on requirments and to design and instal a suitable system or a consultant being employed to advise, design, obtain estimates and supervise the installation, the consultant is merely employed to advise and prepare a performance specification. Specialist sub-contractors are then approached, for example on heating and air conditioning work, lift services, or electrical works, for estimates, and the contract is awarded to the sub-contractor who for the lowest prices (after checking by the consultant) will undertake to design, fabricate and instal all the necessary trunking and accessories, etc. and who will purchase and instal all the necessary plant and equipment to fulfil the requirements of the performance specification. Sometimes the checking process is dropped and the lowest estimate accepted with the onus put fair and squarely on the sub-contractor to fulfil the requirements. Even more often the consultant's services are dispensed with at the ordering stage since he is not normally employed to supervise installation as the detailed design is not his. It will be seen therefore that the prescriptive design is passed to others who may or may not be better qualified, both academically and practically, to design and select the most appropriate materials and equipment for the purpose but who will most certainly be influenced to some extent by those commercial considerations from which the professional is normally free. For example new and novel plant and equipment often comes with an attractive discount to the installer to facilitate its introduction and acceptance on the market.

It is to be hoped that no architect, surveyor or engineer advises a client to proceed with the preparation of a performance specification for the sole reason that, having done so, there can be no blame put upon the professional consultant in question. We must assume that all who do so have sound reasons for giving such advice, possibly for example the better use of specialist technical resources, or even just a saving of time, because otherwise, of course, the procedures involved in such a recommendation can appear to be a complete rejection of all professional responsibility and liability. It is thought that no client could possibly be advised to accept this situation without equally valid substitute remedies being available in lieu should something go wrong. Advice to proceed without such equally valid safeguards as would be available in the normal client/professional adviser relationship would amount to negligence in itself.

In normal circumstances, the responsibility for the failure to select and specify materials and components to satisfy the client's requirements would usually lie with the architect, surveyor, or engineer and the client's remedy would be against the professional concerned. In the circumstances involving a performance specification, this responsibility would devolve on the specialist contractor who had been selected to prepare the design and supply the materials to fulfil the requirements. It would be necessary therefore for the contractor to provide equivalent protection to the client to that provided by the indemnity insurance of the professional. Considerable care would have to be taken to ensure that this cover was available over the years since if it was dependent on continual annual premiums the cover would cease if the specialist contractor either failed to keep up the payments or went bankrupt, a not infrequent occurrence in the building industry. It would therefore be sensible for the insurance provision to be purchased outright by means of a single premium, a costly item and one which would be passed on to the client as part of the estimate. However, to procure cover for what may be fairly novel forms of building construction in this manner is not easy and, although it may be obtainable, the price may be considered much too high in relation to the cost of the work, to say nothing of the conditions which might be imposed on both contractor and client by the insurer.

It is not thought that there is a great deal of scope for the use of performance specifications in works solely confined to repairs and alterations. More possibilities may exist where extensions to property are involved provided the long term protection for the client can be provided as discussed above and, even then, in fairly limited circumstances where it can be shown that there are real and definite advantages to the client. Despite advocacy for the use of performance specifications as being more logical and more likely to bring to the benefit of the client the full advantages of the specialist contractor's skill and up to the minute expertise it is just those qualities of newness which are likely to produce results now currently under a cloud. Clients would do better requiring their professional advisers to accept the full responsibility for their decisions in the manner of preparing normal prescriptive specifications. Likewise, professional advisers should have the courage of their convictions and make decisions on what are the proper materials and components to satisfy their client's requirements. The decisions should be based on their own experience, eschewing newness for newnesses sake, derived either from previous jobs or from examining examples of other's work, experience likely to be far less biased than that derived by others in the commercial field. Professionals are far better qualified to make the necessary judgements in fact than anyone else and it is, after all, what professionals are paid to do.

As to the future of the idea of performance specifications, drafting has proved to be difficult as it has not been easy to decide on the full scope of the requirements in a definitive form in view of the lack of experience with the method. Some of the more obvious requirements can become overlooked on occasions because older forms of construction have proved adequate in the past and satisfactory performance is taken for granted. We all know of new walling systems which keep out the wet but which induce excessive condensation and roofs with excellent low thermal transmittance values but which let in the rain. It is probably that the scope envisaged originally for the use of performance specifications was too ambitious for most practitioners except for those in the very largest of organisations where there can be a tendency to experiment at the client's expense and, unfortunately, often without his knowledge or prior approval. More likely success with the method will be on a national basis by an extension of existing Standards and Codes to encourage manufacturers to arrange for production of components to specified levels of performance which have been agreed by users as meeting the majority of their requirements.

374

CONTENTS

Statutory Consents

Chapter 4 was devoted to a consideration of the law relating to building works in the broadest sense and, as part of his Feasibility Study, the architect or surveyor will have completed a good deal of preliminary work. Perhaps, as previously mentioned, this will have involved an application for outline consent under the Town and Country Planning Acts, to ensure that the scheme meets with the general approval of the Local Planning Authority in respect of what section 22 of the Town and Country Planning Act 1971 terms "development". This is defined, in a very all embracing way, as the "carrying out of building, engineering, mining or other operations, in, on, over or under land or the making of any material change in the use of any buildings or other land". The outline application may therefore have been related to a change in the physical appearance of land by new building and the subsequent use of that building or a change in the physical appearance or bulk of an existing building on the one hand or a change in the nature of its existing use on the other.

It is now that the architect or surveyor has to open his original file and look out the names of the central or local government officers with whom he had previous discussions in order to pave the way for the submission of the formal applications for consent under the various statutes enacted by Parliament in respect of Town and Country Planning, Public Health and the wide range of more specialist Acts referred to in Chapter 4.

Frustrations can often occur at this stage of the project. For one thing, the Planning Officer or other official concerned in earlier discussions at Feasibility stage, who was so helpful and informative, will be found to have left the department and all that remains are some hurriedly written notes or records to instruct the man or woman who will replace him. The sinking feeling that this news imparts will probably be matched with the gloomy sensation of having to start to "tell the story all over again" probably to rather more unsympathetic ears. Be that as it may it is now necessary to take the final sketch scheme or worked up drawings in draft form, already prepared, for discussion with all the appropriate officials or inspectors administering the statutes or regulations with which it has been decided at Feasibility stage the project must comply.

By this time the scheme will have proceeded to such a stage that the series of meetings with officials will probably be lengthy and detailed since it will be in consequence of decisions taken at, or after, these meetings that the fully developed scheme will be prepared ready not only for the receiving of formal consents but also for sending out to obtain tenders. To save time it is usual for the two processes to be run together so that the receipt of consents will roughly coincide with the receipt of tenders. This is yet another reason, of course, for ensuring that applications will receive a consent not a refusal. It is no use having to ask for revised tenders. Accordingly all the complexities of the scheme will be explained to officials who, in turn, will indicate not only the scope in general of their requirements but also the precise fine details as well.

At the discussions mentioned in the previous paragraph it is usual to obtain the forms which have to be submitted to obtain the necessary consents and to discuss the range of plans and details which will be required to accompany them. Again, with a view to ensuring that a consent is obtained, it is well worthwhile to consider arranging a further meeting with the officials for the time when the forms have been completed in draft along with the necessary detailed drawings. A final check that all is in order (this usually consists of demonstrating to the officials concerned that everything required has been incorporated either in the form as previously discussed or in an equally satisfactory alternative form) will render the subsequent submission of applications for consent and the receipt of those consents hopefully a mere formality. If it has been necessary to think of alternative solutions to problems between the two meetings and the alternative is to be submitted, the need for clearance becomes all the more obviously necessary.

The need for completeness and thoroughness at this stage cannot be overstressed. It arises in two ways. There is in the first place the need to ensure that formal consents are not sought until all problems have been solved and all decisions are taken relating to or affecting the works for which the consent is being sought. This is in order that there are no loose ends which will later need either additional or amending consents. What can happen so often if care of this order is not exercised is that consequential effects of later decisions render earlier consents either invalid or inappropriate and this may well result in extra costs on the contract to make everything tie-in effectively. This tieing-in process leads naturally to a consideration of completeness in another form in that there is a need for all applications to be looked at as one and not in isolation. All require to be considered together and at about the same time, complete in themselves, but all interlocking favourably. To put it at its simplest a proposal for a form of construction satisfactory to pass the By-laws or Building Regulations will not necessarily meet with the approval of the local planning authority. It is at this stage that they must all be re-considered in a final summing up process of cross checks, although obviously much will have been done in this regard as the scheme has developed.

The architect or surveyor will have submitted applications as agent for the client and will receive consents in the same capacity. Most application forms allow for this and it is not usually necessary for the building owner to be involved except where, for example, financial assistance by way of grants is being sought. The sort of checks which might otherwise have been made, should applications have had to be channelled through the client, are therefore usually absent and make it all the more necessary for the architect or surveyor to ensure that forms are completed satisfactorily, all questions are answered in full and all supporting details by way of specifications and drawings sent in. If notices to other holders of interests in the property are involved, for example, under Town Planning regulations, these should also be despatched at the same time and not left until later when they can easily be forgotten.

It is to be hoped that by this stage sufficiently good relations have been established with officials during previous discussions so that they can be expected, if not actually relied upon, to telephone if something in the application is either not clear or would appear to be heading for a refusal if not amended. If officials have been antagonised by rudeness or bombast at earlier meetings they will take a mischievous delight in not saying anything and instead recommending the Council or Authority to issue a formal refusal thereby necessitating a fresh application and causing unnecessary delay. If nothing is heard from officials for a couple of weeks, other than a note of acknowledgement, a word on the telephone does not come amiss to ensure that the Council or Authority concerned has all it needs to proceed to issue a consent and, of course, the architect or surveyor should hold himself in readiness to attend to make initialled amendments to forms or drawings if that proves to be necessary.

The architect or surveyor will eventually receive the consents from the authorities to whom application has been made and, as already stated, will receive them on behalf of the client. As such, it is his responsibility to check that the consents are satisfactory in all respects for the purpose. This involves reading the small print as well as the words of the basic consent decision. Often consents are issued subject to conditions. These need careful consideration and while they might already have been anticipated, if the pre-planning already discussed has been properly carried out, it is still important at this stage to ensure that they can be complied with and that at the end of the day the main consent will be valid because the conditions have been fulfilled. Furthermore consents for one aspect of the works may specifically state that they exclude consent under another statute. If that is the case then a check must be made to ensure that that other aspect has indeed been taken care of.

If a consent is not in order in some way or other, or there is some doubt in the architect or surveyor's mind that a consent is not all it should be, immediate steps must be taken to investigate the situation and to obtain the proper consent which is required. This is particularly important since the Council or Authority will naturally assume that what is issued satisfies the building owner unless it is informed to the contrary. Later its inspector will appear upon the scene when the works are perhaps well advanced and could conceivably be the cause of additional costs to the client either to make the consent match works already completed, which may or may not be possible, or alternatively, and probably much more costly, require alteration works so that when these are completed the consent will be matched. The client could perhaps rightly say that such extra cost had been incurred because of the neglect of the professional adviser to carry out the simplest of checks. He might then seek to recover those extra costs from the architect or surveyor.

To underline the importance to the architect or surveyor of ensuring that what is built has all the necessary approvals either in advance of construction or that it will obtain such approvals or the certificates necessary for occupation under, for example, the Fire Precautions Act 1971 or the Health and Safety at Work Act 1974 on completion, mention need only be made of what happens when a building is sold. A price is usually agreed on the basis of the building as it stands and on the use currently being made of it. When the purchaser's solicitors start to make their enquiries and ask to see all the consents, approvals and certificates there will be consternation and severe repercussions if some of those necessary have never been obtained and others are incomplete. If there is no satisfactory way of securing the required consents in an entirely satisfactory form the property may prove to be unsaleable or only saleable at a price considerably lower than might otherwise have been the case had all the consents been in proper order. The Court of Appeal case of *B. L. Holdings Ltd.* v. *Robert J. Wood and Partners* has already been mentioned on Page 33 where a firm of architects found themselves in Court but succeeded in resisting liability on a claim in negligence where a mix up with the planners allowed an office building to go forward to construction but on completion could not be occupied because it lacked an Office Development Certificate. The architects succeeded in this case because of the complexity of the law relating to the size and the method of measuring buildings in relation to the need for such certificates which had confused the local Authority as well as the architects. However, it is easy to envisage other circumstances where it would not be possible to resist such a claim if it related to aspects of ordinary planning, constructional details or safety and use of a building. As said repeatedly before, clients approach architects and surveyors because of their professed expertise to solve just those problems and are entitled to assume that the basic necessities, at least, of any project are being attended to.

In relation to private consents as distinct from statutory consents it will be obvious that the same degree of care is required. Even though members of the legal profession may be involved on behalf of the client their task is to ensure that the words used in any legal document are appropriate for the purpose in legal terms only and that the document itself is also appropriate. It is the responsibility of the architect or surveyor to ensure that all consents, whether statutory or private, are obtained and are appropriately phrased in words and shown on plans to cover what is required *before,* and that is the operative word, works are commenced. If a client wishes to proceed with works before either statutory or private consents are formally obtained, and are accordingly legally binding, and against professional advice then in some cases the architect or surveyor may well consider it necessary to obtain a full indemnity in writing from the client to the effect that no responsibility can be accepted for any loss suffered by the client on account of the premature start. Even if the written indemnity is not obtained every architect or surveyor would be well advised to have on file, together with an acknowledgement of receipt by the client, a letter setting out the architect's or surveyor's position culminating with advice on the dangers of proceeding prematurely and a disclaimer of responsibility. Clients in a hurry or with a deadline to meet will on occasions be happy to take these risks, or at least if not happy, be prepared to accept the dangers involved, but it must be the clients sole decision nevertheless, however much the architect or surveyor may be involved in weighing the assessment of those dangers.

Private Consents

While most schemes of new building or refurbishment require statutory consents in some form or other the need for private consents will depend on the extent to which the proposals impinge on the rights of others with an interest in the property concerned and on neighbours. Possible matters for concern have been mentioned in Chapter 4 for consideration at the Feasibility stage. Apart from party walls in London and Bristol and excavations near buildings in London, however, there are no statutory procedures for obtaining those private consents which may be required. These have to be obtained by negotiation with, perhaps, recourse to the Courts if a successful outcome is not possible. The way these negotiations are handled will depend to a very great extent on the type of proposal, the character of the rights of other parties from whom the consents are to be obtained and, not least, on the attitude adopted by those other persons or organisations as already ascertained at the Feasibility Stage. If the consents required are seen in advance to be numerous, complicated and likely to be difficult to obtain then specialists, usually solicitors and surveyors, may have to be brought in to handle the details from an early stage, using drawings and specifications as may be required and provided by the architect or surveyor. In some circumstances in such cases the architect or surveyor will be in charge of the project and the specialists will accordingly be under his control and will report to him but in other cases there may well be a separate Project Manager appointed by the client under whom both architect or surveyor and specialist will operate.

In many cases, however, the introduction of a specialist will not be warranted and it will be for the architect or surveyor to make the approach to others entitled to the benefit of the rights or restrictions and to progress the negotiations to a successful conclusion or alternatively, to court action in conjunction with the client's solicitor in order to secure any necessary declarations to permit the project to proceed with impunity. It is worth considering briefly how such negotiations might proceed under the various categories of case likely to arise before proceeding to give much closer consideration to the statutory provisions governing procedure relating to possible disturbance of easements for party walls and support in London. While these statutory requirements have to be followed only in London they nevertheless provide useful guidelines which can be adapted as required for the conduct of negotiations in other parts of the country where there are no statutory requirements.

Restrictive Covenants

There is a tendency for architects and surveyors to believe that any covenant restricting the size, character or type of development which can be carried out on a site is an anachronism and the mere fact that it was imposed many years ago must automatically mean that it is obsolete. The neighbourhood around the site to which the covenant applies may well have changed completely in character and while this is certainly one of the grounds which the Lands Tribunal can take into account in considering an application for discharge or modification of a covenant under Section 84 of the Law of Property Act 1925, modified by Section 28 of the Law of Property Act 1969, there are also others. The Tribunal has to take into account all the facts of the case. Whether for example the modification or discharge of the covenant will injure the interests of that person or persons for whose benefit it operates and whether the provisions of the covenant are still sensible and practicable under modern conditions. An example may be cited of the possible dangers to professional advisers in a case reported in the "Times".[1] A restrictive covenant, incorporated in a sale of land to preserve a view from the vendor's own property was disregarded and the land built on. It was decided in the Court of Appeal that damages were not sufficient and an injunction was granted requiring demolition. One can only speculate in the absence of further information on who allowed the owner of the offending building to get as far as building it. If he had an architect or surveyor it is to be hoped that an indemnity was extracted from the owner otherwise the professional adviser could well be considered negligent in the circumstances and accordingly liable for the loss.

The fact that the Tribunal is empowered to discharge or modify a restrictive covenant if this is now against the public interest and award a monetary sum if this will suffice to compensate the person or persons injured, should not be taken as an indication that the covenant will automatically be swept aside as the pros and cons will certainly be subject to detailed analysis and the case for modification or discharge has to be very carefully prepared and presented. This means, of course, the expenditure of money and, if not more significantly, time.

If there is only a single beneficiary to the restrictive covenant, negotiations could begin against the background of the likelihood or otherwise of the Lands Tribunal lifting the restriction. However it is one thing to proceed on the basis that the Lands Tribunal will discharge a restrictive covenant which may seem quite obviously ridiculous under present day circumstances but quite another to assume that an elderly crank determined to be as difficult and obstructive as possible will also see reason. It would, of course, be advantageous to obtain agreement to have a restriction lifted without any cost being incurred at all, if that were possible, but it would be highly unlikely even in simpler circumstances. It is therefore usual at the time of the initial approach for the architect or

(1) *Wakeham* v. *Wood*. Court of Appeal report 21 August 1981.

surveyor, with the client's approval, to offer to pay the reasonable costs of the beneficiary in obtaining professional advice from a solicitor and surveyor of his own choice.

In the case where a restriction seems obviously out of date it is probable that even though the professional advisers to a beneficiary would privately agree that he had no case in the Lands Tribunal and advise him accordingly; nevertheless they would almost certainly seek some financial consideration for their client as part of an agreement to discharge the restriction. The building owner and his advisers would then have to consider whether the amount of compensation requested was reasonable in the circumstances having regard to the cost of delay which would be involved in telling the beneficiary that his demands were outrageous and then taking the case to the Lands Tribunal on the relative assurance that the outcome would be favourable and all the costs would be recovered from the losing beneficiary. This latter aspect is not, however, necessarily a surefire assumption and depends very much on how reasonable the applicants have been prior to the appearance before the Tribunal and whether the beneficiary has been perverse or not in his attitude. Since it is a "developer", in whatever sense, normally seeking the removal of the restriction it is often considered quite reasonable that he should meet the costs of any application to the Lands Tribunal for removal of a restriction and Counsel often advise that proceedings be pursued on that basis. Even if an applicant succeeds in not only getting the restriction removed but also obtains his costs before the Tribunal from the losing beneficiary he will have nothing to compensate him for the cost of delay. Accordingly what might at first sight have appeared to be cynicism in the demand for compensation made by the beneficiary and his advisers takes on a different light. The demands are in reality fully justified in that it is they who have recognised that, to a great extent, the beneficiary holds the key to the earlier realisation of the profit to be made from the new development. Time means money.

It will be very much a matter of bargaining on the amount to be paid if the beneficiary is attracted by the scent of money and an agreement prepared by solicitors with the payment made on completion of the document before the work commences will provide a satisfactory outcome to the negotiations. The architect or surveyor will need, of course, to be involved in the drafting of the agreement and the supply of appropriate annotated plans, since the client will be placing implicit reliance on his professional advisers to clear this hurdle prior to the commencement of the work on site.

Just occasionally, however, the beneficiary of a restrictive covenant will be totally unwilling to concede or agree anything and will be immune to blandishments. He will ignore any professional advice given to him or even refuse to consult professional advisers in the first place. "I know my rights", he will say, however out of date and unreasonable the covenant may seem to be. In these circumstances delay will be inevitable and the necessary application for the discharge of the covenant will have to be made to the Lands Tribunal. It will be necessary in this event for the client to obtain the services of Counsel experienced in such cases who will know how best to present the evidence and who will give an indication of what type of evidence is required in the particular circumstances of each case.

Where in the past large plots of land have been sold for development in smaller plots the restrictive covenant is not necessarily made solely for the benefit of the vendor but may exist also for the benefit of each of the purchasers of the smaller plots. In these cases, it is probably almost impossible to obtain separate agreements with all the beneficiaries of a satisfactory nature and more than likely it will be necessary to take a test case to the Lands Tribunal. Complete success in obtaining a discharge of the covenant against one will mean that the other beneficiaries will have to accept the fact that the covenants are worthless. Of course, it is just as likely however that the Lands Tribunal will award compensation, usually the difference in value of the beneficiary's property with and without the benefit of the covenant plus all costs. The award of compensation to one will then determine the amount of compensation which has to be paid to the remainder, although there are often complex negotiations for valuers to carry out when there are differences in size and location affecting the value of the various properties belonging to the beneficiaries.

Superior Landlords

It is obviously necessary that applications for consents from superior landlords are served upon the right person or persons and sent to the right addresses. This is not always as easy as it sounds and it may be necessary to call upon the aid of the client's solicitor if the matter is anything other than straightforward and particularly if there are a number of superior landlords to be consulted. Often a single superior landlord will examine the drawings, make his own notes, send them to his surveyor and then to his solicitor so that a careful reply can be drafted but this is not always the case by any means.

Application for consent to building works from superior landlords should be sent off at the earliest possible opportunity since, as there is obviously no obligation upon a superior landlord to respond within a given time limit, it must be assumed that consideration and, hopefully, consent to any proposal will be leisurely. Nothing is worse than having to negotiate with a superior landlord against pressure of time for consent to work in which he has little interest and failure to make application at the appropriate moment can lead to a most difficult situation. Obviously, some approach should have been made at the Feasibility stage but this is not always done, particularly when there seems an obvious advantage to the landlord to agree, but in any event such an approach is not likely to have gone into much detail. Usually the tenant has to rely on the type of response that the superior landlords "see no reason why consent should not be given subject to further consideration of detailed plans in due course".

On the subject of detailed plans, it is unwise for the architect or surveyor merely to extract one of the complete sets of drawings from the rack and send it off to the superior landlords with a short, possibly curt, note asking for consent as soon as possible. If the superior landlord is a private individual he might be horrified to be handed a large package by the postman and open it to find only a mass of incomprehensible drawings. It is likely, if he has property interests, that he knows when to take advice and he will probably have a surveyor or architect of his own whom he may instruct to act for him from time to time. It is therefore worth ascertaining whether he wishes to be represented or not in which case the detailed drawings can go to the right source at once. So far as larger organisations are concerned, such as property companies or Government Departments it is, again, unwise to send off a bundle of drawings without first of all paving the way and finding out not only the right person who will deal with the matter but whether, by means of early preliminary meetings, there are any particular requirements that can be taken into account and dealt with before the drawings are completed and sent off. Furthermore, in some cases which involve Board or Committee approval much more will be needed. In order to see that the scheme survives intact the architect or surveyor may well, in order to protect his own client's interests, have to give thought to presentation just as if he were an expert witness and not only compile the case for his client but also prepare attractively presented duplicated documentation for the requisite number of Committee or Board members setting out the proposals in the form of a suitably worded statement accompanied by attractive sketches, plans and photographs. His client will no doubt wish him to attend in order to present the submission for approval and be able to answer questions from his own detailed knowledge, whether during the day or perhaps even in the evening, and then be prepared to pay him for this service, as consent is obviously crucial.

The consent of superior landlords is usually incorporated in a licence related to clauses in the lease from which occupation of the property is derived. Drafts of this licence must be seen by the architect or surveyor who will possibly have been asked initially to provide an appropriate description of the works together with annotated drawings for attachment. He will probably be asked, and if he is not asked he should insist on being consulted, to check the final draft to ensure that it is satisfactory for the client's purposes and this task must be given close attention and all wording and drawings given detailed scrutiny as he is the professional most closely involved. It will be no use blaming the client's solicitor at a later date if the licence fails to mention some important aspect or a vital drawing is not included.

The licence will usually also provide for the payment of all the costs incurred by the landlord in providing the licence. Solicitor will speak to solicitor on legal costs but the architect or surveyor will probably be asked to advise upon the reasonableness or otherwise of the charges proposed by the architect or surveyor employed by the landlord. The word "proposed" is used here as it is important to ensure that the basis of charging is agreed in advance and incorporated in detail in the licence otherwise an acrimonius argument can ensue if they are merely expressed as "reasonable" or "proper" charges. Now that there is a tendency for all recommended scales to be abolished it could be a matter of conjecture and dispute as to what is reasonable in the circumstances. There has never been any mention of fees for such work in the publications of the RIBA but the recommended scale in the RICS Conditions of Engagement for Building Surveying Services 1981 edition is considered to be basically reasonable except that it bears harshly on the lessee where the total value of the work is taken. This figure could be boosted by sub-contractor's work, which may arguably cover work which is not an alteration in the strictest of senses. Furthermore the architect or surveyor in charge of the project needs to be wary of those professional advisers acting for landlords who consider that they are entitled to exercise a supervisory role over the works and will seek to charge a fee accordingly. The character of the work is advisory only, to the extent that the lessor's professional architect or surveyor is to see that the works are carried out in accordance with the terms of the licence in a reasonable manner, not necessarily in accordance with his own, perhaps, very demanding idea of standards in materials and workmanship.

The following recommended scale is taken from the 1981 edition of the RICS Conditions of Engagement for Building Surveying Services, one of the few scales still remaining in force from the now generally abolished RICS Scale of Professional Charges, July 1971 edition, which was reprinted with amendments to September 1981:

Approval of Plans

Scale 28   For approving plans submitted by Lessees and inspecting buildings during progress.

(a) Existing Buildings:

3% on the first £2,000; 2% on the next £8,000; 1% on the next £10,000; 0.5% on the next £80,000 and 0.25% on the residue.

Minimum fee £10.

(b) New Buildings:

0.75% on the first £50,000 and 0.20% on the residue.

Minimum fee £10.

Notes:

This scale is intended to apply only to cases where the surveyor having approved the plans, is responsible to his client for ensuring that the work is carried out in accordance with them. (It does not cover work in connection with certification or approval of payments.) The scale should be reduced where the work is less than this, and where approval of plans only is involved the fee should be by arrangement.

Adoption of the scale is considered reasonable provided care is taken to ensure that the percentages are charged on the cost of the alterations or improvements and not on the repairs and renewals (these being the Lessee's responsibility entirely) being carried out at the same time in the case of works to an existing building. In the case of a new building the percentages should be applied to the basic structure costs and the costs of services and finishes but it would be unreasonable to expect the client to pay a percentage on the cost of his own special finishes or features unrelated to any clause or requirement in the lease.

It will be noted that the fee scale provides for approval of plans and for inspections. The work on the former will already have been carried out by the time the licence has been signed. As for the inspections these will be for the future and it would be reasonable for both sides professional advisers to agree on the number of inspections which it would be reasonable to consider included in the agreed fee assuming the works proceed according to plan and for provision to be made for an additional fee per inspection necessitated by errors or bad workmanship needing to be corrected.

Completeness and thoroughness have been mentioned before on many occasions and apply equally in the realm of obtaining and complying with superior lessor's consents. The architect or surveyor should be obtaining consent on behalf of his client for a fully settled scheme and not something in outline with many gaps remaining to be completed. Obtaining consent for a scheme which is no more than an outline and then proceeding with works is a recipe for disaster. The landlord's representative will appear and say "Oh but you are not carrying out the works in accordance with the licence". Unfortunately that will probably be true since some difficulty which should have been anticipated, had the scheme been properly and fully worked in advance, has prevented the work from proceeding according to the original inadequate plan. The need for amending licences should be avoided for obvious reasons wherever possible.

Easements

Difficulties over the question of easements often occur and this is hardly surprising as the law on the subject is difficult and its interpretation in individual cases even more so. Quite recent cases for example, appear to have completely upset rules that were thought previously to have been established much to the dismay of experts in the field, whether lawyers, architects or surveyors. It is not just case law that is baffling however. The lay client finds the common law rules relating to easements obscure and difficult to follow. Most clients are fully aware that in order to preserve a right of way over other land, it has to be kept in use but many are taken aback when they are told by their architect or surveyor that they cannot demand a right of access upon their neighbour's land in order to repair their own wall at their own expense. Unless an easement has been acquired there is no way in which access can be obtained if the adjoining owner does not allow it and that is the law of the land. The frustrations over this particular problem are growing so acute that the Law Society at present has the matter under consideration. One lawyer has said, rather sadly, that the modern philosophy of standing up for your rights had a number of unwelcome side effects and this was one of them. The lay client is also dumbfounded to be told that should his neighbour, whether he be a private individual or Government Department, suddenly decide to demolish the adjacent terrace house, there is no automatic right for him to be able to demand that his newly exposed flank wall is covered or protected since an easement for protection against

389

weather is not known to law[2] although a local Authority has some powers under S.29 of the Public Health Act 1961. Finally, bewilderment occurs in relation to the support of land. Most people realise that there is a natural right to the support of land, so that you cannot carelessly excavate the soil upon your own property and allow a collapse of your neighbour's land next door. There is, however, no natural right to the support of buildings; such a right can only be acquired. If a house owner builds a new garage and studio extension along the boundary with his neighbour's land and, five years later, is horrified to notice cracks in the structure and, peering over the boundary fence, sees that his neighbour has dug a large trench nearby both he and his surveyor may be convinced that the cracking is due to the excavation carried out but the question of liability may be far from clear. Lawyers will enter into a welter of argument as to whether the soil would have slipped as a result of the new excavation, had there been no new building upon it, or whether the amount of slip was caused by the weight of the new structure. To the lay client who sees an obvious injustice; namely that the man next door has done something that has caused him injury, the deliberations of the lawyers will seem exasperating. Why can't they get on with things? Whose side are they on?

It is the very difficulties arising out of easements in relation to the rights of others which suggest that architects and surveyors should proceed very warily where they exist. It has been stressed at the Feasibility stage where the essential duty of the architect or surveyor lies in ascertaining from his inspection of deeds and the site whether easements do exist or not and if they do exist whether it is reasonable to proceed on the basis that they can either be "accommodated" within the scheme, or diverted or extinguished, perhaps on payment of compensation.

Perhaps the main difficulty with easements is that unless something is done about them before work commences they will remain like an unexploded bomb ready to go off when least expected. For the peace of mind of all concerned they need to be defused before work commences. A further difficulty is that in the absence of agreement with the person entitled to the benefit of the right they cannot be extinguished or altered. A right of way cannot be arbitrarily stopped up or diverted. The Feasibility Study will have concluded either that the project can proceed with the right of way undisturbed or that enquiries have revealed that it can be stopped up or diverted by agreement. Obviously in the case of rights of way, rights of drainage and the like an assessment of this nature can

(2) *Phipps* v. *Pears* (1965) 1QB 76.

usually be made at the Feasibility stage but it is very different in the case of rights of support or a right to light. Here the building owner or developer is charged not to do anything to disturb those rights while the beneficiary of those rights cannot usually do anything about preventing possible disturbance until an actionable nuisance occurs i.e. his building is deprived of support and damage occurs or the right to light is sufficiently obstructed to give rise to a cause of action. It is when this happens and Court proceedings are commenced that the client turns to his advisers and says "How on earth have you got me into this mess – didn't you realise these people would grumble?". The fact that the grumbling may also cause him considerable loss in financial terms will eventually also dawn on him and it will be then that he will turn to his architect or surveyor and say more sharply "You should have warned me of this before we started to build". No client wishes to become involved in a court action if it can be avoided and will certainly react strongly if an injunction is sought and successfully obtained by an aggrieved neighbour to stop his precious scheme in full flight.

It will be seen later when the terms of the London Building Acts (Amendment) Act 1939 are considered in relation to party walls in the Inner London area that a statutory procedure also exists within the area where the Act applies governing the service of notices and subsequent action when it is proposed to excavate at certain levels within ten and twenty feet of the foundations of neighbouring buildings. In their response, adjoining owners can in certain circumstances require the building owner to underpin the foundations of their own building. This procedure will be considered in some detail since, although it has no statutory force outside London, it prescribes a method of dealing with this aspect of construction which is so sensible that it can well be adopted for use elsewhere. Obviously the time limits of the Act cannot be insisted upon but other aspects of the "ritual" could be followed by agreement. The successful conclusion of negotiations could provide for work to be carried out under a short form of agreement made between either the two owners, or their respective representatives, and with an agreed schedule of condition attached to obviate future arguments on the state of the adjoining owner's premises before the work started. Such an agreement would, it is considered, absolve any architect or surveyor of any charge of negligence in respect of his own client's interests vis-a-vis those of a neighbour, which could conceivably arise if the architect or surveyor proceeded entirely on his own. Should some defects develop in the neighbour's property at a later date, and be validated by comparison with the agreed Schedule of Condition, the fact that two professional advisers reached agreement on the method of working, underpinning, soil consolidation, piling or whatever would serve to narrow down very considerably where any fault or blame if any may lie. It may well be, in these circumstances of faults occurring, a matter of bad workmanship by the contractor to be put right at his expense, although on such critical matters a very close series of inspections of the work would no doubt be provided for in the agreement by both professional advisers before ground or concrete foundation work was covered up. Procedures adapted from those set out in Chapter 12 could be used specifically to avoid such a happening. At worst it may amount to a matter of misjudgement by both professional advisers but probably not negligence.

It is recommended, therefore, that where excavations for sites outside London are to be carried out adjacent to other buildings, the very full procedure of notification, disclosure of intentions, offers of payment of adviser's fees etc. all in accordance with the London procedure which is designed to secure agreement and is described later in this Chapter, should be followed. If agreement cannot be reached there is nothing to prevent both professional advisers, with their respective client's authority, agreeing to the appointment of an "arbitrator" to decide what would be best to protect the adjoining owner's structures and for the building owner/developer to agree to be bound by such decision.

Of course, it is unfortunately possible to come across adjoining owners who are so antagonistic to the idea of new construction next door they will do all they can to thwart its progress. This may extend to refusing to discuss anything or to consider any proposals whatever, saying merely that it is up to the building owner/developer to do what he is able by law to do but woe betide him if he puts a foot wrong. Such a neighbour may then proceed to erect notices on his premises with the inscription "Ancient Lights" in the hope that their warning will frighten off the developer. If that fails the neighbour will then with baleful eyes watch everything that goes on next door during construction, a practice so un-nerving at times to contractors that they will actually make mistakes which they would normally avoid in other circumstances.

At least in this situation the building owner's architect or surveyor will have done, hopefully, all he could do to secure agreement with neighbours, so that it will not be possible to criticise him for being forgetful in this regard. What he has then to do, of course, is to ensure that each subsequent event in the construction process will permit no scope for the neighbour to take action against his client. This means, of course, in relation to works near buildings that they are of such a nature and so carefully controlled that the risk of damage to adjoining premises is reduced to the barest minimum. It is essential for all steps in this regard to be extremely well documented so that should some question arise at a later date as to what was done, a satisfactory, clear and positive answer can be given. Design decisions, state of excavations on inspection with dates and notes, along with dates and notes covering all aspects of supervision need to be retained, together with the file copies of all letters, notes of meetings etc. covering the approach to neighbours.

As already discussed in Chapter 4, even the experts in the particular field, let alone practising architects and surveyors, can be put in a quandary over rights of light. If the inspection of a bare site, or an existing building, together with the deeds and due considera-tion of any time factors involved, shows that rights of light do exist for the benefit of neighbouring property then the only sure way of avoiding any possible trouble is either not to build, in the case of a bare site, or in the case of an existing building not to exceed the outline of that building in any scheme of refurbishment. Of course, if the proposed development involves knocking down an existing building and putting up a new one then, of course, one can always do this with impunity in regard to this aspect of the law, provided always that the bulk of the new building is precisely the same as the old. However not many developers would be happy with advice to that effect and there is always a tendency to propose a building somewhat larger, allowed as of right in any event within certain tolerances under planning legislation. Even if it is proposed to put up a new building in place of an existing, and of the same size and shape, the architect or surveyor will be surprised to find how the neighbours will subsequently be convinced that the new building is much bigger than the old. It is for this reason, though there is also a further sound reason having regard to the owner's liability for Development Land Tax, that it is vital for the architect or surveyor to advise the client to meet the expense of preparing drawings both in plan and elevation but, particularly, with sections through all critical points in the existing buildings before they are demolished and for these drawings to be retained very carefully for subsequent reference. Even if there were no party walls involved in the demolition it would be sensible for these plans to be sent to the adjoining owner with an invitation that their accuracy be agreed in advance of demolition (the fee for this service being met, of course, by the building owner/developer but the selection of appropriate professional adviser being left to the adjoining owner) so as to avoid subsequent wrangles over what was on the site before. Such a step will avoid reliance being placed on such statements as "Oh you could see much more sky from this window before that was built" and which in the absence of plans cannot be disproved. Drawings of both the old and the new being available will render such subjective judgements worthless.

The real quandary for the architect or surveyor arises when he can see that the scheme which he is putting forward is going to interfere with existing rights. What is he to do then? How far can a building owner proceed to obstruct the light to a neighbour's property before that owner has a right of action in nuisance and if that owner does take action what will the outcome be? What likelihood is there of the Court granting an injunction to stop building, with all the consequences that would entail and even to remove the obstruction? Alternatively would the Court award compensation and allow the obstruction to remain? Clearly, as discussed in Chapter 4, the experts have been proved wrong on at least two occasions over the last few years and the law, at the time of writing, now suggests that it would be highly imprudent to proceed with building works when the possibility of Court action exists, likely in itself now, it seems, to be successful. It is not thought that many clients would wish to take such risks in the face of strong professional advice but they would, of course, wish to explore all possibilities of removing those risks.

Consequently there would need to be an attempt at obtaining an agreement with the beneficiary of the right. The approach would obviously, in view of its importance, need to be made at an early date in the formulation of proposals and as soon as a reasonably positive sketch scheme was available to enable the full extent of the obstruction to be gauged. No doubt with the aid of drawings to enable a comparison between the old and new proposed situation to be made the approach will be on the basis that the proposals will not give rise to an actionable nuisance and an invitation will be extended to the adjoining owner to agree formally that this is the case. If the adjoining owner is in doubt it is good tactics for the building owner to say he will be happy, of course, to pay the reasonable fees of an independent consultant of the adjoining owners choice to advise him on the proposal. This will amount to a preliminary skirmish only because the objective, in view of the present state of uncertainty, must be to obtain a formal legal agreement whereby in receipt of a payment in compensation the beneficiary waives his rights as they may exist in respect of the proposed scheme as defined. Nothing short of a binding agreement will suffice in the circumstances to eliminate the uncertainty and in this respect it is to be preferred that the building owner pays the consideration and obtains his agreement rather than that the adjoining owner agrees informally or even by letter with the proposal. If that should happen the adjoining owner may then find it all too easy to change his mind when the works are proceeding saying "I had no idea it was going to be like this". It is an unfortunate fact that lay persons, however knowledgable and even when taking professional advice, do not always fully appreciate the significance of information on drawings even though they may maintain, and give every impression, that they do. The adjoining owner in these circumstances may feel that he has been misled, however unwittingly, engage another expert and immediately apply for an injunction. It is to avoid this sort of eventuality that the binding agreement is essential in advance of construction.

Depending on the size and character of the proposed building works and the number of neighbours involved benefiting from rights of light, it will probably be necessary, once matters are seen to be progressing, for the client to have the advice of a professional valuer to determine an appropriate level of compensation payable, as well as for the client's solicitor to become involved in the preparation of the agreements. The amount of compensation generally revolves around the difference in value of the adjoining owner's property with the light formerly passing to it and its value after the neighbouring development has taken place.

Often the adjoining owner will demand a figure for compensation far in excess of that determined in accordance with the formula mentioned in the previous paragraph. He will ask for this on the grounds that his agreement is enabling the building owner to derive additional profit from his building works which he would not otherwise be able to obtain. If this is indeed the case then it may be that the building owner can in fact "afford" to pay a higher level of compensation in order to secure if not 100% of that additional profit at least a substantial proportion. If that is not the situation and, after all, not all building works are carried out purely for profit, or the adjoining owner is being too greedy and expecting too large a slice of the cake, then, if he is promptly advised that the scheme will be redesigned so as to avoid any compensation being paid at all it is surprising how often a changed attitude will materialise and the demand will be toned down.

Totally unreasonable demands and a refusal to moderate them to something within reason, or a failure to reach any agreement with an adjoining owner, may leave the building owner with only one of two alternatives. He may either have the scheme redesigned to remove all possible causes of action or decide entirely on his own volition to proceed with the works as already planned with the possibility of a court action looming distinctly ahead for the future. The second alternative would have to be on his own volition since no architect or surveyor, let alone a right of light expert, could possibly advise a client to proceed in view of current uncertainties in the law. In fact he might even be considered negligent if he allowed the client to proceed without issuing suitably firm warnings.

Private and Statutory Procedures involving Party Walls and Statutory Proceedings for Excavations in London

The Law of Property Act 1925 now governs the question of works involving party walls in England and Wales outside London and Bristol. Prior to the passing of this Act, the owners of properties separated by a party wall were tenants in common in respect of the wall, that is, it was owned by them jointly. In the absence of either owner being able to show that he owned the whole wall, the law would assume joint ownership to be the case so that while either tenant in common could take the initiative and carry out repairs to the wall, there was no right of contribution from his neighbour. The right of repair, however, extending to demolition, re-building or underpinning was a wide one as the work could be put in hand without legal objection from the other co-owner of the wall provided that his use of the wall was not imperilled, but thereby lay the rub. On the other hand, however, a co-owner could not impose additional loads on a party wall which might damage its stability since this would prove injurious to the property of both co-owners. Up to 1925 each of the two owners had a half interest in the whole wall, termed an undivided moiety, and this is the situation which has continued to exist in London where matters of repair are controlled by a local statute. As a result, although there were rights for each tenant in common, it was often difficult to secure agreement to carry out repairs or alterations to the wall since it could be argued that the wall was being imperilled when almost anything was being done to it.

With the passing of the Law of Property Act 1925, the situation was altered. Under Sections 38 and 39 of the Act all party walls that were at that time considered to be owned by tenants in common and any future walls, vested in a like manner, were deemed henceforward to be severed longitudinally along the centre line as between the two owners, each party having such rights of support and user over the half of the other owner as existed on 1st January 1926 or which might have existed but for the Act. As a result each owner now has a divided moiety in the wall and can do more or less what he likes with his own half without reference to the owner of the other half, provided that he does not interfere with

396

the rights of the adjoining owner so far as his use of the wall and rights of support are concerned.

> "(in the case of a party wall or structure) . . . that structure shall be and remain severed vertically as between the respective owners, and the owner of each part shall have such rights to support and use over the rest of the structure as may be requisite for conferring rights corresponding to those which would have subsisted if a valid tenancy in common had been created".

Since the passing of the 1925 Act there has been no right for an owner to repair the other half of the wall at his own expense, as existed before 1925, even without the co-operation of the adjoining owner. Now under Section 39 of the 1925 Act an owner can apply to the Court for a declaration of his rights in a party structure, since the Court is now empowered to settle any dispute as to rights and interests upon the application of any interested party. The situation therefore outside London is that where no local legislation exists any matters which extend beyond the half way line have to be dealt with by agreement between the adjoining owners both as to how work is to be put in hand and completed and as to how the cost is to be shared. On a failure to reach any agreement an owner is empowered only to carry out work to the wall wholly from his own side and within his own boundary, so as to effect any necessary repairs, but there may, of course, be cases where this is insufficient to secure a proper repair or a desirable alteration and he will then be forced to take legal action to obtain a declaration of the Court. A negative remedy, as a last resort, is to enlist the assistance of the local authority to exercise its statutory powers to require the repair of the wall.

Debate has never ceased between architects and surveyors in London and those in other parts of the country as to the advantages and disadvantages of the respective procedures relating to party walls. The specific references in Sections 38 and 39 of the Law of Property Act 1925 and Part V of Schedule I of the Act are minute compared with the detailed legislation relating to party walls in London and are nothing like so far reaching in terms of time limits and the settlement of disputes between the surveyors appointed for that very purpose.

London architects and surveyors point to the fact that they are empowered under statute not only to settle differences between owners on each side of a party wall, and to do so without recourse to law, but that there is also a procedure for settling disputes between the "surveyors" appointed under the Act. Architects and surveyors outside London maintain that the 1925 Law of Property Act provisions work well in the vast majority of cases but there is the undoubted disadvantage that in cases of difficulty where the situation is not clear or cannot be resolved by agreement recourse can only be made to the County Court or High Court, depending on the cost of the work, as the 1925 Act requires that the matter must be decided by a Judge. On the other hand there is not a cumbersome procedure to be followed outside London before comparatively minor work can be carried out from one side only of the wall, a set of procedures which tends to bring the London system into disrepute among owners because the continual requirement to appoint surveyors smacks to the layman of rules and regulations invented by architects and surveyors for their own financial benefit.

Outside London there is no statutory code of practice which states that a notice of intended work has to be served, although any prudent architect or surveyor would probably do this in any event out of courtesy to an adjoining owner even if no work was being carried out beyond the half way point. No work may be carried out in a negligent fashion although it is difficult to see how the adjoining owner or his surveyor can judge whether work is negligent or not without being given notice and, often, the only remedy is an action to require the proper reinstatement of the wall or to work disturbed. The consequences of the Act, providing that each owner has a right to repair his half of the wall, may seem to some architects and surveyors to smack of the requirement in "The Merchant of Venice" that Shylock should take his pound of flesh and no more. It is difficult to envisage how work other than the comparatively superficial can be carried out to half a party wall without affecting the remainder. Perhaps, however, the greatest difficulty outside London is that a building owner cannot require a contribution from the adjoining owner as a simple preliminary to carrying out work to their joint benefit, nor can he automatically assume the right to enter on the adjoining owner's land for any purpose.

A study of the contrasting procedures to be followed in dealing with works to party walls in London as against those elsewhere in England and Wales shows that there are advantages and disadvantages in each. However the logic of London, and only the central part at that, retaining a different legal principle in the ownership of such walls and a set of procedures handed down, albeit adapted to modern circumstances, since medieval times is obscure. It is not as though the development of London as a city has been all that different from other cities since all are fairly congested, with much use of terrace construction separated by party walls, or that buildings are constructed so differently in London as to warrant a separate system. Nor is the system so obviously better (except perhaps in respect of a set timetable for progressing works) as could be said of the system of separate building control which has developed and also continues to exist over the same central area of London, with a locally applicable Building Act with By-laws administered by the District Surveyors appointed under statutory powers. The District Surveyors, all of whom have to be in possession of a certificate of qualification obtained by examination, form the basis of the higher degree of technical control exercised in London over building matters, certainly up to the time when the Building Regulations were introduced for general application elsewhere throughout the country. The District Surveyors provide a powerful body of opinion backed up by their undoubted success over the years in preventing serious constructional failures in London, in contrast to elsewhere. They form a significant group, along with leading architects and surveyors practising in London, within the professional institutions which have considerable influence at times when changes in legislation are being mooted. These groups while consistently maintaining that London methods are better than elsewhere have as yet been lukewarm in assisting attempts to introduce a uniform procedure for party walls and a system of building control applicable throughout the country.

Another possible reason for the apparently long entrenched position found in London regarding procedures for party walls may lie in the one main advantage that these procedures possess over those applicable elsewhere. Generally in London development can proceed at a brisk pace since time wasting opposition is given little scope. The character of the business areas of London show that clearance and redevelopment has always taken precedence over preservation. Fears that this policy might be hampered by any changes proposed would no doubt help to reinforce arguments against any such proposals.

It is perhaps idle to speculate how long this situation will remain unchanged although there are currently proposals for wide ranging changes in the system of control for building works which seem likely, on this occasion, to embrace London. Suggestions, however, that the London procedures for party walls be extended to the rest of the country or that the Law of Property Act 1925 provisions now be applied to London are both, perhaps, inappropriate and instead a system incorporating the merits of both and removing the disadvantages would seem to be preferable. Such a system would probably change the principle of ownership in party walls in London to that applying elsewhere, thus allowing the simpler range of works affecting only one half of the wall to be carried out without the elaborate procedure of notices and the employment of professional advisers. Outside London, the procedures for notices, the timetable, payment for works and the settlement of disputes currently in use in London could become operative when it was found necessary to carry out works affecting both sides of the middle line of the wall. At the same time penalties for non-compliance with procedures would be up-dated and incorporated, since at present recourse must still be had to the Courts if a neighbour fails to comply with the statutory procedures in London.

Subject to what has been said above in criticism of London procedures, it is an undoubted fact that they do offer a sensible means of progressing matters when major works are involved to party walls at the same time as generally protecting all owners' interests, when properly followed. As indicated previously when easements of support were discussed, the procedures will be considered in detail since they form a useful guide as to the steps which might well be taken to secure agreement even where they do not apply under statute and a building owner and his professional advisers are only able to negotiate and persuade an adjoining owner towards agreement without being able to reach a result at the end of the day.

The procedures in London must be followed at the correct statutory time stages, preferably well in advance, and be complete in themselves; for example there is no use serving party wall notices without the excavation notices if they too are necessary, and vice versa. If notices are not served then the building owner may find himself subject to an injunction obtained by the adjoining owner to stop the works proceeding. The injunction will apply until the procedures are followed. This could involve what could be some two months' delay at least unless the building owner is prepared to sacrifice his entire bargaining position and agree to all demands made by an adjoining owner as the price of an expedited settlement. The blame for this will be placed entirely on the building owner's professional adviser since it is his task to obtain all such Awards if they relate to party walls in London or, for that matter, party wall Agreements outside London, and to do so before works are commenced.

Party Walls inside London

Some London architects and surveyors have a tendency to assume that a full legislative framework for dealing in party wall matters sprang into being, newly formulated, on the 1 January 1940. Nothing could be further from the truth. It is, of course, true to say that the current practice and procedure for dealing with party walls inside the metropolis is contained in Part VI of the London Building

Acts (Amendment) Act 1939 but nevertheless the first Ordnance relating to party walls, known as Fitz-Ailwyn's Assize of Buildings, was passed in 1189. The Assize, the subject of the Ordnance, dealt with the election of twelve men in a Court to decide a dispute which might arise between neighbours concerning boundaries but the remarkable nature of the document concerns the provision for the rights and duties of adjoining owners in the repairs to and use of party walls. Perhaps the most memorable measure in legislative terms, however, concerned the Act for the rebuilding of the City of London in 1667 following the Great Fire, which not only contained far reaching provisions to limit the spread of fire in the future but also laid down a code of practice for dealing with party walls.

It should, however, be remembered that the provisions of Part VI of the 1939 Act are not only a re-codification of earlier Acts over an extremely long period of time but also the result of much experience gained in the field of party walls. Part VI of the Act is a rare example of legislation where a layman can refer to the wording of a particular provision to see what is intended without having to consult legal opinion. Experienced practitioners say that it pays to turn to the wording of the Act in individual cases to ascertain the precise meaning of a particular section. That this process is continually rewarding is more than one can say for a good deal of more recent legislation in housing and allied fields. It is as well to remember, however, that the 1939 Act only applies to the former London County Council Area, part only of the area covered by the Greater London Council, which has existed since 1963. The changes in 1963 were extensive and part of the Greater London Area is outside the control of the London Building Acts. It is therefore desirable when dealing with a party wall matter to ascertain if the property is situated inside or outside "London" as covered by the Act and as a preliminary to deciding what type of legislative umbrella will control the procedure. It is useful for offices to have retained large scale maps showing the boundary lines of the old LCC area and accordingly the extent of the ambit of the 1939 Act.

The London Building Acts (Amendment) Act 1939 is described in the introduction as to be read and construed as one with the London Building Acts of 1930 and 1935 so that it can be correctly described as the London Building Acts 1930–1939. The Act itself is divided into twelve parts and includes a large number of provisions relating to buildings, ranging from pure construction, means of escape in case of fire, dangerous and neglected structures, restrictions relating to special and temporary buildings, to such matters as the naming and numbering of streets and regulations as to sky signs. The section of the Act of primary concern at this stage however, is Part VI

"Rights etc. of Building and Adjoining Owners". Before proceeding to the importance of the definition of a party wall under the Act however, section 54 might be highlighted at the outset in advance of the other provisions. It is as follows:

> "Nothing in this Part of the Act shall authorise any interference with any easement of light or other easement in or relating to a party wall or prejudicially affect the right of any person to preserve any right in connection with a party wall which is demolished or rebuilt and to take any necessary steps for that purpose."

While this section underlines the importance for the architect or surveyor acting for the building owner to inform himself as to the existence of any easement which an adjoining owner might enjoy, it is also worth stressing that since the Act is carefully framed so as not to interfere with the rights of either a building or adjoining owner so far as an easement is concerned, the presence of such easements cannot be used to block or delay the progress of procedures under the Act and it is customary for party wall surveyors in London to proceed with the necessary preparation of the draft Award and Schedule of Condition entirely without prejudice to, for example, an adjoining owner's right of light, a proceeding that is often misunderstood.

A vital section of Part VI of the Act is Section 44 dealing with the definition of "foundation" and "party wall". This is as follows:

> "In this Part of the Act unless the context otherwise requires the following expressions have the meanings hereby respectively assigned to them:
>
> "Foundation" in relation to a wall means the solid ground or artificially formed support resting on solid ground on which the wall rests;
>
> "Party Wall" means – (i) a wall which forms part of a building and stands on lands of different owners to a greater extent than the projection of any artificially formed support on which the wall rests; and
>
> (ii) so much of a wall not being a wall referred to in the foregoing paragraph (i) as separates buildings belonging to different owners;
>
> "Special Foundations" means foundations in which an assemblage of steel beams or rods is employed for the purpose of distributing any load.

It is particularly important to grasp the meaning of both subsections (i) and (ii) as a party wall may be entirely outside the ambit of one sub-section while being included in the other.

The rights of owners of adjoining lands where the junction line is not built on are contained in Section 45 of the Act as follows:

45 – (1) where lands of different owners adjoin and are not built on at the

line of junction or are built on at the line of junction only to the extent of a boundary wall (not being a party fence wall or the external wall of a building) and either owner is about to build on any part of the line of junction the following provisions shall have effect: –

(a) If the building owner desires to build on the line of junction a party wall or party fence wall –

   (i) the building owner shall serve notice of his desire on the adjoining owner describing the intended wall;

   (ii) if the adjoining owner consents in writing to the building of a party wall or party fence wall the wall shall be built half on the land of each of the two owners or in such other position as may be agreed between the two owners and the expense of building the wall shall be from time to time defrayed by the two owners in due proportion regard being had to the use made or to be made of the wall by the two owners respectively and to the cost of labour and materials prevailing at the time when that use is made by each owner respectively;

   (iii) if the adjoining owner does not consent in writing to the building of a party wall or party fence wall the building owner shall not build the wall otherwise than at his own expense and as an external wall or a fence wall as the case may be placed wholly on his own land;

(b) If the building owner desires to build on the line of junction a wall placed wholly on his own land he shall serve notice of his desire on the adjoining owner describing the intended wall;

(c) where in either of the cases described in paragraphs (a) and (b) of this sub-section the building owner builds a wall on his own land he shall have a right at his own expense at any time after the expiration of one month but not exceeding six months from the service of the notice to place on land of the adjoining owner below the level of such land any projecting footings and foundation making compensation to the adjoining owner or the adjoining occupier or both of them for any damage occasioned thereby the amount of the compensation in the event of difference to be determined in the manner provided in this Part of the Act.

(2) Nothing in this section shall authorise the building owner to place special foundations on land of the adjoining owner without his previous consent in writing.

It is as well to note however, that before making application to an adjoining owner for consent to place special foundations on his land the implication of future expenses must be borne in mind as set out in sections 47 (1) and 56 (5) of the Act.

Section 46 is one of the most, if not the most, important section of Part VI of the Act. It is as follows:

46 – (1) where lands of different owners adjoin and at the line of junction the said lands are built on or a boundary wall being a party fence wall or

the external wall of the building has been erected the building owner shall have the following rights: –

   (a) a right to make good underpin thicken or repair or demolish and rebuild a party structure or party fence wall in any case where such work is necessary on account of defect or want of repair of the party structure or party fence wall;

This is the main sub-section which gives the building owner the right to carry out substantial work to a party structure or party fence wall. Under this sub-section the cost of the work is to be apportioned between the two owners according to the use that each makes of the party structure (see sub-section (1)(a) of section 56 which is set out in full on pages 431–433)The valuation of the necessary proportion of the repairs in connection with work to a party wall can be complicated by the fact that the necessary thickness will be regulated by reference to statute. It should be stressed at this point that although a wall complies with the definition of a party wall under section 44, section 46 envisages payment of the cost according to the benefit of the owners each side of it. Where a tall building adjoins a low one, for example, the owner of the low building should not be asked to pay half the cost of the whole wall, but only half the cost of the wall that he requires having regard to the statutory regulations assuming both buildings to be the height of the lowest. Sub-section (a) is therefore an important one and of the sub-sections that follow (b), (c) and (d) are included mainly to deal with matters that are necessary to bring buildings up to date and into conformity with the statutory regulations.

   (b) A right to demolish a timber or other partition which separates buildings belonging to different owners but is not in conformity with the London Building Acts or any bye-laws made in pursuance of those Acts and to build instead a party wall in conformity therewith;

Under this sub-section the cost is to be apportioned between the owners according to the use that each makes of the party structure (see section 56 (1) (b)).

   (c) A right in relation to a building having rooms or storeys belonging to different owners intermixed to demolish such of those rooms or storeys or any part thereof as are not in conformity with the London Building Acts or any bye-laws made in pursuance of those Acts and to re-build them in confirmity therewith;

The cost, again, is to be apportioned between the owners according to the use each makes of the re-built storeys or rooms. (See section 56 (1) (c)).

   (d) A right (where buildings are connected by arches or structures over public ways or over passages belonging to other persons) to demolish such of those buildings arches or structures or such parts thereof as are not in conformity with the London Building Acts or any bye-laws made in pursuance of those Acts and to re-build them in conformity therewith;

Once again the cost under this sub-section is to be apportioned between the owners according to the use that each makes of the buildings, arches or structures that have been re-built. (See section 56 (1) (d)). The following sub-sections (a), (f), (g) and (h) are distinguished by the fact that in every case they are to be carried out at the sole cost of the building owner with incidental expenses where specified. They are as follows:

(e) A right to underpin thicken or raise any party structure or party fence wall permitted by this Act to be underpinned thickened or raised or any external wall built against such a party structure or party fence wall subject to: –
   (i) making good all damage occasioned thereby to the adjoining premises or to the internal finishings and decorations thereof; and
   (ii) carrying up to such height and in such materials as may be agreed between the building owner and the adjoining owner or in the event of difference determined in the manner provided in this Part of this Act all flues and chimney stacks belonging to the adjoining owner on or against the party structure or external wall;

The cost is to be defrayed solely by the building owner (section 56 (1) (e)) and it should be stressed that agreement as to the nature of the materials employed must also be settled between the building and adjoining owner's surveyors, since it is no good pressing the use of fletton bricks upon an adjoining owner who requires a Victorian chimney stack to be raised in stock bricks to match the original.

(f) A right to demolish a party structure which is of insufficient strength or height for the purposes of any intended building of the building owner and to re-build it of sufficient strength or height for the said purposes subject to: –
   (i) making good all damage occasioned thereby to the adjoining premises or to the internal finishings and decorations thereof; and
   (ii) carrying up to such height and in such materials as may be agreed between the building owner and the adjoining owner or in the event of difference determined in the manner provided in this Part of the Act all flues and chimney stacks belonging to the adjoining owner on or against the party structure or external wall;

405

Once again the cost is to be a matter for the building owner alone but in this case the Act specifies that a fair allowance is to be made for disturbance and inconvenience that is caused to the adjoining owner (see section 56 (1) (e)).

(g) A right to cut into a party structure subject to making good all damage occasioned thereby to the adjoining premises or to the internal finishings and decorations thereof;

Here again the cost is to be a matter solely for the building owner (see section 56 (1) (e)).

(h) A right to cut away any footing or any projecting chimney breast jamb or flue or other projection on or over the land of the building owner from a party wall fence wall external wall or boundary wall in order to erect raise or underpin an external wall against such party wall party fence wall external wall or boundary wall or for any other purpose subject to making good all damage occasioned thereby to the adjoining premises or to the internal finishings and decorations thereof;

In this case the cost again is to be laid at the door of the building owner alone (section 56 (1) (e)).

(i) A right to cut away or demolish such parts of any wall or building of an adjoining owner overhanging the land of the building owner as may be necessary to enable a vertical wall to be erected against that wall or building subject to making good any damage occasioned thereby to the wall or buildings or to the internal finishings and decorations of the adjoining premises.

Here again the cost is to be borne by the building owner (section 56 (1) (e)).

(j) A right to execute any other necessary works incidental to the connection of a party structure with the premises adjoining it;

This is a general clause which covers matters that might be strictly excluded under previous sections and the cost is dealt with in a manner that is applicable to each individual case (section 56 (2)).

(k) A right to raise a party fence wall to raise and use as a party wall a party fence wall or to demolish a party fence wall and rebuild it as a party fence wall or as a party wall.

This sub-section is framed to deal with party fence walls alone and under its terms the cost is to be borne by the building owner alone. (Section 56 (1) (e)).

(2) For the purposes of this section a building or structure which was erected before the commencement of this Act shall be deemed to be in conformity with the London Building Acts and any bye-laws made in

pursuance of those Acts if it is in conformity with the Acts which regulated buildings or structures in London at the date at which it was erected.

(3) Nothing in this section shall authorise the building owner to place special foundations on land of the adjoining owner without his previous consent in writing.

The provisions of Part VI of the Act are basically both sensible and reasonable since, where the work of raising a party wall is done purely to suit the purposes of the building owner, he is required to pay all expenses unless the adjoining owner intends to make use of part or all of the new raised structure. The provisions in the Act for the compensation of the adjoining owner for disturbance and the payment of his costs under this heading are sparingly granted in certain cases only and this fact should be noted as the payment of such costs is unusual and can by no means be claimed as a general right for work carried out under the Act. The reason for the inclusion of compensation in 56 (1) (e) (ii) is self-evident but is unusual. In the case of consent for special foundations on adjoining land (sub-section 3) future expenses may also be involved and it is necessary to refer to sections 47 (1) and 56 (5) as previously mentioned.

In all matters relating to party walls the influence and consent of the District Surveyor will be fundamental to any final agreement. It should always be remembered however, that the District Surveyor has his own authority outside Part VI of the Act and any provision that may be exercised by the building owner may later, either in essentials or details, be drastically altered by the intervention of the District Surveyor. It should also be remembered that "raising a party wall" under the provisions of Section 46 may well include not only adding to it in terms of height but also by extending its depth in the case of forming a basement. It should also be remembered that a District Surveyor will deal with an existing wall as a party wall if it is used as such but if it has been improperly formed or used as a party wall without consent it might be open to the building owner's surveyor to object to the adjoining owner benefiting from the raising or modification of the wall in the future unless the minimum prescriptive period of twenty years has elapsed.

The need for notice under Section 45 of the Act where the junction line is not built on has already been referred to but the section which deals with those notices that are most commonly served is Section 47. This is as follows:

(1) Before exercising any right conferred on him by Section 46 (Rights of owners of adjoining lands where junction line built on) of this Act a

building owner shall serve on the adjoining notice in writing (in this Act referred to as a "party structure notice") stating the nature and particulars of the proposed work the time at which it will be begun and those particulars shall where the building owner proposes to construct special foundations include plans sections and details of construction of the special foundations with reasonable particulars of the loads to be carried thereby.

(2) A Party Structure Notice shall be served –

    (a) In respect of a party fence wall or special foundations at least one month; and

    (b) In respect of a party structure at least two months;

before the date stated therein as that on which the work is to be begun.

(3) A Party Structure Notice shall not be effective unless the work to which the notice relates is begun within six months after the notice has been served and is prosecuted with due diligence.

The rules governing notices generally under the provisions of the 1939 Act are summarised in tabulated form on Pages 410 and 411 while section 124 of the Act setting out the manner in which they are to be served is reprinted as Appendix 2 to this chapter on pages 435–6. Notices under the Act must be in writing and although no particular form is necessary printed forms are generally employed prepared both by the Royal Institute of British Architects and the Royal Institution of Chartered Surveyors. There are three aspects to the service of notices under the Act, all of which must be correct. The first is that accurate information must be provided; the second is that the notice should be served in the proper manner and thirdly that the timing, that is to say the time limits provided in the Act, should be strictly adhered to. Provided that all these elements are in order, the notice should be a good one. It is a common misapprehension that works have to be specified in extensive and precise detail in a notice relating to work to party walls but this is not so. As long as the intention is made simply and clearly in one, or at the most a few sentences, the building owner's duty under the Act is discharged. The surveyor who serves notice on an "owner" is referred to the original definition included in the 1930 Act Section 5 since incorporated in the 1939 Act:

> An "Owner" is a person in receipt of the whole or part of the rents and profits of any land or tenement or in occupation thereof otherwise than as a tenant from year to year or for any less term.

It will therefore be appreciated that the definition of an "owner" is a very wide one indeed. A tenant for more than a year of part of a house is an owner.[3] A minimum term to define ownership of one

(3) *Fillingham* v. *Wood* (1981) 1 Ch. 51.

408

year certain and then from year to year would presumably exclude a tenancy for a single year only and excludes a statutory tenant under the Rent Acts who has a right to possession only granted under statute and not a true tenancy. The definition would however, include all lessees with a shared maintenance responsibility for a block of flats. Where the owner cannot be found and a notice is required under the Act the matter may be referred to the County Court and although a procedure is available under such circumstances for nailing a notice to the front door of the property concerned, this is fraught with danger and cannot be recommended. The risk element can be illustrated by the instance of where the owners are abroad or are a married couple in process of obtaining a divorce with one of the parties living away. In cases of multi-occupation, personal enquiry at the site is vital.

It should in particular be emphasised that in serving party structure and party fence wall notices under the Act (either published by the RIBA or RICS) it is necessary to insert the appropriate sub-section to Section 46. The correct service of the notice is vital as not only does the whole progress of the building contract depend upon it, together with the investment of a great deal of the building owner's money but possibly a substantial proportion due from the adjoining owner as well. Furthermore the degree of care required in the drafting and serving of notices cannot be over-emphasised. The architect or surveyor should also look ahead. Upon opening up and with the intervention of the District Surveyor, items of work may be necessary which were not foreseen at the outset of the building contract and underpinning, for example, could be included in a notice even although it is hoped that this will not be necessary at the outset. The need for service of a second notice once the works have started is to be avoided if at all possible. It should be added that an intention to underpin must be clearly stated in a notice and in this connection Form C published by the RIBA is badly drafted and in this and other cases the RICS forms are to be preferred. It is necessary when completing notices to be clear in intention and specific in wording rather than general. A particular point to emphasise is that notices should never be invalidated by a covering letter. All too often architects or surveyors feel that a formal notice couched in uncompromising terms is not likely to lead to agreement, particularly if the matter is pressing and they then include a covering letter saying for example that their client will pay for the whole of the cost which may be inappropriate under the circumstances. Finally, it should be stressed that the architect or surveyor should always have available his written authority in order to produce this if necessary having served notice under the Act. Such precautions are vital in cases

(continued on page 411)

SERVICE OF NOTICES UNDER SECTION 124 OF THE LONDON BUILDING ACTS (AMENDMENT) ACT 1939

Section of 1939 Act	Subject Matter	Time Limit for Notice	R.I.B.A. Form
5/6	Where junction line is not built on	One month and not exceeding six months	E and F
47	Where junction line is built on	Party fence wall or special foundations one month. Party structures two months with six months time limit.	A and B (Plans)
48	Counter-notice by Adjoining Owner Note: Dissent under Section 49 within fourteen days	Within twenty-one days after service of the notice in relation to special foundations or one month in relation to other matters	
50	Intention to build within 10ft and 20ft of Adjoining Owner's building	One month plus plans and Sections	C and D (plans)
50	Counter-notice by Adjoining Owner	Fourteen days in the case of underpinning or foundations	
52	Excavation of Sites abutting on narrow streets or ways	Four weeks notice of place where plans and sections can be inspected	
53	Breaking open or entering upon premises	In emergency such notice as is practicable otherwise fourteen days	
55	Selection of Third Surveyor	Where a difference arises or is deemed to have arisen	G
57	Security for expenses	One month	
58	Account of expenses	One month's notice of objection upon receipt of account	

410

NOTES

(1) Notice C should give a definite intention to underpin.

(2) The provision on form D for the appointment of a surveyor is not really necessary and in form E is premature as a difference has not yet arisen. In form F the appointment is still not necessary. The only "difference" can be over compensation. The provision is also premature in forms A and B.

(3) Under Section 48 the position requiring dissent within fourteen days and twenty-eight days for the counter-notice is a curious one.

(4) Exemptions to notices comprise firstly work under dangerous structure notices, secondly work in respect of Crown property and thirdly in cases where a wall is not a party wall.

(5) Section 50 notices must be accompanied by drawings.

FORMS PUBLISHED BY RICS

Recently six forms have been produced by the Royal Institution of Chartered Surveyors. The forms which were drafted by a working party of surveyors specialising in work relating to party walls are:

- Party Structure Notice;
- Acknowledgement of Party Structure Notice;
- Ten Foot/Twenty Foot Notice;
- Acknowledgement of Ten Foot/Twenty Foot Notice;
- Line of Junction Notice;
- Selection of Third Surveyor.

The party structure and ten foot/twenty foot notices, together with acknowledgement forms are partly carbonated to facilitate the completion of the acknowledgement form by the adjoining owner.

The forms are available from Surveyors Publications

(continued from page 409)

of difficulty, for example, where the adjoining owner ignores notices and correspondence and an Award is made and action taken under Section 53.

Under Section 47 (4) of the 1939 Act there is specific reference to dangerous structures.

(4) Nothing in this section shall prevent a building owner from exercising with the consent in writing of the adjoining owner and of the adjoining occupiers any right conferred on him by section 46 (rights of owners of adjoining lands where junction line built on) of this Act and nothing in this section shall require him to serve any party structure notice before complying with any notice served under the provisions of Part VII (dangerous and neglected structures) of this Act.

Section 48 of the 1939 Act deals with counter notices. The section can be set out in detail.

(1) After the service of a party structure notice the adjoining owner may serve on the building owner a notice in writing (in this Part of the Act referred to as "a counter notice").

(2) A counter notice –

    (a) May in respect of a party fence wall or party structure require the building owner to build in or on the party fence wall or party structure as the case may be to which the notice relates such chimney copings breasts jambs or flues or such piers or recesses or other like works as may reasonably be required for the convenience of the adjoining owner;

    (b) May in respect of special foundations to which the adjoining owner consents under sub-section (3) of Section 46 (Rights of owners of adjoining lands where junction line built on) of this Act require them to be placed at a specified greater depth than that proposed by the building owner or to be constructed of sufficient strength to bear the load to be carried by columns of any intended building of the adjoining owner or may include both of these requirements; and

    (c) Shall specify the works required by the notice to be executed and shall be accompanied by plans sections and particulars thereof.

(3) A counter notice shall be served –

    (a) In relation to special foundations within twenty-one days after the service of the party structure notice; and

    (b) in relation to any other matter within one month after the service of the party structure notice.

(4) A building owner on whom a counter notice has been served shall comply with the requirements of the counter notice unless the execution of the works required by the counter notice would be injurious to him or cause unnecessary inconvenience to him or unnecessary delay in the execution of the works pursuant to the party structure notice.

In the event of serving a counter notice the adjoining owner must pay for the expense of work that he requires to be carried out in order to suit his convenience (Section 46 (3)).

Under Section 50 of the Act provision is made for underpinning buildings within ten feet of the proposed new building or structure.

(1) Where a building owner –

    (a) Proposes to erect within ten feet from any part of a building of an adjoining owner a building or structure independent of the building of the adjoining owner and any part of the proposed building or structure will within the said ten feet extend to a lower level than the level of the bottom of the foundations of the building of the adjoining owner; or

    (b) Proposes to erect within twenty feet from any part of an independent building of an adjoining owner a building or structure any part of which will within the said twenty feet meet a plane drawn downwards in the direction of the building or structure of the building owner at an angle of forty five degrees to the horizontal from the line formed by the intersection of the plane of the level of the bottom of the foundations of the building of the adjoining owner with the plane of the external face of the external wall of the building of the adjoining owner;

He may and if required by the adjoining owner shall subject to the provisions of this section at the expense of the building owner underpin or otherwise strengthen or safeguard the foundations of the building of the adjoining owner so far as may be necessary.

(2) In any case to which sub-section (1) of this section applies the following provisions shall have effect: –

(a) At least one month before beginning to erect a building or structure the building owner shall serve on the adjoining owner notice in writing of his intention to do so and that notice shall state whether he proposes to underpin or otherwise strengthen or safeguard the foundations of the building of the adjoining owner;

(b) The said notice shall be accompanied by plans and sections showing the site of the building or structure proposed to be erected by the building owner and the depth to which he proposes to excavate;

(c) Within fourteen days after service of the said notice the adjoining owner may serve notice in writing on the building owner that he disputes the necessity of or requires as the case may be the underpinning or strengthening or the safeguarding of the foundations of his building and if the adjoining owner serves such a notice a difference shall be deemed to have arisen between the building owner and the adjoining owner;

(d) The building owner shall compensate the adjoining owner and any adjoining occupier for any inconvenience loss or damage which may result to any of them by reason of any work executed in pursuance of this section.

(3) On completion of any work executed in pursuance of this section the building owner shall if so requested by the adjoining owner supply him with particulars including plans and sections of the work.

(4) Nothing in this section shall relieve the building owner from any liability to which he would otherwise be subject for injury to the adjoining owner or any adjoining occupier by reason of work executed by him.

An important sub-section is (2) (d) where provision is made for compensation payable to the adjoining owner and occupier in respect of any inconvenience loss or damage in connection with underpinning. This could be very important and indeed costly in commercial premises where loss of trade is concerned and should be distinguished from the compensation for damage specified in Section 45 (1) (c) which deals with footings on the land of an adjoining owner. There is also the requirement in the Act for the repayment of the adjoining owner's expenses for disturbance and inconvenience in cases where the building owner carries out work not of repair but of improvement for his own convenience under Section 46 (f).

Section 51 of the Act deals with the execution of works and is as follows:

(1) A building owner shall not exercise any right conferred on him by this Part of the Act in such manner or at such time as to cause unnecessary inconvenience to the adjoining owner or to the adjoining occupier.

(2) Where a building owner is exercising any right conferred on him by this Part of the Act lays open any part of the adjoining land or building he shall at his own expense make and maintain so long as may be necessary a proper hoarding shoring or fans or temporary construction for the protection of the adjoining land or building and the security of the adjoining owner.

(3) Any works executed in pursuance of this Part of the Act shall –

    (a) comply with the provisions of the London Building Acts and any bye-laws made in pursuance of those Acts; and

    (b) subject to the foregoing paragraph (a) be executed in accordance with such plans sections and particulars as may be agreed between the owners or in the event of difference determined in the manner provided in this Part of the Act and no deviation shall be made therefrom except such as may also be agreed between the parties or in the event of difference determined in manner aforesaid.

Section 52 of the Act deals with notice of excavation of sites abutting on narrow streets or ways. It is as follows:

Where a building owner proposes to erect any building or structure or carry out any work in relation to a building or structure on land which abuts on a street or way less than twenty feet in width the following provisions shall have effect if the erection of the proposed building or structure or the carrying out of the work involves excavation to a depth of twenty feet or more below the level of the highest part of the land immediately abutting on the street: –

    (a) Notices stating the place (being a place situate at a distance not greater than two miles of such land) at and the hours during which plans and sections of so much of the proposed building structure or work as relates to the excavation may be inspected shall be exhibited in a prominent position on the land or on any existing building or on the boundary wall fence or hoarding (if any) surrounding the said land or building in such a manner as to be readily legible from every street or way on which the land abuts;

    (b) The notices shall be exhibited at least four weeks before any such work of excavation is begun and shall be maintained and where necessary renewed by the building owner until such work of excavation is begun;

(c) The plans and sections referred to in the notices shall until the work of excavation is begun be open to public inspection without payment at the place and during such reasonable hours as are stated in the notice.

Although this section applies when the street or way is less than twenty feet in width the proposed new building does not necessarily have to abut upon it since the section operates when excavations in connection with the work are to extend twenty feet or more in depth on land immediately adjoining the narrow street or way.

Section 53 of the Act deals with the power of entry by the building owner. It is as follows:

(1) A building owner his servants agents and workmen may during usual working hours enter and remain on any premises for the purposes of executing and may execute any work in pursuance of this Part of this Act and may remove any furniture or fittings or take any other action necessary for that purpose.

(2) If the premises are closed the building owner his servants agents and workmen may if accompanied by a constable or other police officer break open any fence or doors in order to enter the premises.

(3) Before entering any premises in pursuance of this section a building owner shall give to the owner and occupier of the premises –

(a) In case of emergency such notice of his intention to enter as may be reasonably practicable;
(b) In any other case fourteen days notice of his intention to enter.

The important point to stress is that the correct procedure has to be obeyed to the letter in the service, preparation and observance of the necessary time limit in connection with the notice. Any omission may cost the building owner dear.

Dissent from notices and the settlement of differences is dealt with in detail in Sections 49 and 55 of the Act and are set out here in full. Section 49 is as follows:

If an owner on whom a party structure notice or a counter notice has been served does not within fourteen days thereafter express his consent thereto in writing he shall be deemed to have dissented from the notice and a difference shall be deemed to have arisen between the parties.

Section 55 of the Act is considerably longer and contains the whole machinery for the appointment of surveyors, the steps to be taken in the event of a surveyor failing to be appointed and, once appointed, a surveyor's failure or incapacity to act. The section also covers the Award of the third surveyor including provisions as to costs and appeals. It is as follows:

Where a difference arises or is deemed to have arisen between a building owner and an adjoining owner in respect of any matter connected with any work to which this Part of the Act relates the following provisions shall have effect:

(a) Either –
  (i) Both parties shall concur in the appointment of one surveyor (in this section referred to as an "agreed surveyor"); or
  (ii) each party shall appoint a surveyor and the two surveyors so appointed shall select a third surveyor (all of whom are in this section together referred to as "the three surveyors");

(b) If an agreed surveyor refuses or for ten days after a written request by either party neglects to act or if before the difference is settled he dies or becomes incapable of acting the proceedings for settling such difference shall begin de novo;

(c) If either party to the difference refuses or for ten days after a written request by the other party neglects to appoint a surveyor under sub-paragraph (ii) of paragraph (a) of this section that other party may make the appointment on his behalf;

(d) If before the difference is settled a surveyor appointed under sub-paragraph (ii) of paragraph (a) of this section by a party to the difference dies or becomes incapable of acting the party who appointed him may appoint another surveyor in his place who shall have the same power and authority as his predecessor;

(e) If a surveyor appointed under sub-paragraph (ii) of paragraph (a) of this section by a party to the difference or if a surveyor appointed under paragraph (d) of this section refuses or for ten days after a written request by either party neglects to act the surveyor of the other party may proceed ex parte and anything so done by him shall be as effectual as if he had been an agreed surveyor;

(f) If a surveyor appointed under sub-paragraph (ii) of paragraph (a) of this section by a party to the difference refuses or for ten days after a written request by either party neglects to select a third surveyor under paragraph (a) or paragraph (g) of this section the superintending architect or in cases where the Council is a party to the difference the Secretary of State may on the application of either party select a third surveyor who shall have the same power and authority as if he had been selected under paragraph (a) or paragraph (g) of this section;

(g) If a third surveyor selected under sub-paragraph (ii) of paragraph (a) of this section refuses or for ten days after a written request by either party or the surveyor appointed by either party neglects to act or if before the difference is settled he dies or becomes incapable of acting the other two of the three surveyors shall forthwith select another surveyor in his place who shall have the same power and authority as his predecessor;

(h) All appointments and selections made under this section shall be in writing;

(i) The agreed surveyor or as the case may be the three surveyors or any two of them shall settle by Award any matter which before the commencement of any work to which a notice under this Part of this Act relates or from time to time during the continuance of such work may be in dispute between the building owner and the adjoining owner;

(j) If no two of the three surveyors are in agreement the third surveyor selected in pursuance of this section shall make the award within fourteen days after he is called upon to do so;

(k) The Award may determine the right to execute and the time and manner of executing any work and generally any other matter arising out of or incidental to the difference:

Provided that any period appointed by the award for executing any work shall not unless otherwise agreed between the building owner and the adjoining owner begin to run until after the expiration of the period prescribed by this Act for service of the notice in respect of which the difference arises or is deemed to have arisen;

(l) The costs incurred in making or obtaining an award under this section and the cost of reasonable supervision of carrying out any work to which the award relates shall subject to the provisions of this section be paid by such of the parties as the surveyors making the award determine;

(m) The award shall be conclusive and shall not except as provided by this section be questioned in any court;

(n) Either of the parties to the difference may within fourteen days after the delivery of an award made under this section appeal to the county court against this award and the following provisions shall have effect:

   (i) Subject as hereafter in this paragraph provided the county court may rescind the award or modify it in such manner and make such order as to costs as it thinks fit;

  (ii) If the appellant against the award on appearing before the county court is unwilling that this matter should be decided by the court and satisfies that court that he will if the matter is decided against him to be liable to pay a sum (exclusive of costs) exceeding one hundred pounds and gives security approved by the county court and to prosecute his appeal in the High Court and to abide the event thereof all proceedings in the county court shall be stayed and the appellant may bring an action in the High Court against the other party to the difference;

(o) Where an appellant against an award brings an action in the High Court in pursuance of the last preceding paragraph the following provisions shall have effect:

   (i) If the parties agree as to the facts a special case may be stated for the opinion of the court and may be dealt with in accordance with or as nearly as circumstances admit in accordance with the rules of the court;

417

(ii) In any other case the plaintiff in the action shall deliver to the defendant an issue whereby the matters in difference may be tried;

(iii) The issue shall be in such form as may be agreed between the parties or in case of dispute or of non-appearance of the defendant as may be settled by the court;

(iv) The action shall proceed and the issue be tried in accordance with or as nearly as circumstances admit in accordance with the rules of the court;

(v) Any costs incurred by the parties in the county court shall be deemed to be costs incurred in the action in the High Court and be payable accordingly.

It will be noted that under Section 55 the parties have the alternative of either agreeing to the appointment of one surveyor, known as the "agreed surveyor", or each party can appoint his own surveyor, whereupon the two surveyors so appointed are under a duty to select a third surveyor so that the trio are then known under the Act as "the three surveyors". It has become so much a part of London practice for each side to appoint a surveyor who then agree in turn upon the appointment of a third surveyor that Section 55 (a) (i) where an agreed surveyor is appointed is infrequently used. Owners seem rarely to be sufficiently sure of the impartiality of a single surveyor appointed under the Act to allow matters to proceed on this basis. Furthermore any saving in fees is usually only to the benefit of the building owner so that there is little inducement to the adjoining owner to give up the feeling of greater security which the appointment of a surveyor to act solely in his interest engenders.

It is a curious feature of the Act that the word "surveyor" is not defined and indeed there is nothing to prevent an accountant, or indeed a cost produce broker, from acting as a "surveyor" under the Act, although his right to claim "professional" fees would no doubt be contested by a professional surveyor acting on the other side. Usually however, for obvious reasons, professional architects, surveyors or engineers are appointed to act. Irrespective however, of the nature of the appointment, the Act is constructed in such a way as to ensure that matters progress without being frustrated by any ignorance of constructional details or the proceedings of the Act. Reference to Section 55 (c) where if either party to the difference refuses, or for ten days after a written request by the other party neglects, to appoint a surveyor then the other party may make the appointment on his behalf illustrates this point. The Act also makes provision in subsequent sections for the surveyor's incapacity or neglect to act.

It is at this stage that an interesting metamorphosis occurs. Once the agreed surveyor, or more commonly the two surveyors are appointed under the terms of the Act, they cease to have the normal client/surveyor relationship and now take up a quasi-judicial role which is strictly defined and limited by statute from now on. Once a surveyor is properly appointed and his appointment duly made in writing, his authority under the Act can only be terminated by firstly, completion of the work on the one hand or, secondly, the surveyor's inability (i.e. due to death) or neglect to act, in which case he is then passed over and another appointment made, or, thirdly, by variation due to a Court Order. It should be emphasised that once a surveyor is appointed his instructing owner cannot then, for example, in a fit of pique, on finding his advice unpalatable, terminate his appointment. It is hoped, however, that this will not lead to any tinge of arrogance on the part of a surveyor, particularly a surveyor acting for an adjoining owner, as it is all the more necessary in view of the powers given to him under the Act, to take particular pains to keep his instructing owner fully informed as to what is happening and, in particular, to make him feel that the surveyor concerned is acting wholeheartedly in his best interests. Work to party walls often leads to great anxiety in owners and the surveyor must identify with his client's feelings and take pains to give not only advice but reassurance even in small points which may seem trivial to him but which may be a source of continual worry to the owner concerned.

In view of the wide powers conferred by the 1939 Act it is vital that written authorities of appointment are scrupulously made. The Act gives extensive powers to a surveyor, or to one or more surveyors, which may culminate in actually breaking in upon premises and at the outset of each particular case the surveyor does not know what complications may arise in the future. He is well advised therefore to ensure that his authority is completely effective as he may have to produce this for inspection under a number of different circumstances. An architect or surveyor may already have a contract between himself and his client at the outset of a party wall matter but at this point, he should give considerable thought as to whether, upon his appointment as a surveyor under the 1939 Act, any conflict is likely to arise in the future. In small and relatively straightforward cases, the architect or surveyor dealing with constructional work acts as the building owner's "surveyor" while a second surveyor is appointed on behalf of the adjoining owner. Both surveyors then concur in the appointment of a third surveyor. Conflict does not normally arise to any great extent under such circumstances but in the case of larger projects it has become increasingly the case for surveyors who are specialists in matters relating to party walls under the 1939 Act to be separately appointed apart from the professional adviser actually dealing with the works. There is an enormous advantage in making such an appointment in that the party wall surveyor can make it clear that he is dealing with matters as they relate strictly to the Act itself and his duties are not blurred by any responsibilities relating to supervision of work, for example, or a request to achieve a reduction in rates during the period when the work is being undertaken which might lead to difficulties and possibly conflict in the relationship with a client and the quasi-judicial role under the terms of the Act on the other.

Under any circumstances however, a surveyor should at the outset of his appointment under the Act inform his client as to what is involved and assist him in drafting the actual words of his appointment. There is no printed form which can assist in this connection, which is just as well as the circumstances of each case may differ, but some such wording as "I hereby appoint Mr. John Smith to act as my surveyor in all matters relating to the party wall between Nos. 30 and 32 Hyacinth Avenue under the terms of the London Building Acts (Amendment) Act 1939 and to sign all necessary documents under that Act on my behalf" should provide sufficient authority.

Once a surveyor is authorised to act under the terms of the 1939 Act, he must not only prove to be competent in the different branches of the work which will be needed, such as knowledge of law and construction but he may also be charged with the duty of apportioning building costs, for example where an adjoining owner serves a counter notice under Section 48. In addition however, and just as importantly, he has to have intimate knowledge of the 1939 Act as his duty will then be to press matters forward to a conclusion since the alternatives to a happy culmination are bleak, amounting as they do to neglect, death or intervention of the courts. A surveyor instructed under the Act should always have the object of a successful conclusion of the party wall negotiations firmly in his mind particularly in the case of the surveyor to the adjoining owner who should try to act in a helpful manner and not simply be a piece of grit in the machinery. The building owner's surveyor on his part should attempt not merely to obey the letter of the law but to see things also from the point of view of the adjoining owner's surveyor, to be helpful and human so far as his instructing owner is concerned and to produce, or have produced, specially drawn plans showing details of the party structure or party wall for inclusion in the Award. All too often an adjoining owner's surveyor is handed an enormous wad of drawings accompanied by a letter and notice under the Act suggesting that the building owner's surveyor is merely fulfilling an irksome duty and he would rather that neither the adjoining owner or his surveyor existed in the first place. This is both unfortunate and unnecessary. In the event of one of the two surveyors failing to act the provisions of Section 55 should be followed promptly. If a building owner's surveyor appoints a surveyor on behalf of the adjoining owner in default and the surveyor so appointed should be so unreasonable as to die, the building owner's surveyor is under a duty to make another appointment at once. In the event of a surveyor failing to act he should receive ten days' written notice, whereupon the other surveyor can act in his default and it should always be remembered that under the terms of the Act any two of the three surveyors appointed under the terms of Section 55 (a) (ii) are empowered to make an Award. If the third surveyor is nervous of this proceeding, he can always be asked to make an Award on his own. If the third surveyor neglects or refuses to act he also must receive ten days' notice whereupon, if he fails to react, another appointment can be made.

Finally, in conclusion of this section, it should be emphasised that the appointment of a building owner's or adjoining owner's surveyor under this section of the Act is a personal one. An appointment cannot be made in the name of a company or partnership, nor can work be carried out by one surveyor and documents be signed by another. This can pose problems for large firms of surveyors although in theory it should not, since there is no reason why assistants should not be appointed. There is nothing to say that only partners can accept appointments. Problems can also arise with companies and central and local government where the concept of an individual acting at times seems somewhat alien to normal office practice.

The third surveyor appointed under Section 55 (a) (ii) has the sole duty under the further sub-sections (j) to (m) to make an Award in the prescribed manner and within the time limit laid down in the Act in the event of the other two surveyors not being able to arrive at an agreement. This task is crucial to the smooth running of the machinery under Part VI of the Act and it is vitally necessary that the first task of the building owner's surveyor on learning of the appointment of the adjoining owner's surveyor is to submit suggested names for the appointment of a third surveyor before any other steps are taken. It would seem that this should be a simple task but it is often not the case. An architect may wish to appoint another architect experienced in this work while the adjoining owner's representative under the Act, who could well be a surveyor, might have no knowledge at all of the names submitted and may wish to make counter suggestions as to eminent surveyors he knows who, he feels, are more experienced. It should be emphasised however, that at the price of a slight wrangle at the outset of the relationship between the building owner and adjoining owner's surveyor, it is vital that an appointment is made at once. There is sometimes a tendency towards dodging the problem by simply specifying that a third surveyor shall be appointed by the "President for the time being of the Royal Institution of Chartered Surveyors" and this suggestion seems to be increasingly favoured by Councils as it appears on the surface to give a flavour of impartiality to the proceedings. Hard talking however, is necessary to overcome this suggestion as the practicalities of party wall negotiations simply do not allow of the time consuming procedure that will be necessary to involve the selection and appointment of a third surveyor by this means once a dispute between surveyors has arisen. It is also necessary for another reason. Under sub-section (f) of Section 55 of the Act, if one of the two surveyors already appointed refuses or for ten days after a written request by either party neglects to select a third surveyor, reference is to be made to the Superintending Architect of the Greater London Council or, in cases where the Council is a party to the difference, to the Secretary of State. One can imagine that this process is likely to take some time and it is far better to invoke it at the outset of the proceedings. Differences are just as likely to arise at the outset of the matter as at a later stage and in the interests of all parties it is necessary that the appointment is made without delay. This is usually done by completing the appropriate form obtainable from either the Royal Institution of Chartered Surveyors or the Royal Institute of British Architects. It is not strictly necessary to employ a printed form but this has the advantage of including all the necessary information so that there are no obvious omissions. It is of course only proper professional procedure to ask the consent of the nominated third surveyor before completing the form. If this is not done due to an oversight it does not mean that the third surveyor cannot or will not act when the time comes but it would be embarrassing for example if it was found that the third surveyor already acted for one of the parties in another capacity.

The third surveyor should be skilled in work under the 1939 Act, as a matter of specialist activity, and should preferably be a man of eminence in his profession. It should not be forgotten that while the two surveyors may have complete confidence in the third surveyor, justice must also be seen to be done over a matter of considerable consequence to their appointing owners. Both owners each side of a party wall, peering from the upper windows as the third surveyor waves goodbye, will be considerably impressed by his silver hair and his general bearing, if such be the case, so that when his pronouncement duly arrives it will be accepted without question. Here it is worth adding that the instructing owners should be told at the outset the name and address of the third surveyor and the procedure and appeal machinery under the Act. Such a letter will be filed, and in most cases happily not be needed, but in the event of a substantial difference when one owner asks his surveyor what is to happen next it is as well to remind him of the existence of a letter that he will no doubt have forgotten all about. It is an odd omission in the Act that there is no procedure for jointly invoking the intervention of the third surveyor since either of the two surveyors can request the third surveyor to decide a particular matter without reference to the other. In practice however, should a difference occur, it is normal for the two surveyors to correspond, set out the area of the difference and refer this jointly to the third surveyor who then decides between the parties. Under the terms of the Act, the third surveyor has to act within ten days of being asked to do so and has then to make his Award within fourteen days. Practised third surveyors in view of the time limits under the Act will be very outspoken about any sloppiness on the part of either of the two surveyors. Notice to the third surveyor must always be in writing and the two surveyors must have their authorities properly executed for his inspection. He will wish to see the Award if it has been executed and of course all relevant documents. The third surveyor will then usually ask for an undertaking for payment of his fees irrespective of whether agreement is reached between the parties or whether he decides between them. The former happens more frequently than is often thought. Another misconception is that the third surveyor will settle everything within ten days flat. Most experienced surveyors take the limit of the time allowed to them if the case is anything other than simple and it is merely necessary for the third surveyor to respond to a request to act within the ten days allowed under the Act, but little more. It is too much to expect a busy professional man to leap out of his office at a moment's notice and solve all problems with the wave of a wand. It is often disconcerting to surveyors experienced in this type of work to realise the depth of enquiry that an experienced third surveyor will invoke. It will be embarrassing for the building owner's surveyor to find that the third surveyor questions the service of his original notice and the third surveyor's display of knowledge relating to the sub-sections in the Act can, if the building owner's surveyor is not up to the same level of knowledge, make him feel very small indeed. However the intervention of the third surveyor can often prove extremely helpful since, in most cases, he will realise at once that the two surveyors really wish to arrive at a decision to overcome a particular problem. They welcome the third surveyor's experience and are often only too glad to see him arrive.

The experienced third surveyor will generally call the two surveyors together, either in the office or on the site, to find out what the matter is all about, examine documents, carry out his inspection and then promise to give his decision. Where certain vital documents are missing or inadequate or if the matter is a complicated one, the third surveyor will set a time for further submissions or meetings. An experienced third surveyor never allows the matter to go into limbo. He always follows the matter through as a matter of regular procedure keeping a wary eye on the provisions of the Act. The reason why he calls for meetings and requires information by correspondence is a simple one. It is necessary for each surveyor to feel that he is a party to the proceedings and that the matter is not being discussed out of his hearing, however inocuous such a discussion may be. Finally, when the third surveyor's Award is obtained, the parties are often surprised at its brevity. This is another characteristic of the experienced third surveyor who also probably acts as an arbitrator in other types of dispute as well. Such a man will bear in mind the expression of a distinguished judge who said that "arbitrators often arrive at a correct result for the wrong reasons" and few third surveyors or arbitrators will give hostages to fortune. He will also be unlikely to refresh the mind of either of the two surveyors of the appeal machinery which exists in the Act against his decision. He will feel quite rightly that this is a matter for the two surveyors themselves. The last message of the third surveyor will be limited quite simply to where his Award can be collected upon payment of his fee by either party. He is likely to have earned it. The problems that arise over Part VI are likely to be complex, ranging from costs and security when buildings are "laid open", responsibility for repair due to fire damage and whether notices served are valid or may have expired. Detailed knowledge and experience of the Act is required of a third surveyor.

The authority for the settlement of differences under the Act is set out in Section 55 (i) (j). The scope of the Award, its costs and the provisions relating to the machinery for appeal to the county court or High Court are set out in subsequent sub-sections and no one reading them can have the slightest doubt as to the importance of an Award being correctly drafted, executed and delivered; which includes copies being sent to the instructing owners at once so that the appeal machinery is not rendered invalid.

Nothing divides party wall surveyors so much as the need for adopting another form of words to those that they have found to be tried and tested over the years. This is a particular problem for the adjoining owner's surveyor who, receiving a draft Award that he feels to be inadequate has to undergo the agony of re-drafting clauses which although similar to those with which he is familiar, may vary to an irritating degree.

The party wall Award first of all recites the facts of the case. Here it should be emphasised that the name and address of the building and adjoining owners have to be accurately and correctly stated and that each must have full authority. Particular care must be taken in the case of companies and partnerships for example and if the name of a company should alter during the course of the proceedings, this should be notified to all parties. Following the names and addresses of the owners the authoritative sections of the Act and the names and addresses of the three surveyors should also be inserted followed by the facts of the case as they relate to the party structure. Whether the wall is a party wall or party fence wall, forms part of an independent building or whatever form it takes and is agreed, should be recorded. The existence and the precise identification of the drawings and schedule of condition (to be referred to later) should be specified as should an outline and brief specification of the work so that the nature and extent of this can be identified as it relates, needless to say, strictly to the party structure.

The obligations of the building owner should be specified simply but in an all embracing manner and in a way that is strictly related to the matter in question. This is where a building owner's surveyor has a duty to draft a party wall Award that is strictly related to the matter in question before submitting it to the adjoining owner's surveyor. This is far preferable to clipping a large number of duplicated sheets together covered with ball point scrawl since this carries little conviction. A party wall Award should be drafted anew in every case.

The clauses that define the nature and extent of the building owner's obligations normally include the question of cost, either at his sole expense or shared as the case may be, and will include provision as to the necessary shoring and support. One matter that is often overlooked is the need for specifying adequate security protection either in the case of commercial or residential buildings. The building owner is again held responsible for making good all damage whether structural or decorative and for adequate insurance. Here again the advice of the insurance broker should be sought as there are many aspects of insurance that could well be overlooked by the two surveyors other than damage caused to property or persons as a direct result of the work. A further necessary provision in the Award is for the right of access to be agreed and stated either at reasonable times or upon reasonable notice to be given by the adjoining owner's surveyor in respect of the building owner's side of the party wall and the building owner's surveyor in respect of the land and premises of the adjoining owner.

One of the most important parts of the Award is to recite the agreement between the surveyors as to access for the work i.e. whether this is to be carried out from the building owner's side only or whether access from the adjoining owner's premises is necessary, together with agreement as to screens or hoardings, the removal of rubbish and the hours in which the work can be carried out. It must always be remembered that the hours specified will be of vital importance to the contractor who will eventually hear with something less than excitement of the conditions imposed upon him. Such restrictions should be thought out with great care, relating to the particular case. It will quickly be realised why when reasonable working hours in weekdays, excluding public holidays, may be satisfactory for a private house, weekend and bank holiday working might be the best time for building operations to be carried out in respect of offices. Finally, in connection with the work, it is customary for an Award to specify that this is to be carried out in accordance with specified regulations and byelaws and to the satisfaction of the District Surveyor and also that the work is to be carried out in a proper and workmanlike manner in sound and suitable materials. It is also customary for the works to be specified as having to be carried out with reasonable expedition after commencement and without causing any unnecessary inconvenience to the adjoining owners or occupiers.

A most important point in the Award, certainly so far as the adjoining owner's surveyor is concerned, relates to the question of fees. It is necessary that the fee of the adjoining owner's surveyor is agreed as this is due upon the Award being signed. Some surveyors take the view that they will not execute the Award unless the cheque is handed over at the same time, while others feel that this is improper and that the Award should be executed and published first and that the fee, although due on the publication of the Award, if not proffered at the time, be requested subsequently. Whatever the position regarding payment, care is needed in drafting the particular clause relating to the adjoining owner's fee. It should be possible, and indeed it must be possible, for the adjoining owner's surveyor to work out the cost of his work insofar as this is foreseeable and while it is customary for a lump sum plus VAT to be inserted in the Award, it is also common and good practice for the extent of the foreseeable work to be clearly defined. For example the fee will include work carried out to the date of execution of the Award and will prudently cover further inspections to the site together with a final visit for checking the schedule of condition. The need for any additional work over and above that envisaged should however, be specified under this particular clause as requiring a further fee perhaps at a rate per visit to the site or on the basis of an hourly rate with provision for inflation if the job will be a long one.

Just as the question of fees should be made clear so should the right of the two surveyors to make any further Award or Awards which may be necessary. It is impossible to envisage the progress of a complicated building operation in every possible circumstance and the need for a further Award or Awards may well be necessary. It is also desirable for a clause to be inserted to the effect that the Award shall be null and void if the permitted works do not start within say twelve months of its date of execution. This is an obvious precaution against uncertainty due to unforeseen delay. It is also customary for the fact, although set out clearly in the 1939 Act, that nothing in the Award should be held as conferring or affecting any right of light or air or other easement to be restated. Although this may not be strictly necessary it is included along with other clauses which repeat sections of the Act as a reminder to building and adjoining owners and, of equal importance, to contractors, of the scope of the Award in full without the necessity for others to refer to the Act itself.

Once the Award is drafted and agreed, the document should be carefully executed. The Award itself, the drawings and any Schedule of Condition should be signed. The signatures of the two surveyors should be correctly witnessed on the Award, a fact often overlooked, and the Award should then be published, which merely means that it should be sent out to those affected by its contents. It is necessary for the Award to be sent to the building and adjoining owners and it should not be overlooked that in the event of a number of adjoining owners being involved, each one requires to be treated in exactly the same way. This underlines the need for small practical drawings relating to the party wall alone being incorporated in the Award for convenience, instead of voluminous plans relating principally to other work. Copies of all Awards need to be sent by the building owners surveyor to the contractor for retention on site by the general foreman and with instructions that the terms are to be followed implicitly. Depending on the circumstances of particular jobs copies of the Award may also need to be sent to others, for example solicitors or foundation engineers and this point should not be overlooked.

Schedules of Condition

An agreed schedule of condition is an appendage to an Award or Agreement, as are the agreed plans, but the schedule of condition is such an important document in itself that it requires some comment. A schedule of condition describes the condition of the structures on the adjoining owner's side of the party wall at the time that the Award is entered into and before any works are commenced. The need for this is obvious since, in the event of any settlement or movement in the party wall once the building work is commenced, the extent of the remedial work necessary can be adequately judged. The obvious need for such a document becomes apparent when an architect or surveyor is called in to inspect a house where work had been carried out to the party wall but no schedule has been prepared. The wife of the adjoining owner will be totally convinced that every crack which she can see has been caused by the work carried out next door, whereas the probability is that most of the cracks were old. People do not always scrutinise their walls and ceilings in detail and it is only when the sound of banging can be heard from next door that a crack is noticed for the first time and nothing can remove the impression that it is the result of the work being carried out. Only the evidence from a schedule recording the crack before work was commenced and signed by the two surveyors concerned will convince the adjoining owner otherwise.

Schedules of condition can be prepared in a number of ways. The most painstaking, but correct way, is for the two surveyors to carry out their inspection together each agreeing and recording notes separately. This procedure makes the subsequent checking of the draft schedule prepared by the building owner's surveyor an easy matter for the adjoining owner's surveyor as he can simply tick off the items in the typewritten draft in the order and wording that they appear in his notes. In order to save time however, dictating machines and other aids are brought into operation, often with dubious benefit. Attempts are made at times to introduce photographs but while these are satisfactory as additions to a properly drafted schedule, they can never supersede it. Again, in the case of an old property, perhaps rather neglected with various forms of cracking, there is no alternative but for the surveyors to get out their clipboards and to agree sketches that can later be duplicated and included with the completed schedule. Such sketches save a considerable volume of complicated wording.

It should always be remembered that many people other than the building owner's and adjoining owner's surveyors will examine a schedule of condition. Contractors, in particular, should be sent a copy in view of insurance implications. The importance of adequate and authoritative schedules of condition is emphasised in France, where a surveyor who is an independent legal official is instructed to prepare the schedule. He may be accompanied by the surveyors acting for the respective parties during his inspection and will listen to representations but once he prepares the final document this is regarded as being impartial and binding and has the full backing of the law. Whatever the status of the surveyors concerned however, it is necessary that the schedule which results is both full and comprehensive. There is a tendency, particularly in smaller cases for the surveyors acting for the building and adjoining owner merely to refer to the condition of the plasterwork, decorations, joinery and detailing of the party wall itself or, at most, the rooms immediately adjoining the party wall on the adjoining owner's side. Such a proceeding is fraught with danger to the building owner as anything not included in a schedule of condition must imply perfection in the adjoining property and in the event of partial or serious settlement, the lack of the requisite information can prove highly embarrassing and most unfortunate as the building owner will not have a leg to stand on to resist any subsequent claim. This is particularly so in frame construction where movement on one side of a structure is promptly transferred to the other. Another important aspect of party wall work is that inherent defects revealed by excavation or opening up should be recorded quite separately from patent defects in the adjoining owner's premises recorded before work begins. The preparation of supplementary schedules is a vital part of the surveyor's duty hopefully, in the case of the adjoining owner's surveyor, at an additional fee.

The rectification of defects revealed as a result of inspection once the work is completed with the schedule of condition in hand, is a matter of negotiation according to circumstances. The adjoining owner's surveyor should always remember that an election to carry out repairs as a result of damage by the building owner is less satisfactory than an undertaking to indemnify the adjoining owner in money terms. The builder's workmen are not the right people to carry out careful remedial work as the contract will have ended and the building owner's contractor, feeling he should be elsewhere, will have little sympathy with repairing cracks and redecorating rooms for a completely strange employer. The lack of mutual sympathy is normally fatal to such a relationship. The advantage of a cash settlement is that however inadequate, it does at least enable the owner to select his own builder to carry out the necessary repairs and the building owner and his surveyor will not, then, be involved.

In preparing schedules of condition surveyors must always bear in mind the unexpected. In one case for example the District surveyor, arriving on the scene to inspect the party wall, demanded that a rotted bressumer to the adjoining owner's property be replaced forthwith, together with the necessary remedial work. Fortunately the adjoining owner had been warned about this defect previously but he was extremely bitter that, but for the work to the party wall, the District Surveyor would never have arrived in the first place and he would not have been asked to spend a good deal of money at that particular time. Just as the building owner cannot be held accountable for such a misfortune, he must be philosophical if relationships between him and his neighbour deteriorate in such circumstances.

Party Wall Legislation and Procedure

An extremely useful and authoritative booklet has very recently been published by the Royal Institution of Chartered Surveyors on the subject of Party Wall Legislation and Procedure. The booklet, prepared by a group of surveyors specialising in work relating to Party Walls discusses procedure inside and outside London and contains appendices with specimen standard notices, a draft award, a typical extract from a schedule of condition and typical letters for the guidance of party wall surveyors. The booklet is regarded by the authors as required reading by all who are engaged in this field of work.

Appendix 1 to Chapter 9

London Building Acts (Amendment) Act 1939
Sections 56–59 – Expenses

56.—(1) The following provisions shall apply with respect to the apportionment of expenses as between the building owner and the adjoining owner:—

(a) Expenses incurred in the exercise of the rights conferred by paragraph (a) of subsection (1) of section 46 (Rights of owners of adjoining lands where junction line built on) of this Act shall be defrayed by the building owner and the adjoining owner in due proportion regard being had to the use which the two owners respectively make or may make of the party structure or party fence wall;

(b) Expenses incurred in the exercise of the rights conferred by paragraph (b) of subsection (1) of the said section together with the expenses of building any additional party structure that may be required by reason of the exercise of those rights shall be defrayed by the building owner and the adjoining owner in due proportion regard being had to the use which the two owners respectively make or may make of the party wall or party structure and the thickness of such party wall or party structure required for support of the respective buildings of the two owners;

(c) Expenses incurred in the exercise of the rights conferred by paragraph (c) of subsection (1) of the said section shall be defrayed by the building owner and the adjoining owner in due proportion regard being had to the use which the two owners respectively make or may make of the rooms or storeys rebuilt;

(d) Expenses incurred in the exercise of the rights conferred by paragraph (d) of subsection (1) of the said section shall be defrayed by the building owner and the adjoining owner in due proportion regard being had to the use which the two owners respectively make or may make of the buildings arches or structures rebuilt;

(e) Expenses incurred in the exercise of the rights conferred by –
    (i) paragraphs (e) (g) (h) (i) and (k) of subsection (1) of the said section;
    (ii) paragraph (f) of subsection (1) of the said section in so far as the expenses are not expenses incurred in the exercise of any rights conferred by other paragraphs of the said subsection and also a fair allowance in respect of the disturbance and inconve-

nience caused where the expenses have been incurred in the exercise of the rights conferred by the said paragraph (*f*);
shall be defrayed by the building owner.

(2) Expenses incurred in the exercise of the rights conferred by paragraph (*j*) of subsection (1) of the said section shall be defrayed in the same manner as the expenses of the work to which they are incidental.

(3) Any expenses reasonably incurred by the building owner in executing any works in pursuance of a counter notice served on him by an adjoining owner under section 48 (Counter notices) of this Act shall be defrayed by the adjoining owner.

(4) If at any time during the execution or after the completion of works carried out in the exercise of the rights conferred by paragraphs (*e*) (*f*) (*j*) or (*k*) of subsection (1) of section 46 (Rights of owners of adjoining lands where junction line built on) of this Act any use of those works or any part thereof is made by the adjoining owner additional to the use thereof made by him at the time when the works began a due proportion of the expenses incurred by the building owner in the exercise of the rights conferred by any of the said paragraphs regard being had to the additional use of the works made by the adjoining owner shall be defrayed by the adjoining owner.

(5) Where in pursuance of section 45 (Rights of owners of adjoining lands where junction line not built on) or the said section 46 of this Act consent in writing has been given to the construction of special foundations on land of an adjoining owner then if the adjoining owner erects any building or structure and its cost is found to be increased by reason of the existence of the said foundations the owner of the building to which the said foundations belong shall on receiving an account with any necessary vouchers within two months after the completion of the work by the adjoining owner repay to the adjoining owner so much of the cost as is due to the existence of the said foundations.

(6) Where under this section expenses are to be defrayed in due proportion regard being had to the use made by an owner of a party structure party fence wall external wall or other work regard shall unless otherwise agreed between the building owner and the adjoining owner or provided in the award also be had to the cost of labour and materials prevailing at the time when that use is made.

57.—(1) An adjoining owner may by notice in writing require the building owner before he begins any work in the exercise of the rights conferred by this Part of this Act to give such security as may be agreed between the owners or in the event of dispute determined by a judge of the county court for the payment of all such expenses costs and compensation in respect of the work as may be payable by the building owner.

(2) Where in the exercise of the rights conferred by this Part of this Act an adjoining owner requires a building owner to carry out any work the expenses of which are to be defrayed in whole or in part by the adjoining owner or where the adjoining owner serves a notice on the building owner

under subsection (1) of this section the building owner may before beginning the work to which the requirement or notice relates serve a notice in writing on the adjoining owner requiring him to give such security as may be agreed between the owners or in the event of dispute determined by a judge of the county court for the payment of such expenses costs and compensation in respect of the work as may be payable by him.

(3) If within one month after receiving a notice under subsection (2) of this section or in the event of dispute after the date of the determination by the judge of the county court the adjoining owner does not comply therewith the requirement or notice by him to which the building owner's notice under that subsection relates shall cease to have effect.

58.—(1) Within two months after the completion of any work executed by a building owner of which the expenses are to be wholly or partially defrayed by an adjoining owner in accordance with section 56 (Expenses in respect of party structures) of this Act the building owner shall deliver to the adjoining owner an account in writing showing –

(*a*) particulars and expenses of the work; and

(*b*) any deductions to which the adjoining owner or any other person is entitled in respect of old materials or otherwise;

and in preparing the account the work shall be estimated and valued at fair average rates and prices according to the nature of the work the locality and the cost of labour and materials prevailing at the time when the work is executed.

(2) Within one month after delivery of the said account the adjoining owner may give notice in writing to the building owner stating any objection he may have thereto and thereupon a difference shall be deemed to have arisen between the parties.

(3) If within the said month the adjoining owner does not give notice under subsection (2) of this section he shall be deemed to have no objection to the account.

59.—(1) All expenses to be defrayed by an adjoining owner in accordance with an account delivered under section 58 (Account of expenses) of this Act shall be paid by the adjoining owner and in default may be recovered as a debt.

(2) Until an adjoining owner pays to the building owner such expenses as aforesaid the property in any works executed under this Part of this Act to which the expenses relate shall be vested solely in the building owner.

Appendix 2 to Chapter 9

London Building Acts (Amendment Act 1939 Section 124

124.—(1) Subject to the provisions of this section and of section 125 (Service of documents relating to dangerous or neglected structures) of this Act any notice order or other document (in this section referred to as a "document") authorised or required by or under the London Building Acts or any bye-laws made in pursuance of those Acts to be served by or on behalf of the Council or a local authority or by the superintending architect or the district surveyor or any other person on any person shall be deemed to be duly served –

(a) where the person to be served is a company if the document is addressed to the secretary of the company at its registered office or at its principal office or place of business and is either –

    (i) sent by post in a prepaid letter; or
    (ii) delivered at the registered office or at the principal office or place of business of the company;

(b) where the person to be served is a partnership if the document is addressed to the partnership at their principal place of business identifying them by the name or style under which their business is carried on and is either –

    (i) sent by post in a prepaid letter; or
    (ii) delivered at the said place of business;

(c) where the person to be served is a public body or a corporation society or other body if the document is addressed to the clerk secretary treasurer or other head officer of that body corporation or society at its principal office or (if there is no office) at the premises to which the document relates and is either –

    (i) sent by post in a prepaid letter; or
    (ii) delivered at that office or the premises as the case may be;

(d) where the person to be served is a builder if the document is addressed to the builder at the place of address stated in his building notice (if any) or in default thereof at his office or any one of his principal offices or if a copy of the document is affixed on some conspicuous part of the premises to which it relates;

(e) in any other case if the document is sent by post in a prepaid letter addressed to the person to be served or delivered to that person at his usual or last known residence or place of business in the United Kingdom.

(2) Any document which is authorised or required to be served on the owner or occupier of any premises may be addressed "the owner" or "the occupier" as the case may be of those premises (naming them) without further name or description and shall be deemed to be duly served –

(a) if the document so addressed is sent or delivered in accordance with paragraph (e) of subsection (1) of this section; or

(b) if the document so addressed or a copy thereof so addressed is delivered to some person on the premises or where no person is found on the premises to whom it can be delivered is affixed to some conspicuous part of the premises.

(3) Where a document is served on a partnership in accordance with this section the document shall be deemed to be served on each partner.

(4) For the purpose of proving the service by post of any document it shall be sufficient to prove that it was properly addressed and was put into the post.

(5) For the purposes of this section a document shall be deemed to be a document which is authorised or required to be served on a person if it is authorised or required to be notified given or transmitted or (in the case of a demand) if it is authorised or required to be made to that person and in this section the expressions "served" and "service" shall be construed accordingly.

Chapter 10
Tender Action

CONTENTS

During the time taken for preparing the documentation and for obtaining the necessary agreements and consents, dealt with under the previous Chapter, the architect or surveyor will have started to give serious consideration to the personnel and firms upon whom the ultimate success or failure of the scheme will depend. The professional team comprising architect or surveyor, consulting engineer, heating and ventilating engineer, quantity surveyor and possibly other experts covering a wide range of specialised matters ranging from the structure to the layout of the garden will by now have completed their preliminary documentation and be well embedded in the proposed scheme. Those responsible however, for carrying out the work on the site will not have been selected and careful thought must now given to this aspect of the matter. First, however, it may be necessary to consider who is to be appointed to perform the watchdog role on the site during the progress of the works, on behalf of the client since it may be necessary to make this appointment well in advance.

The Clerk of Works

The architect or surveyor may have recommended in his feasibility report that a Clerk of Works is appointed. This might be due to the fact that the contract is an unusually large one on the one hand or unduly complicated on the other. Since, in the case of the reconstruction of a Tudor house, for example, where a high proportion of day work labour is inevitable, it may well repay the employer to engage a Clerk of Works to assist in looking after his interests on the site. The position of the Clerk of Works is a curious one. Under the JCT Contract Forms he is nominated and directed by the architect or surveyor but appointed and paid for by the client direct. He therefore acts "under the directions of the architect" but not as his representative. He cannot therefore issue instructions and is present on the site "solely as inspector" and for this he has to rely on the provisions of the contract which will require the builder to offer him every reasonable facility to carry out his duties. Contrary to what is often said, or thought, or even accepted on the site, the Clerk of Works has no power to approve work actually carried out. To anyone engaged in other fields such as manufacturing, the arrangement must seem a very odd one. A candidate, chosen by one man under whose direction he acts, responsible to another man by whom he is paid, engaged to spend his time on land in the control of a third

439

man who is responsible for merely granting him access and facilities hardly seems likely to be the basis for a harmonious relationship. However, this makes no allowance for the qualities of the men who become professional Clerks of Works and their, by now, well accepted place in the building team. To anyone who has watched an experienced Clerk of Works deal with his duties, the impressive nature of his performance is nothing short of amazing when one considers the fragile basis of his relationship with the various parties under the contract. It says a great deal for the personality and ability of the men who take on this particular role. It also says a great deal for their knowledge of human nature and tact in dealing with all types of people. It is, of course, an unhappy fact that matters sometimes go wrong. The employer who regards the Clerk as his own personal watchdog, not only on the builder but upon the architect or surveyor as well, is not unknown, and Clerks have been known to pander to this. Similarly, there are Clerks who are downright negligent, others who are autocratic and upset the builders or exceed their duties, but such characters are rare. Clerks of Works are generally able to meet the conflicting demands of the various personalities engaged in the project such as the quantity surveyor who requires neat accurate records, meticulous and tidy daywork sheets and competent certification of contractors information. The architect or surveyor on the other hand is much more concerned to receive the assurance of the Clerk of Works that he was present to inspect certain work in order to ensure that it was correctly carried out before being covered up in the exceptional case where an entirely trustworthy Clerk of Works is entrusted with such an important duty on behalf of the architect or surveyor.

The Journal of an experienced Clerk of Works makes interesting if not awkward reading at a later stage, recording as it does, verbal instructions by the architect or surveyor, conveniently forgotten and never confirmed, mishaps on the site, human problems and difficulties that give a fascinating background to the contract that does not appear in the rather bland weekly progress report forms provided to the architect or surveyor and regarded as the "weekly chore". Like the Site Agent there are times when the Clerk of Works is expected to be everywhere at once and it is little wonder if he becomes irate when endless people arrive unannounced at his site hut and demand to see him as a matter of right. This often, however, has the satisfactory effect of uniting the Clerk of Works and the Site Agent together in mutual sympathy against such intrusions.

In large projects the contractor will no doubt hear about the appointment of an eminent Clerk of Works with the satisfaction that a first division football team hears of the appointment of a well known and respected referee. On smaller projects however, the architect or surveyor who may be at a loss to know how to nominate a suitable candidate must rely either upon enquiry to the Institute of Clerks of Works, advertise, or make painstaking enquiries with the help of professional colleagues. The first requirement is to match the trade background and general experience of the Clerk of Works against the requirements of the project. While it is traditional that a Clerk of Works graduates from the primary trades such as bricklayer, carpenter or joiner, the increasing complexity of technology on the building site has widened the scope for possible entrants to this particular type of post to an enormous degree and enquiry as to the range of ability available is almost always amply re-paid. The second requirement is to ensure, so far as is possible, that the Clerk nominated has the confidence of the employer while the third requirement is to determine, by conversation, if the attitude of the Clerk is right for the job. There is little point in employing a Clerk of Works who has a prejudice against the scheme, or displays a hostile or arrogant approach, for obvious reasons. If a Clerk of Works of the right calibre cannot be found it would probably be best to do without a Clerk of Works completely. Cases where professional advisors have been found to be liable to employers due to negligence of the Clerk of Works or, worse, his fraudulent activities, make depressing reading. In an early case an engineer employed to superintend work for a local Board remonstrated against the appointment of a Clerk of Works and, later, when faults were found, pleaded, understandably, that he was not responsible for errors made by the Clerk of Works. The Official Referee in the case found however, that since the engineer had relied upon the Clerk of Works he was liable and, even more so since he had known in the first place that the Clerk of Works was unreliable. This decision was later upheld.[1] In another case, an architect appointed a Clerk of Works who gave it as his opinion that certain beams did not require to be replaced. The architect relied upon this opinion but it was later found that new beams were necessary and the architect paid the penalty for relying upon the Clerk of Works' opinion.[2] Perhaps the leading case on this question however, is *Leicester Guardians* v. *Trollope* (1911) 75 JP 197. In this case negligence was alleged against a firm of architects when dry rot was found in flooring of a building, four years after completion of the works. The dry rot was found to have affected timber flooring laid over concrete at ground level and it was put to the Judge that the architects were negligent in not

(1) *Sanders* v. *Broadstairs Local Board* (1890) Hudson.
(2) *Lee* v. *Bateman (Lord)* 1893.

441

seeing that the construction was properly carried out under the terms of the contract. The defendant architect, sole survivor of the partnership responsible for the work, alleged that it was the duty of the Clerk of Works appointed by Leicester Guardians to exercise the supervision that was necessary and he counter-claimed for damages suffered as the result of the Clerk of Works appointed having been incompetent. The decision of the Court was however, that while a Clerk of Works was engaged to supervise details of the work, the problem in this case did not arise from a mere detail but a fundamental error and therefore the architect was liable in negligence.

The position of the Clerk of Works should be contrasted and distinguished from the position of a resident engineer under the terms of the ICE Contract. The conditions of the contract in the latter case define the duties and powers of an engineer's representative, whose authority is notified in writing to the contractor by the engineer personally. The duties of watching and supervising the work extend to testing and examining materials to be used but no automatic power is vested in the resident engineer to vary the obligations of the contractor under the terms of the contract or to give instructions for extra work on behalf of the promoter. So far the duties of the engineer's representative do not sound dissimilar from those of a Clerk of Works under a JCT Form of Contract since they are restricted to "watching and supervising the construction, completion and maintenance of the works" but nevertheless the resident engineer has a much more fundamental role under an ICE Contract, particularly in larger contracts, where he may be a fully qualified engineer in his own right. In such a case the fundamental difference between the JCT and ICE Forms of Contract emerges in that the engineer may delegate to his representative on the site any of the powers and authorities that are vested in himself provided that he gives the contractor a copy of all written authorities. Directions by the resident engineer are then binding upon the contractor as if the engineer under the ICE Contract had issued them personally. The resident engineer under the ICE Contract retains a power to disapprove defective workmanship or materials and the contractor is entitled, if disatisfied with any decision of the engineer's representative, to refer the matter to the engineer himself under the ICE terms of contract who may then, if he sees fit, reverse or vary the decision.

The General Contractor

Once the selection of the employer's representative, if there is to be one on the site is dealt with, there next comes that most vital and important area of consideration, the question of the main contractor. It is often said that the best service an architect or surveyor can provide to his client is in choosing a good contractor and this is all too true. Most professional advisors are fortunate in that they have built up good honest professional relationships with numerous firms of contractors in the past whom they trust and by whom they are trusted. To hear that Bill Smith for example will be appointed as Site Agent, that Dexter Morris will be in charge of joinery and that Jim Brown will be available to hang the expensive papers upon which the appearance of the large reception rooms will ultimately depend is music to the ears of the architect or surveyor. It is sad that the traditional firm comprising long term trusted employees capable of dealing with every trade is giving way to the type of firm with one or two main employees who operate a system that is largely based on sub-contract work but such is the case.

Just as the employer, in terms of capital, can be large or small, a vast organisation or a single person, so can the contractor. He can range from the single jobbing man of independent outlook with motor car, workshop attached to his house with his devoted wife to act as receptionist and secretary, to small firms with one or maybe more Directors ranging in size from anything between six and twenty men engaged in various trades including supervisory grades. At the upper end of the scale are the vast constructional and civil engineering firms who operate not only in this country but also abroad and who have a staff of all sorts and types, measured in thousands, including architects, designers, engineers, quantity surveyors and all types of consultants in the complex services that are such a growth feature of the building industry today. Such firms may also run research and testing departments and have an enormous technical capability. Their experience, particularly in fields where building and engineering work run together is so enormous that it is little wonder that they suggest "package" or "in house" services and become irritated at the suggestion that they need to work under outside supervision.

Since the very large firms, provided that they can keep competitive and gain the necessary contracts, are able to offer the best terms of employment and therefore gain the best labour and assistance possible, this forces the medium sized or smaller firms into a position of some difficulty. It has often been said that the task of attempting to decide what size and type of firm will suit a particular contract best is made easier by the fact that most firms of repute will only tender for contracts in the particular range that suits their size and scale of operation. However, due to the "stop go" of building operations during the past decade, this could well be far from the truth. There is now a considerable danger that in times of depression or financial stringency certain firms, desperate to keep their labour force together, will be tempted to undertake contracts beyond their capacity with unhappy results. The small firm which takes on a large contract beyond its experience, relying on sub-contracted labour and ends up in considerable difficulty is a common enough feature of the building industry but, equally guilty is the large firm who, to increase their cash flow, take on a number of small contracts that they are unfitted to deal with. It is not the biggest, the smallest or the cheapest contractor who provides the best results for a particular contract. It is the contractor who is used to dealing with the type of work in question and who can instantly assess the potential risks and advantages and who has the resources to cost and subsequently run the contract with an experienced and efficient labour force and supporting office staff. The most successful contracting firms do not entertain any work offered until they are able to decide if the appropriate time and resources in terms both of labour and finance are available to deal with the project efficiently. It is an illuminating paradox that, while professional advisors feel a growing need to advertise their services, the most efficient small or medium sized building firms advertise least and are always busy. The need for good builders is constant and if a firm is successful, the word spreads quickly. It is for this reason that the architect or surveyor who requires a good firm in a particular locality is wise to make his own local enquiries and allow plenty of time before the commencement date for the contract. If the professional advisor is able to select the "right" contractor for his client the employer is a lucky man indeed.

It is said, and wisely, that outside the great city centres the best type of building contractor is the established local firm which restricts its operations, purposely, to within a radius of 50 miles and which has, for very many years, built up relationships with local sub-contractors so that it is able to seize any opportunity within its scope, know exactly what it takes on in the way of building or construction work and possesses a tried and tested labour force. The vast national building firms with regional offices complain that such a suggestion amounts to prejudice but experience does show that in the medium range of contracts, which after all comprise the vast majority, central control and lack of commitment to a particular area tends to put them at a disadvantage. It is however, emphasised that in particular this applies to the smaller or medium range of contractor dealing both with rehabilitation and new work. It therefore follows that good local companies know their business very well and are not likely to be easily ordered or cajoled into relationships that they dislike.

The architect or surveyor will, at the feasibility stage, have looked into the question of local firms available to carry out the work, if such a firm is appropriate, primarily to avoid the embarrassment arising from a lack of local labour which may introduce an unduly high cost element at a later stage if a large national company is used.

Tendering Procedures

So far contract documentation has been discussed which is aimed at setting out the terms as clearly as possible upon which the building work will be completed. Having decided upon the type of contractor in the broadest sense the next stage is to find a particular contractor to carry out the work. For this to be achieved there are three established methods of selection. They are as follows:

1. Open Tenders

Under this basis the number of contracting firms allowed to tender for any given project is unrestricted and, indeed, the whole basis of this procedure is that all comers are actively encouraged to compete for the project, in some cases advertisements being placed in the national or local press to elicit the widest possible number of enquiries from contracting firms who might be interested in submitting a tender. Some public projects even have to be advertised abroad under EEC requirements.

2. Selective Tenders

In this case as in the case of inviting open tenders, the basis is to ensure competition between contractors competing for the building project but here the number of firms invited to tender is strictly limited, the firms approached being carefully selected according to their general size and ability to carry out the particular work concerned and in the hope that a close set of competitive prices will be obtained. Selective tendering can either be arranged in a single stage or in two stages whereby the successful tenderer for the first stage of the project enters into a negotiated contract for the second stage, this being largely arranged according to information obtained from the first stage.

3. Negotiated Tenders

Where a contracting firm has particular expertise or is by its size and geographical locality the only likely candidate to carry out certain work, a negotiated tender with this particular firm can be

445

arranged by the architect or surveyor on behalf of the employer. Obviously, the advantages of this method of proceeding must be such that they outweigh the disadvantages of forgoing the more normal competitive tendering procedure. If, for example, the type of work contemplated is unsuitable for open or selective tenders or there are special circumstances where, for example, the contractor is involved in financing arrangements, negotiated tenders are often employed. As mentioned earlier, negotiated tenders may be invoked as the second stage to the normal selective tendering procedure and an obvious case where a negotiated tender would be worth considering would be where a contractor has satisfactorily completed certain work and is then invited to carry out further precisely similar work in the same geographical locality a very short time afterwards.

The open tendering procedure is constantly criticised on the basis that it is wasteful in resources and potentially dangerous since the building surveyor or architect in charge of the project can learn little or nothing about the numerous firms who are likely to be interested with the result that the successful tenderer may be financially unstable or technically incapable of carrying out the work. This criticism, however, ignores the fact that some bodies are bound under their own rules to advertise for open tenders so that everything is seen to be fair and above board. Certainly the criticism of aspiring contractors who grumble that it is difficult to obtain invitations to tender for the best type of work as the established contractors "have it all their own way" has some validity. It is true that architects and surveyors tend to favour established firms and the reasons for this are not hard to find. The biggest danger, however, in entering into the open tendering procedure is that it is likely to scare off competent and established contractors who reason, rightly or wrongly, that the contract will be awarded to a cheapjack firm and that there is little point in their wasting their valuable resources in terms of office and managerial time in competing for a contract that they are very likely not to win. Such firms are, not unnaturally, convinced of the virtues of the selective tendering procedure and it is generally assumed that the architect or surveyor is similarly convinced. This however, is not quite so. Obviously professional advisers feel happiest when they can engage firms whose expertise and stability are beyond reproach but it is not merely a matter of pride but a matter of crucial importance for a set of really competitive prices to be obtained and most architects and surveyors will make room for newcomers provided that they are convinced of their track record to date.

It is no easy matter for the architect or surveyor to guide the employer as to the correct firms to approach. Established builders can and do go downhill or can be taken over with glum results and often the retirement of one or two men in a medium sized firm can create difficulties. The employer, naturally, will have one single interest in mind which is the amount of the tender and often, the first suggestion of a certain "freeze" between the Employer and his professional adviser comes about when, alongside the names of several established firms the employer wishes to add a few more and the architect or surveyor will accept none of them. The employer assumes, naturally, that his adviser is conservative and, worst, uninterested in opening the list of tenderers to a wider selection of newly formed firms who, he feels, might provide a better price. The adviser on the other hand, having suffered in the past, and knowing that the cheapest price can often prove in the end to be the most expensive, adopts an "over my dead body" stand on the grounds that this battle is likely to prove the most important in the entire campaign. Considerable tact is often needed on both sides at this stage in the proceedings so as to keep relationships on a tolerable level. It is only natural that the Employer should sit wistfully looking at an attractive advertisement issued by a contracting firm promising that "the ability of our management team combined with the experience of our operatives on the site leads to highly competitive prices well below other firms". The art here is to achieve a balance and to invite the employer to sit in at interviews with prospective firms whose suggested nomination he has advocated or to visit their offices with him. Often such interviews lead to much subsequently hilarity during subsequent conversations with the employer who by then has completely lost his enthusiasm for the thrusting candidates that he himself put forward and whose introduction he so enthusiastically suggested.

It is, accordingly, at this stage, that the architect or surveyor has to decide as to the firms whose names he will submit to the employer for selective tendering. He should do so on the basis that every contractor chosen to tender should feel that his nomination has been made in good faith and that he will be invited to carry out the work if he is successful. Most employers will see the force of this and will accept that any provision in the contract documents giving him the right to accept any tender, not necessarily the lowest, is purely a protective measure. If the employer does not consider himself to be morally bound in the matter, although fortunately most do, the whole tendering procedure becomes at best a farce and at worst a confidence trick on some unfortunate contracting firms. The shoddy arrangements that sometimes take place where firms are chosen to tender against a favoured firm whose price, originally too high, is then "re-negotiated" bring everyone concerned and particularly the architect or surveyor into disrepute. It is the professional adviser who suffers in the long term and it serves him right. He should never be a party to such dubious practices.

It is unlikely that the professional architect or surveyor will be at a complete loss for names of contractors to approach under the selective tendering procedure but he may wish to add a bit of fresh air to the list, so to speak, by approaching firms who are recommended to him but about whose work or circumstances he knows little. Since firms vary so enormously not only in size but in skills, he should be able to find out at once where the basic strength of any unfamiliar firm of builders lies. It may be in management supposing for example that they do a great deal of estate development for local government authorities or it may be in the constructional skill of the work force. Since the majority of contracts involve small or medium sized firms, accurate analysis of their strength and weaknesses is vital.

It is of course an obvious truism to say that the size of any prospective firm must be related to the size of the contract envisaged since it is obviously not sensible to send large jobs to small firms or, for that matter, small jobs to large firms although this second alternative is less likely to be fraught with the same basic risk element as of the first. The small jobbing firm is likely to be used to specifications divided into physical areas or a "room by room" basis rather than trade breakdown and a complicated specification or Bill of Quantities will leave it nonplussed. The architect or surveyor who asks a small firm to tender for a project and then sends it a mass of complicated documentation that leaves the staff astounded has only himself to blame just as a large firm, invited to tender, upon receiving a small specification is likely to return it with regrets either immediately or, more embarrassingly, at a much later stage. A visit to the offices of prospective firms and a request to see some of the work which has been completed or is on hand may be time consuming and appear to be a dreadful nuisance to the fully engaged but such visits are rewarding as the visitor hardly ever leaves the offices of the firm concerned without a fairly firm idea of whether they will or whether they will not do for a particular job. A filthy builders yard littered with half opened cartons of materials, a slack and slovenly office staff or a neglected site lacking supervision are hardly likely to inspire the architect or surveyor. By the same token, the builder and two companions who arrive late for an appointment in a large and battered saloon car wearing hand made boots, leather jackets and shirts open to the navel also do not inspire confidence particularly when they clap the building surveyor or architect on the back, call him squire and suggest that instead of all this paperwork "Jack could make a start on Monday provided that an advance could be made for the purchase of materials".

It is here that any professional adviser has to admit to some prejudice. In fairness to him or herself it must be said that the whole responsibility for the success or failure of the scheme will depend upon the firms selected for tendering and the employer who so enthusiastically suggested the inclusion of a particular firm in the list of tenderers and endorsed their nomination is likely, if they turn out to be unsatisfactory, to forget, by some mysterious process that he ever had a hand in their selection and he will then blame his professional advisor for not having made a better choice.

It is, therefore, when the architect or surveyor sees a tidy and well run yard, a businesslike and courteous office staff and a site well attended by various trades in a well ordered progression that his spirits will lift. Nevertheless it is hoped that the professional surveyor or architect will keep an open mind in a changing society for evidence of excellence which might arrive, heavily disguised, in a manner to excite his worst prejudices.

The vital point governing the invitations for and submission of tenders is that the whole procedure should not only be fair but be seen to be fair as well. In order to achieve this state of affairs however, a good deal of effort and expertise is needed and few architects or surveyors have not experienced problems in this direction during the course of their professional careers. Coming as it does, at a very early stage in the relationship between the architect or surveyor, his employer and the contractor, ill feeling due to treatment that is considered to be unfair can have a sad effect on the relationship of the parties ever after. "Once bitten twice shy" is particularly true of building contractors who are prone, understandably, to build suspicions on minimal evidence of favour being given to another party due, sadly, to less than happy experiences in the past. They also have long memories. The architect or surveyor who yields to pressure from the employer to accept a particular tender, other than the lowest, generally finds that he has to live with the consequences of this decision for a very long time and sooner or later he may regret ever having made it. The person who takes the view that the tenderer who succeeds is automatically satisfied and that the rest will soon forget about the whole business is misguided. The tenderer who succeeds, if unfairly selected, is bound to have the uneasy feeling that when it comes to sharp practice his turn may come next while the others are not at all likely to forget about it but will carefully make a note of the architect or surveyor's name and address for future reference. It is too easily forgotten that the submission of tenders costs a very great deal of money and any builder who is treated unfairly, no matter what size the contract may be, has every right to complain.

It is thus of enormous importance that the list of tenderers is finally slimmed down to include only those firms in whom the architect or surveyor has complete confidence to carry out the work.

It is often difficult at the best of times to hold successfully a fair balance between tenderers. It is therefore sad when mistrust is generated from sloppy office work. When time is tight, documents dated for a particular day that arrive one week later will simply infuriate a contractor, while intimate correspondence with some firms and not others will generate suspicion. We have said earlier that the contractor is on the lookout for signs indicating unfair treatment at an early stage and is apt to view quite inocuous correspondence or meetings with others as having a suspicious flavour about them. It is vital for the architect or surveyor to be totally frank and open with all parties and to take elaborate, even extreme pains to let it be seen that this is so. By the same token he should always remember that he is acting as agent for the employer and that the normal rules of agency apply, in that he must ensure that a satisfactory relationship is created from the legal point of view by not making a commitment on his client's behalf that is in excess of the authority granted to him.

The two most common causes of failure in adequate procedure for inviting tenders are, firstly, that the time allowed for the submission of the tender is inadequate and, secondly, that there are one or more flaws in the architect or surveyor's documentation. When both these errors occur together, the result can be a nightmare. It is not uncommon for a contractor, pressed for time, particularly as this is not his fault, to ask for an extension of time, a request which, if granted, will infuriate the other contractors who may well, at grave inconvenience, have burned the midnight oil in order to comply with the architect's or surveyor's original request. Most architects and surveyors will, if pressed, admit that they have been in the awkward position where a contractor asks for more time and quotes, as a reason, some valid problem in the documents.

The key to obtaining satisfactory tenders does not, however, automatically lie in allowing a longer period of time for their submission. Too long a period may simply result in the fact that a busy contractor's office will put the documents away in a drawer, only realising from a diary entry at the last minute that the deadline is close, resulting in a mad panic to produce a price on time. This is, of course, likely to happen in any event, even in well regulated offices, but the most helpful step that the architect or surveyor can take to assist contractors comes well before the formal invitation to tender. Contractors say that a preliminary enquiry as to whether they wish to receive a formal invitation to tender is of the upmost benefit particularly if this gives all the information that is needed on which to make a judgement. The amount of information needed to make this procedure worthwhile however, even in this preliminary enquiry, is often a matter of amazement.

Code of Procedure for Single Stage Selective Tendering

In January 1977, the National Joint Consultative Committee for Building produced, in collaboration with the Department of the Environment, the Joint Standing Committee of Architects, Surveyors and Building Contractors in Scotland and the Joint Consultative Committee for Building, Northern Ireland, a totally authoritative booklet entitled "Code of Procedure for Single Stage Selective Tendering". The Code was prepared for all who commission building work, whether they be private clients or public authorities, and deals with the use of traditional single stage tendering by a selected list of tenderers. The Code says that single stage selective tendering is the most appropriate method of obtaining tenders for the majority of building contracts although, in contracts where it is desired to secure the early involvement of the contractor before the development of the design is completed, two stage tendering procedures may be adopted, and a companion code for this procedure is in course of preparation.

Since the general principles of the Code are fully supported by the Department of the Environment and take into account the NEDO Reports, it is obviously required reading for architects and surveyors. It also has the merit of being both well written and short, considering the ground it has to cover.

Appendix A to the Code sets out in detail a form of preliminary enquiry for invitation to tender and suggests that the architect or surveyor provides the following information even at this early stage.

   a. Job . . .
   b. Employer . . .
   c. Architect . . .
   d. Quantity Surveyor . . .
   e. Consultants with Supervisory Duties . . .
   f. Location of Site . . . (Site Plan enclosed)
   g. General description of Work . . .
   h. Approximate cost range £ . . . to £ . . .
   i. Nominated Sub-Contractors for major items . . .
   j. Form of Contract . . .

Clause 23(j)(i) of the Standard Form of Building Contract will/will not apply. (See Reference 1)

Clause 23(j)(ii) will/will not apply. (See Reference 1)

Clause 31 Parts . . . will apply. (See Reference 2)

k. Percentage to be included under Clause 31E if applicable . . .

l. Examination and correction of Priced Bill(s) (Section 6 of the Code) Alternative 1/Alternative 2 will apply. (See Reference 1)

m. The Contract is to be under seal/under hand. (See Reference 1)

n. Anticipated date for possession . . .

o. Period for completion of Works . . .

p. Approximate date for despatch of all Tender Documents . . .

q. Tender Period . . . weeks.

r. Tender to remain open for . . . weeks. (See Reference 3)

s. Liquidated Damages (if any), anticipated value £ . . . per . . .

t. Details of Bond requirement if any.

u. Particular Conditions applying to the Contract are . . .

References

1) Delete as appropriate, before issuing.

2) Complete by inserting Parts A, C, D and E, or Parts B, C, D and E, or Part F.

3) This period should be as short as possible.

The Contractor who receives this information certainly cannot complain that he has not been fully informed as to what is proposed. "Good tendering procedure", says the Code, "demands that the contractor's tendered price should not be altered without justification. Difficulties have arisen when an examination of the priced bill(s) reveals errors or a discrepancy between these prices and the tender figure". The Code lays down, in Section 6, alternative methods of dealing with this situation before the contractor's offer is accepted. The first alternative does not permit the correction of errors in priced Bill(s) of Quantities, the second does. The choice between the alternatives however, must be made before contractors are invited to tender.

The Code says that it should be a condition of tender that obvious errors in pricing or significant errors in arithmetic discovered before the acceptance of the contractor's tender should be dealt with in accordance with one of the alternatives in section 6 of the Code.

When selecting the short list of contractors, says the Code, the financial standing and record of the firms concerned should be considered together with their recent experience of building at the required rate of completion over a comparable contract period, together with the firm's general experience and reputation in the area in question. The Code also adds that consideration should be given to whether the management structure of the firm is adequate for the type of contract envisaged and whether the firm will have adequate capacity at the relevant time. The final recommendation under this section of the Code that approved lists should be reviewed periodically to exclude firms whose performance has been unsatisfactory and to allow the introduction of suitable additional firms is obviously aimed at the very large organisation. Smaller localised firms with one or two partners are hardly likely to need to compile such lists.

The Code of Procedure suggests that an appropriate period of time between the preliminary enquiry and the despatch of tender documents might be from four to six weeks although in some instances a period of three months would not be unreasonable. In cases beyond three months, the preliminary invitations should be confirmed a month before tenders are invited. The Code also gives interesting advice in suggesting the number of tenders to be invited according to the size of the contract at 1977 prices. The following scale is suggested.

Size of Contract	Maximum number of Tenderers
Up to £50,000	5
£50,000 to £250,000	6
£250, 000 to £1,000,000	8
£1,000,000 plus	6

A caveat is included regarding specialised contracts in the engineering field involving relatively high tendering costs and in such cases the maximum number of tenderers for contract values above £250,000 should be reduced to six and four respectively. Once the list is settled, one or two further names should be appended so that these may replace any firms on the list who do not take up the preliminary invitation to tender.

Once the contractor, says the Code, has signified initial agreement to tender it is in the best interests of all parties that such acceptance should be honoured. If in exceptional circumstances a contractor has to withdraw his acceptance, he should give notice of this intention before the issue of tender documents. If, for any reason this is not possible, notice should be given not later than two working days after receipt of the tender documents.

After the latest date for the acceptance of the preliminary invitation, the final short list of tenders will be selected, and firms which notified their willingness to tenderers, but are not included in the tender list, should be promptly informed.

The Code is precise in what is expected from both architect or surveyor and contractor. It is aimed at excluding problems arising from difficult circumstances so that the final choice of contractor will be simple – the firm offering the lowest tender. It is, accordingly, at this point that the final opportunity is given to the architect or surveyor to carry out fine tuning to all his documents in order to make sure that they are complete, without omissions and that they do not conflict in any way. It is no shame to discover an error at the last minute and indeed it is much better to discover it sooner rather than later. If there is a tendency to collect all the documents at the last minute in a mad panic to catch a particular post, something is almost certainly bound to go wrong. A few moments of thought are always worthwhile and if any discrepancy is found there should be enough time available to put the matter right. Often an addendum or note pinned to the documents can be hastily drafted and cause more trouble and confusion in the end.

The architect or surveyor should have an office procedure that is geared to deal with queries prior to tender. All too often a contractor's query over the telephone is answered but not fully recorded and queries should always be dealt with instantly and confirmed in writing. It is an excellent rule for the remaining tenderers to be sent copies of both the enquiry and the reply. This avoids the danger that one contractor, having heard that another contractor has been in touch with the office may wonder what has been going on.

On the day stated in the preliminary invitation, all tender documents should be despatched to the tenderers and the Appendices B and C in the Code which gives suggested formats for "Formal Invitation to Tender" and "Form of Tender" should be copied since the conditions of tendering should be absolutely clear so that all tenders are submitted on the same basis. Competition should be on price only so all other matters such as the contract period should be specified as basic conditions of the contract and not be subject to variation. It is for this reason that the NJCC strongly recommends the use of the Standard Forms of Building Contract in unamended form. If alterations to the Standard Forms have to be made it essential that they be kept to an absolute minimum, that they should not be undertaken without serious prior consideration and that they are then "drafted by a person competent to ensure that all consequential alterations to other clauses are made". The Code suggests that the contractors attention should be specifically drawn in the preliminary invitation to any alterations made to the Standard Form of Contract and, where appropriate, reasons should be given. This is so that the implications of such amendments may be considered by the tenderers prior to acceptance of the invitation and minimise the risk of subsequent queries at tender stage.

The Code does not lay down a hard and fast time that should be allowed for the preparation of tenders since this should obviously be determined in relation to the size and complexity of the job. The Code, however, does state that a minimum of four working weeks should normally be allowed but for major projects, smaller works without quantities or in other special cases, a longer period may be necessary. The tender period must be sufficient to enable the tenderer to obtain competitive quotations for the supply of materials and for the execution of works to be sub-let. The latest time for submission should be specified as an hour of a day and should be chosen to allow as short a time as possible to elapse before opening the tenders. Tenders received after time should be promptly returned unopened to the sender and should not be admitted to the competition. If Bills of Quantities are issued to tenderers in sections, the time of tendering should be calculated from the date of issue of the last section.

The Code says, understandably, that for fair competition, it is essential that the tender documents for each contractor are identical and also that the tenderers should not attempt to vary that basis by qualifying their tenders. If a tenderer considers that any of the tender documents are deficient in any respect and require clarification, or contain unacceptable alterations to the Standard Form of Building Contract not previously set out in the Preliminary Invitation, he should inform the issuing authority, the architect or surveyor, with a copy to the quantity surveyor, as soon as possible and preferably not less than seven days before the tenders are due. If it is decided to amend the documents either the issuing authority, the architect or surveyor should inform all tenderers and extend the time for tendering if necessary.

The Code says directly that a tenderer who otherwise submits a qualified tender should be given the opportunity to withdraw the qualifications without amendment to his tender; if he fails to do so his whole tender should be rejected if it is considered that such qualifications afford the tenderer an unfair advantage over other tenderers. Under English law a tender may be withdrawn at any time before its acceptance but under Scots Law a special form of wording is needed. If provision is to be made for a tender to be withdrawn at any time before its acceptance, the words "unless previously withdrawn" are to be inserted in the tender after the words "this tender remains open for consideration . . ." This clause is not, however, contained in tenders issued in Scotland by the Department of the Environment.

Tenders should be opened as soon as possible after the time laid down for their receipt and the lowest tenderer should be asked to submit his priced Bills of Quantities as soon as possible and in any case within four working days except in Scottish practice where the priced Bills, contained in a separate envelope, endorsed with the tenderer's name, should be submitted at the same time as the tender.

The next step is for all but the three lowest tenderers to be informed immediately that their tenders have been unsuccessful, as this information, as the Code justly says, is critical in relation to a contractor's stragetic tender planning. In order to serve the employer's interests in the event of the lowest tenderer withdrawing his offer, the second and third lowest tenderers should be informed that their tenders were not the most favourable received but that they will be approached again if it is decided to give further consideration to their offers. They should subsequently be notified at once when a decision to accept the tender has been taken. In Scottish practice, the envelope containing the Bills of the lowest tenderers should be opened and the Bills examined or alternatively, the three lowest tenderers should be advised that their offers are under consideration and the envelopes containing the Bills of the three lowest tenderers should be opened and the Bills examined. Otherwise Scottish practice follows the English procedure and the remaining tenderers whose offers are being rejected should be informed accordingly.

Once the contract has been let, every tenderer should be promptly supplied with a list of tender prices and in Scotland the practice is that every tenderer should be supplied with a list of the firms who tendered (in alphabetical order) and list of the tender prices (in ascending order of value).

The next stage is for an examination of the priced Bills of Quantities supporting the successful tender to be made by the quantity surveyor who should treat the document as confidential. On no account, says the Code, should any details of the tenderer's pricing be disclosed to any person other than the architect or surveyor or other appropriate consultant except with the express permission of the tenderer. The object of examining priced Bills is to detect errors in computation. If the quantity surveyor finds such errors he should report them to the architect or surveyor who, in conjunction with the employer, will determine the action to be taken under whichever is appropriate and has been selected in advance of the following alternatives.

Alternative 1

The tenderer should be given details of such errors and afforded an opportunity of confirming or withdrawing his offer. If the tenderer withdraws, the priced Bills of the second lowest should be examined, and if necessary this tenderer be given a similar opportunity. An endorsement should be added to the priced Bills indicating that all rates or prices (excluding preliminary items, contingencies, prime cost and provisional sums) inserted therein by the tenderer are to be considered as reduced or increased in the same proportion as the corrected total of priced items exceeds or falls short of such items. This endorsement should be signed by both parties to the contract.

Alternative 2

The tenderer should be given an opportunity of confirming his offer or of amending it to correct genuine errors. Should he elect to amend his offer and the revised tender is no longer the lowest, the offer of the firm now lowest in the competition should be examined. If the tenderer elects not to amend his offer, an endorsement will be required as in the clause above. If the tenderer does amend his tender figure, and possibly certain of the rates in his Bills, he should either be allowed access to his original tender to insert the correct details and to initial them or be required to confirm all the alterations in a letter. If in the latter case his revised tender is eventually accepted, the letter should be conjoined with the acceptance and the amended tender figure and the rates in it substituted for those in the original tender. In Scottish practice the lowest tenderer or each of the three lowest tenderers should be given an opportunity of confirming his offer or amending it to correct genuine error.

Once a tender is found to be free from error, or the tenderer is prepared to stand by his tender in spite of an error, or a tender on amendment is still the lowest, this should be recommended to the employer for acceptance.

Should the tender under consideration exceed the employer's budget the recommended procedure is for a price to be negotiated with this tenderer. The basis of negotiations and any agreements made should be fully documented. Only when these negotiations fail, should negotiations proceed with the next lowest tenderer. If these negotiations also fail, similar action may be taken with the third lowest tenderer. If all these negotiations fail, new tenders may be called for.

A final section is added to the Code under the subheading "Post Tender Period". Although this period does not strictly fall within the scope of tendering procedure, "action taken within this period" says the Code "is so critical to the successful outcome of any project as to justify comment". The NJCC then recommends that a due period be allowed for through project planning and for the contractor to organise his resources. Undue haste to make a physical start on site may result in extensive and costly variations which can lead to prolongation and not reduction of the total construction period. Regard also should be had, however, to the fact that unnecessary delay in achieving a start on site may involve the employer in extra costs whether or not the contract is based on variation of price conditions. These points, says the Code, should be borne in mind when determining the anticipated date for possession of the site.

The procedures set out in the Code are so sound that they should not be departed from even in the smallest cases. Obviously, the procedure will differ slightly where a quantity surveyor is not involved but tenders are best opened in the presence of witnesses and the architect or surveyor should then carry out a methodical check to ensure that each tender is complete and that there are no obvious anomolies. Variations introduced that might be construed as a "counter-offer" rather than a tender should be rejected and an arithmetical check on the winning tender carried out as soon as possible after opening so that, if an error is detected, the architect or surveyor is then able to telephone the successful tenderer to ask if he wishes to "stand by his figure". This is normally enough to set the alarm bells ringing and it is usually not long before a phone call is received from the contractors saying that an unfortunate error has been made and trusting that a revised price will be accepted. The recommendations of the Code should, in the author's view, be strictly followed hereafter.

For supplementary reading to the Code a most useful pamphlet entitled "Tender Action" has been produced by the Quantity Surveyor's Division of the RICS compiled by working parties of the Junior Organisation Quantity Surveyor's Standing Committee. This contains many interesting points of particular reference to larger contracts.

Whatever the type of contract selected, the documents, once drawn up and executed, are not intended to be put away and forgotten about. It is a common myth that once the documents are signed the various parties then shake hands warmly and "get down to brass tacks". Such a sentiment, while heart warming is totally misleading. The agreed terms of the contract are to be kept alive in the memories of the parties or their representatives and reference to what was originally agreed must be continually made so as to avoid the most obvious and frightening errors. Similarly, once the documents are signed, the architect or surveyor is advised not to heave a sigh of relief and start thinking of other matters straight away but to carry out an immediate spot check to ensure that all is in order. How many practitioners for example, follow the requirements of the Standard Method of Measurement Clause B4 which requires provision of a Schedule of Clause Headings and Appendix Items, with full information on options, alternatives and inserts. Any supplementary conditions or amendments to the Conditions should be inserted in full, unless they are standard and published for general use and the recommendations of this clause should be followed strictly.

There are of course problems with any type of contract. The architect or surveyor who commences work under a Lump Sum Contract may subsequently wish that he had chosen a Measurement and Value Contract if the building work runs into complex and unforeseen difficulties. It is more likely however, that he may have more cause to regret entering into a Cost Plus Percentage Contract and wish later that he had devoted the time and effort to setting up a Lum Sum Contract. There is nothing to prevent an existing contract being discharged, and a new contract formed in its place by novation but it should always be remembered that the terms of the original contract must be satisfied or amended to the approval of all the parties concerned. Again, a new contract may be implied from events rather than by formal agreement. If the original contract has been abandoned or circumstances have altered to a fundamental degree so that the original conditions are no longer applicable, the work may proceed in a manner that is so far outside the terms of the original contract that a new one is implied. Such an alteration must go to the root of the matter however, since this will not, obviously, apply to mere variations only.

A great deal of building and maintenance work is carried out annually simply upon an exchange of letters with perhaps a simple specification, priced, in addition. There is nothing wrong with this. If an architect or surveyor draws up a JCT Form of Contract with Quantities for the repair of a garden gate his partners will suddenly realise that things have been getting on top of him lately. On the other hand, merely because the contract is a very small one does not mean that the paperwork can be slapdash or intermittent. On the contrary; it is essential to keep abreast because work on larger contracts with a pre-ordained time scale and printed documentation helps to keep the architect or surveyor along the right lines from the clerical point of view, while there is seldom enough time in busy offices to dictate letters over small matters and these tend to be overlooked.

One of the writers once met a developer at a party who pointed out someone at the other end of the room and said "we have both carried out hundreds of thousands of pounds worth of work on merely a handshake". The subsequent bankruptcy of both parties does not invalidate the one central fact that success in building operations depends on mutual trust and, if this central element fails, the contract will fail with it, however sophisticated the paperwork. Nevertheless, by the same token, the architect or surveyor must always remember that he is the agent for the Employer and he is expected to be diligent in taking the necessary steps to protect his interest.

Part 4
The Work in Progress

Chapter 11
Commencement of Work

CONTENTS

Introduction

It is at this point that the duties of the architect or surveyor undergo a fundamental change. The tasks of design, administration and assessment are now largely superseded by an altogether different role in which the architect or surveyor steps down from his platform into the arena, so to speak, and takes up the role of a practical man of affairs.

The contents of Part 4 of this book may not be to the taste of everyone. They will not please the skilled designer with an abhorrence of personal confrontation, nor will they please the architect or surveyor who has found out, too late, that his client, now the Employer is over-demanding, unreliable or erratic. Nor will they please that same individual who has been pressurised into making an early start on the site with vague instructions and inadequate documentation. It is, of course, for these reasons and many others that a number of architects and surveyors prefer to opt out at this stage of the proceedings, accepting a reduced fee in order to rid themselves of the troubles to come. While understandable, this viewpoint is misguided. It is not that such action is perfectly legitimate but in so many cases the wish to "jump off the bus", so to speak, arises from the fact that the architect or surveyor has a nasty feeling that if he proceeds further in the matter he will become hopelessly embroiled in a situation that will prove very costly in terms of time, and therefore money, and probably injurious to his reputation as well. However, considered quite coldly, the architect or surveyor is best advised to press on and see the project through to completion in most normal circumstances. If he does not do so he is bound to be seen in a light that is positively disadvantageous in any event. In pocketing his reduced fee and passing over all his plans and documentation to others, he takes, what must be, a severe risk. The lay client, struggling in difficult circumstances, may be in no mood to be fair minded when he or she rings up his or her previous adviser to complain at the way matters have turned out nor is the contractor who has made a muddle of his site arrangements likely to accept full responsibility when it is too easy to point to a set of documents, largely incomprehensible to the client, and blame the architect or surveyor instead. He, by his very absence, has given away not only his role to monitor the contract but also to act as advocate in his own defence.

From now on there are likely to be surprises in store for everyone. The contractor may be taken aback to find that the pleasant man that

464

he talked to at tender stage has undergone a complete change of personality and become suspicious, touchy and, in certain ways, unreasonable. The architect or surveyor on his part may discover with horror that the contractor, previously so efficient in his administration, now lets the paperwork lag behind while the Employer, previously so relaxed over the whole project, now develops an obsessive mania for detail when there are much more serious things to worry about.

It is, therefore, for all these reasons, that Part 4 of this book forms a very large section indeed. If some may feel that it is too long, ample reasons have been given and more will follow to stress why site supervision is so important and why, if adequate procedures are not adopted from now on, every aspect of professional practice dealt with so far could well be put at risk.

Site Meetings

It may now be assumed that the main contract has been let. It is of course not necessary that this should occur before work starts on site since, in certain cases, nominated sub-contract work can commence before the main contract is placed. This is more likely in the case of new work but in the vast majority of cases the main contractor will have been selected and the contract executed before any work whatsoever is carried out.

Before the work actually starts on site there are a number of points which the architect or surveyor must consider. The first is his own position. A contract now exists between the main contractor and his own client to which he is not a party. The contractual obligations will apply irrespective of his own position which is merely to undertake certain specified duties referred to in the contract document. It is true that these are fundamental to the success or otherwise of the bargain struck between the employer and the contractor since obviously, if appropriate documentation is not fed through to the contractor this will frustrate the contract entirely as will the architect or surveyor's failure to certify payments. Nevertheless the contract is in existence and now has its own momentum. The obligation rests with the contractor to assemble the necessary workforce, order the requisite materials, produce a programme for the work if this is a contractual requirement or, alternatively, proceed with the works under a previously agreed programme and achieve completion with due diligence. It cannot be emphasised too strongly that the contractor has freedom to carry out the actual building operations in whatever order he chooses and occupy the site in the manner that he finds most convenient unless anything to the contrary is stated in the contract documents. It is for this reason that many experienced contractors become restive when the architect or surveyor lays down the law on the facilities to be granted for a fixed series of meetings on the site, with everyone present, at what is seen as a committee composed of representatives from the various firms concerned with the work; the structural engineer, the quantity surveyor, the main contractor and the primary sub-contractors. If the intention of the architect or surveyor is then to take the chair at the meeting, record minutes, and in short act as he would as if he were in charge of the local tennis club, he is likely to be reminded of one or two facts. The first is that the site now belongs to the contractor to all intents and purposes and the second is that while the architect or surveyor is enabled under the terms of the contract to inspect the works as they progress, this is a far cry from many of the fond ideas that are held about "controlling the works". There is, in fact, no good reason why the main contractor should not take the chair at his own site meetings and ignore the architect or surveyor altogether. This would be a fairly crushing repost to any professional architect or surveyor who oversteps the mark and demands too much. Of course, in practice, this does not happen as the architect or surveyor is, in most cases within the scope of this book, seen by all as best suited to organise site meetings and record the decisions taken and this fact is generally recognised and accepted. Nevertheless his organisation of site meetings must be sensible. The architect or surveyor and the main contractor may be heavily involved in a contract which obviously means a great deal to them but they must not be blinded to the fact that others, particularly sub-contractors, may have a limited involvement only. With many other irons in the fire, they may not take kindly to being hauled out to attend a series of meetings where a great deal of time is spent in discussing matters over which they have little or no interest. If a series of meetings are planned at fixed intervals with the intention that everyone should turn up, attendance may be satisfactory on the first, say, two occasions, but, after that, excuses will become more and more perfunctory as the attendance level at subsequent meetings drops sharply. The art of arranging site meetings is to ensure that there is a two way desire for attendance. On the part of the architect or surveyor, coupled with the main contractor, there will be a desire for information from the sub-contractors who, on their part, are equally anxious for information to be provided to them.

It is fairly common practice for the first meeting to be held at the offices of the architect or surveyor as a preliminary to work starting on the site. This practice has a good deal to commend it. For one thing the various personalities can be introduced to each other since, although the representatives of the architect or surveyor, quantity surveyor and consultant engineer may very well know each other they may not be known to the contractor and his two representatives who will probably turn up, nor will they be known to the representatives of the primary sub-contractors. At this meeting a good deal of preliminary ground can be covered and the architect or surveyor is well advised to prepare a short agenda of matters that can be usefully discussed as preliminary items. These might comprise the following:

1. The Contractor's Programme
According to the contractor's responsibility under the terms of the contract his obligation to produce the programme can be raised as a first essential item.

2. Matters under the Contract
Two of the main and most obvious items under this heading are the question of indemnities and insurance. Clause 18 in the 1963 JCT Contract Form is replaced by a new clause 20 in the 1980 Form which contains similar provisions relating to indemnities and here, the intention of the Joint Contracts Tribunal is to re-distribute claims by third parties. If a claimant sues against one only of the parties to the contract so that there is a risk of judgement being obtained against him only, this clause enables the other parties to be joined in the action. It is still not clear, however, under this clause whether the Employer is responsible for personal injuries to the architect or surveyor and the continuing anomaly remains that if the Employer contributes in even the smallest degree, possibly due to negligence by his architect or surveyor, the whole of this indemnity clause fails, as far as he is concerned, so that it therefore has little value from his own point of view.

Insurance, which is now governed by clauses 21 and 22 of the JCT Contract Form 1980, replacing the earlier clauses 19 and 20 of the 1963 Form is dealt with under two distinct categories. The clauses drafted to protect the contractor in his obligations to the Employer deal firstly with third party risks where the liability of the contractor extends to personal injury or damage to property including that of the Employer, although there is no reference to any excess or limit on possible claims. The question of insurance is a study in itself and the services of an insurance broker are ideally necessary to determine matters in the interest of both the Employer and Contractor and in particular to decide whether an endorsement on the contractor's own third party policies are necesary or whether special provisions should be made.

The second section relating to insurance of the works has been criticised in that it ignores the commercial interest of the Employer and the architect or surveyor must ensure that these provisions are adequate and fair. Contractors with a poor record may find difficulty in obtaining insurance which, of course, may apply equally to sub-contractors and the question of ensuring that excess cover is obtained is important so as to prevent problems arising if a claim is lodged with possible disruption of the work. Again it must be stressed that the advice of insurance brokers must be sought both as regards the amount of the total cover and other subsidiary points under clauses 21 and 22 of the JCT Contract Form 1980.

The question of bonds for due performance of the work by the contractor to undertake and complete all his responsibilities will have been brought up at an early stage but the final agreement of the terms and execution of the bond must now be completed. The importance of a bond arises from the attraction that it holds for the Employer but, from the architect or surveyor's specialist point of view does very little for the relationship between the parties. If a contract cannot depend upon willingness on all sides for its completion, no amount of artificial inducement is likely to help much in this direction and the question of a bond should only be raised and agreed upon under the most unusual circumstances. Bonds are sometimes required in cases relating to party walls in London for example where an adjoining owner's surveyor makes a request for a bond against the building owner but such circumstances are rare. Otherwise the circumstances where a bond is required should be such that the request is eminently reasonable and even then the extent of the bond should only cover the strict amount of the protection needed and the level of surety should be accurately judged in this respect. Performance bonds are more directly related to engineering contracts under clause 10 of the ICE Contract conditions while bonds for retention or maintenance are generally called for in order to protect the retention monies where a need arises.

Where the employer feels that the idea of a bond might be ideal to cover certain circumstances, he should be warned by the architect or surveyor that the cost of entry into a bond is bound to increase the price of the tender as this is just another factor in the long string of financial arrangements to be made by the contractor and the additional facility is hardly likely to be offered free of charge. Perhaps the main drawback against bonds is that the main contractor, while charged with a duty of entering into a bond, may know very well that the real reason for the additional security required is due to anxiety about the sub-contract arrangements but he may, nevertheless, have no power to pass on a proportionate share of expenses and may thus feel that he is being penalised by bearing a disproportionate amount of the total sum.

The whole question of bonds and sureties is, again, a matter for specialist lawyers, accountants and insurance brokers and the architect or surveyor is well advised to take appropriate advice if in doubt.

It cannot be emphasised too strongly that total disclosure and complete honesty is required in relation to all dealings of the type discussed. So far as indemnities and insurance are concerned, the reasons are obvious. Just as the contractor has a duty to declare with total honesty all matters relating to his own circumstances that might affect the question of insurance so has the architect or surveyor the same duty to make total disclosure of all information on behalf of his client. Contractors of any size normally deal through a broker and enter into an "all risk" insurance policy annually which covers third party liability as well. The documents should obviously be available for inspection, except where particular arrangements relating to insurance have to be made, but the onus is very much upon the contractor to discuss and deal with any points of special-ised risk so that he is likely to at least have to think about the project and consider special risks, for example the storage of petrochemicals, while the architect or surveyor may wrongly assume that the whole question of insurance is outside his province. This may be costly since, should he fail to disclose some circumstance that might relate to the contract at a later stage affecting the insurance cover, the Insurance Company concerned could then legitimately deny liabil-ity and the insurance scheme could well become vitiated.

3. Nominated Sub-Contractors

It is an excellent rule for nominations to be completed before the first meeting on the site is held. It is a pity that so much friction occurs between main contractors and nominated sub-contractors although this can often be overcome by better handling of the situation by the professional advisers concerned. Late nomination of a sub-contractor leading to irritation between sub-contractor and main contractor should be avoided wherever possible. The practice of introducing nominated sub-contractors to the main contractor at the earliest possible stage is so obviously beneficial that one wonders why it is not more often followed. The reply, obviously, is that life is no longer like that. With modern pressures it is fashionable for certain nominations, steelwork sub-contractors for example, to be made well in advance of the selection of the main contractor while other nominations are left until nearly the end of the contract.

Should late nominations be unavoidable, it is an excellent idea for a list of possible nominees to be supplied to the main contractor if at all possible so that he can express a preference or render disapproval.

4. Statutory Consents and Approvals

The position regarding consents and approvals should be discussed and any outstanding matters dealt with. These often relate to details and calculations required by the District Surveyor or Building Inspector from the consulting engineers or nominated suppliers for example. Often large schemes however are held up due to the fact that the consent for a minor aspect of the work has been initially overlooked or subsequently held up.

5. Party Walls and Rights of Light

In large cases specialist surveyors dealing with party walls or rights of light will have been introduced to the scheme but in other cases it is necessary that the full procedure has been carried out and any Awards or agreements finalised. Again any defects in procedure can cost the employer dear in terms of delay.

6. Structural Information

Often the first information required for the scheme to be started, that of sufficient detailing regarding the structure, is lacking. Details might be needed from the structural engineers or this may be due to the fault of the architect or surveyor. Complete frankness when at fault and promise to deal with the matter in haste is what is required here.

7. Service Installations

The position regarding all mains and other services should be discussed and any problems brought out.

8. Site Access and Site Dimensions

Any problems that may hold up complete access to the site must obviously be brought up at an early stage and it is a good rule for the contractor to be requested to carry out his checks of dimensions and report any discrepancies at once. He should also be invited to examine adjoining structures and buildings, undertake plumb line surveys and do everything to satisfy himself that there are no unusual problems at this stage rather than stumbling across them later on.

9. Concrete

It is worth including this item as a separate heading as details of ready mix concrete designs must be submitted to the consulting engineer as soon as possible and the delay in obtaining cube test results from the laboratory may be inconvenient.

10. Information Required

It is at this stage that a schedule of information required under the contract with appropriate dates can be requested by the main contractor and this, in larger cases, takes the form of the contractor's "information required schedule". This may cover a host of matters ranging from Party Wall Awards setting out to ground floor, builders work in relation to lift installation, mechanical services and sanitary and other fittings and steelwork.

11. Notice Boards

The question of a notice board on the site and appropriate names can be considered at this stage.

At the conclusion of the first meeting the architect or surveyor, having taken notes, should produce these in clear form for circulation as soon as possible. The notes should first of all detail those present and set out the various points discussed and conclusions arrived at in succint form with, either underneath each item or in the right hand margin, the name of the person or firm responsible to take action under what has been agreed. The note should end with the date and time of the next site meeting and a distribution list appended below.

Later site meetings should continue the form of notes already formulated, in similar sequence, but other items, of course, will be included and others extended. The fact that the notes of the previous meeting were accepted should be recorded at subsequent meetings and additional space allowed to discuss and record the question of progress. The contractors monthly progress review should be produced in readable form so that it can be studied by everyone. The actual or planned progress made against completion is best set out in the form of percentages against each stage of the contract such as preliminary work, sub-structure and super-structure while the progress position measured in weeks should be clearly stated as against that planned for the contract.

Certificates and Payments

Once the first site meeting is over with a date fixed for the next, the architect or surveyor can ensure that his arrangements for the certification of work in progress and the issue of interim certificates are in order. Where quantity surveyors are involved of course, valuations will be provided at arranged intervals and these will include the names of the parties, the date of the interim valuation giving gross and net figures. Unless the architect or surveyor notifies the quantity surveyor that any work is not in accordance with the contract, the amount of the valuation is simply subject to the agreed retention with the amount of money certified under previous interim certificates deducted from the total. Where however, a quantity surveyor is not employed the architect or surveyor does well to check his own relationship with the client. Circumstances may vary and although we have dealt with problems in this area, it is as well for the architect or surveyor to warn the client that monetary arrangements are now due to be made and what is expected of him, re-affirming or correcting the timetable set out in the Feasibility Study. However well instructed, certain clients will nearly always delay payments until the last possible moment on the principle that as long as money is in their bank account it is earning interest for them rather than somebody else. An architect or surveyor however who encounters problems upon the issue of the first interim certificate is either extremely unlucky or should be blamed for his inadequate preparatory groundwork. Again he should be sure of his contractural position regarding the question of variations and delays. Every form of contract has specific requirements, as we have studied earlier, and the architect or surveyor who is not aware of the particular provisions whether of duty by the contractor for notification or his own duty of confirmation will get himself into an early muddle from which the contract may never recover.

The General Foreman or Site Agent

It is hoped that the site agent or general foreman will be present at the first meeting and if so the architect or surveyor should seek him out for a general discussion. It is rare that the architect or surveyor will be able to exercise control in the choice of general foreman or site agent who is the employee of the contractor and is chosen to exercise control and organisation on the site and to supervise the work in progress. The site agent has such enormous powers including the rejection of materials and the dismissal of unsatisfactory labour that his abilities, or lack of them, and his general competence in the various fields that are necessary have an enormous influence on the contract. An older general foreman may have little or no academic training, having graduated from the primary

472

trades such as bricklayer, carpenter or joiner. The younger man however, is far more likely to have received a Polytechnic education or have his City and Guilds examination in a trade. It is often said that a foreman who has graduated from joiner for example, will apply a severe test of adequacy in this direction, but may neglect the concrete work. This is misleading and unfair. It is far more likely that the foreman of works will tend, with maturity, to develop a good knowledge of all trades and to be generally found either in the site hut valuing the excellence of paperwork on the one hand or alternatively, has to be searched out since he will proclaim a massive disregard for "bumf" and prefer to spend his time trudging around in the rain "with the lads". The architect or surveyor who can establish frank and open relations with the general foreman at the outset of the contract is a happy man but, if he cannot, suspecting that the general foreman is suspicious, arbitrary, and, that most difficult thing to pin down, possessing a bland knack of disregarding questions that do not suit him, then misery may result. While a request can be made for the foreman to be changed, it must always be remembered that such men are prized above rubies in the building trade and may not only be a firm friend of the contractor but have his entire confidence. Such a request is rather like asking a bank manager to sack his chief clerk. Only under dire circumstances should such a request be made and, like every other relationship on the building site, the architect or surveyor should endeavour to get to know the general foreman, assess his character, and have sympathy with his strength and weaknesses, endeavour to support him where possible, and to find ways to compensate for his deficiencies. This is not so arrogant as it sounds. From the time that the architect or surveyor first appears on the scene, the general foreman will be quietly assessing his character in turn, sizing up his capabilities and making notes to make similar compensations in just the same way.

General Principles of Site Inspection

The focus of this chapter now changes from the preliminary steps to be taken just before works begin on site to the time when the architect or surveyor receives his call from the contractor to carry out his first inspection of the site, or, alternatively, where he himself makes an unheralded visit. From this time forward his role changes from dealing with the rather pleasant preliminaries which are, after all, rather academic, since, if a problem presents itself it can be worked out either in discussion or on the drawing board, to the actuality of the contract in operation where the stakes will prove costly if matters go wrong and scapegoats may have to be found. If anyone thinks that site inspection is easy they only have to look at the publications of the Building Research Establishment to receive some sobering information. In an interim report on low rise housing issued jointly by the BRE and the National Building Agency, inspectors found a wide range of faults in construction. One, in particular, may be instanced. This was the failure to fix metal straps correctly, essential for the purpose of acting as a tie between roof and wall structures. In a very large number of cases the ties were incorrectly fixed so that they were ineffective and the interim report questioned whether designers were even aware of the need for straps to act in both compression and tension. In addition to this, two further research projects of the Building Research Establishment, looking into the question of how far quality is achieved in housing construction, have shown that quality control on building sites is severely lacking. In a study based on observations of twenty seven sites involving contracts for central or local government valued at between one hundred thousand pounds and twelve million pounds, 501 "quality related events", i.e. anything that requires any responsible member of the contractor's staff to pause in his work to consider the quality or "rightness' of what was being built or proposed, were noted. Of this total, 36 % of "quality related events" were concerned with workmanship while 57 % were related with project information. The study showed that simple lack of care was far more common than lack of skill; that difficulties with project documentation were dominated by unclear or missing information which could also be considered an expression of lack of care by the designer and that while the site staff were more successful in dealing with workmanship problems in their own area of responsibility, they were less successful in dealing with problems of design, when they had to refer to people outside the site. The main conclusion to be derived from the table was the disturbing point that for no less than 39 of the "quality related events" there was no successful solution. It is accordingly with these depressing findings that the architect or surveyor has to equip himself to monitor quality control on what he may, understandably, regard as his own pet project.

It is hardly surprising that no reference is made in the JCT Forms of Contract as to the number of inspections that the architect or surveyor will provide for the particular project. The contract is drawn up between the employer and the contractor and although the role of the architect or surveyor is fundamental to it, his monitoring duties are not referred to. The contract does, however, enable the architect or surveyor to function as his employer's agent in the certification of payments for example, and by other clauses that give him power to carry out his duties by having access to the works and to the contractors workshops at reasonable times. More surprising perhaps is that detailed reference as to the extent of the architect or surveyor's attendance duties such as the frequency of inspections, for example, is not made in the contract between the architect or surveyor and his client. It would not be unreasonable, one would have thought, for the employer to require a minimum number of periodic inspections to be made and for this to be recorded in the terms of the agreement. The truth is, of course, that at an early stage in the proceedings the architect or surveyor does not know himself how many inspections are we likely to be entailed in the project and any guess-work as to what is likely to be needed may be widely inappropriate. The degree of attendance relies very much upon circumstances and any pre-determined arrangements at an early stage may subsequently prove to be totally valueless. This is not to say, of course, that the architect or surveyor will not have discussed the whole question of the nature and extent of his duties of inspection with the employer and he would be remiss if he did not, but merely specifying the frequency of a certain number of visits in a programme of inspection, while possibly helpful in the matter of costs and expenses, will not provide any protection against future claims of negligence. The Courts are not satisfied with evidence that a professional man has gone through the motions of his employment. They wish to hear evidence as to whether he has discharged his duties under the terms of the contract adequately or otherwise.

It has long been established in Common Law that an architect is not expected to be constantly on the works and to supervise every detail but nor, on the other hand, is it sufficient for him to turn up occasionally, ask for certain matters to be put right, and then vanish. His duty seems to be to devote such reasonable inspection of the work as will enable him to give an honest certificate that it has been properly carried out in accordance with the terms of the contract.[1]

It has been established, moreover, that while the architect or surveyor is not required personally to check or measure every detail he must check substantial or important items, such as the bottoming for a cement floor, which are about to be covered up. As mentioned earlier, a pattern has been evident in recent years from published reports of Court cases which highlight the duty of care of a professional architect or surveyor in certain areas. These are, firstly,

(1) *Jameson* v. *Simon* (1899) 1F (Ct. of Sess) 1211 and *Cotton* v. *Wallis* (1955) 3 ALL ER 373.

to ensure that work has been adequately carried out before it is covered up for good and the opportunity is lost of taking any remedial steps, secondly, that particular care in inspection is needed where there is a risk of an accident that might cause injury or death and, thirdly, that a professional man is seen to have failed in his duty when the employer's rights of restitution are completely signed away by negligent certification.

Since the contract between the architect or surveyor and his client is personal to both parties, the law regards with suspicion any attempt to water down the responsibilities of the one towards the other. Accordingly, although an architect or surveyor may depute some parts of his duty to subordinates, he does not, by doing so, avoid his own responsibility by saying that the fault was theirs and not his.[2]

Standards regarding the duty of care expected of a professional man tend to alter and an interesting case of 1955 in this connection is that of *Cotton* v. *Wallis*. In this case the defendant entered into a contract under the then current standard RIBA Form with a contractor for the erection of a house costing £1,910. The plaintiff was the architect appointed by the defendant. Clauses in the contract provided that the . . . "Contractor shall carry out and complete works in accordance with this contract in every respect with the directions and to the reasonable satisfaction of the architect" . . . "and the whole of the materials and the workmanship is to be the best of their respective kinds and to the full satisfaction of the architect who shall be at liberty to reject any materials and require any unsatisfactory work to be carried out to his full satisfaction". It was also provided that . . . "any defects, shrinkage or other faults which shall appear within the defects liability period (six months following completion) and shall be due to materials and workmanship not in accordance with this contract" . . . "shall within a reasonable time after receipt of the architect's written instructions be made good by the contractor at his own cost." Plaster and paint-work were found to be defective and the floor tiles were stained. The architect drew these facts to the contractor's attention and wrote asking him to make good the defective tiles but those used to replace the stained tiles did not match the remainder and this was the position at the end of the maintenance defects period when the plaintiff certified final payment. Subsequently the plaintiff brought an action for his fees against which the defendant client brought a counter-claim for damages for failing to exercise professional skill in

(2) *Leicester Guardians* v. *Trollope* (1911) 75 JP. 197. 2. *Armstrong* v. *Jones* (1869) Hudson.

supervision of the contract work. It was decided on appeal that although the plaintiff architect had no dispensing power to pass bad work, yet the low price of the work was a material factor in the determination whether the architect could certify work to his reasonable satisfaction, and accordingly no case of professional negligence had been made out.

An ominous, if brief note, to this reported case says that Denning LJ dissented and it is doubtful if a subsequent hearing in the Court of Appeal would have produced a similar outcome.

With this in mind on turning to the Conditions of Appointment and Engagement for both architects and chartered surveyors one wonders what Lord Denning would have had to say about them. They are in many respects similar, particularly in that they both attempt to limit the extent of the architect or surveyors duties of inspection. Regarding the architect's conditions prior to 1982 Hudson writing on building contracts says "it is thought that the intention is to make it clear that the architect is not warranting compliance by the contractor with the building contract" but one detects a certain flavour of the raised eyebrow in the expression "it is thought". From this one can deduce that the section of the Conditions in force prior to 1982 dealing with inspections had not recently been tested in the Courts and one trembles to think what would have happened had it been.

Section 1 "Extent of Surveyor's Responsibility" of the General Conditions of Engagement dated 1981 for Building Surveying Services published by the RICS under para 1.3.4 "Site Visits and Inspections" is as follows:

> "During the course of the building works, the surveyor shall make periodic visits to the site to monitor the contractor's workmanship and progress; to check on the use of materials; to check on the works' conformity to specification; and to report generally on the progress and quality of the works having regard to the terms of the contract between the client and the contractor. The surveyor shall not be expected to make exhaustive or continuous inspections."

The following disclaimer, included in the 1979 Conditions has now been removed.

> "The sole purpose of such periodic site visits is to enable the surveyor to inspect the work of the contractor so as to protect the client, as far as is practicable, against deficiencies in that work. The surveyor does not undertake to supervise or to be responsible for the operational methods, techniques, sequences or procedures adopted by the contractor; nor the safety precautions adopted in connection with the work undertaken by the contractor; nor does the surveyor undertake responsibility for any failure by the contractor to carry out and complete the work in

477

accordance with the terms of the contract between the client and the contractor."

In the case of the RIBA, similar phraseology for site inspections was covered under three separate clauses in Part 1, General, of the pre-1982 Conditions of Engagement, published in October 1977 thus:

1.3 Responsibilities

1.33 the architect shall advise on the selection and appointment of the contractor and shall make such periodic visits to the site as he considers necessary to inspect generally the progress and quality of the work and to determine in general if the work is proceeding in accordance with the contract documents.

1.34 The architect shall not be responsible for the contractors operational methods, techniques, sequences of procedures nor for safety precautions in connection with the work, nor shall he be responsible for any failure by the contractor to carry out and complete work in accordance with the terms of the building contract between the client and the contractor.

1.6 Inspection

1.60 During his on-site inspections made in accordance with clause 1.33 the architect shall endeavour to guard the client against defects and deficiencies in the work of the contractor, but shall not be required to make exhaustive or continuous inspections to check the quality or quantity of the work.

The above clauses had in fact been effective in the RIBA Conditions since July 1971 but if the edition which came into effect in October 1966 is consulted it is interesting to note the appearance of the disclaimer towards the end of para 1.34 above which is included in 1971 but was not before. The October 1966 Conditions of Engagement had this to say in Part 1, General Conditions, about site supervision and nothing else:

1.1 Responsibilities

1.16 the architect shall give such periodic supervision and inspection as may be necessary to ensure that the works are being executed in general accordance with the contract; constant supervision does not form part of his normal duties.

In the RIBA Architect's Appointment 1982, inspections during the progress of the works are dealt with in two separate parts. The

478

section of the booklet, Part 1, describing the Preliminary and Basic Services normally provided by the architect sets out, under Work Stage K: "Operations on Site", the following:

Inspections

1.22 Visit the site as appropriate to inspect generally the progress and quality of the work.

While under Part 3, setting out the conditions which normally apply to an architect's appointment, below a heading "Site Inspection" appears:

Inspection

3.10 The architect will visit the site at intervals appropriate to the stage of construction to inspect the progress and quality of the works and to determine that they are being executed generally in accordance with the contract documents. The architect will not be required to make frequent or constant inspections.

The disclaimer, carried over from the previous conditions, in respect of the contractor's work is now placed more logically before the above paragraph under the heading "Contractors sub-contractors and suppliers" thus:

Responsibility of the contractor

3.9 The client will employ a contractor under a separate agreement to undertake construction or other works. The client will hold the contractor, and not the architect, responsible for the contractor's operational methods and for the proper execution of the works.

There is of course the first "condition" set out in Part 3:

Duty of care

3.1 The architect will exercise reasonable skill and care in conformity with the normal standards of the architect's profession.

But even so, as in the case of the published conditions by the RICS, the wording cannot be said to provide much guidance or indication to the client as to the scope of the architect's or surveyor's responsibilities for seeing that the scheme which has been, hopefully, so carefully prepared on paper, is to be completed in accordance with the documentation. In fact it is clear that there has been a progressive retraction from the more encouraging phrases which

479

used to appear in the published conditions, such as inspections "to ensure that the works are being executed in general accordance with the contract" (pre-1971 RIBA Conditions) and periodic site visits so as to "protect the client, as far as is practicable, against the deficiencies in that work" (pre-1981 RICS Conditions). The idea now put forward by the professional bodies seems to be that architects and surveyor's will only inspect and monitor progress and quality and "determine", whatever that word may mean in this context, that the works are being executed generally in accordance with the documentation but do little else and the impression given to the public is distinctly feeble and unfortunate. An experienced client may not need to insist on more precise words being added to any agreement with an architect or surveyor, if he has a knowledge of the law, but is still likely to do so just the same. The less experienced client, however, might consider he has a right to expect more from his architect or surveyor in the way of "periodic inspections" to ensure that he is getting what he is paying for, so far as it is possible to do so. If he agrees to the wording put forward in the published conditions (and many will be persuaded to do so, knowing little better) and he is let down, the law may provide its support, despite the wording, but it seems a pity that architects and surveyors, collectively, have not sufficient confidence in their ability to put forward a form of words more positive and encouraging to clients for use in agreements when seeking their services.

To the lay client it must appear that the Conditions of Appointment, or Engagement as the case may be, to which he is normally invited to agree, provide for the architect or surveyor to inspect the works during their progress and yet for example, to absolve him from any duty to step up the number of visits and to exert pressure on the contractor when the going gets tough. The client, who will remain docile in the early stages of the work will suddenly become interested when the finishing stages are reached and, particularly if he lives at the house which is the subject of work in progress will complain loudly if any of the workmanship falls short of the standard of craftsmanship that he himself has, in his own opinion, achieved. "Call that bloke a joiner", he says, "I could do much better myself". More irritatingly however, he then expects the supervision given not only to increase in terms of time but in its nature as well. "That bloke is coming back here tomorrow – can you come over and make sure he does it (unspecified) correctly? I have to go to work". The implication that "he" has work to do while his hired hand can only just about be trusted to take over is wounding but not so serious to the architect or surveyor as to provoke a decision that visits in future will be in the form of pre-emptive strikes. Some architects or surveyors are practically forced into yielding to entreaties to be site foreman in cases for example where work is being done for a neighbour who is a close friend. Thinking philosophically that the job must, surely, soon be over the architect or surveyor will be drawn into obsessive and unpaid attendance. But upon yielding thus, are the dangers over? No; they are not. "If that is what their painting is like" mutters the client, darkly, "I often wonder what the foundations must be made of—" and then, turning to the architect or surveyor "I hope you saw all the work done from start to finish". Any expostulation then about the architect's or surveyor's duty will fall upon very deaf ears. The fact is that the client has, in his own eyes, forced his architect or surveyor to carry out his duties properly when, before, he was clearly not sufficiently interested in the job to do so.

Discussions, sometimes heated and almost always at a late stage in the contract, end by the architect or surveyor reminding his client that in the RIBA Architects Appointment or the RICS Conditions of Engagement presented to him and discussed earlier, mention is made of the appointment of a Clerk of Works should frequent or constant inspection be necessary. This simply infuriates the client. "If you must employ a bunch of bodgers and you tell me they cannot be ordered off the site then you must see that they do the work properly. That is your job."

Architects or surveyors, however, must obviously press the point that if a client requires to be absolutely sure of perfection in every respect then he must incur the expense of employing a Clerk of Works to act as his representative on site on a permanent basis. Why should the architect or surveyor accept any responsibility when all he can provide is periodic attendance? This attitude, perhaps valid in the case of larger contracts, falls down in smaller cases as it overlooks two important facts. In the first place it is very expensive for the client to employ a Clerk of Works on any other than the largest of contracts, certainly well beyond the range of the typical job envisaged by this book, which would become highly uneconomic as a result of such employment. The architect or surveyor might reasonably reply that if that is the price of a good job as distinct from a dubious one, so be it. That however is a very short sighted view as it is the architectural and surveying profession who are in the market offering a service to satisfy clients requirements. If clients requirements are not catered for at a reasonable level of cost commensurate with the service provided, clients will be more tempted to turn to the specialist contractor who will offer a package deal with a guarantee. The viewpoint also overlooks the second aspect in that it has demonstratably been proved on untold occasions in the past that it is perfectly possible to produce sound buildings given the good will of a reliable contractor and the monitoring inspections of the architect or surveyor who prepared the scheme. The professional man can be there to answer the inevitable queries which must arise out of any attempt to represent building works on paper and in words and to see that everything intended is completed generally under the terms of the contract between client and builder.

What the architect and surveyor are offering to do, however, for approximately the last third of the scale fee and of something like a mere quarter of the additional cost of employing a clerk of works is to use their best endeavours within the limitations imposed by periodic inspections to see that the terms of the contract are fulfilled. Given the skills of an experienced architect or surveyor in recognising faulty procedures, poor materials and bad workmanship, this is a sound business proposition, if not a bargain, of which lay clients would be foolish not to take advantage. Who better than the originator of all the thought behind the scheme and the writer of the specification to see to its translation into fact, certainly preferable to, for example, the lay client, the client's "builder" friend, the client's son who is studying to be a quantity surveyor or someone else with a smattering of building knowledge? To some extent it may be said that the professional expertise brought to bear on the task of supervision by the architect or surveyor is superior in many ways to the day to day watchfulness of the clerk of works who, even when employed, still has to refer to the architect or surveyor. However, as with any business proposition or bargain it is only sound, or a bargain for that matter, if the client obtains a full and thorough service through the adoption of a proper sense of responsibility in the architect or surveyor who undertakes the task. Giving great thought to the matter beforehand by providing proper detailed instructions to the contractor, determining the right choice of contract, selecting the right builder and working out his own suitable pattern of progress inspections are merely a few of the areas of responsibility required.

Lamentably, this sense of responsibility is the aspect to which sufficient attention has not always been given in the past. All too often, if carried out by the architect or surveyor himself, inspections are treated as a pleasant jaunt out of the office. If, however, architect or surveyor are busy on the next scheme or some other knotty problem demands attention in the office, inspections are delegated to an inexperienced assistant with insufficient control exercised over his actions, or, more often, inaction. Firms where the earning of the last third of the scale fee is often thought of as a "doddle" and, perhaps, where the loss made on the earlier stages of the work programme can be recovered, are often in for a shock. In fact, site inspections are an onerous responsibility and one to which as much attention is required as is devoted to the earlier stages of the scheme if the duties under the Conditions of Engagement are to be fulfilled. All the good work put into the earlier stages of the commission can be thrown away by lax supervision. If a flippant attitude to the task is all that can be mustered then in many ways it would be better not to undertake supervision work at all. To duck out in this way however, would be a sorry admission of failure in a professional architect or surveyor and it would not be surprising if the public's opinion of the professions dealing with building declined even further if this attitude became prevalent.

The question arises now as to how much attention is required for the architect or surveyor to fulfill his duties under the requirement for periodic inspection. Two degrees of attention have already been mentioned; the architect or surveyor visiting only rarely by prior appointment and the draughtsman or junior assistant sent on his behalf. It is thought reasonable that both of these would be considered an insufficient response to the duty imposed even though they would be said to comply with the strict wording of the Conditions of Engagement. At the other extreme there might be the architect or surveyor with one job only on his hands at the time and who has made provision to attend at the site nearly every day for some hours. This does not conflict with the wording of the RIBA Architect's Appointment or the RICS Conditions of Engagement and the client could indeed count himself fortunate in being provided with such close attention to his affairs bordering on the exhaustive or continuous inspections of a site architect. What the contractor would think is another matter. He no doubt would consider it rather obsessive and extreme and depending upon how the supervision was exercised it may be his men would find it a pain in the neck. Most contractors and their workforce like to feel they are being trusted and no workman likes to have someone looking over his shoulder all, or very nearly all, of the time.

What then might be said to be the proper number and frequency of visits to satisfy the duty undertaken by the architect and surveyor to carry out "periodic visits", "to monitor the contractors workmanship" and "to check on the works' conformity to specification". A moments reflection, will of course, provide the answer that no particular rules can possibly be laid down. The characteristics of each job are different as are those of each contractor and most certainly of the work force employed. What can be said is that the architect or surveyor must carry out a sufficient number of inspections of such duration as are necessary to enable him to provide to his cleint, if asked, at the end of the contract, an assurance that, subject only to the limitations imposed by the periodic nature of the inspections, work has been completed in accordance with the contract documents. Everyone realises, and indeed the point will be discussed later, that architects and surveyors cannot indemnify clients against malpractices that may occur while they are not present. It is for this reason that the issue of a Final Certificate is not to be taken as evidence of the completion of the contract in accordance with the documents and it does not operate as a release for the contractor. On the other hand the establishment by the architect or surveyor of procedures and arrangements with the contractor and his workforce on site inspections will considerably lessen the opportunity for such malpractices to flourish. It is a full appreciation of what can be done in this respect coupled with a fuller understanding of the difficult and time consuming nature of the task accepted by architects and surveyors which needs to be stressed.

For example, to comply with the RIBA Architect's Appointment or the RICS Conditions, it must be fully understood that site inspections fall into two distinct categories. The first category covers those inspections made at various stages during the course of the works where it is vital to see that features are constructed in a satisfactory manner before they are covered up by further work. These inspections are usually made by arrangement; the general foreman notifying the architect or surveyor that such and such a feature is ready for him to pass. The second category comprises those inspections made between the arranged visits when the architect or surveyor will descend upon the works unheralded to see that matters are progressing according to the standards laid down. It is vital that these inspections are not by prior arrangement and indeed on no account should they fall into any kind of pattern which can be discerned by the contractor; they must be totally irregular. In the case of the first category much can be said in the specification by way of clauses requiring matters to be left open until passed by the architect or surveyor but the specification cannot hope to cover everything and, accordingly, it is usually necessary to come to an early understanding with the general foreman as to what stages require his notification. The corollary, or other side of the coin, is that the architect or surveyor must hold himself in readiness to make inspections at reasonably short notice otherwise he will be in danger of delaying the contractor unreasonably and risking the possibility of a claim for an extension of time on the contract. Of course, on a strictly cost effective basis architects and surveyors will find that because of all the differences possible between various types of job some will cost more to supervise than others. Some with a good contractor, sound foreman and a reliable workforce may well prove the "doddle" hopefully anticipated. Others where, perhaps, the specification and drawings have not turned out to be quite the perfect model intended, perhaps in a case where the owner had imposed restrictions on opening up before the works began and where nothing turns out as anticipated, the foreman is newly promoted and the workforce recalcitrant, can prove to be a perfect nightmare.

As time goes on, the architect or surveyor can see what perhaps was only likely to be a modest profit slipping away entirely. In the normal course of events architect or surveyor must in circumstances such as these, just grin and bear it but resolve to try and prevent similar circumstances arising again since it could be fatal to skimp matters of attendance at this stage. Better a much reduced profit or even none at all than to risk a claim for negligence. However, what if the architect or surveyor in the early stages can foresee difficulties of this nature arising? It may be possible to see trouble ahead from the character of the client as he presents himself at the beginning of the relationship or, perhaps, from the builder or even from a dawning realisation that the contract has one or two nasty problems glossed over at documentation stage but looming nearer as the time comes to start the work. One thing however, is certain. Most difficulties occur when the time that should have been available to prevent them has passed.

The only ground therefore for the architect or surveyor to claim extra fees incurred by a neurotic client or a bad builder is the rather negative statement that the surveyor "shall not be expected to make exhaustive or continuous inspections". In defence of the RIBA Architect's Appointment and the RICS Conditions of Engagement it may be argued that it is not usually possible to tell what degree of supervision is likely to be required until the architect or surveyor has had experience firstly of the site conditions and secondly of the contractor. By the time, however, that his experience of both of these is a gloomy one it will certainly be too late to impose conditions regarding extra fees upon his client. In certain obvious cases, however, where the contractor is nominated by the client and is unknown to the architect or surveyor, some basic understanding about the number of inspections would only be prudent so that if it were found necessary for an increased number of visits to be made, further costs could be chargeable accordingly. Similarly, in daywork contracts or unusual building operations, the architect or surveyor could either by design, or inadvertently, undertake a role nearer to that of Clerk of

Works than the monitoring role envisaged by the Conditions of Appointment or Engagement and here again the architect or surveyor would be foolish if he did not formulate an agreement in advance as to what was expected of him under such circumstances. In any event the client is entitled to know what services he can expect for his money and will certainly be interested, to say the least, to know what the architect or surveyor intends to do. It is at the feasibility stage of the contract that the client is likely to listen to the architect or surveyor's recommendations regarding the amount of site inspection and is likely to be guided by him accordingly. The stage of detailed design and documentation is not likely to alter the situation and once the work has started, however, the opportunity is certainly lost for altering the terms of the engagement. Since there are few guide lines to assist him, the question of site inspection must depend upon the judgement of the architect or surveyor according to the particular case involved and in assessing what is needed he will call heavily upon his past experience of other contracts. For reasons mentioned earlier, clients unfamiliar with building operations do sometimes expect what might be termed close supervision, particularly if works are being carried out to the family home and client and family are remaining in occupation. It is best to clear away any misconceptions at a very early stage of the contract in this respect.

Site inspections will often be made by the surveyor or architect in person but are also likely to be undertaken by assistants. There is, of course, nothing wrong in this, but it must be recorded, however, that the architect's or surveyor's assistant becomes his "representative" under the terms of the JCT Contract and therefore has not just a right but a duty to arrive at decisions on behalf of his principal. In large contracts an assistant may even be resident at the site in lieu of a Clerk of Works and paid for by the client but in the case of the bulk of the contracts carried out within the scope of this book, inspections are usually carried out on about a week to week basis, sometimes being varied by day to day inspections at certain crucial times and sometimes, in certain other types of work, month to month inspections being sufficient. It is a paradox in that the speed with which a small job progresses often necessitates site inspections at more frequent intervals than is the case with a large job. What is important is that inspections should be irregular, as already discussed, and not conform to a pattern although there will be those occasions when specific items will have to be inspected when completed before the next stage of the work can be allowed to proceed. Although assistant and principal may sometimes attend together, it is vital for the proper performance of the contract that the assistant has received an adequate amount of experience if he is to attend frequently on his own. Although the Form of Contract may require the surveyor or architect to confirm verbal instructions given on the site within seven days, there is barely time in most cases for the assistant to seek confirmation from his Principal in a five day working week so as to ensure that the instructions arrive in time and passive reliance on the contractor to confirm instructions in lieu is an abdication of the architect's or surveyor's duty. It might reasonably be asked why the assistant should not telephone his Principal from the contractor's hut but few people who are aware of what life is like in a modern architect or surveyor's office would recommend such a course. A short-tempered architect or surveyor, dragged from a meeting with clients to decide on a point that is imperfectly described to him at a distance of many miles may be in no better position to decide the matter than his assistant. Of course, major matters will be referred to him as he is the responsible party under the terms of the contract but under such circumstances the contractor will have recognised that a decision of some consequence has to be made and will, in all probability, have allowed sufficient time for it to be dealt with.

The assistant must be able to sign order sheets for variations on behalf of his Principal and most architects or surveyors see that each contract has a properly bound order book for that purpose with detachable copies for the contractor's and the office file and, where applicable, for the quantity surveyor and Clerk of Works with the original or top copy being retained in the book on site until completion. The book should be labelled with the name of the contract and each order should be correctly numbered in sequence with the name of the party to whom the order is addressed together with a description of the items, the date and the assistant's or Principal's signature. The number of the order is particularly important as this will be used as a reference in the case of later correspondence. The use of such a book to deal with and answer contractor's queries is not advocated since most queries will be answered without any aspect of a variation becoming involved. The contractor should keep a separate book for this purpose. It is only when an answer to a contractor's query involves a variation that the order book should be used.

An experienced contractor may have respect for a particular architect or surveyor but if he never sees him and only makes contact with an assistant who is so indecisive that he has to refer back to his office on each occasion, control of the contract may well be lost. This is not, however, to suggest that any decision is better than none. Any assistant who correctly hesitates before making a decision, say, between two rival manufacturers of hardware, will, if he has encouraged a sound relationship with the contractor draw upon the latter's long wealth of experience. It is true that the contractor may have an axe to grind or may be scornful of innovations but his help may also be invaluable. An assistant who fails to consult the contractor and invariably reports back to his office over the smallest matter may slowly close the door to any form of worthwhile consultation and will forfeit one of the most precious benefits available to him; that of the contractor's co-operation. It is only by attendance on the site, canvassing the views of others outside his office, balancing one factor against another and using his own judgement that an assistant will mature. He is bound to make mistakes and if he does so it is vital that the contractor and principal have a link so that the situation can be recovered without loss to the client. In this respect the order book with its removable copies for both architect or surveyor's and contractor's office records can be of considerable assistance since the copy brought back by the assistant to the office after a site visit can enable a Principal to monitor the decisions being taken on his behalf and, if necessary, countermand them. The assistant must, however, assume responsibility sooner or later and if he signs for extra work or a variation that has become necessary and his Principal, on his next visit, says to the contractor that his assistant has overstepped the mark, the contractor will then act as an advocate of the assistant and will loudly commend his wisdom and general foresight. The prudent contractor will however, often defer carrying out work which he considers has been hastily or incorrectly ordered by either assistant or Principal so as to give time for reconsideration.

A great deal is implied at law in the duty of the architect or surveyor, or of either's assistant, visiting the site in a monitoring capacity but just as much is implied by common sense. The contractor has his own obligations under the contract and the architect or surveyor or assistant should recognise this. The role of the architect or surveyor is to ensure that the contract is concluded to the satisfaction of all parties, not least that of the contractor who should benefit financially from the contract by receiving a fair profit. An architect or surveyor is extremely ill-advised to regard himself as his client's agent to the extent of chiselling down the contractor's measure of remuneration by any means that he can. He might well provoke a response that will surprise him. Draconian powers may well be granted to the architect or surveyor under the terms of the contract but it is very unwise to unleash these unless it is absolutely necessary. An instruction, for example, to cease work following a disagreement may have disastrous consequences and an autocratic refusal by the architect or surveyor or an assistant to consider any alternatives that may help the contractor if he finds himself in a real difficulty or, indeed, to have any sympathy with the contractor's position at all, may result in a breakdown of communication with equally lamentable consequences. The architect or surveyor or an assistant should always bear in mind that there are areas in any building contract where they must tread delicately and with tact. They cannot directly interfere with the particular sequence of work which the builder has planned, unless this is likely to prove disastrous, or where the client particularly requires it, in which case the contractor's consent should be sought, and any extra expense accepted. Similarly, since the responsibility for the design and construction of shuttering, for example, and in many cases strutting and shoring lies with the contractor under the terms of the contract, who will only have priced for the work which he considers to be necessary, a formal requirement for extra work may well be countered with a request for a variation order. Nothing however, can relieve the architect or surveyor of his duty to step in where he feels that matters are not right and on many occasions a quiet suggestion will be picked up quickly by the contractor who will then take the necessary action without any fuss. Such cases are, of course, to be contrasted with the occasions where the architect or surveyor himself is responsible for the design and direction of temporary work. Again, since the contractor, in the main, is required to set out the works and be responsible for accuracy and make good errors at his own cost, an intervention by the architect or surveyor or an assistant may be welcomed but, again, this can be contrasted with the case where a contractor finds an ambiguity in the drawings or layout plans and asks for the architect or surveyor's decision so that he may receive confirmation of the correct design before starting upon the next stage of the work.

Just as the architect or surveyor or an assistant must tread delicately in certain areas, they should follow an established pattern of courtesy on their visits to the site. If a Clerk of Works is employed by the building owner contact should be made with him alone and he should be kept fully aware and made a party to any appointments for visits or decisions that may affect his work. Just as importantly, his authority should not be undermined by ill-judged comment. A foolish architect or surveyor who criticises his client's Clerk of Works in the hearing of the builder would expect to receive news a little later on that the drawings proved to be wrong, his assistant did not arrive for an appointment, and the client who arrived unexpectedly yesterday, was most dissatisfied. A more confidential chat with the Clerk of Works would have revealed that the error in the drawings was of no importance, the assistant, who had suffered a puncture on his moped had only arrived a little later than expected and that the client was in fact dissatisfied over his wife's choice of door fittings.

While the Clerk of Works is employed by the building owner, due consideration must also be extended to the contractor and his team where no Clerk of Works is employed. The general foreman should always be requested to attend a meeting rather than be ordered to be present as otherwise an unattractive alternative may be presented "I was due to supervise the unloading of the roof trusses but as I had to be present at your meeting I sent the lorry away". Later, an extra charge may be presented for the lorry's wasted journey.

The builder and his team are expert in deflating the arrogant and capitalising on mistakes whether they call in the penalty or not. They are skilled in negotiations and naturally manoeuvre to get the contract completed their way. There is no reason why this should not be so. They are in business and if they do not look after themelves, no one else will. They will have plenty of sympathy with an inexperienced assistant only if he is frank and open and does what he says he will do. The assistant who tries to cover up and put the blame on someone else will receive short shrift. Building contracts, particularly smaller ones, are a matter of shifts and balances. A builder will not care if he never deals with a bombastic and autocratic architect or surveyor again but, with one whom he likes and respects, he may not wish to lose the opportunity of further work and will go some way to see that problems are cleared up without too much fuss.

Just as the architect, surveyor, or assistant, are courteous with the contractor and do not criticise him in front of his employees, so the same degree of courtesy should extend down the line. It is permissible to talk to the carpenters or bricklayers and indeed it is vital for the architect or surveyor or assistant to do this in order to establish, if nothing else, that he has some human qualities, but comments should be restricted under normal circumstances to straightforward enquiry and appreciation of work completed. The architect or surveyor can then go back with the contractor to his hut, where they will be alone, and let off steam if he so wishes. The same rule applies to the tradesmen who are working on the site. One of the great pleasures in the architect's or surveyor's life is to talk to knowledgeable craftsmen and learn about their skills and their approach to the work in hand just as one of the great pains is to deal with operatives who are incompetent or lazy. In most circumstances, however, after a wary period to see if the architect or surveyor or assistant are "on the catch" relaxation becomes general and the professionals can then learn a great deal of information that may be new to them.

The architect or surveyor should always take considerable trouble to establish good relations with the site foreman who might vary from being a man of advanced years, skilled in paperwork as well as building experience, to a young man recently promoted from being a craftsman such as joiner or plumber. If the latter's views are uncompromising, it should be remembered that the builder, who is the only one who knows his true worth, will be keeping an anxious eye upon him and indeed this may be his first contract. Good foremen are always in short supply and the best have graduated from the primary trades. The benefits of obtaining the confidence of a good foreman are inestimable and the architect or surveyor or any of their assistants who antagonise the general foreman or fail to take advantage of his particular experience are fools. It is very rare to find a really poor foreman and regrettably it has to be said that when relationships deteriorate with that worthy, it is usually the fault of the architect or surveyor or perhaps the client.

Little so far has been said about the building owner but it should always be remembered that the lay client may be quite unused to the sort of upsets that are commonplace on the building site. After all, the layman does not normally visit the factory where his car is being made or his lawyer's general office where his affairs are being discussed. It is probably just as well that he is unconscious when he is in the operating theatre. A client considers it quite natural however, that he should have unrestricted access to the building site (after all, "who is paying", he would like to know) and is often put out at attempts to curtail his activities. However, with all due understanding to the building owner, the different trades and occupations on site demand a wide range of abilities and differing types of temperament in the work force employed. Add to this the fact that there are likely to be a wide variety of different ages and social backgrounds and that everyone has to work together under one roof, it is not surprising that when various members of the team are questioned, their replies will be individual to say the least. The general foreman, by his age and his undoubted knowledge and experience, used to be, and still is, in many cases, able to control the diverse range of human beings under his charge but latterly, and particularly with the growth of sub-contracting and the introduction of specialist firms, this tight control can be lost, the pattern changing with various groups reporting back to the builder at his office once they have completed their particular section of the work.

An experienced architect or surveyor or an assistant from the office will not be put out of countenance when he listens to an elderly carpenter who does not have a good word to say about a youthful electrician upon whom he is attending in order that they may jointly fix wiring under wood floorboards. Nor is the surveyor surprised if the joiner does not have a good word to say about the plumber or if all trades turn around and furiously denounce the plasterers and the painters. It must however, be admitted that while on a good Friday the surveyor sees such inevitable rivalry as a necessary part of the creative process, on a bad Monday with a streaming cold he may regard it as a perfect nuisance. The main reason why all architects and surveyors, united on this matter if no other, try to keep the lay client from visiting the site unless closely chaperoned is because of the disastrous effect some unforeseen encounter can have upon him. The assistant, architect or surveyor who accompanies the client is advised not to accost a solitary figure working silently in the corner in the hope of gaining information as to the progress of the work. The results may prove to be disappointing:

Assistant:	"This is the owner. He is Mr. Elias J. Snaggs, President of Leisure and Water Sports Industries Inc. He would like to know how things are going."
Plumber:	"I am glad he likes water as he is likely to see a lot of it."
Assistant:	"What do you mean?"
Plumber: (holding out a plastic object)	"Look at that. I told the boss what to get but he comes back with these. Anything to save fourpence. Water! your bloke is likely to be wading around in three feet of the stuff with these things put in."
Assistant:	"Is Mr. Jones about?"
Plumber:	"Not likely. You won't see him again now he's got his new girl friend."

We have so far dealt with those areas where the architect or surveyor or his assistant are well advised to tread with some delicacy. We now turn to the other side of the penny, since, in supervising the building work, approving the type and nature of materials employed and workmanship generally, the architect or surveyor or his representative have a direct and responsible role under the terms of the contract. Indeed this role is crucial since, once poor materials are passed or defective workmanship is accepted for payment, the client has little recourse to any other remedy than litigation with results that are often painful to everyone. We have already referred to the obvious but vital need for the architect or surveyor or any assistant to be competent in this respect. Not only have they the duty of judging the standard of the work as they see it at the time but also in trying to estimate whether things are likely to proceed smoothly until the next visit. Whoever is inspecting should therefore keep his eyes about him; refer to the drawings and specifications constantly and ask questions firmly and courteously. The omission of a membrane in cavity wall construction or the stop end of a gutter may well result in saturation and dry rot to the interior of a house and, with so many people coming and going on the building site, obvious omissions are made and whoever is inspecting must not be afraid to speak up. They should also watch out for defective workmanship and again point out anything that strikes them as being unusual or peculiar. It should not be thought that in doing this the architect or surveyor or his assistant will spend his visits in an atmosphere of chilly hostility. If he is pleasant in his manner, appreciative of the good things that he sees, apologises when he is at fault and is uncomplicated and direct in his approach, there is no reason why this should be so. Pointing the finger at one particularly horrible example of workmanship may reveal that "the gov'nor" was forced last Friday to introduce a man who was no good and who was promptly removed. Discussion will then reveal that everyone was extremely pleased to see him go and that the "gov'nor" has been warned in no uncertain terms that no one wants to see him come back. It should always be remembered that a craftsman who may spend months working at a house is likely to take a pride in the result of the work carried out by himself and his colleagues many of whom he may have known for years. If they see an effort being made to ensure that the working conditions are satisfactory, they are likely to respond and will certainly eye a young assistant with a benign air when he asks the builder to lay protective coverings on newly completed floors or staircase joinery and will be rather tickled if he enters into the usual wrangle in the continual and often unavailing attempt to ensure that materials are not left uncovered in the open air and that bags of cement and plaster are promptly stored under cover, with labels exposed, immediately on being unloaded from the lorry.

It is hoped that the architect, surveyor or assistant will do all they can to get on well with the Clerk of Works as ill-feeling here can prove disastrous. Even if an assistant does not feel that the figures produced by the Clerk of Works to check labour and materials are relevant to him personally, he should always look at them seriously and must learn to understand them. In daywork contracts the labour sheets are vital since, unless these are checked and followed up immediately, evidence of work may be lost and, in the absence of a quantity surveyor, severe difficulties may result in consequence. If a daywork contract is to be undertaken, it is vital that the costs should be agreed immediately after the sheets are received and the client notified. Suggestions that this turns the architect or surveyor into a site supervisor are absolutely correct as this is precisely what daywork contracts do in fact entail. The alternative to spending time on the site and checking daywork sheets is perhaps to spend them in a witness box at the High Court.

An assistant must not be afraid of making a fool of himself and joining in the general laughter when he puts his foot in it. It is easy to do this when one is young but later on, an assistant will be looked to for answers and will find it difficult to display ignorance. While it is possible that something that looks odd may be in order and in accordance with the contract, it is just as likely not to be and most architects and surveyors will remember instances in their early professional years when they did not speak out or were comforted with bland assurances which later turned out to be false. Thus experience is gained on the principle of "once bitten twice shy".

Perhaps the two most difficult areas for an assistant to deal with are, firstly, problems arising from variations in the original design and, secondly, the selection of different materials as alternatives to those specified, if this should be necessary. Often a well intended alteration, perhaps at the request of the client, such as a change in the position of a door, may lead to unforeseen complications later and the assistant may well be presented with such a problem and urged to find an immediate solution with the bricklayer and joiner standing by. He may be rash to do so. There are occasions when everything must be brought to a temporary halt and the matter looked into in rather greater detail as otherwise complication will mount on complication leading to a difficult situation nearer completion when it may be very difficult to put matters right. The question of new materials is one that can also rarely be satisfactorily resolved on the spot. If blocks of "slabbo" are being fixed to sections of "globbo" and the contractor says that he is unable to obtain the necessary "bondo" adhesive which the manufacturers recommend but that he has been able to produce "fixo" as an alternative, he may profess that he is in a difficulty but so will be the assistant who has a natural desire to help the contractor on the one hand but also feels that he cannot detract from the contractor's responsibility for the successful execution of the work on the other. Merely saying that the contractor must use the new adhesive at his own risk is hardly helpful as the contractor knows this already. He is not likely to seriously believe that in submitting the name of a new adhesive to the surveyor's assistant that this relieves him of all responsibility. He is more likely to feel that the surveyor's assistant may be more abreast of the technical digests and might have knowledge that could assist him. The matter might end with the architect or surveyor or the builder phoning the manufacturers, sorting out the matter between them, and recording the decision in the order book.

All architects, surveyors and their assistants should do all they can to smooth over points of difficulty. There may be an obvious coolness between the builder and a nominated sub-contractor and the builder may infer that he has not been properly made a party to an agreement between the architect or surveyor and a sub-contractor even although he is supposed to be responsible for it. There is often some truth in this and it is rather unwise of some architects or surveyors to make a great fuss of a nominated sub-contractor in the presence of the main contractor as this may lead to a certain taste of sour grapes. The practice of agreeing to aspects of the work with a nominated sub-contractor and failing to notify the main contractor can lead to all types of unimagined difficulty. This may sound obvious but provides a source of conflict more often than one might think.

Some of the general principles to be followed on all site inspections have now been discussed irrespective of whether the visit may be by prior arrangement or not. Now it is necessary to consider the procedures to be followed during the course of a typical job to ensure that at the completion the architect or surveyor can truthfully say that he has seen that most, if not all, of the critical points have been completed satisfactorily. Architects or surveyors know what these critical points are but it is necessary to establish procedures with the contractor so that he knows when to pause and call the architect or surveyor. In discussion it will often be found that what the professional man thinks of as a critical point is not necessarily the same as the contractors. In establishing these procedures and requiring them to be followed it is important to try and overcome the traditional impression which always seems to exist with contractors and their workforce that the purpose of the site inspection is to try and catch out the contractor in some improper practice. If site inspections do degenerate purely into a game of "hide and seek" then all trust must have been long lost. Any worthwhile contractor will readily acknowledge his duty and desire to complete a contract in a proper and workmanlike manner and will readily agree, if asked, that the architect or surveyor as agent of the employer also has an equally responsible duty to perform to see it to a satisfactory completion in the same manner.

Hopefully the contractor can be persuaded to adopt an attitude of some pleasure in consciously demonstrating to architect or surveyor that this or that item has been completed in accordance with the requirements. Such an attitude can be encouraged from the commencement of site work and suggested procedure to achieve this at all stages, will be discussed in the following chapter.

The architect or surveyor is well advised to obtain for himself the printed pads of forms produced either by the RIBA or the RICS for use in connection with building contracts. Such forms can be specially prepared and printed with the name of the architect or surveyor or his firm and cover the whole range of instructions likely to be issued under the terms of the contract from authorising variations to certifying, notifying or directing payments to be made. In the case of the forms issued as certificates for example, stamped with a serial number for reference in the architect or surveyor's office, spaces are provided for the basic information such as the site address and description of work and the name of the employer and his address against whom the certificate is drawn. The date of issue, the instalment number, contract and valuation dates and job reference have all to be filled in along with the name and address of the contractor to whom payment is to be made. The amount of the contract sum with gross amount due less retention is to be inserted in the form giving a calculated net amount which, less other sums previously certified gives, finally, the amount of the payment due to the contractor under the particular certificate concerned, which sum is exclusive of VAT. Separate copies are provided in pad form individually coloured for the contractor, employer, architect or surveyor and quantity surveyor to retain.

The architect or surveyor must, right from the outset of the contract, be careful not to overcertify payment when the various stages for issuing certificates are reached as set down in whatever type of contract is employed. Variation orders or instructions which will vary the contract sum should be carefully checked and provisional or prime cost sums and specified retention percentages must all be dealt with as stipulated under the terms of the contract.

Late payments by the Employer to the contractor or by the contractor to sub-contractors whether nominated or otherwise can disrupt the whole contract and confuse the system of cash discounts. The architect or surveyor should act firmly to ensure that the employer first of all honours his certificates and secondly takes a tough attitude with the contractors should they drag their feet over payments to sub-contractors. There are unfortunately some firms who delay payments to suit their own internal cash flow position which is a perfect nuisance. Nothing undermines confidence so much as trouble over money payments and this is one good reason why the architect or surveyor should maintain his own papers in impecable order so that no blame can be attached to him. There will be machinery under most contract provisions for monies to be paid direct to a sub-contractor where the main contractor defaults in payment but care should be taken, and advice sought if necessary under the provisions of the JCT Contract Form 1980 which are complex and as yet to a large extent untested.

In discussing the question of inspection in detail, the approximate order of construction is taken for the typical project envisaged by this book, that of an extension to an existing building with substantial repairs and improvements to the main structure. There will be digressions, as appropriate, for larger or smaller contracts or where the scope of the work is different in the case, for example, where similar repairs are being carried out to a number of buildings.

Chapter 12
Inspection of Work

CONTENTS

Section A
The Structure

Temporary Works

Arrangements for shoring must be made by the architect or surveyor and the duty of specifying what is needed falls squarely upon his shoulders. The architect or surveyor's responsibility for temporary works is wider than is generally supposed. He is not merely liable for positive errors in his specification but also for neglect to take action. In a leading case on the subject an architect's duty was found to extend to all persons likely to be closely and directly affected by his acts and omissions. Thus when a wall which had been purposely left standing after demolition but which then proved to be dangerous and collapsed, injuring a builder's workman, the architect could not escape liability merely on the grounds that his duty was only to his client. The Court of Appeal found that he should have foreseen that the builder's workmen would be affected by his carelessness and he was held to be responsible for the matter jointly with the contractors and the employers of the unfortunate workman.[1]

On large contracts, of course, the whole question of shoring is now a field for the specialist and the vast temporary structures formed of tubular steel noticed by the public in the heart of cities are set up by particular firms skilled in this work to the designs of an engineer. For most of the contracts envisaged within the scope of this volume, however shoring and temporary work will be a matter for collaboration between the architect or surveyor and the contractor, mainly employing timber both from the point of view of its familiarity and its adaptability with, possibly, the provision of steelwork either in the form of rolled steel joists to provide the appropriate rigidity for needles and the universal adjustable steel props which have proved such a boon to the small building firm in recent years. So useful are these props in fact and so inexpensive to employ that there is a danger that too much may be expected of them. One of the writers remembers a graphic story told to him by a colleague who was running a contract to take out and re-form the ground floor

(1) *Clay* v. *Crump & Sons Ltd.* (1963) 1QB 533. Also reported in the Estates Gazette, 21 September 1963 at Page 835.

accommodation of an old three storey commercial building in a south coast country town, bordering a fork in the main road. Unable to forget about the job over the weekend he travelled to the site and, with his torch on Saturday night, crawled through the mass of steel props, supporting the upper structure, to see that all was in order. He spent a restless night apprehensive lest a car should swerve off the road and bring down not only the props but the entire building as well. Fortunately, however, his doubts were dispelled when the workmen arrived on Monday morning and the amount of temporary steelwork gradually diminished.

The desire for economy in temporary work on the grounds that only a short time will elapse before the permanent works are constructed, in spite of its obvious lack of logic, nevertheless has a curious appeal. Since the lives of people can be put at peril, quite apart from the value of property, the cost of adequate temporary work must be faced. Building owners seldom object to the cost of adequate provision in this respect if properly advised. Failures have generally occurred due to a combination of two things; in the first place the architect or surveyor is unaware of the full extent of his duties and secondly the contractor has taken an unnecessary risk.

Shoring should be designed on the drawing board in the same manner as the permanent work. There is ample experience from the past to guide the architect or surveyor in this respect and the contractor should, it is to be hoped, have considerable experience of his own from other similar jobs. However, the provision of temporary work such as shoring is a classic case where success can only be achieved through a combination of sound design and adequate site supervision. The whole point of shoring is that the design provides for the weight of a structure to be taken on the the temporary work without any jarring or subsidence. But the shoring itself must first have a firm anchorage or base. Finally, the task must be accomplished of dismantling the temporary work in stages while the weight of the structure is gradually taken by the new work. The use of timber with folding wedges to allow for careful pinning up and to compensate for changes in temperature and humidity has been long established and extended by the use of the universal adjustable prop. Although considerable care is often taken in the preliminary operations carried out, the maintenance of shoring is often neglected. As mentioned earlier, shoring often remains in place for far longer than was contemplated and here the risk is that it will be entirely forgotten about so that in time defects gradually develop. The surveyor must always remember that periodic visits to supervise maintenance and to ensure that it is being carried out are a vital necessity.

There is little use in carefully designing shoring either in the form of lateral support to a wall as raking or flying shores or in making careful provision for carrying the weight of a structure by dead shoring to enable repairs to be carried out below if site supervision is lacking. Old walls bulge and lean. Rotted wood timbers concealed below a coating of rendering provide unpleasant surprises. Previous support, assumed to be present in an old structure from cross walls or partitions, often turns out to be non-existing. For all these reasons an initial site survey with plans and specifications of necessary arrangements for shoring may prove to be quite unsatisfactory if, on opening up, such features are revealed. The surveyor must be on the site with everyone else at an early stage in the work and not merely leave matters to the contractor. The latter naturally enough has enough worries on his mind at this time without having to find fault with the architect or surveyor's instructions and there have been cases where a nod is as good as a wink and Charlie's hand slips and a section of old and irreplaceable wall comes crashing down which was an important visual feature of the building under repair. Everyone naturally is very sorry but the architect or surveyor and his client are more sorry than the others.

There are therefore sound reasons why the precise steps to carefully pack out the face of an old irregular wall when using raking or flying shores should be specified by the surveyor. In the design of raking shores it is a basic principle that the thrust from the rakers must be counter-balanced. This may not be achieved due to an unexpected weakness in the structure, either on the plane of the vertical wall piece, or alternatively, in the composition of the brickwork above the needles. The lack of adequate measures to provide internal strutting or over-tightening wedges to a bulged wall may have disastrous results however well the raking shores are designed. Conversely, lack of adequate construction in the shores themselves either by way of foundation movement where the sole plate is carried on an inadequate grillage, unsatisfactory or inadequate lacing of timbers and similar matters may have a disastrous effect. Skill and understanding of the purpose of shoring is needed with both raking and flying shores. In the latter case, it may not be possible to form horizontal shores at actual floor levels but, if formed between window openings, wall pieces must be stiffened so that they are totally rigid otherwise the thrust from the horizontal shore will exert undue pressure on the unrestrained brickwork.

In the case of dead shoring it is obviously necessary not only to anticipate the type of load to be carried since, while a number of point loads can be sustained by providing a dead shore at each point, distributed loads where, for example, a wall plate carries a line of floor joists, need a rigid beam at the head of the dead shores or a "head tree" with dead shores and cill to provide continuous support. Similarly, dead shores in a vertical line, formed to take the load away from a wall must link up the main structural elements internally. This may seem obvious but up to now the architect or surveyor may only have been able to measure the building before any parts of the structure have been opened up so that it may only be at this stage when demolition has started that he will come across the surprises that old buildings have in store for everyone. Distributed loads may not after all be carried by horizontal beams as anticipated and floor joists may be suspended in a totally unexpected way while single floors may turn out to be of double or some irritating type of composite construction that frustrates the simple provisions made for dead shoring. Again, the surveyor may have accepted the comfortable principle of needle support for dead shoring in that reasonably sound brickwork may be expected to have the capacity to be self-supporting over distances of 1.5 to 1.8m. In old brick or stone walls however, which are poorly bonded or where the materials have crumbled, the intervals planned for needles may be inadequate or in some extreme cases the condition of the wall is such that further reinforcement or new brick or stonework has to be formed before needles can even be inserted. The need for needles to be totally rigid appears to be obvious but the writers have seen cases where any old sections of timber have been used and in one case a timber needle with a notable horizontal split along the line of the grain. This is where, it must be said, the introduction of steel offers much comfort.

The ground or floor base for cills to take dead shores must be inspected by the architect or surveyor. If a weakness develops in the base for one or more dead shores, leading to differential settlement in the structure above, the consequences are miserable for the architect or surveyor. Another weakness often found in dead shoring is that diagonal bracing is often neglected or omitted. A further item often conveniently overlooked is the need to strut window and door openings. Finally, the man with a heavy hammer should always be watched. Wedges in all types of shoring should be sufficiently tightened to take the load but not overtightened. Jarring when dust from a course of bricks over a window or doorhead can be seen proclaims that such bond there may have been now has been lost. Old walls are fragile and if shoring is not carried out with care, the whole point of employing it in the first place may be defeated.

While the provision of scaffolding and its maintenance may be a matter for the contractor, the architect or surveyor does well to inspect tubular steelwork and pass on any comments as he sees fit since there have been a number of disturbing cases of scaffolding collapses. Even if he is not primarily responsible, the architect or surveyor would not wish to be involved in such a case as this. Scaffolding boards on putlogs must be secured and ladders not merely left in place but tied to the framework. Some of the old painted ladders delivered to building sites have been rotting away quitely for years and these must be removed. Similarly the provision of appropriate coverings for protection of pedestrians, night lamps and the like are all legitimate fields for the architect's or surveyor's comments should shortcomings be seen. The architect or surveyor must also stress the importance of measures for safety and, when an instruction has been issued by the contractor regarding the use of safety helmets, the architect or surveyor should be sure that he wears one himself as an example.

Finally, before leaving this topic, we might stress the importance of safety in another context. Parts of the existing structure near building operations should be protected. In particular the care of trees is often overlooked where these are adjacent to routes taken by vehicles. Site safety from thieves or vandals is equally important as this can seriously affect and hold up a contract. Broken sanitary ware, graffiti on walls, smashed windows and the like have a disproportionately depressing affect on the morale of the building team. It has been known for the leadwork in a terrace of fourteen newly built houses to be stolen again and again, six times in all, on a site which was very vulnerable to thieves.

Excavations

The need for particular care and attention in regard to excavation work and foundations has long been known but has been highlighted in recent times.

In the late 1970's a good deal of publicity was rightly given to the alarming problems encountered by the National House Building Council due to faults found in the construction of new dwellings. Of the claims submitted to the Council for major structural defects, the overwhelming majority – 91 % – were claims in respect of defective sub-structures due partly to the use of bad land for building but also due to faulty infilling of sites prior to construction. We have written elsewhere[2] of the difficulties experienced by developers in recent years in finding adequate ground for building purposes, often owing to zoning restrictions, following on from the natural reluctance to allow good agricultural land to be used for building. These alarming faults however, caused the National House Building Council to take

(2) Structural Surveys of Dwelling Houses, published by the Estates Gazette Ltd.

drastic steps to limit their liability. The new six-point plan they produced contained a number of restrictions, among them being the requirement that private developers and builders should inform the Council two months in advance of any building land being found to be suspect so that special precautions, such as the employment of a consulting engineer, could be taken. A definition of what constituted bad ground was, from that time onward, included in the Council's general specifications. A further alteration however, was even more interesting in its implications. This went so far as to require the provision of suspended floor construction wherever infilling on sites would be in excess of 600mm. This was due to the fact that the Council had been forcibly made aware of the horrifying implications arising from the increased use of unweathered shale. Shale infill had been used in the north east for years with complete success but in the past shale had only been taken from the tips in relatively small quantities where it had remained exposed to the elements for a considerable period of time. The house building boom of the previous decade involved the use of unexpectedly large quantities of shale which had been allowed insufficient time to weather so that chemicals such as gypsum and alum had not leached out. The unweathered shale, when used as an infill, tended to swell from chemical change leading to sudden lifting in floors and superstructures. The defects were, for a while, quite inexplicable to the builders concerned but nevertheless led in some cases to the need for advanced structural repairs, and in some cases total rebuilding.

The repercussions from the spate of problems from poor foundations or bad ground in the 1970's have been widespread and one consequence has been the way in which the duties of the builder's site supervisor, building inspector and surveyor or architect have been re-defined in the Courts. The most famous case in this field is perhaps *Anns* v. *London Borough of Merton* (1977) 2 ALL ER 492 where the House of Lords decided, notwithstanding the doctrine of caveat emptor, that an owner/builder owed a duty of care in respect of the condition of the property to subsequent owners. It held, secondly, following the decision of the Court of Appeal in another well known case, that of *Dutton* v. *Bognor Regis UDC* (1972) 1 QB 373, that a building inspector who was the employee of a local authority could also incur liability in respect of the failure of foundations which he had passed as being adequate but which subsequently proved to be defective. As was widely expected at the time the decisions in these two cases led to others.

In the case of *Stewart* v. *East Cambridgeshire DC* (1979)[3] a house

(3) Estates Gazette 15 December 1979. Page 1105.

was to be constructed on a gravel pit that had since been filled and although the local authority called in consulting engineers, subsequent settlement occurred and the structure of the house proved to be defective. In this case, however, it was held that the building inspector, having followed the advice of the engineers as to the depth of foundations necessary, had done all he could to inspect the trenches and ensure that they were adequate. Since deep piling only would have prevented subsequent settlement and damage to the house, the case then turned on the single point as to whether the building inspector could have been expected to have taken any further steps or to have acted in any different way. The Judge found however, that since a building inspector only had limited qualifications and could not be expected to exercise the same standard of knowledge or care as a civil engineer, chartered architect or chartered surveyor, he had done everything that could reasonably have been expected of him and that he had not accordingly been negligent. The result of this case leads one to the logical if gloomy conclusion that, had the building inspector been a chartered surveyor for example, he would have been found negligent.

In the case of *Acrecrest Ltd.* v. *W. S. Hattrell & Partners and the London Borough of Harrow* (1979)[4] the plaintiffs constructed some blocks of flats in Harrow in 1971. There were two defendants, the first being the firm of architects employed to design the flats and supervise the work, the second being the local authority for the area who were involved as administrators of the Building Regulations. The architects had originally specified strip foundations to an approximate depth of 1,075mm but since evidence of tree roots was found in some of the foundation trenches, the building inspector specified that some parts of the foundations had to be increased to a depth of 1,500mm. Subsequent to construction however, severe cracking occurred to the structure and the Judge found, upon the evidence supplied, that the cause of the cracks was due to "heave" or the swelling of the sub-soil by the absorption of water. It was submitted in evidence and accepted by the Judge that the moisture would normally have been absorbed by trees but since the original fruit trees on the site had all been taken away and a row of Elms, which were later, after the flats were built, found to be suffering from Dutch Elm disease, were felled, the moisture content of the sub-soil was much higher than it otherwise would have been.

Since the architects admitted negligence, the case proceeded against the second defendants only who were the local authority, or more specifically the building inspector in this instance, who denied

(4) Estates Gazette 15 December 1979. Page 1107.

liability. It was however, found by the Judge that if a 1,500mm foundation depth had been specified throughout the whole site, the damage would have been either prevented or at least reduced and the case then revolved around the duty of care to be expected from the building inspector of the London Borough of Harrow in the supervision of the foundations. It was decided firstly that, following the Anns case, the building inspector did indeed owe a duty of care to the person or organisation relying upon his supervision of the foundations and whose interests were later adversely affected by a breach in that duty. The second and more interesting point, however, arose when the local authority submitted that, even if their building inspector was negligent in not requiring foundations 1,500mm in depth throughout the site, they were responsible only for the foreseeable consequences of this negligence. This should not be inflated by the extra damage due to the subsequent removal of the Elm trees owing to their infection from disease. The judge, decided however, that even with the knowledge available in 1972, there were enough foreseeable hazards to render the inspector negligent in not requiring 1,500mm foundations throughout the site as the damage was of a type which could reasonably have been foreseen and that the defendants were therefore liable for such damage notwithstanding the fact that the precise manner in which it occurred was not in itself foreseeable.

This case highlights the dangers to the professional man that are implicit in the concept of foreseeable risk. Although all the planning and design work has been completed, the results of tests and analysis of the sub-soil known and approved, nevertheless it is at this stage before the first sod is cut that the architect or surveyor should look around the site, clear his mind of his clients and his own pressures and try to foresee any risks that may suddenly become recognisable at the last minute. If the reader quite reasonably enquires whether it is not too late to make alterations in the design or construction at this last stage, it should always be remembered that the last chance of avoiding some future disaster might well be lost in a few days or even a few hours. The architect or surveyor is urged to look round the site, examine the surface soil and vegetation and look over adjoining land, if this is sufficiently near, so as to make himself aware of any new conditions or conditions not previously observed.

Where building contracts for the substantial repair of houses involve the replacement of part of the structure, including services, and the construction of new additions will involve excavation, it is a convenient starting point to assume that the ground is untouched except for a number of trial holes dug to a substantial size

900mm × 900mm to a depth of say 2,700mm provided with covers which the architect or surveyor should have specified in order to avoid any possibility of an accident. The scene is set therefore for the architect or surveyor and the builder, armed with the results only of the analysis from soil samples supplied to the laboratory to walk across and examine the trial holes to ensure that these are not waterlogged, for example, due to some unforeseen set of circumstances, before the excavators arrive. Even if soil sampling has been carried out by auger, perhaps more common nowadays, perambulation of the site is still advisable with the results of the soil analysis as a prelude to the works. After all, the soil sampling cannot tell the whole story.

Such a precautionary review of the situation before the arrival of the contractors work force will probably be combined with an introductory visit to those who are perhaps going to remain in occupation of existing premises while, say, an extension is being built. The architect or surveyor will introduce the contractor and his foreman to the lady of the house, in the case of domestic premises, or the office or factory manager where a commercial or light industrial building is concerned. The arrangements for keeping the respective parties apart during building operations will be settled, their respective areas for operation will be defined and methods to protect existing premises from the ravages of nearby building operations will be discussed and settled. In the case of domestic premises the preservation of as much of the existing garden as possible will loom quite considerably in the minds of the client and his family. In whatever circumstances however, it will be necessary for the architect or surveyor to ensure compliance with the decisions taken at that time so that relations get off to a good start and do not deteriorate later owing to encroachments by either party on the sphere of the other. Undue restrictions imposed by either the architect or the surveyor or the client at the time specification and drawings are prepared can be counter-productive in the long run and it may well be necessary to agree variations in this respect with all parties at this time for the sake of future relations if the contractor presses the point.

Temporary fencing and protection works of the above nature will be inspected, probably at the same time as the contractor asks the architect or surveyor to check the setting out of any new extension which he is entitled to do under the terms of the JCT Form of Contract. The contractor will set up profiles beyond the immediate area of the work to show the extent of oversite clearance and the line of foundation trenches both for external walls and internal partitions. The centre line of walls will be indicated on the profiles probably with a stout nail so that with twine stretched taughtly between the profiles, the surveyor will be able to check by himself using a steel tape that the dimensions on site correspond with those indicated on the drawings. He must also check the setting out for squareness by measuring diagonals carefully to ensure they are identical for proposed rectangular structures if that is what is intended. Sometimes it may be necessary to use a level or theodolite for setting out more complicated shapes and of course the same instrument would be needed for checking purposes. The former instrument will of course be required for checking at a later stage on the level of ground floor or basement slabs which is a factor on which the architect or surveyor both have to agree with the contractor under the terms of the JCT Contract. It is very important that the architect or surveyor is quite clear in regard to his responsibility for agreeing the setting out of new structures. If he is not available to do so and cannot make himself available or if he declines to attend to check on the principle "Oh, I expect it is all right" then his client will have to accept the sizes as provided by the contractor or the client will have to pay to have them altered and possibly recover the cost from his professional adviser. Once, however, the setting out at ground level has been checked and agreed, the responsibility for establishing correct dimensions and levels subsequently rests squarely on the contractor and any mistakes will fall to be corrected at his expense not on that of the client.

When existing premises remain occupied the connection between the new extension and the old building is often one of the last items to be performed under the contract. It is therefore vitally important at setting out stage to ensure the relationship between the two is going to turn out as intended, otherwise there will be more than red faces involved if wall or floor surfaces do not line up where expected. The tolerances which might be acceptable in some cases of entirely new construction do not apply to alterations and extension work and a degree of precision, unfortunately not familiar to some contractors, is required and has to be insisted upon.

In former times when top soil was removed and excavation, both over the site and for foundations and other purposes, was carried out by hand, the architect or surveyor had the valuable benefit of being able to ask the foreman of the excavating team how his men were finding things and receiving a suitably informative reply, highly coloured perhaps in the event of unpopular obstacles such as large lumps of stone being unexpectedly encountered. The speed, or rather lack of it, of the traditional excavating process gave the architect or surveyor plenty of time to walk around the site and form his own conclusions as to what was being exposed without in any way holding up progress. The difficulty under present circum-

513

stances, convenient though modern excavating machinery may be, even for a small contract, is that the process may finish almost as soon as it starts and the surveyor then finds himself being pressed for a decision to approve the excavations almost before he knows that digging has begun. A problem with modern excavators is that whereas top soil can obviously vary in depth from say 65mm to 650mm, the excavator is likely to set his machine to clear the site to an average depth of 230mm to 250mm irrespective. If the architect or surveyor does not arrive quickly and the machinery is deployed elsewhere, a cry of outrage will greet his request that the machine be returned to the site as more excavation is needed. Similarly, where trenches are excavated by machine, the surveyor often has to be content with examining the spoil from the excavation himself rather than receive an appraisal of any deleterious matter found by a labourer from his own experience with a spade. It is for this reason that the architect or surveyor has to be particularly careful, when trench bottoms are compacted, that no injurious matter remains.

If the architect or surveyor has not been able to inspect the excavations in progress, not as unlikely a situation in present day circumstances as we have seen, he will no doubt receive a peremptory telephone call to the effect that the foundations are ready for inspection and approval and the building inspector will be summoned to attend if the surveyor will name the day and time, "preferably tomorrow, as the machines will be leaving then". The opportunity will then arise to put some of the onus of following the specification straight back on to the contractor. The contractor should be asked whether he is sure that all requirements have been followed, that all deleterious matter removed, all bottoms made ready and the excavations free of water. If the contractor is quite satisfied he can be told by all means to send the machine away as, of course, in the unlikely event of any further work required it can be dealt with by hand tools. The contractor should also be told not to contact the building inspector until such time as the excavations have been approved by the architect or surveyor. The contractor's response to this reply to his telephone call is often quite salutory. There will be a momentary silence and then a promise to phone back when a check has been made.

By taking this attitude at the beginning of the contract the architect or surveyor will make it quite clear that the contractor is to satisfy him in the performance of the specification not to present him, as is so often the case, with a half prepared site which will cause the architect or surveyor many trips backwards and forwards until he is satisfied. Contractors know perfectly well what is required but the natural tendency is to the minimum of excavation. The contractor is not responsible for subsequent defects due to foundation failures if the foundations have been approved by the client's representative and the local authority, (always supposing there has been no deliberate concealment by the contractor of bad conditions or workmanship). Accordingly, many contractors are happy to summon the architect or surveyor when only the minimum has been done and await directions "to take out a bit more here" and so on. Unfortunately many surveyors and architects are guilty of a similar attitude themselves in relation to the local authority and are quite prepared, supposedly in their client's financial interests, not to instruct the contractor to do more work than will satisfy the building inspector. No self respecting architect or surveyor should adopt this attitude since as the case of *Stewart* v. *East Cambridgeshire DC* mentioned on page 509, established, he is expected to have a greater professional knowledge and exercise a greater degree of care than the building inspector and therefore must, in his client's interests, be the prime decider of what is satisfactory or not. It would seem degrading for an architect or surveyor to accompany a building inspector on a tour of excavations and wait to be told that further work needs to be done before the building inspector will pass the excavations except in very rare circumstances, related probably to special needs in a particular area. What should happen is that the contractor thoroughly satisfies himself in the first instance, then calls the architect or surveyor and it is at this point that the architect or surveyor must allow himself time to make a very thorough inspection and check the work so far carried out on the site.

It is probably best for the architect or surveyor to check first that the excavations are dimensionally in compliance with the requirements of the specification and drawings. The contractor's setting out will already have been verified but the twine will be needed again to be stretched out along the centre line of walls and partitions so that not only are the widths of the foundations trenches checked but also that the sides are equidistant from the centre line. Any deviation in excess of about 20mm to 30mm will require correction by the contractor at his expense since it is important that walls sit centrally on foundations so as to avoid any tendency to tilt. Next, a level will be required so that the surveyor can check that the depths below the datum for the clearance of oversite vegetable soil and for the bottoms of foundations have been achieved. Depending on whether the site is sloping or not this will either be a simple operation or one complicated by the need to check that sufficient space has been allowed to form the appropriate overlap of a minimum of 300mm at changes of level (or the depth of the foundation whichever is the greater) without any part of the bottoms of the foundation being too near the surface. The contractor will be eager to point out any excavation in excess of the requirements of the specification and drawings, and the reason for it, but not so keen as to indicate any at a lesser depth. The check at this stage will however, establish precisely whether, and by how much more or less, the excavations depart from the requirements of the specification and drawings. A careful record, of course, will be taken with measurements so that any variations by way of saving or extra can be valued at a later date.

The architect or surveyor will next wish to walk the excavations and with his own eyes examine the oversite surface and the sides and bottoms of the trenches. He will be looking to see whether the contractor's men have missed any pockets of rubble, waste material, decaying wood or household refuse and that any footings from old walls, trees or bush stumps and roots have all been removed. This is particularly important since an extension to a house is more often than not built over part of the existing house garden which, in its day, may have been the repository for all sorts of rubbish when the original house was built and subsequently may have had its levels altered by the construction of terraces, steps and paths not to mention the enthusiastic gardener's attentions in the way of planting. Any such areas found must be dug out and this work is much better done by hand under careful supervision so that a satisfactory bottom and clean sides are formed. Some of the past history of the garden may be seen in the sides of the trenches and these must be examined for evidence of made up ground, particularly if made up or any other poor ground is in strata form and dips down so that it appears in the bottom of the excavated trenches. If this is the case then the poor ground must be taken out and a new sound bottom found over the affected area at a greater depth.

To conclude, the final stage of the architect or surveyor's inspection will consist of sounding the bottom of the trenches to be sure that what is seen at the bottom of the excavations continues for a reasonable depth below and is not just a few inches of good soil overlying an area of poor ground. The soil investigation will already have provided information to establish that this could not be the case over the whole of the site, otherwise the desirability of using a form of foundations other than the strip foundations being discussed here, would have arisen. The architect or surveyor will be looking for pockets of poor soil which might give cause to partial and differential settlement at a later date in the new structure. The architect or surveyor will therefore need to check the bottom of excavations at about intervals of a metre along the line of all new walls and partitions, but paying particular attention, and perhaps halving the interval between probes, to corners and wall junctions where the effect of partial settlement would be particularly severe. The testing would be carried out with pointed metal rods about 19mm in diameter driven down into the soil with a sledge hammer for a depth equivalent to about $1\frac{1}{2}$ times the width of the foundation, down to the lowest level of the stress envelope. If rods are chosen of a length equivalent to this depth plus the depth proposed for the concrete foundation, or slightly more if required, then if all is well the rods can be driven down and be left as markers or indicators for the appropriate depth of concrete when this is placed at a later date. On being driven down, sound uniform soil will be indicated by decreasing penetration on each blow as the depth increases. If the penetration per blow suddenly increases then a weak strata will have been discovered and it will be a matter of further investigation and excavation to establish the full extent and for the weaker soil to be removed.

The architect or surveyor having satisfied himself that a satisfactory bottom for the foundation has been prepared, even if this involves going away and making a further visit or visits at a later date, will no doubt agree at this stage the extent of the variations from the work set out in the specification and shown on the drawings. Arrangements can then be made for the building inspector or district surveyor to attend for the now hoped for formality of giving his approval under the Building Regulations or By-Laws as the case may be. The architect or surveyor should of course accompany the officer on the inspection in order to answer any questions as to why extra excavations may have had to be carried out and of course the architect or surveyor will wish, himself, to see the outcome of any verification probes which the officer may himself wish to see carried out. Should any probes be made equidistant between those made by the surveyor he can at least feel satisfied that any remaining pocket of weak soil must be very localised indeed. Even if such a pocket had been missed and not taken out, the likelihood of damage to the structure would have been highly unlikely, given the ability of unreinforced foundation concrete to span a metre or so in normal circumstances, without deflection. Such a discovery could however, lead to a joint decision to excavate and remove the pocket of poor soil in the event of it being found, to extend the removal to the full interval of a metre between the architect or surveyor's probes and to the full width of the foundation above. More likely, however, if it was a smaller pocket, that both inspector and architect or surveyor would be able to agree the size and extent of some mesh reinforcement for the bottom of the concrete foundations at that point as an added precaution.

Once the excavations have been approved the contractor can be instructed to fill any additional excavation, over and above that specified, with weak concrete 1:12 to bring to the level of the underside of the foundations shown on the drawing and proceed to concreting the foundations as soon as possible. No sensible contractor allows his excavations over this period to become damaged by the weather and thereby need re-bottoming, involving as it does additional labour, and either restoring to the correct level with weak concrete or, if he prefers, with extra brickwork above the foundation concrete but nevertheless all at his sole expense. However, it is wise to suggest to the contractor that he takes the necessary precautions against bad weather with trestles, tarpaulins or polythene as he may decide and furthermore to ensure, should the weather in fact worsen, that such precautions have been taken before the concreting begins. A special visit should be made for this purpose if necessary. Bad weather, however, is not the only cause of water appearing in the excavations. Water can also rise in the excavations where these are below the water table or due to other reasons.

For example, if it is the case that the position of a building is such that surface water will drain towards it, land or other drains should be laid to divert the water away from the site. Under such circumstances, of course, the architect or surveyor will have made any necessary and appropriate provision, in advance of this stage, in his specification. However, it is also necessary that all excavations should be cleared of ground water before concrete is laid but here pumping operations should be carried out with care and should not be permitted to disturb the ground outside the limits of the excavation or remove the grout when concrete is freshly-laid. Many architects and surveyors will have seen a rich brown slurry pouring from pumps when this happens. The discovery of an unsuspected spring occurs on occasions but the important thing here is for the architect or surveyor to prevent the builder from merely covering up the source or attempting to block it temporarily. The more expensive but necessary measure of draining the outlet of a spring clear of the site is, for obvious reasons, absolutely vital, and architect or surveyor and contractor will need to investigate the best way for this to be done. Ingenious attempts to divert the water to discharge into a nearby storm water system of drains may not meet with the approval of the inspector from the local authority who may have some forceful words to say on the subject.

Other problems of course do arise during the excavation process and the architect or surveyor needs to ensure that the sides of the excavations for foundations are well formed and vertical. Problems often occur in loose ground or clay soils where the sides may dry out and crumble. As a result the sides of the excavation will fall into the trenches and although planking and strutting will prevent this and the builder may originally have made adequate provision in this respect, it is just possible that the figure for this work may have been pruned, along with a number of other items in order to provide a more acceptable tender. As a result the contractor may be inert when it comes to making tiresome arrangements for extra labour and materials when he knows that the ready mixed concrete truck is on its way. In cases where the architect or surveyor suspects that soil is mixed with the concrete he must require part of the foundations to be taken out in order to see what has happened. It is not necessary to enlarge upon the unpopularity of such a step. The contractor often assumes that blinding the foundations trenches with a thin layer of concrete is quite adequate and will last for days if necessary. The current British Standard Code of Practice however, specifies that excavations in clay, soft chalk or other soils are liable to be affected by exposure to the atmosphere and that trenches should be concreted as soon as possible after they have been dug. Where this is not possible the bottom of the excavations should be protected immediately by 75mm thickness of lean concrete additional to the foundation concrete and, in order to obtain a dry hard bottom, the last few inches of excavation should only be removed immediately before concreting. Special circumstances such as this should, of course, be covered by the specification. Clay however, is notoriously difficult to consolidate, even when quickly excavated and back filled and it is of course preferable in all cases that the concreting be carried out as quickly as possible.

It is understandable, in the circumstances, that contractors pressurise architects and surveyors to make quick decisions and move with expedition at this time. The architect or surveyor must correspondingly make himself available to attend when required within a reasonable time and, in order to ensure that the Employer's interests are fully protected, to attend, perhaps surprisingly to the contractor, at other unexpected times. Inconvenient this may be perhaps, but, on the other hand, there can hardly be a more vital stage in building operations and on no account should the architect or surveyor allow the contractor's desire for speed to prevent the proper examination and consideration of all the available evidence to enable the correct decisions to be taken at this time before authority is given for the concrete to be laid.

Where reinforced concrete foundations are provided, the bottom of any excavation must of course be covered with a 75mm thickness of plain concrete additional to the reinforced concrete, or be covered and protected by building paper or other means so that the reinforcement can be correctly positioned and so that any admixture of the soil in the concrete forming the cover to the reinforcement may be prevented. It can be extremely difficult always to ensure that such recommendations are carried out on the site but vital to do so. In the noise and confusion of busy building operations, standing in a thin drizzle of rain, the architect or surveyor might think wistfully of the pleasant task of drafting a specification in a dry office but one matter that he must certainly enforce is the adequate preparation of ground to receive reinforced concrete foundations since otherwise, if sufficient attention is not given to the bed and spacing of the reinforcement rods, dire results may follow. Although the duty of supervision may be in the hands of consultant engineers so many mistakes have been made in the past from haste or thoughtlessness that the architect or surveyor must keep his eyes open even if he cannot intervene on the site but merely puts a telephone call through to the engineers office.

Particular care should be taken in the excavation and layout of trenches for drains and services. These are likely to be below the level of the underside of any adjacent foundations but they should not be formed nearer than a line drawn at an angle of 45° to the horizontal from the nearest lower edge of such foundations in stable soils, and 30° in the case of wet clays. If it is essential to construct trenches within these limits, the trenches should be filled with weak concrete up to the level of the underside of the adjacent foundations or alternatively, the foundations should be specifically designed to suit the new conditions. Often if unexpected obstructions occur which mean that a drain trench cannot run in the straight line shown on the drawing, consultation is necessary to re-plan the drain run and perhaps provide an additional manhole and extra excavation may well be needed at this stage. Otherwise the architect or surveyor may find that the new drain is formed to a gentle parabola on plan so as to overcome the obstruction without fuss leading to subsequent perplexity when the drain is later blocked following completion of the contract. Excavation of the land at the point where the drain is thought to be then leads to the complete puzzlement of all parties.

The alterations in the standards recommended for drainage installations by the Building Research Establishment and other bodies are fundamental when compared with traditional methods and this, combined with the fact that a wide variety of materials is now available for both rigid and flexible pipe runs may sound as if drain laying is simpler and more straightforward than in times gone by. The reverse is the truth. The defects in existing drains highlighted by the Building Research Establishment and referred to elsewhere[5] show that far from defects in drains becoming less

(5) The (Repair and Maintenance) of Houses, published by the Estates Gazette Ltd.

common, failures are on the increase, both in design and construction. Architects and surveyors must keep themselves abreast as to information on the nature and cause of failures in drains varying from traditional problems, such as cracking in rigid pipes due to poor jointing or the incorrect use of modern materials, to poor design and construction in pitched fibre pipes or flexible joints used in wrong conditions, so as to be better aware of what to watch for during construction. Many faults occur from careless or incorrect back filling and the architect or surveyor does well to control and regulate both the quality of the back fill, whether granular or otherwise, to see that this is properly compacted in layers and, should local difficulties occur in the ground necessitating an alteration from the specification, that the correct types of alternative pipe are employed. A common fault is to employ the incorrect type of pipe and construction where pipes run below or through brick walls. Faults have also been found in modern drainage installations at the linkage points with soil pipes and manoles, often when purpose made concrete manholes are employed to save the cost and labour of forming brick built manholes of conventional pattern.

The architect or surveyor must also keep an eye on trenches dug for the public services. The Water Authority will only bring its supply to the boundary of the site in new construction but also within the context of this book old water mains may need renewal and although the depths may be pre-determined, nevertheless correct excavation and bedding of the pipes is just as important here as elsewhere. Other authorities like to use their own labour in providing services to a building which makes sense from the point of view of their ultimate liability, but co-operation with the main contractor is essential in order to ensure that the work is properly carried out.

We have already referred to the problems found, particularly in post-war houses, due to the use of unsuitable materials and what the engineers call, in a graphic phrase, "aggressive ground conditions". Of nearly 2,000,000 tons of waste material produced annually in this country, half consists of mine or quarry waste while the remainder is essentially formed of industrial or domestic debris. While industrial wastes include such items as inert hard granular material such as slag, pottery debris or brick rubble, contamination with chemicals, particularly those that are likely to be injurious to concrete, is always a potential hazard. Any acidic content is dangerous and the calcium salts contained in cement are soluble in nearly all mineral or organic acids. Other "aggressive" wastes include copper compounds, creosote, glucose, glycerine, gasworks lime, vegetable oils, sewage, sugars and particularly sulphates.

Sulphates are notorious for the disastrous effect they have upon concrete. The chemical products of sulphate attack occupy a larger volume than the original compound. This expansion causes rapid disintegration since cracked zones display new cement paste for further attack so that an almost continuous cycle is set up. It should not be forgotten that until recently, high alumina cement was occasionally used when sulphates were found to be present until it was found that the high temperatures generated during hydration caused more problems than the sulphate attack which it was intended to prevent.

It is for all these reasons that the architect or surveyor must look very carefully at all hardcore delivered to the site to see that it is in accordance with the specification. The constituent parts may be soft or liable to crumble into material that is too fine for the purpose and then be unsuitable, or worse, contain deleterious materials such as lumps of old wood, plasterboard, branches of trees or just plain rubbish. Unsuitable hardcore must be ruthlessly refused. The methods by which hardcore is laid must also be supervised with care. The use of a roller to consolidate layers no thicker than 225mm must be employed with caution as a heavy roller will reduce hardcore to a rigid mass and totally destroy its drainage characteristics, either by crushing the larger lumps into small particles or by forcing the hardcore into the sub-soil so that the interstices are filled. It should not be forgotten that the composition of hardcore is prescribed for a purpose and is not simply a cheap way of providing a sub-layer to concrete. Since ash is now hard to come by the surveyor will hardly ever see the surface of the hardcore blinded with this material but a layer of sand will then be needed and it is hoped that the specification will also provide for a layer of polythene or bitumen felt lapped 150mm at joints and turned up against the outside or partition walls for a depth equal to the thickness of the oversite concrete and finishes. This sheeting will serve to separate the two structures of wall and floor so that they can settle independently if necessary and will also act to prevent the cement from the concrete penetrating into the blinding and act as a barrier to damp rising into the slab which, in some circumstances, might carry sulphates which would attack the cement in the concrete.

It is not unusual for paths or garage entrances, main sewers and drains to be constructed before the extensions are erected and the current British Standard Code of Practice sees no objection to this practice and indeed regards it is as being advantageous. Excavations for driveways or paths, however, being shallower than for buildings, are more likely to have soft spots requiring greater depth of hardcore, but drainage of the sub-soil is vital as otherwise frost action can break up the surface. The question of existing land drains on a site should never be overlooked and cases have been known where an existing system of drains has been cut, with dire results at a later stage. Heavy lorries continually passing and re-passing on hardcore laid to a driveway, before the tarmacadam surface is provided, may have a ruinous effect and this point should be brought to the builders attention since, although his interest at the time may centre largely in the delivery of materials, adequate completion of the site works depends on care at the commencing and middle stages of the contract. The stability of the surface of the driveway and paths depends very much upon the quality of the base and the provisions made for drainage. The hardcore should be firm without uneven or soft areas and rolling should be firm but not excessively so. Detailing is important from the point of view of drainage, and manholes should be carefully formed and finished so that the road surface can be bedded neatly around them. Concrete access roads or paths should be laid in bays to allow for expansion and the joints filled to prevent growth of moss or weeds. Particular care should be taken to clear out mud and rubbish from surface water gulleys and drains at the completion of the contract, a point which is often overlooked.

Concrete Work

During the years following the Second World War the future of new construction whether for domestic, commercial or industrial purposes seemed to lie in the use of reinforced concrete. Recently however, a spate of failures has been revealed to a horrified general public arising from the use of the wrong materials or additives, such as High Alumina Cement or calcium chloride, or basic failures in workmanship and supervision such as a laxity in ensuring that concrete is both able to pass between reinforcing rods where these are laid horizontally to floor or roof slabs. It seems inconceivable that anyone could specify aggregate that cannot pass between reinforcing rods to provide the appropriate cover but it needed the blast of a bomb in Northern Ireland some years ago to alert those concerned with modern buildings to the fact that in many recent structures there is a fair chance that reinforcing rods may be provided with a bare minimum of enclosing concrete or, in some cases, no concrete to speak of at all.

We are not concerned with major failures in concrete construction within the terms of this volume but any architect or surveyor who has passed under a motorway bridge or who has examined the exterior of a concrete building in detail will have noticed tell tale signs of brown staining which indicates that the cover for the reinforcement rods is quite insufficient. The sad fact is that in small projects, as in large ones, failures in concrete construction occur because the pouring or laying of concrete is always rushed without any good reason. It is true that the rise of specalists and sub-contractors has meant that the provision of reinforced concrete may now be one of many specialist activities but this is not necessarily so in the case of smaller contracts. "Readymix" trucks will be seen poised for instant departure while the concrete is frantically poured and tamped as if everyone's life depended on the work being completed as speedily as possible. It is quite beyond reason that hours spent in the careful calculation of reinforcement and the accurate specification of the constituent parts of concrete should be rendered useless due to needless haste or sloppy workmanship. The fact remains however, that more and more discoveries are being made to show that this is precisely what has happened and there can only have been a lamentable lack of close supervision by contractors of their workforce and of periodic supervision by surveyors, architects and engineers.

On all sites where concrete is to be made it is necessary for the architect or surveyor to ensure that the constituent materials are sound and adequate. Sand for concrete work, for example, should be "sharp", an expression which may mystify the trainee architect or surveyor, but the difference between a good pit sand and the type of sand that one sees on the sea-shore cannot be mistaken. Salts should be excluded from concrete and one traditional way of making sure that sand is not salty is to wet a sample with the tip of the tongue. If the central heating contractor and his assistants in fashionable jeans and sweaters pass by at the particular time, glances will be exchanged to the effect that there is obviously an eccentric loose on the building site, but the architect or surveyor will have to bear this, in common with many other professional duties, with fortitude. It is of equal consequence to ensure that there is no deposit of clay or loam in the sand delivered to the site and the traditional way again of ascertaining if sand is clean is either to rub some particles in the hands or alternatively between two sheets of white paper. If in further doubt, the method of mixing sand in a glass jar with water is still valid. If allowed to settle for three hours any clay or impurities will rise to the top and if in excess of 6% of the total depth this can be pointed out to the contractor who will have to be told to reject it.

Sand is one of the building materials that is most commonly found to be impure when delivered to the site and every effort must be made to ensure that only clean sand is delivered and used. Sand should also be well graded from 5mm down and it is as wrong to have too many large grains as it is to have too many small grains; there needs to be a fair balance of all sizes of grain from the maximum size to the minimum but with the balance tilted slightly in favour of the larger. Selecting a sample and examining it closely should give a good indication of whether it is well graded or not. If a batch of sand has to be rejected for one reason or another, the contractor will not be complying with the specification and should be asked to produce a certificate for the next batch from his supplier to guarantee that the sand complies with the appropriate British Standard. The point will have been made and it is probable that the contractor will test the next batch himself before the surveyor has the opportunity to see it, as he will probably not wish to be caught out again.

A further problem can arise from old or contaminated bags of cement hopefully brought from another job where these were turned away by the site supervisor. Old or stale cement can be slow to harden and be of reduced strength so that old bags with hard lumps which cannot be easily powdered in the hand must be rejected. On the other hand, however, fresh cement will set very quickly, perhaps preventing the mix being properly placed and tamped if too much is being attempted with one batch. Once the set has started the concrete must be left as it is and not be subjected to further movement, for example, being stirred while additives are poured in. Any measures to retard or speed up the setting or hardening of concrete should be viewed with suspicion, require the closest of supervision and should only be adopted in exceptional circumstances. If sulphate resisting cement has been specified the surveyor will of course check that this indeed has been supplied. Proper storage is vital.

It goes without saying that the water used in concrete construction must be pure, at least fit for drinking, and this seems self-evident until one has had some experience of the strange shifts to which builders are occasionally put in order to supply water to the site. Architects and surveyors should take much more pains than they often do to ensure that fresh water is available to the contractor rather than merely putting in a standard clause in the specification saying that the contractor is expected to make his own arrangements regarding water supply.

The remaining constituent of concrete, the coarse aggregate, is of vital importance since it forms the bulk of the concrete mix. Even grading of aggregates is a necessity for all concrete work but it is also important that the coarse aggregate for the weaker plain concrete in foundations, beds for drains and for oversite work does not get mixed up or confused with the aggregate for the stronger concrete required for reinforced work. This may happen when work is being carried out within an existing building as well as on an extension and also perhaps where work is proceeding on a number of adjacent buildings but the work is at different stages in each. For plain mass concrete in foundations and oversite the range of particles can be from 40mm down to 5mm but for reinforced work the maximum size should not exceed the size of the reinforcement being used otherwise it will not pass between the reinforcing rods and between the rods and the shuttering. Obviously it is not too bad if the aggregate intended for reinforced work becomes used for mass concrete, although uneconomical from the contractor's point of view since he can hardly claim the difference in cost from the client as an extra. However, as discussed, it can be disastrous if the reverse happens.

The architect or surveyor can check the grading of the aggregate delivered to the site by taking a bucketful from the centre of the batch and tipping it on to a hard smooth surface, mixing it thoroughly, flattening to a pile about 100mm high and dividing it into quarters. It is necessary to ensure that the sample is a fair one as in the normal course of delivery the finer material in any batch tends to end up on top. Taking from the centre of the pile should overcome this difficulty. Two of the quarters from opposite corners should be stored as a future reference sample whereas the remainder can be re-mixed and spread out for closer examination. It should now be possible to assess whether there is a fair balance of material of all sizes from the largest specified to the smallest. At the same time, by taking a fistful of the aggregate and squeezing it into a ball it is possible to gauge whether it contains too much clay or loam. If the aggregate is clean the ball will fall apart when the hand is opened; no material adhering to any other.

In the same way as with the supply of sand, aggregates can be obtained from reputable suppliers with a certificate and guarantee that they comply with the appropriate British Standards, washing and sieving being carried out mechanically at the plant so that the batches delivered are clean and well graded. Most contractors are only too happy to reassure the architect or surveyor with the production of certificates and it is perhaps only when the architect or surveyor is not shown such certificates and believes that the contractor is using his own material that he may wish to check on sizes and cleanliness in the way described.

All the good work put into the design and specification of concrete work will come to nought if the making and placing is carelessly carried out. By now the surveyor will be getting to know the particular characteristics of the chosen contractor and even though these may be highly encouraging it is important that he pays special attention to the aspect of concrete making not only at the beginning of the contract but all the way through, irrespective of whether the concrete is being made by hand or machine.

Plenty of water in the mix makes life easier for the operatives but produces weak concrete and therefore it is essential to ensure that just the right amount of water is used to produce a mix of suitable workability to allow proper compaction. The amount of water required will depend to some extent on the characteristics of the aggregate being used. Aggregates with sharp edges and rough surfaces, for example some produced from crushed stone, require more water than aggregate with rounded edges and smoother surfaces such as river gravel. Workability is measured by the slump test, familiar to all students of building construction. Given the same ingredients and proportions in the mix, consistency of strength for a particular area of work, for example foundations, is maintained by frequent slump tests during the work's progress but particularly at times when the concrete is being made from a newly delivered batch of aggregate. The architect or surveyor will wish to see a slump test at the beginning of concreting so as to ensure that the operatives know what is expected and call for a test on the occasion of each visit while concreting is in progress.

Correct proportioning of the other materials for different mixes of concrete is vital to ensure consistency of strength and the architect or surveyor will wish to see that operatives are aware of their responsibilities in this respect by ensuring that deep narrow gauge boxes of the correct size according to the mix are being used and that filling is being carried out on a clean level surface and one that can easily be kept clean so as to avoid adulteration. At the time he should run through with the operatives the proportions of the mix to be used so that for each 50kg bag of cement all are aware of the volume of fine and coarse aggregate required and that proper allowance is being made for bulking as necessary if the sand is wet.

Obviously in most cases for foundation work a mechanical mixer will be provided and these are undoubtedly a considerable aid to the production of concrete of consistent strength and good quality provided that they are properly used. The first mix of the day should be rejected since it will undoubtedly be too weak, most of the cement and fine aggregate adhering to the paddles and drum, hence it is probably best to run the machine with cement and fine aggregate in the first place. For consistency it is important that the mixing is carried on until the colour and texture of the mix are even throughout. The time required for this must be noted and the same mixing period used for each batch. Cleanliness is also essential and the mixer will require cleaning after each run. If mixing of small batches is necessary by hand then the same principles apply as to proportioning except that the cement content should be increased by 10%. Hand mixing requires the materials to be turned at least twice when dry and twice when wet with just sufficient water being added through a rose but again the final result must be a uniformly coloured and textured mix.

It should not, of course, be necessary to remind contractors that concreting and indeed many other building operations such as bricklaying and plastering should be suspended during cold weather whenever the temperature is below 5°C. Even if the temperature rises above this level during the day it is imperative to ensure that the materials used are not still frost covered. Sand and aggregates must be protected overnight if there is the least danger of frost. Asking the contractor after the event if concreting has ceased will only elicit the bland assurance "but of course". It is far better for the surveyor to make an unheralded call to ensure that this rule is being followed otherwise the affected parts may subsequently be covered up to cause possible troubles at a much later date. The concreter may make application to continue concreting in cold weather so as to avoid undue delay and if the precautions to be taken have not been set out in the specification it will be necessary to agree these with the contractor there and then. Because supervisors found it impossible on site to limit the use of calcium chloride to the mere $1\frac{1}{2}\%$ which is considered safe against its corrosive effect on the steel in reinforced concrete, its use is now generally forbidden, although there is no real reason why it should not be used in mass concrete. The difficulty on site would be to ensure that it was indeed used solely for mass concrete, so that the total ban is probably more sensible, particularly as other accelerators are readily available. Alternatively, increasing the cement content, the use of rapid hardening cement or heating the mixing water and aggregates can be considered as alternatives.

Increasingly for urban work nowadays concrete is ready made and delivered to the site in large vehicles. In most cases if the distance is comparatively short it is made elsewhere under controlled conditions and merely kept agitated on the journey. However, it can also be mixed from materials and water stored on the vehicle towards the end of the journey so that it arrives freshly mixed, if longer journeys are involved, and there is thus a danger of initial set. The idiosyncracies of individual operatives can be overcome by the use of ready made concrete and it is usually considered that a far greater consistency of quality can be achieved. Unless specified by the architect or surveyor, however, the option is one for the contractor to exercise since the obtaining of concrete by

528

this method is probably somewhat more expensive than by using his own men and equipment. The makers will supply a certificate to the contractor setting out the details of the mix so as to confirm that the specification has been followed. The certificates should obviously be retained and related to the positions where the particular batch was placed and to any samples which may be sent for testing.

The requirement that concrete, to avoid initial set, must be placed in position within a maximum of thirty minutes after mixing, leads to the scenes of frenzy on most building sites already mentioned. Admittedly the requirement is a severe one but it is important for the architect or surveyor to ensure that compliance does not entail the mix being rushed along in wheelbarrows over bumpy terrain and then being tipped from a substantial height. This happens all too often. Heavy jolting of a dry mix while being moved will cause the mix to consolidate. Segregation of the particles will occur when the coarser material sinks to the bottom leaving a mixture of watery cement and finer particles near the surface and this can happen either from bumping around during tansportation or dropping from a height. Chutes may be required to assist placing in foundation trenches and it is, of course, essential to arrange for the minimum length of travel from the mixer, or that ready mix lorries deliver as near to the required spot as possible. Clearly though this is not always feasible in the case of extension work and the need to barrow through a building is not uncommon, necessitating the careful arrangement of boards to avoid undue jolting.

Once in position the concrete must be compacted to ensure that all entrapped air is excluded and no voids result in the completed work. This then this involves gently moving the concrete mix around so that all air escapes to the surface and in particular no pockets remain below the larger particles of aggregate or below reinforcement bars. This can be done by hand using a sharp 13mm steel bar which is preferable to any other method for concrete in reinforced lintols, beams and columns to ensure proper cover to the steel. In drier mass concrete work and sometimes also with heavily reinforced features hand compaction can be very wearisome and the use of mechanical vibrators is now common. However, in cases of a mix with a fairly high water content, the careless use of a vibrator will cause an excess of fine material and water to come to the surface. Compaction is complete when air bubbles have ceased to appear.

Besides being protected against the effects of hot sun or strong drying winds when freshly mixed and during transportation and placing so as to prevent the immediate onset of the initial set, concrete needs to be cured so that the mixture of water and cement completes the appropriate chemical reaction as the concrete hardens. It is therefore necessary to prevent water drying out for at least a period of four days, preferably seven, but double this time in winter and discounting any frosty days. The concrete accordingly needs to be covered with hessian or sand and kept moist by watering or covered with polythene in summer to prevent drying out. In winter the covering would need to be of polythene or building paper obviously without the involvement of water if there is a danger of freezing. It is important that coverings are kept close to the surface of the concrete since loose coverings can create wind tunnels and result in a quicker loss of water than would have been the case had no covering been used at all. The architect or surveyor on his inspections will need to keep a note of when particular items are cast so that later he can check that the proper time for curing has been allowed.

We are not concerned here with the reinforced concrete construction which is the province of a consulting engineer, such as for example, columns, reinforced concrete walls and suspended floor slabs since the engineer will also be employed to supervise the construction of his design, and will, of course, need to pay particular attention to construction and daywork joints. However, even with large areas of oversite concrete, it is best to lay in alternate bays, and to allow all shrinkage to be taken up before filling the gaps between bays. By this method pronounced shrinkage cracking can be obviated and in the unlikely event of movement in the slab this can be controlled to some extent along the defined construction joints making any subsequent repairs easier. This method is, of course, in direct contrast to the case of a length of foundation which in underpinning is cast in alternate lengths and allowed to harden before the next adjacent length is placed. Here the intention is that the completed length of foundation should act as one homogeneous mass and it may be appropriate to rebate construction joints and provide metal dowels. Equally, it is necessary to ensure that the surface of the first placed section is hacked to remove laitance and to expose the aggregate and that the surface is well wetted and covered with a thin layer of a grout consisting of equal proportions of cement and sand to assist the bond between the two sections.

In the size and type of work generally envisaged by this book the value of testing concrete cubes may seem a little doubtful. Taking six cubes from each grade of concrete as is normally provided for is by no means any substitute for the frequent but irregular inspections which the architect or surveyor makes to ensure that, so far as possible in the absence of a Clerk of Works, the client is to obtain work in accordance with the specification. Obviously a great deal of concrete making will continue in the absence of the architect or surveyor but the establishment of the right procedures at the outset coupled with some closely intervalled but unheralded inspections thereafter should be sufficient to provide the client with the best protection possible. However, the knowledge that work carried out in accordance with the specification is producing concrete of the required strength is an added reassurance and therefore on one of the inspections of concrete making, covering each grade of concrete, the architect or surveyor may direct that samples be prepared for testing and in due course receive the results from the laboratory. In the very unlikely event of low results it may be that a section of work will have to be taken out and replaced and at appropriate timings careful examination will need to be made to ascertain whether there is evidence to suggest similar failings in other batches.

In a single one off extension, coupled with repairs and alterations to an existing building, it is probable that the only reinforced concrete work would consist of the provision of lintols over door and window openings and perhaps of a longer beam or beams over openings connecting the two parts of the completed work, although in the latter case it is usually much more sensible to use steel beams. For lintols on a small job it is usually wise to specify precast members from a reputable manufacturer and the site work as such would then merely be limited to ensuring that what was specified was in fact obtained and that the lintol was installed the correct way uppermost and with a proper and adequate bearing at each end. Should however, precast units not be specified then the surveyor will need to check the size of lintol box, size and positioning of reinforcement, cranking and hooking of the ends of bars to form anchors and that reinforcement is clean, rust free and not contaminated with oil or grease. The rigid fixing of reinforcement by spacers and wiring within shuttering or for that matter at laps of mesh reinforcement employed in larger areas is a fiddly job and one all too easy to skimp in the hope that when the concrete is poured all will be well but, if it is not, nobody will notice for a long time. The results of this type of carelessness and lack of supervision have already been mentioned. Should a long beam have to be cast in-situ the architect or surveyor will need to ensure that shuttering is adequate for the purpose. All too often site work of this nature on small jobs tends to be carelessly carried out and as a result when the concrete is poured the joints open and there is a leakage of fine material producing cellular rather than homogeneous concrete. Shuttering must of course be clean before concrete is poured. A useful tip to remember in the casting of long beams is to ensure either that there is thorough wedging of the shuttering in the middle of the span or that the shuttering is deliberately set up so that there is a slight camber in the finished soffit of the beam to overcome the optical illusion of sagging when the soffit is exactly horizontal.

Finally, in specialist work such as underpinning, the surveyor needs to take particular care. It is commonly held that underpinning methods are crude in this country compared with France, for example, where gauges are often installed to record the slightest deviation in the structure. Such refinements are rarely seen here except where specialist contractors are employed.

Apart from ensuring that the order set out for underpinning is followed and that sections are properly jointed to form a homogeneous mass a particular point to watch regarding underpinning is the question of pinning up, either by slates or by means of dry packing. Dry packing should be formed in a thin, even layer no more than about 75mm thick, but cases have been known where the thickness has varied from 20mm to well over 150mm when it is useless. It is also pointless to employ dry packing if concrete shrinkage has still to take place. At least two days should be allowed for the new mass concrete to stabilise.

Walls

Completion of the foundation work for an extension or other new structure either by way of concrete strips, reinforced concrete beam on top of piles, or a raft, will be followed by the arrival of the bricklayer or mason, for all structures other than those of timber framing, together with his materials. Everyone involved in exercising care with ground conditions and foundations will ensure, of course, that the loads about to be placed thereon will thereafter be resisted without undue settlement, particularly of the differential variety. External walling, completed satisfactorily, will provide the client with protection from the elements, rain, snow, cold, heat and draughts, vital attributes, everyone would agree, to the success of any building contract. Yet in a Building Research Establishment analysis of the defects referred to its Advisory Service, it was found that half of all defects related to dampness and of those 63% to rain penetration and rising damp with the former accounting for five times the latter. Accordingly, because of the importance of this aspect much thought should have been devoted to the selection of appropriate materials and settling standards of workmanship in the specification and of drawing out satisfactory and appropriate details to satisfy such a basic requirement before tenders were obtained and a start made on site. In the field of totally new building work external walls are nowadays invariably constructed in cavity work but in the realm of repairs and extensions both solid and cavity work will be encountered. If the latter is comparatively newly built it may be in the form usually found for new buildings these days, comprising an outer leaf of clay or other bricks and an inner skin of concrete blocks. On the other hand the clash of new bricks with old may be unacceptable with a new extension in which case both leaves may be specified of concrete blocks, the outer skin to be coated with a coloured rendering as a foil to the original work. Alternatively, the opportunity might be taken to render the old building as well if it had been built of poor bricks, either for the purpose of weatherproofing or to improve appearance, a situation which might also apply to some of the less attractive stone built dwellings of past eras. Since solid brickwork with a rendered finish is satisfactory for keeping out the elements in most circumstances should the old structure be of solid work, rendered or un-rendered, the continuation of such work in a new extension may be considered yet another alternative if, perhaps, doubts are entertained of the capacity of the local workforce to build a cavity wall in a satisfactory manner.

Care in the selection of suitable materials will come to nought if what is selected is not provided by the contractor and this applies most particularly in the case of materials for the exterior walls. Clay facing bricks for the exterior will have been selected for the various positions and according to the degree of exposure of the proposed structure by "varieties", "qualities" and "types" according to the classifications in BS 3921: Part 2 1974 and probably by manufacturer and specific reference number in conjunction with the client. Samples may have already been obtained but, if not, it is important for the architect or surveyor to obtain samples at this stage, before the contractor places the order, so that these can be retained for comparison against those delivered. Invoices and certificates should be retained and seen from manufacturers and suppliers and, of course, the architect or surveyor must carry out his own tests and examination of random samples if in doubt. Clay bricks in any batch are seldom uniform. It is the variations which provide character to the finished brickwork, but the variations must be within certain limits to be acceptable. Sizes must be within the tolerances set out in the British Standard. Bricks must be reasonably true to shape and not twisted and soft underburnt bricks and brittle friable overburnt bricks must be rejected along with any bricks with underburnt nodules of clay on the surface. Although many bricks are now delivered in pallets, damage can still occur in transit and on delivery when precautions are not taken and bricks with damaged arrises should be rejected. It does no harm for the architect or surveyor to examine the first load of bricks delivered in conjunction with the foreman and to extract, and for the foreman to put aside, examples of bricks which will not be considered acceptable, the purpose being for reference by the bricklayer working on the site for the avoidance of doubt.

Similar considerations apply to bricks made of materials other than clay and, of course, the architect or surveyor will have considered the advantages and disadvantages of using calcium silicate bricks to BS 187: 1978 "Calcium Silicate/Sandlime and Flint Lime bricks" in one or more of the six classes available at the specification stage. The uniformity in manufacture of such bricks means that rejection does not normally have to be made on grounds of variation in quality but only on physical damage to arrises in transit or on delivery or in variations in colour if the bricks are to be used as facings externally or in unplastered positions internally. With so many differing classes covering a wide range of strengths for various purposes, it is even more important than in the case of clay bricks to see invoices and certificates and to ensure that bricks to be specifically used in different parts of the building are kept quite separate from each other on site. The British Standard for calcium silicate bricks provides for marking on or in relation to the bricks, for example on an invoice delivery note or suppliers certificate, the name of the manufacturer, the strength class as in Table 2 of the Standard, the work size, length, width, height and whether the brick is hollow or cellular and whether with or without a frog and the number of the Standard. There is provision for the supplier to render a certificate of compliance if requested and, for all except the facing bricks of class 2, a proportion of the bricks in a batch can be colour coded in the manner set out in Table 3 for classes 3 to 7 to assist in easing identification on site.

Natural stone, as a material for solid walls or in the outer leaf of cavity walls, may well be required in an extension to a house in an area where stone in the past provided the predominant building material or, perhaps, to a house of character in an area where stone had to be brought from some distance away. By the time the stage of ordering has been reached, assuming it has been decided that stone will be the material for the external walls, a great deal will already have been done to ensure that the basic material will be satisfactory. In fact, the stone will probably already have been selected after due consideration of the stone used on the original building, of any similar stone buildings in the area concerned, the source of such stone and its current availability or, if not currently available, the possibility of utilising a stone of similar characteristics. More than likely such knowledge would be basic to an architect or surveyor working in a stone area but the information would be more difficult to acquire in the case of an architect or surveyor who practised elsewhere, or if the use of stone in the particular area concerned was the exception rather than the rule. Once acquired, in whatever circumstances, such knowledge would need to be extended to an examination and discussion with the probable supplier at the quarry and examination of any test results relating to durability, absorption and crushing strength and, of course, due consideration of the characteristics of the stone in relation to the basic requirements of a hard stone for rubble walling, greater size and uniformity of stones for coursed work, as against random work, and the working qualities if it is to be used for ashlaring. All these aspects, will of course, need to have been related to the design considerations involved by the proposal. Accordingly, when stone is ready for delivery to site, on the order from the main contractor or a nominated sub-contractor, it will probably be no more than a mere formality to ensure that it is up to the quality as previously agreed with the supplier and that, depending on the type and proposed use, it has not been unduly damaged in transit. With the stone walls entrusted to a contractor well experienced in such work this task would consist very much of a dialogue between the mason and the architect or surveyor.

The availability of cheaper substitutes for natural stone has led many owners to consider the use of such materials should the finances not rise to the use of natural stone. Consideration of the aesthetic rights or wrongs of the use of such material is outside the scope of this section but has been touched upon in Part 1. If materials of this type are to be used then it is essential that they are obtained from a reliable firm of some standing and all the more reason, since the appearance is invariably "skin deep", to check against damage in transit.

A principal constituent of the modern building site is the lightweight or aerated concrete block for use, as we have seen, in either one or both leaves of the cavity wall or in partition work for both load and non-load bearing purposes. In view of the vast array of types for all purposes which are available it is of considerable help when it comes to the task of supervision for the architect or surveyor to have specified the blocks by maker and reference number and if there are to be more than one type of block in use for these to differ substantially in shape and appearance. Checking that the correct types have been delivered thereby becomes a great deal easier and the differences will prevent mistakes arising on site and the possibility of a non-load bearing block being used in a position requiring load bearing material. All concrete blocks selected must be made to BS 2028 1364: 1968 "Precast Concrete Blocks" and the manufacturers certificate to this effect should be seen and retained. The Standard does indeed provide for marking on or in relation to the blocks (for example on a delivery note, invoice or suppliers certificate) the name of the maker or his trade mark, the type of block as in clause 1 of the Standard, its strength as in clause 13, its length, height and thickness and whether solid, hollow or cellular, the number of the Standard and whether aerated or not and, if not, details of the binder and aggregate. A very helpful provision is that a supplier is required to provide information to enable blocks of different strength to be identified on site.

A particular requirement for all walling materials whether of clay brick, calcium silicate brick, natural or artificial stone, but particularly so of lightweight concrete blocks, is for adequate storage on site to provide protection against the elements. A firm level surface raised off the ground and proof against damp penetration from below is required, preferably under a properly constructed temporary shelter or, if this is not possible, bricks or blocks must be covered over with tarpaulins or plastic sheeting. It is surprising how often contractors are neglectful in respect of this necessary precaution and bricks and blocks are piled on bare ground and left to become muddy and saturated.

Other materials for the use of the bricklayer or mason will also need to be seen to be as specified. Cement and water have already been mentioned under Foundations and the same comments apply here. Sands however, for bricklaying, laying concrete blocks and masonry are covered by BS 1200: 1976 "Sands for mortar for plain and reinforced Brickwork, Blockwalling and Masonry", and the sand suitable for mortar for jointing bricks and blocks is not the same as that required for concrete making. Some operatives are not always careful to differentiate between the two. With a view to avoiding such confusion on the site it is wise to specify the use of coarse stuff to BS 4721: 1971 "Ready Mixed Lime: Sand for Mortar", produced under controlled conditions in numerous recommended proportions so that only cement has to be added. Otherwise the architect or surveyor will need to be particularly careful to ensure that the sand is suitable for the mortars intended and is clean and well graded. The provisions of BS 1200: 1976 are useful in that provision is made for the supplier to certify that the sand complies with the Standard and, if requested, details of the source or origin, the group classification, the properties of the sand, its grading and external characteristics will be supplied. There is a requirement for testing, if desired by the purchaser, the cost of the tests being met by the supplier if the batch does not comply, or by the purchaser if it does. Similar provisions apply to sands supplied for other purposes, for example for internal gypsum plastering or for external renderings under different Standards but this does not, of course, prevent confusion reigning on site when batches get muddled up. Ready mixed lime: sand for mortar prepared in accordance with the Standard will be supplied on the invoice, delivery note or suppliers certificate with the name and address of the maker, the designation of the lime: sand mix, the number of the Standard and, if requested, the type of aggregate, the amount and type of any pigment required and the nature and proportion of any admixtures included. Furthermore, the Standard provides that suppliers will be able to advise on batching with cement on site according to the mix supplied.

If the specification provides for cavity walling of a brick outer skin with concrete blocks for the inner leaf, the requirement for wall ties will be for the butterfly twisted wire type, not the vertically twisted flat bar type suitable for use only when the blocks in both skins are of the same size. Having regard to the increasing frequency of reports referring to corroded wall ties, it is to be hoped that ties nowadays will be specified as of copper, copper alloy, stainless steel or other incorrodable metal. BS 1243: 1978, by its retention of galvanised mild steel as a material for wall ties even as amended in 1981 to increase the thickness of the zinc coating, is now being shown as providing, at its lower end, a standard that is hardly adequate in view of the ineffectiveness of much galvanising and the ease with which it and other protective coatings to metal can be damaged under the conditions of many building sites and, over a period of time, by the conditions experienced in the outer leaf of cavity walls. However, if only the bare minimum of BS 1243: 1978 can be afforded it is hoped that the better quality ties can be specified and it is essential for the architect or surveyor to see that ties, if of galvanised mild steel, are not already beginning to rust or that protective coatings are not damaged before the ties are built in. Consideration should be given to using the double triangle type in an incorrodable metal since these ties present much less material within the cavity to collect mortar droppings during construction. It is to be noted that the Committee drafting the 1978 Edition of BS 1243 considered plastic and zinc die cast alloys as possible suitable materials for wall ties but found insufficient evidence of their performance to justify their inclusion. Ties of whatever type must be built in for at least 50mm into each leaf, in the case of butterfly twisted wire types with the "knot" downwards, all sloping down towards the outer leaf and distributed adequately. The specification will set out the spacing for general walling and this is usually followed by bricklayers and masons until corners or piers between openings occur when the requirement to double the number is either forgotten or a lack of common sense is displayed to the extent that a narrow pier is not provided with ties at all because it does not fit in with the pattern. It is most essential that both leaves act in unison at such points where loads are concentrated and the architect or surveyor must make this point quite clear before the bricklayer or mason reaches that part of the work. With skilled operatives it is best to convey such instructions by way of a reminder thus "you will, of course, be doing such and such won't you when you get to so and so because of this and that?". A question in this form does not impinge on the operative's pride and will give him the opportunity of providing a reassuring "of course". The point will nevertheless register that the architect or surveyor will be particularly keen to see that this aspect of the work is done properly. Later during a subsequent visit by the architect or surveyor, the operative may go to some trouble to demonstrate that he has indeed done precisely what is required and may even show that he has done a little more to be on the safe side.

It would be reasonable to broach one particular aspect of an operatives work such as the above with the bricklayer or mason at an early stage of operations but it should not be thought necessary to do so in regard to the basic skills to be exercised. Some matters must be taken on trust to begin with. In bricklaying and masonry work the architect or surveyor will need to look for early signs of bad workmanship in regard to bonding, bedding and flushing up of joints, rejection of defective bricks or stones, failure to maintain perpends in a true vertical line, less than neat corners, cleanliness both of facing work and of ties and cavities, avoidance of projections into the cavity and the proper formation of weep-holes. All these points will need checking but not in an obsessive way to begin with and the eye can be allowed to roam over the work as it is progressing in the early stages on the initial assumption that the exercise of basic skills is to be expected. If correct procedures are not being followed then steps will have to be taken at once to put matters right by pulling down and starting again if necessary with either the same operative, or preferably with another, for if such basic skills cannot be counted upon to begin with then there is little likelihood of subsequent work being satisfactory.

The traditional argument over whether bricks should be laid frog-up or frog-down is settled with authority by the Brick Development Association who say that where maximum strength or weight is required for the brickwork the bricks must be laid frog-up and all joints filled. Where maximum strength is not of prime importance, such as in one or two storey houses, the bricks may be laid frog-down thereby achieving an appreciable saving in mortar. However, for separating walls in dwellings, it is important that the bricks are laid frog-up to give maximum weight and hence meet the "deemed to satisfy" requirements of the Building Regulations so far as sound insulation is concerned.

Every endeavour should be made to keep facing brickwork clean, particularly from mortar splashes, run-off from scaffold boards, paint and bitumen since these are very difficult to remove without damaging the brick face. Scaffold boards should be turned back away from the wall during periods of rain and at the end of the days work. Any mortar which does get on to the brick faces should be removed as the work proceeds with a stiff fibre brush (not a wire brush) as once mortar staining has hardened, removal is difficult. Proprietary cleaning agents should be used only as a last resort and then with great caution. Where there is danger of paint or bitumen spilling on to the brickwork, the walls should be temporarily covered. As the work proceeds, the mortar to the brick joints should be struck off flush with the bricks and then rubbed with a piece of wood. Alternatively, the specification may provide for joints to be weathered or "ironed" to obtain a bucket-handle finish. The fashionable recessed joints of recent years are not recommended for external brickwork by the Brick Development Association.

The mortar being used by the bricklayer or mason must be checked. The specification will no doubt set out the various mortar mixes to be used according to the particular part of the structure being built but it frequently happens that bricklayers ignore such requirements. As long as the bricklayer is not of the belief that really strong cement mortars are what should be used, and some are still very firm in this belief, there is no harm, in normal two or three storey domestic work, in allowing slight variations in specified mixes to suit a particular bricklayer's preference. The important thing is that they should be discussed and agreed between the bricklayer and the architect or surveyor who needs, of course, to make his presence felt early on in this respect. The bricklayer usually prefers a mortar that works easily. "Fatty" mixes of this nature produced with sand containing more than 10% of clay or loam must not, however, be permitted for use. Instead plasticisers to BS 4887: 1973 "Mortar Plasticisers" used strictly in accordance with the makers instructions and in the appropriate mixes, but without over mixing, are suitable for all except the most severe positions such as joints in copings and cills, parapet walls and chimneys constructed in winter and in retaining walls. Plasticisers to the Standard are supplied in packages or containers with the name of the maker or his trade mark marked on, the words "Mortar Plasticiser" in large letters, together with the number of the Standard and the maximum and minimum proportions for use in specific mixes. It is equally important where there is a mixture of units in the wall being constructed to ensure that the bricklayer or mason uses the much weaker mixes, as appropriate, required for building inner leaves and partitions of concrete blocks. It goes without saying that mixing of the constituents of mortar must be by gauge boxes not shovelfuls. When facing brickwork is involved the architect or surveyor should arrange at an early stage for a sample panel to be prepared strictly in accordance with the specification and using the sand which it is intended should be used for the final pointing, or bedding and pointing, if the facework is to be pointed as it proceeds although this is infinitely less preferable. The panel must be allowed to dry out thoroughly for a week or so before the client is invited to give his blessing or, if necessary, further panels are prepared, until he expresses satisfaction. It can be embarrassing if this simple aspect of client relationship is overlooked and on completion the client says that he is not too keen on the appearance and it is "not as nice as what he has seen elsewhere". Of course, architects and surveyors have a more general duty to the environment and may need to persuade clients away from such abominations as the vividly contrasting mortar and brickwork which some prefer.

With all the horrors reported over the last few years of dampness in structures, architects and surveyors should very properly be giving close attention to the quality of the materials used for damp proof courses and membranes which they specify. While many of the problems reported in the fairly recent past have been caused by damaged materials and poor workmanship, the architect and surveyor needs to have regard not only to these aspects but also to the fact that damp proof courses and membranes must last as long as the remainder of the structure. Renewals, if these should prove necessary, are both difficult and expensive. Accordingly while the materials for all damp proof courses must conform to at least BS 743: 1970 "Materials for damp proof courses", there will be many occasions when those materials listed which have given proof over the years of durability such as lead, copper and asphalt, will be preferred to those where the durability has always been known to be shorter or where materials are still thought to be somewhat innovatory, for example bitumen felt, pitch polymer sheets and polythene in both sheet and strip form. Whatever material is selected and in this respect regard must be had to the position where the material will be used and the characteristics, whether of rigidity or flexibility, required for such position, the architect or surveyor must check that his client is getting what has been specified on his behalf. As far as some of the better quality materials are concerned the architect or surveyor will be assisted in this task. For example, in respect of lead by the colour codings related to thickness together with the Standard number and makers name indented thereon and now adapted for the standard thicknesses in BS 1178: 1969 "Milled lead Sheet and Strip for Building Purposes". With other materials of a traditional nature, copper for example, he will need to see certificates and check thicknesses and grades. With newer materials it will probably be more a question of seeing that proprietary products are delivered undamaged and are of the quality described in the invoice, although each roll of bitumen felt complying with the Standard does have to be legibly labelled with the number of the Standard and the Type of felt ranging from "A" to "G" depending on characteristics. Polythene sheeting has to be black of low density not less than 0.46mm thick, packaged in various widths in rolls not less than 8m in length and marked with the BS number.

It is in the nature of things that building works in this country will be carried out at what always seem to be inappropriate times as far as the weather is concerned. Architects, surveyors and contractors always seem to assume good weather and are taken by surprise when conditions, more often than not, cease to be ideal, with the result that precautions against extremes of weather are often omitted from the specification. If this is the case, the architect and surveyor will need to be especially careful in agreeing methods with the contractor to cope with the situation. As mentioned previously, a building site can be quite a pleasant place on which to work in the summer but even then precautions have to be taken against the undue drying effects of hot sun and hot drying winds. Wetting bricks and porous stone, but not saturating, and covering work during the day, at the end of each day and on completion are the principal precautions to be taken for brick and block laying in the summer. In winter months, however, working on site can be most uncomfortable and, far better than varying mixes according to the weather, heating water and aggregates and covering walls as the work proceeds, is to arrange for a proper framed temporary enclosure, erected before the works commence and, preferably, slightly heated, to enable work on all trades to proceed if not exactly in comfort at least out of rain, snow and the blast of freezing cold winds. Delays as a result will be avoided, production will rise and the quality of work will improve. The small additional expense of such enclosures is amply repaid by such improvements and it is surprising that more enclosures of this nature are not specified initially by architects and surveyors rather than have such measures left to the initiative of the more enlightened contractors. An alternative to a full enclosure might be a smaller bricklayer's tent and portable heaters for a section of the work but in either case it will still be important to cover work overnight since, with the heating turned off, temperatures can drop very quickly even within an enclosure, as it also can within a near completed building which is still without its glazing. Depending on the weather and the degree of protection to the works available, the architect or surveyor will need to agree alternatives for specified mortar mixes with air entraining plasticisers, never calcium chloride, for cold weather, the heating and prescribed temperatures for the water and sand and, of course, the avoidance of wetting bricks and stone if work is to proceed when temperatures are below $-4°C$. He should also ensure that mortar is between $16°C$ and $27°C$. Once the procedures for working in cold weather are established it is essential to make the occasional spot check to ensure that they are being followed, including perhaps the odd check at the weekend, or in the evening, to ensure that the methods for covering up at the end of the working day, including the provision of any extra insulation, if necessary, over and above mere sheeting, are being followed.

The foregoing aspects of materials and general workmanship for the construction of walls will require the architect or surveyor's attention on his periodic unheralded visits to the site. Some consideration, however, must now be given to the previously arranged inspections by the architect or surveyor while the walls are being built so that, before work is covered up, the contractor can demonstrate to him, and the architect or surveyor can see for himself, that his specified arrangements for the safeguarding of the building (and thereby the occupants) from the effects of all forms of damp penetration have been followed. Furthermore he will also need to see that the precautions for the avoidance of undue movement in walls which could possibly be a source of danger, or at least anxiety or irritation, to the occupants and which, in themselves, can also be a source of damp penetration, have been followed. All architects and surveyors will agree that safeguards from rising damp are vitally important. Accordingly, when brickwork, blockwork or stonework reaches that point, 150mm or so above ground level or whatever level has been predetermined, as the level for the damp proof course, the architect or surveyor will wish to verify that the work specified has been carried out satisfactorily before further walling is carried out. He will need to see that the material for the damp proof course is as specified, is sound, free from tears and defects, properly bedded and correctly lapped at joints. At the same time he will, of course, wish to see that all partitions are provided with damp proof courses and, also, all sleeper walls if the ground floor construction is to be hollow. If the ground floor is to be of solid construction, then of as equal importance as the damp proof course in walls will be the provision of the damp proof membrane, laid above the concrete and the vital overlapping with the damp proof course in external walls and partitions. It should be noted that it is generally advisable that the two do not actually form a connection which could be disturbed by the slight differential settlement which may arise between walls and slab.

Some other important aspects will also have to be seen to at about this time. The top of the cavity filling must be seen to be at the correct level in relation to the damp proof course, at least 50mm below and finished at the top sloping outwards. So that the space between the two can be cleared of the inevitable accumulation of mortar, the architect or surveyor must see that sand courses are left at this stage below damp proof course level. Eventually, with the aid of a torch and a long crowbar this operation can be successfully carried out on completion of the walling and to the satisfaction of the architect or surveyor in respect of every part of the external walls and before the bricks are finally set in position. Weep holes are also a necessity to enable any water to drain out from the cavity. Following the filling of the cavity, but not before, otherwise there would be a danger of collapse, the return filling to the foundation excavation will have been carried out, together with the formation of the oversite concrete slab, whether this be for the basis of a solid ground floor or on which sleeper walls are to rest. Where backfill is being carried out on the inside, care needs to be taken to see that it is well compacted in layers, not exceeding 300mm at a time. This work is frequently skimped with a minimum of attention given to it so that later, cracks appear in the solid ground floor construction about 200mm to 250mm away from the wall when the edge of the slab settles, as the fill consolidates under its own weight, depriving the unreinforced ground slab of support. Accordingly, it is useful to provide some mesh reinforcement around the edge of the slab for a width of about 400mm to 500mm. Alternatively the back fill of excavated material can be omitted and the floor slabs provided with a dropped concrete edge down to the foundation top.

The contractor, having satisfactorily demonstrated that all precautions in relation to rising damp have been complied with, can now proceed with the general walling to the level of the top of ground floor window and door openings. When this stage has been reached the architect or surveyor will wish to see, in respect of all such openings, that proper precautions against damp penetration have been taken. There is no use leaving this inspection until the time when the lintols have been put in position over the openings as it will be impossible by then to see at crucial points that work has in fact been completed satisfactorily. This inspection, which will require the aid of a powerful torch, can be facilitated if some careful thought is given at the specification stage to the provision of proper closer blocks for use on the inner leaf around openings to avoid undue cutting and, in particular, the practice of using brick bats at this point in an inner leaf otherwise wholly of concrete blocks. Furthermore the proviso that a flexible damp proof course both at cill level and at the sides of openings be extended so that it projects for say 25mm beyond the features concerned will enable it to be seen with ease. In addition to the aspects of damp penetration the architect or surveyor at this stage will also check on the disposition and cleanliness of ties at the sides of openings and also that the bearings provided for lintols are adequate. So often this work is done carelessly, in particular when concrete blocks are used for the inner leaf of a cavity wall, and the lintols are levelled with the use of any old bits of broken material which comes to hand and an excess of mortar. It is better to see that bearings are satisfactory at this stage before the lintols are installed.

To complete the pre-arranged inspections of what might be termed the first "lift" of walling in any new structure, attention will be divided fairly equally on the next inspection between seeing that safeguards against damp penetration have been followed and that adequate precautions to provide the walling with lateral support have been taken. The architect or surveyor will accordingly require to be notified when joist hangers and straps have been built in to the inner leaf to carry the floor joists and for connection thereto at first floor level to provide the lateral restraint to the walls. If the carpenter is also on site and can install his joists and secure the straps as well, so much the better, as this might save another separate inspection at a later date, but it is not a vital point and, in any event, involves the subsequent careful covering of the floor to keep it dry. The straps are needed to all walls, not only to those parallel to the run of floor joists since the bearing of joists by means of hangers is insufficient in itself to provide adequate restraint; only full building in can do this. Straps have to resist both tensional and compressive stresses so that it is vital that they are fixed tight against the cavity face of the inner leaf and that they are not bent in fixing but kept straight and screwed securely to the joists, except where turned over against the walling. It is equally important that the backs of joist hangers fit tightly against the internal room face of the inner leaf and are securely built in to the block or brickwork and it is infinitely preferable that the type with a turn down into the cavity are used which, when specified correctly, make it almost impossible for the hangers to be installed other than accurately. If not well fitted, both straps and hangers should be taken out and reset as, certainly, in the case of the former, they will be quite ineffective. In regard to lintols the bearing has already been mentioned so that there should be no real cause for comment at this stage unless the levelling was inadequate. What does need checking is the vital provision of a damp proof course above the lintol. This must be in one piece, tucked in above the lintol into a joint of the inner leaf, brought down sloping towards the exterior over the lintol and between the outer leaf and the top of the door or window frame. Furthermore, it must extend at least 100mm beyond the limit of the lintol at each end and be turned up slightly at this point to prevent any water running back on the underside towards the inner leaf, or the closer, at the side of the window or door.

In the same way as it has been seen to be necessary to make two pre-arranged inspections of ground floor walling, once it has progressed beyond the damp proof course stage, so it is with the first and any subsequent floor. In each case it will be necessary to check that details are satisfactory when the work reaches window head level and again when the work reaches the next floor level or, in the case of the topmost floor, either flat roof level or eaves level. Clearly the detail at the top of the wall in the topmost storey will govern what inspections need to be made. Should there be a flat roof and parapet then inspections at roof level would be similar to those carried out at the level of lower floors, with a further inspection at damp proof course level immediately above roof level and a further inspection of the damp proof course immediately below the coping. In the case of an eaves finish the architect or surveyor will be looking to see that the weight of the roof trusses or rafters are properly distributed over both leaves, not only from the point of view of supporting the load, but also to provide that element of restraint and holding down as is necessary at the top of the wall as it is lower down. In addition, the architect or surveyor will wish to see that the details are satisfactory and ties in particular are clean before the cavity is closed at the top. Closing the cavity will be the signal, of course, for the final clearing of any mortar droppings from the base of the cavity, an aspect which the architect or surveyor must see to himself as having been done satisfactorily before the sand course bricks are replaced permanently.

Internal partitions, both load bearing and non load bearing, require attention from the architect or surveyor in a similar manner on his periodic inspections and by way of a final check before the contractor is authorised to proceed with plastering. Of course, aspects of damp penetration do not arise to the same extent but the importance of the damp proof course and its lap if necessary, according to detailing, with the damp proof membrane at lowest floor level has already been stressed. Other aspects which require checking are the bearings for lintols over openings, particularly in load bearing partitions, the bonding of partition blocks both at angles and at junctions, the bedding and flushing up with mortar of joints throughout the work, (an item often skimped to a deplorable extent), and the proper building in of frames and linings together with any plates to provide bearings for timber joists or binders.

The completion of the external walls and internal partitions may well result in the bricklayer or mason withdrawing from the site for a while to enable other trades to proceed and, indeed, if pointing up as the work proceeds has been specified, there may only be a few matters, such as flashings or similar features, for him to return to complete. On the other hand, leaving new brickwork to be pointed on completion from a movable staging once the scaffolding has come down has much to commend it and will produce a better finish. In this event the aspect to watch for is that joints are a full 20mm in depth and well brushed out and wetted before the work is carried out and also, as mentioned before, that the work matches the original approved panel. If the opportunity is being taken to repoint the original brickwork or stonework of the main building the architect or surveyor must ensure that raking out to a full depth of 20mm is carried out despite the moans and groans which this requirement will often entail, followed by brushing to remove dust and debris and wetting if the existing brick or stonework should be porous. The specification will, of course, set out mixes for the mortar and the type of joint required related to the type of brick and the degree of exposure and it will be necessary to follow all the precautions discussed already if the work is to be carried out in unduly severe weather conditions.

If external walls are not to be left fair faced then some consideration will need to be given to the supervision required for the application of a rendered finish. As discussed previously such a finish might profitably on occasions be extended to include the rendering of the existing structure so as to link new and old together not, however, forgetting to provide a straight joint between the two, with metal lathing or wire mesh sealed with mastic, so as to induce any subsequent cracking, which might arise on settlement in the new structure, to take place on the junction line. Rendering, to serve its purpose of preventing the penetration of water yet providing a durable finish which is pleasing to the eye, should have a porous texture, be free of cracks, adhere securely to its backing and be evenly and skilfully applied. It is not pertinent here to discuss the considerations which apply to types of rendering, exposure conditions, backgrounds, mixes and methods of application all of which are dealt with exhaustively in BS 5262: 1976 "Code of Practice for

External Rendered Finishes" and which will need to have been considered at the specification stage. However, if both new and old work is to be rendered it may be that the special circumstances and requirements of the old work will need to take precedence over the new. Generally it will be the case that what will be suitable on the old work can be adapted with very little trouble for the new, but the reverse is by no means always possible. A detailed study of the subject of rendering as a repair to existing walls appears in Chapter 2 of "The Repair and Maintenance of Houses" at Pages 162–174.[6] Obviously such an important item affecting the appearance of the client's property will have been discussed and agreed with him at the specification stage as the architect or surveyor would not wish the selection to come as a complete surprise to him.

The materials used for renderings and the workmanship must clearly be of no less a standard than that provided for in the Code of Practice BS 5262: 1976 and certified accordingly, for example sand to BS 1199: 1976 "Sands for external rendering, internal plastering with lime and Portland cement and Floor Screeds", as coarse as possible but also properly graded, and lime to BS 890: 1972 "Building Limes" or it may be that the specification will set out suitable proprietory materials to be used in accordance with the makers' directions. The architect or surveyor will need to check on these aspects, as has already been discussed, in relation to other cement lime/sand mixes for mortar or cement/aggregate mixes for concrete. What does, however, require the architect or surveyor's particular attention in the case of rendering is the need to ensure that the contractor has the work in the hands of skilled labour and that the work is done at the proper time. At this stage of the contract it will be appearance and standard of finish which will share the main consideration along with weatherproofing capability. Badly applied rendering or rendering which has to be patched, however successful it may be in resisting damp, will be a continual source of irritation to the client and certainly no advertisement for either architect, surveyor or contractor. It may accordingly be considered advisable to see work carried out elsewhere for others by the same team as is proposed for the current contract, but obviously in advance of the commencement of work. If this is not possible then it may be that a small area can be selected and for the full number of coats to be applied, again in advance of the main work, and for this to be seen and approved by architect or surveyor and client. Undoubtedly the former proposal is better because the larger the area covered by rendering the better the impression which can be

(6) Published by the Estates Gazette Ltd.

obtained of the standard of workmanship. Furthermore a request for the preparation of a small panel or even one wall as a sample is not likely to appeal to the contractor in view of the continual coming and going of labour which would be involved.

Assuming that the architect or surveyor is satisfied with the skill of the team to do the work, it is vital to ensure that it is not commenced too soon. Rendering should be virtually the last external operation and must, if it is to look satisfactory, be carried out from either a scaffolding entirely separate from the wall or from an independent movable staging. The intention must be for the finishing coat, once completed, to remain untouched, even by ladders, for the remainder of the duration of the contract so that even the refixing of pipes, which will have been taken down to enable the work to be carried out, should be done from the movable staging or a separate scaffolding. Weather conditions must also be considered so that no rendering need be carried out during frosty weather or when there is a danger of frost, while in summer it is essential to work on elevations in the shade if the weather is very hot.

As in the case of other items of constructional work, periodic inspections will need supplementing with set visits. The architect or surveyor will wish to see that the preparation of the background has been thoroughly completed before authorising the application of the first undercoat. Attention will need to be directed to ensuring that raking out of joints is deep enough, any hacking of hard dense surfaces to form a mechanical key has been thoroughly completed (such work having preference to the use of any bonding agent), any fungicidal treatment applied as may be necessary, the whole of the surfaces thoroughly brushed down, any dubbing out in two or more coats, as may be necessary, completed or that any spatter dash application has hardened and cannot be dislodged by the hand. Authorisation to proceed with the first undercoat might well be accompanied by suitable reminders on dampening down before application, combing surfaces to provide a key for the next coat and the protection of newly completed work, so as to allow time for curing and to prevent too rapid drying.

The architect or surveyor will no doubt be attending some time during the application of the first undercoat, to check on mixing and application, but his next fixed inspection will be to check that all is well for the application of either the next undercoat or the finishing coat, if only one undercoat is required. In particular, before authorising the next coat, the architect or surveyor will need to be sure that the preceding coat has thoroughly dried out and, in consequence, that all shrinkage has ceased. At least two full days is required for drying out in summer and a week or sometimes more in winter or wet weather.

Obviously the same procedure must be followed if there is a second undercoat and before the finishing coat is applied. Once the finishing coat has been applied, however, greater care is needed to see that drying out takes place very slowly in view of the thinner nature of most finishing coats. This is to avoid cracking and it is essential to spray the surfaces with clean water for at least three days to keep them damp and to shield them with screens from strong winds and sun for at least two days, ensuring that the screens do not touch or flap against the finished work and cause damage or discolouration.

Carpentry and Joinery

There have been enough stories in recent years concerning dry rot in floors and roofs and both wet and dry rot in external joinery, all appearing within a short time of completion, for architects and surveyors to realise that a great many reputations must have been damaged in the process. The causes of these defects have been attributed variously to poor detailing by designers, the supply of poor quality timber, a reduction in the acceptable size of timbers for reasons of economy but, in consequence, rendering the members more vulnerable to attack, poor workmanship on site and careless-ness in storage and handling of timber and joinery, all acting singly or in conjunction. Clearly clients have been receiving a raw deal and obtaining little protection from their advisers against what must seem to lay members of the public very elementary dangers arising in various forms of traditional building construction. Coupled with tales of structural failures in suspended timber floors and pitched roofs it makes painful reading at a time when there is a plethora of advice available to help circumvent most of the problems. Perhaps here lies one of the problems in itself; the advice is somewhat overwhelming in its quantity and while architects and surveyors have difficulty in keeping abreast and following it entirely what hope has the contractor and the men working on both large and small building sites? In consequence, however, what has become abun-dantly clear as a result is that, given a degree of competence by the architect or surveyor in the field of design and specification, it is he who can provide the protection for the client by the proper exercise of his supervisory powers under the terms of the contract against defects of the nature outlined above. Under these powers it is for the architect or surveyor to ensure so far as is possible that the timber delivered to the site, whether for carcassing or joinery and made up or otherwise, is of itself satisfactory for the purpose, is fitted together soundly and built in such a way as to fulfil its function without deterioration over the life span of the structure. To exercise these supervisory powers in an effective manner it is necessary, as seen in the case already of foundations and walls, to make not only the unheralded periodic checks of materials and workmanship on the site, but also inspections by arrangement at· set stages of progress.

In furtherance of the aim of ensuring that the timber will be satisfactory for its purpose on delivery, care needs to be taken at the specification stage so as to limit any disputes which may arise later on what is satisfactory and what is not. Experience from the past indicates that now, for even proposed average quality structures, where an architect or surveyor is involved, nothing less than top quality stress graded material for structural carcassing work in species at least to satisfy the Building Regulations or By-Laws, pressure impregnated with preservative and top quality joinery, all at the appropriate moisture content from a reputable firm or firms, will do. Whether the architect or surveyor will wish to name the supplier or a range of alternative suppliers for the carcassing timber will be a matter for him to decide, but very often where trussed rafters under the TRDA quality assurance scheme or perhaps a staircase are being selected from a catalogue produced by one of the larger merchants, then it would seem the obvious thing to do, particularly if all the joinery can also be selected at the same time. There is no doubt that the larger reputable merchants have better facilities and better quality control over their products and it is totally false economy to allow contractors freedom to save pence on timber by obtaining inferior material and products. When working in a particular area an architect or surveyor will find it advantageous to establish and maintain contact with one or more of the main local merchants, so as to ensure that he is not only aware of what the market can provide but also so that the better quality material can be made available and be identified as such. For the younger architect or surveyor it can also be a particularly useful way of becoming familiar with the differing appearance of various timbers, of the distinctive tones which are taken up on the impregnation of carcassing timber by the available preserving chemicals and also of getting to know the grading marks used by the firm, all of which knowledge will be of assistance when he comes to check material when it is delivered to the site.

If the supplier is not named in the specification then the architect or surveyor will need to approve the contractor's choice at the time of ordering and it will be necessary in all cases at this stage to check the details of the order with a view to the avoidance of undue cutting of timbers on site. This tends to put at risk the preservative treatment by necessitating the saturating on site of cut ends, a task all too frequently skimped and work which is to be avoided if at all possible. At the same time facilities and methods of storage for the timber should be agreed so that these are available and ready in advance of delivery. So often the material arrives late on a rainy afternoon, catching the site staff totally unprepared, so that when unloaded it is left overnight and most of the next day inadequately protected. Storage in the new structure should be avoided as the atmosphere will be too moist laden for the purpose. Far preferable would be an old unoccupied building or a clean dry garage or shed. If none of these are available then it will be necessary to form a proper self crossing external stack raised off the ground on bearers so that the timbers are flat and will be well ventilated but also completely protected from the weather. It must be made quite clear at this stage that damaged timbers or components, such as trussed rafters, will not be accepted for incorporation in the structure so that the contractor is duly warned against careless handling and will in turn be careful to see that his site staff thoroughly check, if necessary in conjunction with the architect or surveyor, the condition of the timber delivered and those made up items such as trussed rafters.

Delivery of the carcassing timber from a reliable supplier, well known to the architect or surveyor, accompanied by a certificate covering the treatment with preservative with the degree of salt retention given, depending on situation and exposure to hazard in accordance with BS 5268: "Code of Practice for the Structural Use of Timber" Part 5: 1977 "Preservative Treatments for Structural Timber", may be sufficient for the architect or surveyor. If there are any doubts however, he should verify himself that each scantling has its clear and indelible grading mark on one face edge or end with the grader or company responsible identified, if visually graded, or the grade, machine licence number and BS kitemark for machine graded pieces. Timbers with indistinct markings should be rejected and sent back to the supplier. They may be satisfactory but on the other hand they may not and chances should not be taken. If still in doubt the architect or surveyor can check a sample of pieces visually using the criteria set out in BS 4978: 1973 "Timber Grades for Structural Use" to establish whether characteristics in relation to knots, inclined grain, fissures, wane, and growth rate are such as to require rejection of the piece for structural purposes. Whatever checks are carried out on delivery, however, should be extended to include that of moisture content. As moisture content must not be allowed to rise above 22% before building in, this needs to be checked, not only on delivery, but also under storage conditions and on fixing, to ensure that it does not exceed the required level.

Care at the specification stage will facilitate checking on site in respect of joinery items when these are delivered. Selection of good quality standard items of proven success from the catalogue of a reliable manufacturer is a much better proposition on all jobs, except the very largest, than designing and specifying purpose made items. There is then usually no difficulty in recognising manufacturers' labels and identifying marks leaving only the moisture content to be checked when items are delivered. For this reason also in work to existing buildings, it is often better to alter openings to suit proprietory items although, of course, regard must be had to the appropriateness of the item to the building in question, a factor not always given the care it deserves. If purpose made items do, however, have to be designed and specified, much helpful advice on suitable softwoods and hardwoods for joinery and the appropriate workmanship can be obtained from BS 1186: Part 1: 1971 "Quality of Timber and Workmanship in Joinery", together with recommendations for the moisture content appropriate for joinery items in different heating situations. Manufacture may be by the general contractor or by a joinery sub-contractor but, in either case, the architect or surveyor should obtain certificates on the manufacture of the item in accordance with BS 1186 and on its treatment against fungal decay and insect attack coupled with a guarantee for say a period of five years after manufacture. It is always worthwhile for the architect or surveyor to make one or more visits to the joiner's shop while special items are being made. Not only will the architect or surveyor be able to see that his instructions are being followed but minor variations may need to be discussed and agreed. Furthermore, such visits often please the craftsmen concerned who are often only too happy to demonstrate the quality of the wood they have selected and the care to which they are giving the work.

Defects in joinery arise far more, however, from careless handling and poor storage conditions on site than from defective manufacture. It is preferable for this reason for joinery to be retained in the workshop and not delivered to the site until it is very near the time required for installation. If this ideal cannot be achieved, then it is vital that joinery be not only well covered and protected during transit but also kept covered on delivery and stored correctly so as to avoid physical damage, warping and damage from water penetration.

If plywood is to form part of the work then it should, of course, be specified to BS 1455: 1971 "Plywood manufactured from Tropical Hardwoods", otherwise it will be much more difficult to check whether the material will be satisfactory for its purpose when delivered. The Standard requires that all plywood prepared in accordance with its requirements shall carry the manufacturer's name or mark, the country of manufacture, the British Standard Kite Mark, the thickness and two indications of quality relating to appearance and

552

durability. As to appearance both faces are given a grading of 1 to 3, grade 1 being for the best quality face veneer suitable for positions where the sheets will be seen and grade 3 for situations where the plywood is to be hidden from view. For durability the codes used cover the materials used and methods of bonding the ply sheets together; WPP meaning weather and boiling water resistant, BP resistant to boiling water, MR moisture resisting and NT for interior use only. It should not be forgotten that plywood can be treated either with Copper/Chrome/Arsenate or Organic solvent solutions as a preservative and accordingly certificates in accordance with BS 5268: Part 5: 1977, should be obtained when required.

Much the same system is used for identifying that useful material blockboard manufactured in accordance with BS 3444: 1972 "Blockboard and Laminboard" and the surveyor or architect will ease his task of checking the material on site, when it is delivered, if he describes precisely what grade is required at the specification stage. As in the case of plywood, the manufacturer's name, the country of manufacture, the BS number and the thickness, together with two indications of quality, are required to be shown. For blockboard there are only two qualities for face veneer, grade 1 for exposed faces of high quality and grade 2 for backing or for painting and these are expressed as either 1/2 or 2/2 as the case may be although there is also provision for a special grade "S" for selected finishes as agreed between purchaser and manufacturer. As to the quality of the bonding between the pieces of the timber making up the blockboard and the surface veneers three qualities are available, BR boiling water resistant, MR moisture resistant and INT suitable for interior use only.

Architects and surveyors need, of course, to know the limitations in use of chipboard or other particle boards and it is not thought there will be a great call for their use on a contract of medium quality. However, given a decision to use such material, BS 2604: Part 2: 1970 "Resin Bonded Wood Chipboard" provides for the marking of sheets made in accordance with its requirements with the BS symbol, the name, trade name or trade mark of the manufacturer, if made by the extrusion process the word "extruded", if made for the purposes of flooring the word "flooring", the date of manufacture or a date identification mark. The manufacturer should also certify whether the chipboard is of a medium or high density. Sanded and unsanded finishes are available.

Plywood, blockboard and chipboard can all be produced of course, veneered, either with wood or plastic laminates. There is no doubt that much irritation is caused to clients by the use of wood or plastic veneered chipboard in view of the difficulty of making any screw fixing. Provided the architect or surveyor makes the necessary enquiries before specifying the make and type of board he requires, he will not be caught out by being expected to accept an inferior product since, once veneered, all such boards look the same.

Hardboard has its uses at the cheaper end of the market and, if employed, BS 1142: Part 1: 1971 "Fibre Building Boards" should be invoked and one of the seven colour coded types specified. The material must be obtained from a reliable and well known manufacturer whose product is tried and tested and of known quality and performance. Flame retardant qualities are available.

Other components used by the carpenter or joiner, where specified, should be of a good heavy quality and preferably, for the avoidance of dispute, in the case of framing anchors, hangers, straps, fasteners or connectors, from the catalogue of one of the well known manufacturers. Needless to say, such items when made of steel must be protected against rust by galvanising or sheradizing but, furthermore, special care needs to be taken in view of the recommendation that all timber should be pressure impegnated with preservative. In damp situations where timber has been treated with water borne salt solutions there is a danger that the residual salts may attack the protective coating on steel components. It is therefore necessary to ensure that the preservative manufacturer's advice and recommendations to allow time for "fixing" and drying the preservative are implicitly followed to avoid problems of this nature. Preferably the use of organic solvent solutions for preservative purposes to BS 5268: Part 5: 1977 can overcome this problem since these do not attack metal protective coatings and furthermore the use of the pre-vac system of impregnation in conjunction with these preservative solutions provides the additional advantage that it does not raise the moisture content of the timber. Another alternative might be the specification and use of components protected against rust by a plastic coating instead of a zinc coating. Certainly in the case of all metal fastenings the protective coating against rust must be seen to be undamaged at the time the components are used.

Care is needed at the specification stage to indicate whether brass or stainless steel screws and bolts are required and, if so, always to check on site whether they have in fact been provided. If not specified, or if specified and the architect or surveyor is careless about checking, there is little doubt that ordinary steel items will be used.

Mastics are a boon and, if properly specified and applied, are far superior, being resilient and waterproof, to, for example, the old pointing in cement and sand mortar around window and door frames. They must not however, be used as a substitute for proper detailing in some exposed situations. Their very obvious merit leads too easily to such situations and their use needs careful consideration. Obviously there is a need to avoid those mastics which, however, harden and chip in time, those which soak in and stain other materials and those which drip so that having specified a particular make and type the architect or surveyor must see to it that that is the make and type which is being used. Site staff can be forgiven if they assume all such products to be the same, but they do need to be reminded on occasions that this is not the case.

Nobody would deny that the work of the carpenter in particular, working wholly in the field of new construction, has changed quite considerably over the last twenty to thirty years. With the advent of metal connectors, plate fasteners and framing anchors, much of the work of forming joints has become almost obsolete. However, this does not entirely apply to quite the same extent in the field of repair and maintenance and refurbishment and in the connection of new extensions to existing buildings. There may still be the opportunity in such work to employ traditional crafts in an economic manner. However, whether junctions between timber members are formed in a traditional or a current manner, the same basic rules for general carpentry work apply and the architect or surveyor will do well to watch these aspects on his periodic inspections. For example, timbers should be cut cleanly to the precise lengths required and to allow in particular for the full amount of bearing required. The faces of timbers should be cut accurately and straight so that where timbers butt together at joints they do so over the whole sectional area of both members. Care must be taken in nailing so as not to split timbers and it is undoubtedly better, indeed essential in some cases, for nail holes to be pre-bored as well as the holes for screws. Nails should, of course, be of sufficient size for their purpose; in length twice the thickness of the piece of timber being fixed. If bolts are being used the holes bored should be no more than 1.5mm larger than the bolt and both bolt heads and nuts should be provided with washers. Bolts should be long enough for their purpose allowing three turns of the thread to project beyond the nut and care must always be taken to see that nuts are not overtightened so that the timber becomes crushed. The sensible use of timber is another aspect that requires attention; for example it is a simple expedient to turn a joist over should a large knot occur near mid-span and be likely to reduce its strength if left along the lower edge.

The normal unheralded site visits will cover much in the way of checking workmanship to see that matters are proceeding in accordance with the specification but, certainly in the case of the carcassing, the time will come when further work will prevent a final check being made that everything has been carried out properly. Clearly in the case of floors and flat roofs these stages are generally just before ceilings and floorboards are fixed or the underlay or ground-work for flat roof coverings is laid.

In the case of the floor at lowest level, the construction may, of course, be either with the use of sleeper walls or fully suspended from external walls and structural partitions. The vital importance of proper damp proof courses at this level has already been stressed in the section of this Chapter dealing with walls so that at this stage the architect or surveyor will only be looking to see that nothing in the way of this protection against the possibility of fungal decay has been disturbed by other trades since the provision, by the bricklayer or mason, of the appropriate damp proof courses. However, two other aspects are also vital to the success of measures against decay and these are adequate ventilation and cleanliness. Accordingly before boards are laid at this level there must be a check that all debris has been cleared from the sub-floor space and that all ventilation channels are clear in themselves, not only in the outer walls but also in any sleeper walls and partitions. Attention to these aspects will form an important part of the pre-arranged inspection at this stage. Other matters of importance are to ensure that all timber is kept at least 25mm away from the face of all brickwork, blockwork or masonry and that all nailing of timbers to plates or hangers has been properly carried out with the correct number of nails. By the time floorboards are due to be laid, plumbers, electricians and heating engineers will have completed the work of running services so that there will be a need to see that their work has been completed satisfactorily, joints formed properly, no undue bends in pipes, pipes adequately supported and that no reckless cutting of the structural carcassing timber has been carried out, although, admittedly, this is not usually so much of a problem at lowest floor level as it is with upper floors.

At upper floor levels, in checking the structural work before floorboards are laid, the architect or surveyor needs to pay particular attention to two quite different aspects; the strength and rigidity of the floor itself and, once this has been established, the tie of the floor to the external walls to provide those walls with adequate lateral restraint. Accordingly, to deal with the first aspect the architect or surveyor will need to make a final check on hangers, the bearing of the joists on those hangers and the nailing of one to the other and this will, of course, extend to both ends of joists as necessary. If, however, the inner ends of joists are bearing on a structural partition then it is necessary to check at this point that joists are not only adequately nailed to the plate in the partition but also properly nailed to the joists fixed from the other side, where they lap, so that an effective tie is maintained all the way across the structure to the opposite external wall. Particular attention also needs to be paid to the provision, every 2m, and the actual fixing of herring bone strutting so as to provide the necessary rigidity to the floor. To be effective this must be adequately wedged against solid brickwork, blockwork or masonry at each end and accurately cut and fitted between the joists. Solid strutting and unwedged or inadequately wedged herring bone strutting is virtually useless.

In view of frequent reports to the National House Building Council of failures in the trimming around the staircase of new houses, the architect or surveyor will no doubt have taken care in his specification for the jointing of trimmer joist to trimming joists and also for the trimmed joists to the trimmer and will need at this stage to check most carefully that his directions have been followed to the letter for this vital point of construction, irrespective of whether the joists used are of traditional design or, as is more usual now, with plates and straps.

Again, as with the floor at lowest level, there is a need at this stage to check the work of other trades in the provision of services hidden within the depth of the floor and also to check that any notching has been carried out in the manner agreed earlier with the carpenter and appropriate tradesman, so that a floor soundly installed is not unduly weakened by excessive cutting or the cutting of timbers in the wrong places.

Once the strength and rigidity of the floor in itself has been checked, attention can be given to its satisfactory connection to the outside walls for the purpose of providing lateral restraint. These connections are extremely important and all too frequently straps are attached to joists when bent and totally lacking in blocking of any fashion. Fixed in this way straps are well nigh useless for their purpose and it is essential that the architect or surveyor checks that every strap is securely fixed and properly blocked between wall and joist and between the joists themselves, when these are parallel to the wall, so that the strap can be effective should the need arise for restraint in either compression or in tension.

Similar inspections, by arrangement of course, need to be carried out in the case of each upper floor when there are more than one. When it comes to examining the carcassing carried out for flat roofs, however, all the points noted above in connection with floors need to be taken into account along with other essential factors depending on the type of covering proposed. The covering will, of course, have been selected at the specification stage and this will govern the form that the carcassing will take to provide a suitable fall and any integral gutters that may be required. These aspects must all be checked along with the nailing and jointing, the supports for the roof and the tieing to the walls. In regard to the latter it should not be forgotten that in the absence of a weighty parapet any straps must be taken well down the wall to a secure fixing. A turn down over one brick or block is useless as the slightest pull will cause single bricks or blocks to be dislodged in the absence of tailing down from a heavy parapet.

In the case of pitched roofs similar considerations apply. With traditional construction, sizes and spacings of timbers must be checked, joints examined and nailing checked, particularly for continuity of ties, before there is any question of the covering being put on. Roofs formed with trussed rafters need particular attention in view of the ease whereby the metal fastenings can become loosened or even detached by careless handling while trusses are being moved or being placed in position. Accordingly the architect or surveyor should make a particular point in inspecting both sides of every trussed rafter to see that all connections are present and secure. If there is excessive twist or bow a trussed rafter may have to be rejected. Particular attention is also needed in regard to lateral restraint in addition to ensuring that binders and diagonal bracing are securely fixed and are continuous at ceiling tie and ridge levels and abut the brick, block or masonry walls. The check on the fixings should, in particular, extend to those awkward points at the ends where it can be difficult to wield a hammer and in consequence essential nailing is often omitted. The fixing to the wall plate is another point for careful checking to ensure that nailing has not split the timber or disrupted, on one or both sides, the fixing of the metal fastening. Leaving the head 5mm proud helps to avoid this but better still is the provision in the specification of a framing anchor. In precisely the same way as for floors, it is vital to ensure that ties from pitched roofs are properly nogged or packed both between rafters and between the last rafter and the wall and are also fitted tightly against the brickwork or blockwork inner leaf well down inside the cavity, so as to ensure that the tie can act both in compression and tension. If, at the time of inspection the architect or surveyor thinks of the roof as a whole, acting, along with any gable walls, as a strong stiff structure to be made capable of resisting all untoward wind forces, it may be of assistance at this stage of checking. It is unfortunately all too easy, particularly where trussed rafters are involved, to think only of the individual units and to forget the need for proper connections between the units themselves and between the units and the walling. Because of the sequence of operation and because the two trades of bricklayer and carpenter are involved it requires someone, usually a carpenter, to go round to put the finishing touches to such matters as packing out. This is because each connection has to be dealt with individually in view of the fine tolerances involved, however tiresome and time consuming this may be in practice. No doubt the architect or surveyor on one of his unheralded inspections will remind the foreman of this need so that it can be done in advance of his final check, but it will remain the architect or surveyor's duty to ensure that in fact the work has been carried out properly in accordance with the specification and drawings.

Mention has already been made of the need to check the moisture content of structural timber and timber components delivered to the site and of the need to keep this at a reasonably low level by careful storage and covering on site. This is particularly relevant to roof structures for, although a roof covering may keep out the damp, there have been cases of a high initial moisture content, coupled with condensation, causing fungal decay in the timber and corrosion in the thin metal fastenings now used for trusses and rafters very shortly after completion. To avoid this condensation problem the architect or surveyor will have given careful attention in his design to the provision of insulation together with a vapour barrier at ceiling level, which in due course he will have to ensure is installed satisfactorily and is free of gaps which might allow vapour to pass through. What he will need to check at this particular stage is that his provision for the very necessary ventilation in both flat and pitched roof structures has been properly formed in accordance with his requirements. Air bricks must be seen to be in position unblocked and in line to provide cross currents in flat roofs above the level of the insulation. BS 5250: 1975 "The Control of Condensation in Dwellings" suggests a need for 10,000mm^2 per metre length of eaves for ventilation each side to typical dual pitch roofs for domestic purposes and this is usually provided by means of a 10mm slot to the soffit board. This can be useless if subsequently quilting or other loft insulation is allowed to block the clear passage of cross current air, so that it is important at this stage to see that the arrangements are satisfactory on site to prevent this happening. It is for this reason that it is wise to provide stops as necessary to control the position of insulation material.

Generally, the principal carcassing items forming part of an extension to an existing building are the floors and roof structure and consideration has now been given to what steps the architect or surveyor needs to take to fulfil the responsibilities to his client to ensure that these items are completed, so far as it is reasonably possible to check, in accordance with the terms of the contract.

Principles have been established and it would not be difficult to apply these principles in a similar manner to other items of timber carcassing which might also be required. For example, in alterations to existing buildings there is very often a need, apart from renewals of whole floors and sometimes even roof structures, for a timber framed partition, or again, in the new extension it may be decided on structural or aesthetic grounds that one wall should be timber framed. Standards of workmanship as for floors and roof will obviously apply to such items in the same way and the architect or surveyor must see the framing, with all its joints, connections and ties completed, before it is covered up by whatever has been decided as the finishing material or, in the case of external surfaces, any underlay.

Joinery has been included in this section for convenience since so many of the comments on carcassing applicable to the selection of materials, delivery, storage and handling apply also to joinery even though as a finishing item it may seem a little out of sequence. Certainly there is not the same critical concern for the architect or surveyor to see so many items before they are covered up, although in this regard it is advisable to see grounds fixed in position before linings or similar items are fixed. On the other hand, the joinery items, along with many other finishings, are those which are for ever in the eyes of the client and which, in many cases, in these do-it-yourself days are items which the client, acting in whatever capacity, could perhaps just as well have carried out himself. Indeed, many clients able to devote much more time to a job than is economically possible in the building trade will have higher standards for some joinery work than can often be achieved within a reasonably priced building contract and are not slow in saying so. Accordingly the architect or surveyor will need to pay as much attention to these finishing items as he does to the main structural elements, if he is to have a contented client at the end of the contract.

Mention has already been made of the need for careful handling and storage and undoubtedly, given the selection of reasonably good quality joinery from a reliable manufacturer and its safe delivery to the site, most of the defects in joinery are produced because of lack of care in this regard. Rough handling distorts members, opens up joints and physically damages surfaces. Careless stacking does the same thing by introducing stresses which the fittings were not designed to sustain while subjection to damp conditions, far beyond those pertaining in the workshop or likely ever to exist in the completed building, will cause severe swelling as the moisture content of the timber rises. The architect or surveyor must therefore interest himself in this aspect, discuss with the foreman where items are to be stored in advance of delivery, (which itself should be kept back as late as possible and as near to the date of fixing as practicable), and be around, if he is able to be, when items arrive at the site or certainly at least soon afterwards. The foreman must be instructed to check items on delivery and return any which are unsatisfactory or, if in doubt, after discussion with the architect or surveyor. If subsequently, at the time of fixing, any items are found to be defective then these must be held to be the responsibility of the contractor who will have to provide a replacement and meet any additional cost. It can only be to the benefit of the ultimate appearance of the finished work if the architect or surveyor firmly rejects any items at an early stage which he sees either on site, or being installed, and which are below the required quality or are defective or damaged, rather than leaving matters until later when it will be well nigh impossible to enforce his requirements.

Those joinery items on the other hand which are sometimes built in as the work proceeds, for example door linings, need particular care to ensure that they are square and true otherwise, when doors come to be hung, there will be the unhappy spectacle of much planing of edges and a less than fully satisfactory finished appearance. Such features as linings can be so readily damaged subsequent to fixing by the movement of materials and equipment that a little forethought towards providing foam or rubber buffers is a sensible precaution.

Those joinery items which are made up on site such as skirtings, picture rails and architraves should be seen, as the work progresses, to be properly jointed with mitres properly formed, true in shape throughout their length and undamaged. In the unpainted stage it is often difficult to detect those flaws which stand out like a sore thumb when surfaces are decorated with gloss paint, so that the architect or surveyor's close attention to these points at an early stage, can be repaid by the avoidance of difficulties later. It must be stressed that the decorator's art cannot be expected to cover every flaw imaginable. External joinery, for example at the eaves, should be put together with white lead and the architect or surveyor will need to see that the backs of all timbers are primed and in particular that any cut ends are treated with preservative and well primed before fixing.

Should the design call for flush doors internally the architect or surveyor will need to watch carefully that what is specified is in fact delivered if no make or brand name is quoted. One quality of flush door looks much like any other on the surface but BS 459: "Doors" only provides for markings to be included on the hanging or hinge edge in Part 3: 1951 "Fire Check Flush Doors and Wood and Metal Frames (half hour and one hour types)". In this part of the Standard the marking is to include the manufacturer's name or trade mark, the number of the British Standard and the reference, 1 hour or $\frac{1}{2}$ hour, as appropriate. These markings often get removed by planing when the doors are hung and the manufacturers of doors taking part in the TRDA quality assurance scheme are proposing the insertion of a coloured coded plastic plug in the hanging stile to overcome this problem. Neither Part 1: 1954 "Panelled and Glazed Wood Doors" or Part 2: 1962 "Flush Doors" has any provision for marking so that it is essential for the architect or surveyor to obtain a certificate from the maker or supplier of compliance if doors are provided by reference to the Standard and not by manufacturer's reference and catalogue number.

While many joinery items come ready glazed according to the catalogue specification at present, there are still others which will require to be glazed on site. As generally there are no markings on glass, probably the best way of checking that the material specified is in fact being used is to see the suppliers invoice which should give the maker's name and include his certificate of compliance with the classifications set out in BS 952: "Glass for Glazing" Part 1: 1978, "Classification", together with a description of the type of glass, quality, nominal weight and thickness. Also to supplement this examination with spot checks on these items and for condition to ensure that the material is free of bubbles, scratches or wavy surfaces. In particular the architect or surveyor will wish to see whether float or sheet glass is being used according to specification and of which of the two qualities of the former or three qualities of the latter. If obscured or patterned is also called for there will be a need to check on whether the thickness specified is being used as well as the type, the group (governing the price) and the tint. Safety glass in accordance with the recommendations of BS CP 152: 1972 "Glazing and Fixing of Glass for Buildings" or BS 6262: 1982 the latest "Code of Practice for Glazing" may also have been specified for glazing at low level in both internal and external doors and windows and the architect or surveyor will need to see that this is indeed being used. Confusion usually seems to arise in this connection over the difference between Georgian wired cast glass and Georgian polished wired cast glass. The former is a translucent rough cast glass appropriate for roof lights etc. while the latter has a clear polished plate finish. The former will be brought on site by the contractor, if the specification does not differentiate, as it is a great deal cheaper.

The periodic inspections by the architect or surveyor will need to take in matters of workmanship relating to the glazier's craft such as the cutting of panes to the correct size, neither too large so that an overtight fit is provided and therefore likely to cause cracking, or too small, requiring an excess of putty to make up the difference and likely to be a danger should it fall or be accidentally pushed out. The appropriate putties will need to be seen to be in use; linseed oil to BS 544: 1969 a light biscuit colour for glazing to wood, and metal window putty, which is green in colour, for glazing to metal. The former must never be used on metal windows. Linseed oil putties made to the British Standard are packed in containers marked with the maker's name or trade mark and the number of the Standard other than when it is supplied in small plastic bags. Large containers, 12.7kg and above, also have to have a batch number so that if necessary the date of manufacture can be ascertained. In addition the architect or surveyor will need to check that back puttying is carried out, that sufficient sprigs or pegs are used and that there is good close and precise finishing particularly at the corners to the putty. Although no doubt covered by the specification, the architect or surveyor will need to ensure that no putty to glazing in excess of the recommended sizes according to the degree of exposure is carried out and, where necessary, the glass in large squares and in doors and other features subject to vibration is properly glazed in wash leather, accurately cut and fitted with beads secured to the framing by brass cups and screws.

Before proceeding to a consideration of the site supervision involved in the work to provide the other finishes and the services there remains one final but vital feature of the structure to be completed. Although coverings to roofs might be thought of as a finishing, they are so important in protecting the structure below from damp penetration and in keeping the occupants contented in all weathers that it is not unreasonable to elevate them to the status of a structural element in the circumstances. Roofs which leak shortly after completion of the works cause untold damage to the credibility of the building professions and unfortunately there are far too many "masterpieces of architecture" that leak. Clients would wish to have masterpieces of architecture that do not leak but, if given the opportunity, would prefer to have something less of a masterpiece as long as it had a sound roof. Flat roofs with cheap coverings, poorly detailed and inadequately supervised during construction have been the principal cause of damage to many reputations, so that pitched roofs will receive first consideration on the basis that a flat roof will only be provided if there are sound and cogent reasons for it not being possible to provide a pitched roof. This advice is now promulgated by the British Research Establishment in respect of new work and can well be extended into the field of extensions, even although there may be more circumstances necessitating the use of flat roofs because of the difficulties of linking a new pitched roof to an existing. However these difficulties can be overcome in many cases and it is surprising that more consideration is not given to the provision of pitched roofs in extension work.

Coverings for Pitched Roofs

Should a pitched roof be chosen for the extension to an existing building then it is more than probable that the decision will be taken to use the same type of covering as on the existing building, even although the use of new materials will not necessarily match the old because of the age factor. Of course, if the covering on the existing building is very old and nearly worn out, a conscious decision may be taken to renew the covering entirely or, alternatively, to provide a different form of covering in which case, on completion of the contract, the roofs of both old building and new extension will match, allowing the two structures to blend together much better than would otherwise be the case. A decision to change the type of roof covering on an existing building requires very careful consideration, having regard to the possible alternatives, both from an aesthetic point of view and the pitch, strength of timbers, general shape and spans existing in the original roof structure. More often than not, however, it will be a question of using the same materials as on the existing building.

Should it prove to be a case of providing the same form of covering on the new extension as on the existing building then this will almost certainly consist of one or other of the traditional coverings of slates or tiles in one or other of the varying forms. Being in use for many centuries, both the materials and the workmanship for slating and tiling formed the subject of early British Standards and Codes of Practice so that specifying the work is reasonably straightforward for both. Current references are British Standard Code of Practice 142: "Slating and Tiling" Part 1: 1968 and BS 5534, a "Code of Practice for Slating and Tiling" Part 1: 1978 "Design", the first part of an up-dated version in metric terms. Checking that materials specified are being used, however, is still essential as there are plenty of poor quality slates and tiles on sale not conforming to the requirements of the appropriate British Standards. Seeing delivery notes is a vital precaution and the architect or surveyor must also familiarise himself with the means of identification (available from makers or suppliers adopting British Standards) for "Roofing States" prepared in accordance with BS 680: Part 2: 1971, "Clay Plain Roofing Tiles and Fittings" to BS 402:

1979 and "Concrete Roofing Tiles and Fittings" to BS 473.550: Part 2: 1971, together with the different types and grades available within each British Standard range. Very briefly, slates will be provided with a certificate giving the name of source of origin, the name of the colour, vein of rock or particular description by which the slates are known, the thickness and whether graded or ungraded (if graded this would be in terms of the producing quarry for the average thickness of 100 slates), the length and width of the slate (varying widths being stated and if sold as "randoms" or "peggies", the range of length is to be stated). Although many clay tiles have information impressed on the underside there is no requirement in the Standard for actual marking on each unit and all that is required is for the manufacturer to certify compliance, with an added proviso for tests to be carried out if required by the purchaser, the incidence of payment for such tests being agreed in advance. On the other hand concrete tiles are required to be marked on the underside with the manufacturer's name or trade mark while the number of the Standard is to be quoted on invoice and delivery notes. If in doubt on what has been delivered then the architect or surveyor must if necessary take random samples and himself carry out some of the tests laid down in the appropriate British Standard. Although it is unlikely that asbestos cement, either in the form of slates or corrugated sheets or galvanised steel in corrugated sheets (all of which the architect or surveyor will be aware have their own British Standards) will be required, there is a distinct possibility for Pantiles, Roman or Spanish tiles to be needed or other, more recent, innovations in the way of faced concrete interlocking tiles, which have enabled roof pitches to be reduced to such an extent. Here again invoices will need to be seen and checked but, no doubt, also the architect or surveyor will be able to recognise the particular tile he has chosen by its configuration and also probably by reason of the maker's name and identifying mark or brand name on the underside of the tile. Of course, in such instances, the use of proprietory shapes of tile, even though made of materials and in a manner laid down in the appropriate British Standard for the material, means also that manufacturer's recommendations on detailing and in workmanship on site must be followed implicitly. This may cause the architect or surveyor some additional trouble on supervision by way of convincing tradesmen on site that traditional practice will not necessarily suffice. Problems of this nature will be eased by an early discussion with the tiler before work commences so as to ensure that he has all the necessary information and fully understands what has to be done. It is certainly not wise to assume this knowledge.

Slates and tiles are easily damaged on site by rough handling and therefore the architect or surveyor will wish to impress this aspect on the foreman and arrange as necessary, in advance of delivery, suitable clean and dry storage facilities. The foreman must be told that any unsound tiles delivered to the site should be returned as they will certainly not be allowed to be incorporated in the works.

The fixing nail or clip is the other main material item used by the slater or tiler. The Codes of Practice are firm in their advice on these and that they should be non-ferrous and consist either of aluminium, composition (a yellow metal alloy of copper, zinc or tin) copper wire, or cut copper. The architect or surveyor must see as a matter of course that the specified item is being used.

Before the stage of nailing is reached, however, there are vital earlier sequences of operation relating to the underlay to be seen. The covering of a pitched roof of slates and tiles, in whatever form, is basically similar and once the carcassing of the roof structure has been completed and passed by the architect or surveyor the next stage is to provide an underlay of felt and battens. This type of underlay would be provided nowadays even though the existing roof may have had, what may seem at first sight, a more expensive and better quality form of underlay, such as boarding throughout. This is because felt and battens have been demonstrated to be superior in all respects to any other form of underlay. Felt and battens allow the removal of any wind blown rain or snow that may penetrate the tiles or slates without damage to the battens or other timbers, keep out wind blown dust and dirt and keep undue draughts at bay, provided always that they are laid properly. The most vital aspect in the laying is that it should have just that degree of "sag" between the rafters as to provide a clear and uninterrupted channel, from ridge to eaves, for water to drain away below the battens into the eaves gutter. The initial laying of the felt is accordingly an important operation since it must also be properly lapped in both directions, but particularly over rafters in a horizontal direction to provide adequate support at each lap and must be smoothly dressed over the tilting fillet and top of the fascia board and to project at least 50mm over the edge of the gutter. The tilting fillet is a vital feature since this must be arranged to eliminate any possibility of ponding, resulting from penetrating rain or melting snow immediately above the eaves. Following the laying of the underfelt the battens, pressure impregnated with preservative, at the appropriate gauge, can be fixed to the rafters through the felt. Any perforations which are needed through the felt must be carefully arranged, particularly around pipes, where careless cutting can result in water or snow penetration down the side of the pipe into the roof space.

The choice of roofing felt, will, no doubt, have been carefully made at the specification stage from one of the thirteen types in four separate classes covered by BS 747: 1977 "Roofing Felts". These classes provide a range of materials for a wide variety of purposes, including flat roof coverings. It will be found that all roofing felts made to this Standard are now marketed in similar packages with the name of the maker, the number of the Standard, the type of felt and sometimes also the size, length and width and the mass of the roll given on the wrapping. All except types 3G and 3H and the four types in class 4 are colour coded, white for class 1, green for class 2 and red for class 3, where applicable, for ease of identification when unrolled. A felt from class 1 is usually sufficient for an underlay on a pitched roof and with the packaging now a requirement for by the British Standard no confusion should arise and there should be no difficulty on checking that the correct material is being used on site.

When the underlay is complete the architect or surveyor must carry out a pre-arranged inspection to make sure that all those features which will be hidden when the slates or tiles are laid in position have been completed in a satisfactory manner. In addition to the felt and the battens, there will be a number of other items, particularly those of concern to the plumber. There is a possibility that a valley gutter will be required in metal, or secret gutters behind chimney stacks, both of which need to be seen to be of the correct size and not skimped and, furthermore, dressed properly over tilting fillets as well as being properly and securely fixed. In addition soakers at an abutment will need to be inspected, one per slate or tile, securely fixed to the appropriate batten. All such features of detailing and workmanship at abutments or changes of direction and any perforations through the general run of roofing are vital to the long term efficiency of the roof. It needs very little to be done wrongly to upset this efficiency, hence the detailing warrants the use of good quality material with a life expectancy at least equal to that of the material used for the roof covering itself and a high standard of workmanship. Whatever materials are used, however, it is vital for the architect or surveyor to see that all the details are satisfactorily formed before the slater or tiler appears on the scene to do the actual fixing of the slates or tiles, because once this work commences they will be covered up very quickly indeed.

Depending on the type of covering being used and the degree of exposure of the roof the architect or surveyor will have specified requirements on nailing or fixing and also the treatment at the eaves, at verges and abutments and on any special cutting that may be required. In the case of a comparatively small extension to an existing building, the supervisory aspect should consist of no less than one visit by arrangement with the tiler at the commencement of work, at least one visit while the work is in progress and a visit on completion. It must be accepted, however, that it is impractical for various stages of the craftsman's work to be seen before other work is put in hand. The operation of tiling or slating proceeds too quickly for this. A visit is suggested at the commencement so that all the work and any particular aspects can be discussed with the tiler or slater and with the foreman present. On the question of nailing for tiles where this, of course, depends on the degree of exposure, it is probable that the foreman can be charged with keeping a specific eye on seeing that the correct courses are nailed in the absence of the architect or surveyor. On the other hand, the architect or surveyor on his own inspection, or inspections during the course of the work, will probably be able to see for himself that all the correct fittings are being used at verges, ridge, hips, valleys or abutments, that any cutting is only being carried out from a tile and a half so that nowhere is there less than a whole tile at any particular point and, at least on those sections of the roof being worked upon at the time, the nailing or other form of fixing is being carried out as directed. Eventually on completion, the architect or surveyor will need to see that ridge and hip tiles have been securely set and pointed as required, that the necessary pointing has been carried out to any verge and that all flashings have been carefully dressed down over the slates or tiles but yet also securely fixed, wedged and pointed up to the brickwork or stonework as the first line of defence against damp penetration at crucial points. The architect or surveyor approaches this stage secure in the knowledge that he has already seen and approved on behalf of his client the second line of defence now hidden below the surface.

Coverings for Flat Roofs

Should it have been decided that a flat roof is required then the architect or surveyor must exercise a very close degree of supervision over the work in view of the fine tolerances involved and the very narrow margin between success and failure extending over the whole area of the roof. Obviously care must be given to the specification and design of the roof according to the type of covering to be adopted since, although the metals used for this purpose all require broadly similar detailing, the individual metals each have their idiosyncratic requirements which in turn differ from those necessary for asphalt or felt built-up coverings.

Probably the best protection for the client is for the architect or surveyor, once he has decided on the type of covering, to arrange for an estimate to be submitted and for the work to be carried out by a nominated sub-contractor of repute and with the necessary experienced staff to ensure a satisfactory end product. In this connection it may be necessary for the architect or surveyor to see work carried out previously by the firm if he is not familiar with its standards from past experience. An essential pre-requisite for such an arrangement, however, at the specification and drawing stage, is for a meeting to be held with the nominated sub-contractor to discuss the details of the work required, the preparation of the base to the standard necessary before the sub-contractor will do his work and the scope of attendance which the sub-contractor will need from the general contractor. The detailed design requirements for the differing materials used on flat roofs can have a considerable effect on levels of parapets and need to be closely related to existing roof details where an extension is to be joined on to an older building. Failure to iron out all the problems at the specification and drawing stage will lead to the submission of estimates far too low to reflect all the true eventual requirements and much confusion, and probably bad feeling, between the nominated sub-contractor and the general contractor when it comes to the work being carried out. A further consequence would probably be a substantial bill for extras at the final account stage from both.

Architects and surveyors need to be wary of allowing misconceptions to creep into aspects of their relationships with nominated sub-contractors. One that seems to arise frequently is the view that by the appointment of a nominated sub-contractor the architect or surveyor is relieved of his design function and can safely leave all problems to the sub-contractor. This is not so since he is engaged, in the normal course of events, to design all the works except in such cases where a consultant is employed and paid for by the client, for example for heating or electrical services. Accordingly he must exercise his full function on design with all the responsibility which that entails. This does not, however, preclude him from having such discussions as he feels necessary and for completing his design to take into account such advice as he feels it appropriate to accept. This is the ideal to be achieved, because in dealing with specialist sub-contractors it ill-behoves the architect or surveyor to ignore advice given by reputable trade experts, perhaps at a time because a design has reached an advanced stage and there is a disinclination to alter it. This can produce fatal flaws in a scheme and while not all sub-contractors will turn down work when their advice is not accepted, many will introduce a caveat to provide non-liability for all or certain aspects of their work, which would be highly unsatisfactory for the architect or surveyor should matters go wrong and leave him dangerously exposed to claims.

Of course, in regard to the more common traditional sheet metal coverings such as zinc or lead, the architect or surveyor may consider

569

that the staff of those general contractors who are being asked to tender are perfectly capable of carrying out successful work. This might also apply if the architect or surveyor thought that there were a sufficient number of asphalt roofing specialists in the area to merit a certain amount of competition for the work. Detailing is traditional in respect of these coverings and only to be departed from at great risk to the success of the project. Furthermore there are available comprehensive trade association publications for all these materials, and for copper in addition, together with British Standard Codes of Practice (CP 143: "Sheet Roof and Wall Coverings" Part 11: 1970 for lead, CP 143: Part 5: 1964 for zinc, CP 143: Part 12: 1970 for copper and CP 144: "Roof Coverings" Part 4: 1970 for mastic asphalt). Accordingly the architect or surveyor can prepare detailed drawings and specifications for all the requirements in the normal way, but with the knowledge that he is following sound specialist advice.

Whether a nominated sub-contractor, general contractor's staff or a sub-contractor is employed, it still remains the architect or surveyor's responsibility to check that both materials and workmanship are in accordance with the contract.

Where lead is used, checking the material is now considerably simplified by the numerical coding and colour marking adopted in BS 1178: 1969 "Milled Lead, sheet and strip for building purposes". Ends of lead rolls are marked by one of six colours indicating the numerical coding from three to eight, which is also stamped on all sheet and strip together with the British Standard sign and the maker's mark. The numerical coding utilises a number equivalent to the old imperial weight per square foot, for example lead of BS Code No. 5 at thickness 2.24mm, marked red, is the same as the old 5lb lead suitable for flat roofs, depending on traffic. Apart from the coding, the lead should also be checked for cleanliness and freedom from cracks and laminations. Zinc is produced in three gauges and it may be necessary to check the gauge being used by measuring the thickness and weighing a sample. It is usual practice to use No. 14 English gauge, equivalent to No. 21 standard wire gauge, thickness 0.813mm, weight 5.82kg/m^2 for roofing work. BS 849: 1939 "Plain Sheet Zinc Roofing" still governs manufacture and provides that each sheet is branded by the maker and legibly stamped with the appropriate English zinc gauge and the corresponding Standard Wire Gauge. Sheets again must be clean and free from all cracks, blisters and scale, but must also be flat and cut square in the case of zinc. Copper would probably need checking in a similar manner to zinc unless it was possible with the use of both metals to be satisfied merely by seeing the invoice or delivery note. Much would depend at this stage of the contract on the relationship between the architect or surveyor and the particular contractor and undoubtedly checking the thickness and weighing provides the proof of the material which, in the circumstances, the architect or surveyor may feel he needs to have. In the case of copper used for flat roofs on domestic properties, the recommended thickness is 0.457mm and the weight 4.12kg/m². It is important to ensure that the copper is of British manufacture to BS 2870: 1968 "Rolled copper and copper alloys, sheet, strip and foil" and will be certified as such by the manufacturer, and again is clean, flat, cut square and free from all cracks. Aluminium is unlikely to be featured on an extension to an existing building but it too is covered by Code of Practice 143 in Part 7: 1965 "Wrought Aluminium and Aluminium alloys" and BS 1470: 1972 covers manufacture of the metal in sheet form. Normally 0.91mm, of weight 2.52kg/m², is used for domestic work and again it will be necessary to check thickness and weight and that sheets are free of cracks, blisters or scale and are clean.

It is important that the sheet metal coverings are separated from the decking by a material to form an isolating membrane, one which does not stick to the surfaces, allows free movement of the metal, prevents condensation on the underside and reduces the drumming effect which can be produced during heavy rainfall. Bituminous felts are not suitable for this purpose and instead an insulating felt underlay to BS 747: 1977 is recommended by the Code of Practice and the trade associations. Brown type 4A (ii) is considered suitable which is inoderous and weighs 2.3kg/m². A similar isolating membrane is also required under asphalt roofing. This type of roofing felt is not colour coded on the roll but as mentioned previously all the various roofing felts made under this Standard are packaged to show the Standard number and type of felt clearly.

Mention has already been made of the possibility of salts in timber treated with preservative attacking the metal of framing anchors and metal fasteners in humid conditions within roof spaces. A similar danger can arise with sheet metal coverings to flat roofs. Obviously a copper covered roof will come to no harm from timber impregnated with copper/chrome/arsenate solutions but this would not be the case with a covering of zinc or aluminium where there would be a distinct possibility of electrolytic action between the two. It is not thought that the isolating membrane is a sufficient barrier to prevent this happening in some circumstances, since it can only be laid butt jointed, and therefore in these circumstances it is vital that the preservative used for the timber decking is of the organic solvent type.

As with all other building materials, storage on the site is important and a clean dry situation is required for metal and rolls of felt, clear of the ground. Sheets should be stored flat, rolls stored flat, if of lead, or on end for copper, zinc, aluminium or felt and pre-formed sections stored in such a way that they are not deformed, generally laid flat and nesting together.

Although all asphalt available in the British Isles is produced according to British Standards, there are two distinct types, one of which is considered to be of better quality and is more expensive than the other. The architect or surveyor should have no difficulty in distinguishing the two, however, since the blocks which will be delivered to the site with the asphalters pot, will be marked with the BS kite sign and the appropriate number, BS 1162: 1973 for natural rock or lake asphalt, the better quality material, and BS 988: 1973 for asphalt with limestone aggregate, which is a compound of bituminous binders and crushed natural limestone.

Should it be decided for economy or short term reasons to provide a felt roof, then such work, if it is to last even the comparatively short time of 15–20 years anticipated for such material, must be entrusted only to a reputable specialist contractor and never to the general contractor or merely left for a sub-contractor chosen by and in the direct employment of the general contractor. The architect or surveyor will be aware of the categories and weights set out in Table 2 of the British Standard Code of Practice CP 144: Part 3: 1970 for differing types of felt suitable for underlays and the exposed layer on bituminous felt roofs. He will also know that while the purely felt based materials are for really low cost short term work, asbestos based felts are better and must always be used as the first layer of felt on decking and supporting structures where these are of timber, irrespective of the materials used for subsequent layers. Glass fibre based felts are considered to be of the best quality and a properly specified and applied surface in this material will have the best chance of lasting a reasonable period. All these types of felt are made in accordance with BS 747: 1977 "Roofing Felts", as previously discussed, and it is unlikely that the architect or surveyor will be able to recognise the actual difference in materials on site. In the circumstances, he will have to rely on seeing the wrapping to the rolls of felt and the colour coding of the rolls themselves, coupled with the guarantee which must be obtained from the specialist sub-contractor.

All coverings to flat roofs whether of metal or of the built-up type, require a satisfactory decking laid to a proper fall. A basic requirement of such decking is that it should be stable and free from any movement under temporary load, for example someone walking on it, and this involves ensuring that there are no unsupported edges. If the decking is of timber, well seasoned material must be used and tongued and grooved boarding of a minimum thickness of 25mm, well cramped, is to be preferred, although plain edged boarding covered with plywood of weatherproof and boil proof grade, provides an acceptable substitute. Boarding must be laid in the direction of fall, or diagonally, head joints staggered and, most importantly, all nail heads must be well punched home and any screws used must be countersunk. To allow free movement of metal, the surfaces of the decking must be as smooth as possible and all edges rounded if lead is being used. If skirtings or fillets around the perimeter are required against abutments, these should be fixed to the decking clear of the wall to allow for an air space behind for ventilation purposes and to ensure that, should differential movement occur, wall and covering can move independently.

On completion of the work to provide the decking, and this must extend to include all drips, skirtings with any necessary expanded metal lathing, edging strips and the fixing of roof drainage outlets together with all other builders work above the level of the roof covering (for example to parapet walls or copings, the cutting of chases for flashings and work to any other walls at higher level), an inspection should be arranged with the general foreman and preferably also a representative of any nominated sub-contractor, if one should be involved. All the features mentioned in this and the preceding paragraph should then be checked and, subject to the decking being absolutely dry, (no problem if the precautions on temporary covering mentioned earlier have been taken), it can eventually be passed as suitable for covering by the architect or surveyor. It must also, of course, be passed by the sub-contractors representative so as to avoid the sort of embarrassment that sometimes occurs when the sub-contractor's work force arrives with all the necessary materials and equipment only to depart promptly, giving as the reason the incomplete state of the decking and its total unsuitability to take the proposed covering. An argument will then probably develop as to who should meet the bill for the wasted time.

For coverings to flat roofs in metal, it is not thought practical to insist upon work being stopped until the architect or surveyor has seen a stage completed and before work proceeds to the next stage. Obviously however, at least one inspection should be made during the progress of the works and another on completion. In these circumstances it will probably be a case for the architect or surveyor to go over the scope of the work with the sub-contractor's representative, or the foreman if the work is being done by the general contractor, and discuss any points of difficulty or where he considers extra care is needed. If the work is being carried out by a nominated sub-contractor, it is possible for the architect or surveyor to ask the general foreman to keep an eye open for any particular aspects on which he may be concerned. Certainly on his inspection of the work in progress, the architect or surveyor will probably be able to check that the decking is being kept clean before laying commences, that the underlay has been laid properly with butt, not overlapping, joints and properly fixed and that the metal has been correctly welted, with sealants as necessary at side laps, or shaped over wood rolls, but all without undue bending likely to cause work hardening of the metal and corresponding cracks where the metal has been folded. In addition he will be able to see that clips are being provided to cappings as well as to the lower edge of flashings and that flashings are also properly wedged before being pointed. One of the most important items is to ensure that where fixings are made, the correct nails are used, copper for lead and copper, galvanised steel for zinc or aluminium, and this of course applies to the nailing of the underlay as well. The use of correct nails is vital to ensure that no electrolytic action develops between copper and zinc or aluminium, which can lead to rapid corrosion of the metal. The architect or surveyor will also need to look to see that any of the metals in contact with any cement or lime products or where there are dangers of sulphate attack, for example rendering or mortar, are coated with bituminous paint, particularly flashings tucked into brickwork and damp proof courses embeded into brickwork. On full completion of the roof work, the architect or surveyor will look to see that all cappings are completed, all flashings securely fixed into the brickwork or stonework, all drips properly dressed and last, but by no means least, that all rubbish has been cleared off the covering, a point which will need checking again when all works on the contract have been finished since bolts or nails, for example, trodden in or left to allow electrolytic action to occur will cause rapid corrosion in the metal and a hole to form.

For built up roofing of asphalt, the architect or surveyor may consider it necessary, and quite reasonable, to insist that he sees the first coat completed before work proceeds to the second coat and, for felt roofing, that each layer is seen as laid before the next is commenced. If he does consider this essential then he must make himself available at short notice for the necessary inspections otherwise the sub-contractor will be submitting a claim for unproductive time. Where only a single extension is involved there is nothing else on site for the nominated sub-contractor to be engaged upon, in contrast to cases where a number of new extensions, or renewals to a number of buildings, are being carried out.

Even although the architect or surveyor considers that he needs to see each coat of asphalt or layer of felt completed before the next is laid he should still endeavour to visit the site during the progress of the work as well as taking the opportunity to have an early discussion with the sub-contractor's representative on any points likely to cause difficulty, which discussion might well be combined with the pre-arranged visit to pass the decking. Admittedly in the case of asphalt, however, the heating of the blocks to the correct temperature (neither too hot so that the volatile oils are driven off or too cold so that crazing occurs when the material is laid) and the spreading in two coats to the correct thickness is a skilled craft and it is thought unlikely that the architect or surveyor will find much to fault. However, he should ensure that all angles are formed as substantial fillets for the avoidance of subsequent cracking and that where there are abutments between a timber roof and brickwork the asphalt is not tucked in but merely dressed up on the metal lathing of the skirting, ready for finishing at the top with a metal flashing and clips.

In the case of felt roofing, it has already been mentioned that the asbestos fibre based material is a necessity for the first layer on timber roofs and this should be seen to be nailed with galvanised clout nails at 150mm centres generally, but at 50mm spacing at perimeters and at laps. The laps need to be 50mm at the sides and 75mm at the ends of sheets and must be arranged so that they do not obstruct the flow of water off the roof and to break joint in successive layers. If the decking is of plywood, or perhaps in some cases of insulation board, cork or compressed straw slabs, then full bonding of the first layer in hot bitumen with a continuous coating is required, as it is with all subsequent layers of felt. The use as decking of an organic material such as compressed straw slabs requires considerable care in that the makers instructions must be implicitly followed if fungal decay or disintegration is to be avoided. The hazards and possible dangers might well be considered too great to warrant specifying the use of such material in the first place. As with asphalt, care is needed to ensure that the bitumen is not overheated so as to drive off the volatile oils leaving the residue hard and brittle and useless as a bonding agent. Neither too much or too little bitumen should be used in bonding the layers. There must be sufficient to render the bond effective and this can usually be gauged if there is just enough for a small amount to be squeezed out at the edges on rolling. Of course, with bituminous felt it is necessary to provide all triangular fillets in timber, prior to the arrival of the sub-contractors, and still essential to see that the felt is dressed properly at these points and, as before with asphalt, to be finished off with a metal flashing. The architect or surveyor will wish to see, in all cases, that details at edges, abutments and where there are any projections through the roof are all completed in accordance with the drawings supplied to the contractor or, alternatively, in accordance with recognised and approved trade custom as embodied in the Code of Practice. Such details would include any finish, as may be applied, such as asbestos cement tiles as a wearing surface, essential also of course where asphalt sustains traffic other than that for maintenance purposes, or where chippings bedded in bitumen are provided as a light reflective surface. In the latter case it is essential to ensure that all areas within 300mm of any outlets are kept clear of chippings, as must any gutter formed in felt within the main area of roofing.

Mention should also be made of flat roofs where the construction is of concrete. Although not so likely to be required in the case of a typical small extension envisaged to a house or business premises, it may still be convenient in some circumstances to provide such a structure. This could be so when if, as is so often the case, it follows on naturally from the provision of floors in a similar form of concrete construction. These would not necessarily be cast as a reinforced concrete slab but would consist more probably of reinforced concrete beams with clay pots or by way of hollow pre-cast concrete beams. Although aluminium, copper or zinc can be laid on concrete structures, provided accurately positioned composition fixing plugs or preservative treated battens are embedded in the structure to secure the clips and rolls, it is comparatively unusual to provide a covering of lead to a concrete structure. There is no real reason, however, why this should not be done provided the canons of good practice are followed. By far the most common coverings to a flat roof of concrete however, are asphalt and bituminous felt. The combination of the latter coupled with haste in construction leaving entrapped moisture has unfortunately been responsible for unsatisfactory and unacceptable conditions in much new housing since the Second World War.

It is the length of time needed to dry out the structure, and the screed laid to provide the appropriate fall, that makes concrete flat roofs less than satisfactory for comparatively small extensions. This is so even although a temporary roof is provided which, as discussed previously, is highly desirable as a means of keeping all the works dry and, coupled with the provision of side screening, acts as an overall aid to good progress and improved workmanship on practically every contract. At least a month of reasonably good drying weather is required for every 25mm of structure so that, for smaller jobs, cast beams and pots are almost entirely ruled out leaving only pre-cast beams and, of course, the necessary screeding as a suitable form of construction. When it is considered that 75mm is the minimum thickness one would expect to find at the highest point of a dense cement and sand screed laid to falls, it becomes apparent that at least twelve weeks is required for drying out before the roof covering can be applied. Without a temporary roof the difficulties of keeping out rainfall with tarpaulins and polythene sheeting over this period are almost insurmountable.

Accordingly, once the structure has been completed and the screed applied, it will be important for the architect or surveyor to check that sufficient time has been allowed for drying out. In the case where a temporary roof is provided this will involve the keeping of accurate records of the precise date on which the various stages of work are completed and making sure that the interval is correct. Where there is no temporary roof the matter can be more difficult since it is possible that such covers as have been provided against the entry of rainfall may have blown off, or have become at times otherwise ineffective, and the architect or surveyor may well have no actual knowledge of such occurrences. In the circumstances since a visual inspection will be worthless, unless there are pools of water or obvious damp staining, it will be necessary to use a moisture meter and probe below the surface, drilling and making good as required for the purpose. Such a procedure, incidentally, must be adopted in the case of any concrete screeding which is to be covered up entirely by an impervious covering, floors for example, in addition to roofs. In the case of roofs it is essential to employ a moisture meter irrespective of the provision of vents in the covering since these can only be expected to cope with the very last vestiges of residual damp which might remain undetected despite all precautions. This is particularly essential since the design of the roof, of necessity, will incorporate insulation and a vapour barrier so that, in due course, the structure will be totally enclosed apart from the roof vents.

The inspection to check that the concrete structure and screed are ready for the covering to be applied is normally made, as in the case of timber structures, in the company of a representative of the roofing contractors. In all cases, as is the case of any form of flat roof construction, all work above the level of the structure should have been completed in advance, all chases formed and all outlets installed. For a proposed asphalt covering, the architect or surveyor in company with the contractor's representative will need to see that all is ready for the laying of the isolating felt membrane and, for built up felt roofing, that the screed is finished with a wood float and free of all irregularities, gaps or steps and free of any frost damage that would cause the surface to break up. For metal coverings the contractor will expect to see clips or plugs suitable for taking his fixings and these must be secure enough for the purpose not, for example, embedded in some lightweight insulating screed incapable of holding them in position.

The supervision aspects in laying the actual coverings should follow the same procedures as previously described for hollow roof structures in timber, but it is pertinent at this stage to point out that the provision of the vapour barrier below the concrete structure should be delayed for as long as possible for obvious reasons.

Steel Beams

In many instances of a connection between an existing building and a new extension, there is need for either one or a number of wide openings to connect the two together. The beams above such openings are usually more economically formed in steel, from both the cost as well as the size aspect, rather than in reinforced concrete. As a result the architect or surveyor is often faced with the problem of sizing the beam and specifying work where to engage the services of a consulting engineer would hardly be warranted. Many architect and surveyors consider themselves able, however, to size beams for simple domestic or small scale commercial projects and prepare the necessary calculations and details for submission to, and approval by, the local authority under the Building Regulations or GLC constructional by-laws. Bearing in mind the maxim that a little knowledge can be a dangerous thing, the architect or surveyor should only undertake this work if he is entirely satisfied that he has the capability to do it properly. If he is not satisfied on this score then he should either engage the services of an engineer (with the client's authority if he expects the client to pay the fee) or, alternatively, he may be able to utilise the services of the design department of a steel supplier whose costs for the design work, calculations and drawings prepared for, and the obtaining of approval, would be added to the cost of supplying the steel. In the latter cases the aspect of approval of drawings from both consultants and suppliers will arise, as discussed previously in Chapter 7, dealing with drawings prepared by others in the building team in general, and the precautions and procedures outlined in that Chapter will need to be followed. Another aspect to be borne in mind is that if a consultant or supplier is involved, it is better if they ascertain the loading on the beam in question, both by site inspection and a study of the architect or surveyors drawings, rather than to be supplied with the information by the architect or surveyor himself. Designers are used to making approximations in this regard which are quite adequate and permissible in the circumstances. Architects or surveyors can, and do, get bogged down in unnecessary detail which may possibly give rise to an error which, if left undetected, could have serious consequences and for which, obviously, neither the consultant or supplier could be expected to accept any responsibility.

Whoever, in fact, prepares the calculations and specifies the beam it will be necessary for the work throughout to comply with British

Standard 449: "The Use of Structural Steel in Building" Part 2: 1969, in metric units. Steel used in accordance with this Standard is deemed to satisfy both the Building Regulations 1976 and the Constructional By-Laws of the Greater London Council. This will mean, in effect, that a beam of known properties selected from the Tables in another British Standard covering the manufacture of steel beams will have to be used. The British Constructional Steelwork Association and the Constructional Steel Research and Development Association publish a "Structual Steelwork Handbook" which contains a list of the steel sections available with, their dimensions produced under British Standard 4: "Structural Steel Sections" Part 1: 1980 "Specification for Hot Rolled Sections" with further tables to show the structural properties and safe loads for those sections used under various conditions and when made of three of the Grades of steel, 43, 50 and 55 (in ascending order of strength but the first representing "mild steel" in common parlance) provided for under BS 4360: 1979 "Weldable Structural Steels". Accordingly the specified designation for a steel section will have to state its serial size, its mass per unit length in kilogrammes per metre (since the same sized sections are produced in different weights) and an appropriate word for its shape for example, beam, channel or angle, thus "914 × 419 × 388 beam", coupled with the grade of steel required, since the calulations submitted for approval will have been prepared on the basis of the use of such a section.

Although BS 4: Part 1: 1980 makes no requirements as to the marking of products produced to its standards, steel sections made in the United Kingdom normally have the name or trade mark of the manufacturer incorporated on the web during rolling. Some sections may also be provided with details of size and mass per unit length but, if not, the surveyor can at least check the precise dimensions. However, he will not be able to weigh the beam and if unmarked steel is delivered, it must be accompanied by a Certificate that it is in accordance with the size and weight specified. The requirements of BS 4360: 1979 are satisfied if each piece or parcel of steel is legibly marked with the manufacturers name or trade mark and with the cast number, or identification marks, by which the steel can be traced to the cast from which it was made, while Appendix D to the Standard requires steel of nearly all the grades covered to be legibly marked with the grade identification number with the marking to be ringed in paint. In this Standard there is express provision, unlike the terms of BS 4, for certification of the steel by the manufacturers and for this to be extended through to certification by the merchant stockist.

When the architect or surveyor examines the section as delivered, it should be found to be cut precisely for the required length with the ends smoothed, particularly if the section concerned is only part of a longer beam, where the ends must butt together accurately at the joint. The section or sections must also be straight and free from twisting. If not, they should be returned to the supplier.

Steel to be used is best specified to be given a coat of red oxide before delivery to the site. This must be inspected before the casing is applied and damaged areas of the protective coating made good. Whatever method of casing is chosen by the architect or surveyor it is clear that he must see that the beam is properly supported and positioned and that all framework or reinforcement to the proposed casing are secure before the beam is fully encased in accordance with the requirements of the deemed to satisfy specifications in Schedule 8 of the Building Regulations 1976, or of the appropriate sections of the Constructional By-Laws.

The foregoing paragraphs, dealing as they do with the comparatively minor requirement of one or, at most a few beams in steel, is, of course, a great deal less complicated an operation than the case where columns and possibly a whole framework of steel is required. Here it is almost certain that the services of a consulting engineer would be essential or at least the full services of a steelwork specialist sub-contractor. Much liaison work is required by the architect or surveyor and it is he who must see and ensure that full co-operation exists between general foreman and the foreman erector so that the frame is put up truly plumb and level. The general contractor needs to be able to certify to this effect on completion of erection and before any casing of the steel is carried out although, of course, the architect or surveyor will, no doubt, wish to be involved in the matter of checking at the time the work is in progress.

Metal Windows

The need to select windows and other joinery items from a reliable supplier has already been mentioned in connection with wood windows and doors and applies equally, of course, to metal windows and doors. A product of known quality will then be obtained and it will be far simpler for the architect or surveyor to check on site that the client is obtaining what is specified.

Aluminium and steel are the principal metals used in window manufacture. The former is usually anodised while the latter can be used in an alloy to produce stainless steel windows, although these are very expensive. Normally rolled steel bars are used in manufacture and the window is then hot dipped galvanised to BS 729: 1971 "Hot dip galvanised coatings on iron and steel", which is generally considered satisfactory for the climate encountered in the United Kingdom, while fittings are given a ZN3 zinc electroplated coating in accordance with BS 1706: 1960 "Electroplated coatings of Cadmium and zinc on iron and steel". British Standard 990 "Steel Windows Generally for Domestic and Similar Buildings", provides a range of sizes both on a module of 100mm, the "Module 100" units, under Part 2: 1972 and to Imperial units, the "N", "H" and "Z" and Georgian ranges under Part 1 of 1967. There is also another metric W 20 "Preferred Range Specification" to different sections prepared by the Steel Window Association and set out in their Publication SWA 201: 1972 also based on a module of 100mm. Performance standards are laid down in a further Steel Window Association Publication "Specifiers Guide to Window Performance".

The aspect of performance has been receiving attention in regard to all windows, not just those of metal, for some time now and BS 4315: "Methods of Test for Resistance to Air and Water Penetration" Part 1: 1968, "Windows and Structural Gasket Glazing Systems", describes the appropriate tests to be carried out. The performance levels of windows under the methods of test laid down in BS 4315: Part 1 were suggested in a British Standard Draft for Development DD4: 1971 as providing "Recommendations for the Grading of Windows, Resistance to Wind Loads, Air Infiltration and Water Penetration and notes on Window Security". Four grades of exposure, sheltered, moderate, severe (a) and severe (b), are defined and many proprietory ranges of windows are now available in various materials complying with one or more of these grades.

If metal windows and doors are not specified by manufacturer and catalogue number but only by size and reference to a British Standard, it will be found that both BS 990 for Steel Windows and BS 4873: 1972 for "Aluminium Alloy Windows" provide for the windows made in accordance with the requirements of these Standards to be marked or suitably labelled with the name or trade mark of the manufacturer and the number of the appropriate Standard. There is provision in the Standard relating to aluminium windows for testing to BS 4315: Part 1: 1968 and accordingly manufacturers are able to issue certificates relating to performance ratings and for exposure grading. Such certificates should of course be seen and retained.

A great deal of surface damage and frame distortion can be caused to metal windows and doors by careless handling and poor storage conditions on site. The architect or surveyor must see that the general foreman is well primed to watch for this aspect and that, before delivery, proper consideration is given to the proposed storage area so that components are kept upright on battens and in clean surroundings, with nothing else stored on top. Since openings in walls must be of the correct size, plumb and square, it is of course preferable for windows and doors to be fixed, with lugs built in to hold the damp proof course in place at the sides of openings, as the work proceeds. If this is not possible, sand courses must be left at the sides of the opening to enable building in later. In this case building must be carried out to very precise measurements to conform to the window manufacturers opening sizes. In either case, care must be taken to provide for the vertical damp proof course to lap over the frame. Equal care, of course, is needed when metal windows are fixed to wood frames.

Section B
The Services

Cold and Hot Water Services and the Soil, Waste and Rainwater Disposal Systems

All services may be installed by the general contractor if, as is sometimes the case on smaller contracts, the work is fully specified but, more often than not, the electrical service and a central heating system will be installed by nominated sub-contractors, estimating on a separate outline specification prepared by the architect or surveyor. It is comparatively rare, however, for the internal plumbing system above ground of cold and hot water supply, sanitary fittings, waste and soil pipes, together with rainwater gutters and downpipes, to be installed other than by the general contractor. If that is the case, having therefore specified the installation in detail and no doubt shown much, if not all, of it on the drawings the architect or surveyor will need to see, as for other items, that his specified products are, in fact, supplied and installed.

Many of the pipes and fittings used on an internal plumbing installation are covered by British Standard Specifications and there are a number of British Standard Codes of Practice covering various aspects in the design of the installations, compliance with which is normally acceptable by the Water Authority and will secure approval under the Building Regulations or in London, the Local Authority By-laws. This makes the specification somewhat simpler to write and, in the main, it is possible simply to refer to items in accordance with the appropriate British Standard, since there are a number of manufacturers producing items complying with those Standards. What pipes and fittings are specified will, of course, depend on the quality of the work required by the client. Sufficient to say that there are Codes of Practice for "water supply" CP 310: 1965, Sanitary Pipework above Ground in BS 5572: 1978 entitled "Code of Practice for Sanitary Disposal", "Frost Precautions for Water Services" CP 99: 1972, "Drainage of Roofs and Paved Areas" CP 308: 1974 and there are Standards covering copper, lead, polythene in two types, un-plasticised polyvinyl chloride, galvanised steel, cast iron and pitch impregnated pipes, cisterns and cylinders in various materials, ball valves, and even the floats for ball valves, in both copper and plastic.

Specifying pipes and fittings using the appropriate British Standard involves the architect or surveyor knowing the contents of the Standards. The BS Handbook No. 3, "Summaries of British Standards for Building", currently four loose leaf volumes published by the British Standards Institution in 1977 and available on an updating subscription service, provides a precis of all the Standards relating to building, totalling 1,439 in all, including those covered by Addendum Packet A4–1979, without the need to purchase individual standards. The Handbook is sufficient for the purpose of specifying by architects or surveyors and also gives details of the markings incorporated on goods made to comply because in a number of cases there are alternatives from which a selection needs to be made. Such alternatives are also reflected in the identification markings of the products so that it is essential for the architect or surveyor to be familiar with those markings if he is to ensure that his client obtains what has been specified on his behalf.

Of the water pipes most likely to be used on good quality contracts at the present time, copper is probably the first choice. Copper pipes made under BS 2871: Part 1: 1971, "Copper tubes for Water, Gas and Sanitation", from 15mm up to 42mm diameter are stamped with the kite mark and BS number plus the table designation and maker's identification mark every 500mm. If over 42mm they are stamped at the end of each length only. Pipes from Tables X and Y in the Standard can be bent, which is preferable to using elbows, provided bending is done properly to maintain the full bore, but those from Table Z, hard drawn tubes, are not suitable for bending. Pipes from both Table X and Y are satisfactory for capillary and compression jointing and for welding, but those covered by Table Z are not suitable for welding. Annealed copper tubes, suitable for microbore heating installations, were added to the Standard in 1976 under a new Table W and these again are not suitable for welding.

The use of stainless steel is another possibility for high quality work. BS 4127: Part 2: 1972, "High Gauge Stainless Steel Tubes", covers the manufacture of stainless steel tubes suitable for bending and for use with capillary or compression joints. The pipes are made in bores from 6mm to 42mm. The Standard requires the maker to mark indelibly each length of tube of 15mm bore and upwards, at intervals not exceeding 500mm, with the number of the Standard and his identification mark. Other bore sizes can be marked in the above fashion or at one end with a band of adhesive tape possessing waterproof characteristics, 25mm wide, printed with the British

Standard number and the makers mark. The adhesive tape is to be fixed not less than 75mm from the end of pipe.

Plastic pipes are only suitable for running cold water services, but are often used on large contracts where the saving in material costs can make a significant difference. There are two distinct materials in use for this purpose, flexible polythene tube in two degrees of hardness, high density to British Standard 3284: 1967 Type 50 and low density to BS 1972: 1967 Type 32 and the more rigid unplasticised polyvinyl chloride pipes to BS 3505: 1968. As a result there are plenty of opportunities for confusion on site if the architect or surveyor is not sufficiently careful in his specification or lacks knowledge of the identification marks. Pipes in both materials come in different pressure classes, coded longitudinally on the tube or pipe, red class "B" for a maximum pressure of 60 metre head of water, blue class "C" for maximum pressure of 90 metre head and green class "D" for 120 metre head and, as they are more rigid, there is a further class "E", colour coded brown, for unplasticised pvc pipes to take a maximum pressure of 150 metre head of water. With polythene tubing delivered in coils the architect or surveyor will need to look for the maker's name or mark, the British Standard number, the nominal size and the class letter with colour code. Unplasticised pvc pipes are provided with the same information but they are delivered in 6 metre and 9 metre lengths and the information is given at spacings not in excess of 3 metres. Of course, in addition, it is also necessary to check that all fittings are of the correct type and make appropriate to the tube or pipe selected. Suppliers are not averse to palming off oddments and it may be that the contractor might not know the difference.

Galvanised steel pipes are not used so frequently now in new work but it is possible that they could prove useful for extending an existing system. Manufacture nowadays is to British Standard 1387: 1967 and the medium and heavy thicknesses used in building are colour coded blue and red respectively in 50mm wide bands at one end for tubes up to 4 metres in length, and at each end for tubes over 4 metres. No other marking is required by the Standard.

As in the case of galvanised steel tubes, it is unlikely that there will be a requirement for lead pipes in an entirely new structure nowadays but a possibility for use can still arise in connection with existing buildings. Lead and lead alloy pipes for other uses than the transmission of chemicals are covered by BS 602, 1085: 1970, two formerly separate Standards updated and published as one. For water distribution purposes two grades of pipe are set out; Table 3 for cold water services and Table 4 for hot water. Both require that the lead used in manufacture will be of BS 602 Chemical Composition

Standard No. 1 and the manufacturer will certify to this effect if required. All pipes produced under the Standard are clearly embossed with the BS number, the code number of the pipe, which determines the bore in mm, and the nominal wall thickness, together with the maker's identification mark. It would be lead to this standard that would need to be used for connecting galvanised steel pipes to basins, baths, etc.

Cisterns are well covered by British Standards; in galvanised steel to BS 417: Part 1: 1964 in imperial units and Part 2: 1973 in metric units and in two grades "A" and "B", asbestos cement to BS 2777: 1974 and plastic, of either Polyolefin or Olefin Copolymer, to BS 4213: 1975. Each cistern is marked with its BS number according to material, manufacturer's name and reference number related to size, shape and capacity to water line. No difficulty should therefore arise from either specification point of view or site checking. Ball valves are also made to a British Standard, BS 1212: Part 1: 1953 covering the piston type and Part 2: 1970 covering the diaphragm type, while the float can be specified and checked for marking to BS 1968: 1953 for copper or BS 2456: 1973 for plastic, for both cold and hot water use.

Cylinders, in a similar manner, are covered by British Standards, both the direct and indirect type. British Standard 417: Parts 1 and 2, as mentioned above, deals with galvanised steel direct cylinders as well as cisterns and BS 1565 deals with indirect cylinders, Part 1 of 1949 for imperial units and Part 2: 1973 for metric units. For cylinders in copper, the direct type is covered by BS 699: 1972 while BS 1566 deals with indirect cylinders, Part 1 of 1972 for the double feed type and Part 2, also of 1972, for the single feed type. Galvanised steel cylinders have the British Standard mark and number, the grade and thickness, the maker, the capacity in gallons or litres and the maximum working head in feet or metres stamped on. Copper cylinders have stamped on the British Standard mark and number, the maker, the type reference and grade, the maximum working head in metres, the capacity and the thickness of the metal for direct cylinders. Indirect cylinders to BS 1566: Part 1 double feed type, have additional information stamped on concerning the maximum length and location of the heater and the area of the primary heater surface while, for Part 2, the single feed type, there is also the grade and heater class plus the admonition that the "cylinder to be fitted in vertical position only", the maximum permissible quantity of primary water with the water content capacity of the primary heater also added.

There should be no difficulty in checking that the sanitary fittings delivered are as ordered as these will probably be immediately recognisable, having no doubt been jointly selected by the architect or surveyor and the client. The compliance with design principles and manufacture in accordance with British Standards current at the time is a guarantee of quality and the architect or surveyor will do well to persuade the client to select fittings which comply in all respects. The design of such fittings is satisfactory but it has to be admitted that clients often wish to have something different. Provided the fittings are not too novel, manufactured by a reputable firm, supplied with a guarantee and with the usual provision for connections, they will probably be satisfactory but the architect or surveyor may feel, of course, the need to opt out, in writing, of responsibility for efficiency in use and long term durability should there be any doubts in his mind. When they are delivered to the site, sanitary fittings should be checked for any flaws in manufacture or damage in transit. They must, of course, be safely stored and when installed well protected against damage by other trades. The architect or surveyor will need to see to this.

The discharge of waste products to the drainage system involves a further range of pipes which, again, are covered comprehensively by British Standards making specification and the checking of products relatively easy, once a decision on the quality required has been taken. Copper, frequently used for good quality work, either entirely on its own or for branches leading and connecting to cast iron pipes, has already been covered since British Standard 2871: Part 1: 1971 deals also with the larger pipes drawn from half hard material under Table X, which can be bent and which is also suitable for silver brazing and welding. It will, of course, be necessary to provide expansion joints if long lengths are welded.

Lead, previously very commonly used in the same way that copper is so frequently used now to connect outlets from fittings to cast iron pipes, has also already been dealt with earlier since BS 602, 1085: 1970 deals with all sizes of pipes.

Cast iron spigot and socketed soil, waste and ventilating pipes and fittings are provided for in BS 416: 1973. The range is very comprehensive and, of course, the material is much thicker and heavier than that used for cast iron rainwater pipes and fittings so that the architect or surveyor should soon learn rapidly to tell the difference even though, superficially, they may look alike. The soil, waste and ventilating pipes are marked with a figure indicating the nominal bore, the maker's name or trade mark, the British Standard number with the letter "S", if spun as against being cast, and a letter "T" if specially tested at the purchaser's expense to a higher than normal pressure of $0.07N/mm^2$. All soil, waste and ventilating pipes are given a black rust inhibiting coat before leaving the works, probably the most immediately distinguishing feature. Cast iron rainwater goods, on the other hand, covered by British Standard Code of Practice 460: 1964, while also marked with the size, the appropriate BS number and the maker's name or trade mark, are merely given a coat of quick drying grey paint to act not as a primer but merely as a protection against damage during transit and storage.

It is not considered very likely that pitch impregnated fibre pipes will be required for soil, waste or ventilating purposes within the scope of the work covered by this book. Reference to BS 2760: 1973 however, will show that pitch fibre pipes made in accordance with the Standard are legibly marked with the maker's name and the number of the British Standard although with such unpleasantly distinctive material, it is not thought that confusion is likely to arise on site with other pipes or fittings.

On the other hand, there is every likelihood of use being found for unplasticised polyvinyl chloride soil and ventilating pipes, fittings and accessories, in colours black or grey, covered by BS 4514: 1969, as amended to 1978, provided there is no discharge of water exceeding 60°C. For this reason the pipes are considered suitable for discharges from WC fittings and, it may well be thought, generally suitable for baths and basins as well. However, it is impossible to be sure that owners or tenants will not find some reason or other for pouring boiling water down the waste pipes of such fittings and, even with the dilution from the cold water contained in the trap, causing damage to the waste system. In most households the desire to do this would probably be rare, or even non-existent, but with premises for tenant occupation the risk must be considered too great for most owners to take. Where owner occupation is involved, the architect or surveyor can discuss the situation with the client who can then, perhaps, be expected to take the responsibility for ensuring that his family does not indulge in such practices. In the case of waste pipes serving kitchen sinks or plumbed fittings in kitchens, however, it is essential to avoid the use of plastic and keep to a metal because of the much higher temperatures involved, particularly with the use of washing machines. The clear and durable marking for each unplasticised pvc pipe and fitting made under the above Standard consists, in the following order, of the manufacturer's identification, the number of the Standard and the nominal size of pipe. The architect or surveyor must carry out a check on the pipes and fittings, when delivered, as there are numerous systems available which do not comply with the Standards while also checking that all fittings come from the same range and are made by the same manufacturer.

It is convenient at this stage to mention the range of pipes, gutters and fittings available for the disposal of rainwater. Once again the field is well covered by authoritative advice and British Standard Code of Practice CP 308: 1974 provides guidance on the design of installations to provide efficiency in use. Long term durability will depend on the selection of the material for the fittings but may also depend on client's individual preferences and a desired appearance in relation to existing features. The range of rainwater goods available is large and the do-it-yourself market provides many more examples in addition to those covered by British Standards. It is accordingly essential, as we have seen in all other cases, to ensure that the specification is carefully prepared and is precise in its requirements and that what is being put up on site complies in all respects. It is not always easy at a glance to tell the good from the bad and the architect or surveyor must be familiar with the markings on the goods made to the requirements of the appropriate Standards.

The traditional and good quality, long lasting, cast iron gutters, both ogee and half round, and pipes as already mentioned are covered by British Standard Code of Practice 460: 1964. They can be identified by a number, indicating the size of pipe, gutter or fitting and the BS number on each section and the coating of grey paint, as already mentioned, which distinguishes such pipes and fittings from the heavier soil and waste pipes. Not to dissimilar in appearance by shape, and with a galvanised or vitreous enamelled finish yet still of a reasonable quality, though not so long lasting as cast iron, are pressed steel gutters, both half round and ogee, rainwater pipes, fittings and accessories to BS 1091: 1963. Each gutter, pipe length or fitting is indelibly marked with the British Standard number. While the range of matching gutters, pipes and fittings are all made of light pressed steel, there is also a range of heavy pressed steel gutters produced under the Standard over 380mm in girth, for use as box gutters, valley gutters on top of boundary walls, or in similar situations. They too can be either galvanised or finished with vitreous enamel but can also be supplied merely with a coating of a tar based paint. They are indelibly marked in the same way as the light pressed steel gutters.

A joint British Standard BS 1431: 1960 covers "Wrought Copper and Zinc Rainwater Goods", both gutters and pipes, although the gutters are not very commonly used nowadays in view of their propensity to blockage because of the necessary provision of stays to stiffen the construction at regular intervals. Identification marks consist of the makers name or trade mark and the number of the Standard, although there is also provision for the goods to be supplied unmarked, provided the maker certifies that construction and the materials used are strictly in accordance with the Standard.

Aluminium is another metal for which a British Standard is available covering rainwater goods, namely BS 2997 of 1958. Half round, ogee and square section gutters are produced by casting or extrusion or, alternatively, wrought from sheet metal. Round or rectangular pipes are produced by extrusion when, of course, they are seamless, or they may be wrought and seamed. The goods produced to conform with the Standard are either marked indelibly with the makers name or trade mark and the number of the British Standard or, alternatively, the manufacturer certifies that the goods comply with the Standard.

The lack of the need for regular painting can be a considerable attraction to clients and accordingly on cheaper work, or where appearance is not of vital concern, unplasticised polyvinyl chloride gutters, pipes and fittings (UPVC), in either black or grey, may be required. British Standard 4576: Part 1: 1970, as amended in 1978, covers only half round gutters and round pipes and it is surprising that it has not been extended or revised to include other shapes, in view of the rather poor appearance provided by half round gutters in most situations. There are many other plastic alternatives available on the do-it-yourself market and, accordingly, it is essential for the architect or surveyor to check the identification marks on UPVC goods delivered to the site. Gutters and pipes made under the Standard are clearly and durably marked to show, in the following order, the makers identification, the number of the Standard and the nominal size of the pipe or fitting.

Finally, in this section on pipes, there is yet another Standard covering a further non-metallic system of rainwater gutters and pipes, namely asbestos cement to BS 569: 1973, but it is not thought that this material is likely to be required on the typical contract envisaged in this book or that, if it was, it would be mistaken for any other type. Both half round and ogee shaped gutters are produced, together with round pipes, and are all marked with the manufac-turer's name or trade mark and the number of the British Standard.

It is the responsibility of the architect or surveyor not only to specify the cold and hot water installations, together with the soil, waste and rainwater disposal systems, but also to design the layout in detail. Although the soil and waste disposal is usually given close attention because, of course, Building Regulations or By-Law approval has to be obtained, little attention may be given to the running of cold and hot water pipes. Sometimes a contractor will ask for a layout if none is submitted but, at other times, the plumbers will proceed and install pipes as they see fit. Very often the installation will be excellent and, depending on the skill of the plumber, better and neater even, perhaps, than the architect or surveyor would have suggested himself. At other times, the architect or surveyor will arrive on site to find pipes being run all over the place in such a manner as he could never have contemplated. If, however, he has not provided a layout the architect or surveyor has only himself to blame if an extra is required by the contractor to re-run pipes already fixed in position to suit his special requirements. What is suggested is that the architect or surveyor either provides a layout, which can best be done, very often, in the form of isometric sketches, or alternatively, discusses the proposed arrangement in advance with the general foreman and plumber. This latter meeting is essential because even though in the design the architect or surveyor may have followed the three Codes of Practice governing the work, there are still bound to be points of detail to settle or agree in the absence of full layout drawings.

Certainly in the work on site, the archiect or surveyor will wish to see and be sure that pipes will be adequately protected against the effects of bad weather in accordance with the suggestions embodied in British Standard Code of Practice CP 99: 1972. However, before the stage of applying any insulation material to pipes is reached, the architect or surveyor, with the general foreman and the plumbers, will need to see that all the basic rules of good workmanship have been followed and to apply the appropriate tests to the installations. They will look to see that all runs have been properly laid out with no awkward bends, that stop cocks are accessible, particularly on rising main and down services, expansion joints provided where necessary, overflows provided in visible positions, cisterns cleaned out, all joints properly formed, and all pipe runs securely fixed in accordance with the recommendations of the Codes for both horizontal and vertical lengths but well clear of surfaces to be painted. The cold and hot water installations will then be charged slowly with water to exclude all air, preferably with all fittings installed, although it may be necessary to cap off some connections temporarily, if all fittings have not yet been delivered. This will enable a check on soundness to be made on all those joints of runs which are subsequently to be covered up by insulation or casings, or to be hidden within the depth of floors or the thickness of partitions. Now is the time to check not only that the system is leak proof and capable of withstanding a pressure of 3.4 bar for a minimum of 30 minutes, with no loss of pressure on the service pipes in addition, as recommended by the Code of Practice, but also that the system is not going to be one of those that provide a perpetual source of nuisance to the occupier through water hammer and noise transmission. Drawing off quantities of water from all points in turn and allowing the system to refill will test this aspect. The introduction of flexible connections or other means to combat noise can so easily be done at this stage whereas, if left until later, the problems can often be difficult to solve without the necessity for pulling the structure apart. Similarly, joints which leak under pressure in excess of that for normal requirements, as well as joints for distributing pipes which leak under normal conditions, can easily be remade and the system again tested until all is satisfactory.

In the case of soil and waste pipes, size and type of trap, inclination of wastes, connection of anti-syphonage pipes, provision of cleaning eyes as well as jointing and support, as for other pipes, in accordance with the practice of the Code, all will require checking. Joints for any internal rainwater pipes need checking, of course, although externally they are often left unjointed and merely wedged so as to stop them rattling in storm conditions, for ease of identification in case of blockage, or for ease of replacement should that be subsequently necessary. Testing soil, waste and internal rainwater pipes will require open ends to be capped off and the pipes subject to air pressure. Where no water traps are involved, pipes can be tested to 100mm water gauge for a period of five minutes when the pressure should not have dropped below 75mm. With water traps present in the system the test has to be limited to 38mm water gauge pressure over a period of three minutes and the pressure should not have dropped below that level after this period has elapsed. If pressure drops below the required amounts, it will be necessary to have recourse to a smoke rocket, or pressure producing smoke machine, in order to detect the position of the leak and for this to be repaired and to enable the system to be re-tested. Alternatively the bubbling of a soap solution applied around the joints may indicate the position of leaks while the air test is in progress.

Gutters for rainwater disposal should be tested, if not at the same time as the soil and waste pipes, then, certainly, well before completion, by stopping up the outlets, filling the gutters to overflowing and leaving for half an hour or so, when a check can be made to see that all the joints have been soundly made. Obviously, a check will be made by the architect or surveyor on the fall and the fixing of all gutters and, on completion, that all wire balloons have been fitted to prevent clogging of gutter outlets by leaves or debris and the building up of birds nests in the top of ventilating pipes.

Once the plumbing above ground has been checked, authorisation can be given for insulation to pipes to be fixed but, here again, if the architect or surveyor is wise, he will insist on seeing that this work also has been done properly before authorising any of the operations which will obscure pipes once and for all. Very often, there is an argument as to who should do the work of lagging, and the tradesmen drafted reluctantly to do it give the task less than the attention it deserves. If lack of care is not the prevalent attitude, an equally bad mood can exist which suggests that, as the insulation is seldom ever seen, it hardly matters how it is applied or fixed. Those situations where it is difficult to fix lagging, and there are usually some such places, however well laid out the system may be, will be skimped if the architect or surveyor does not take care. Strict compliance with the Code of Practice and the fixing of insulating materials in accordance with the manufacturer's requirements are absolute essentials for this work.

Central Heating Installation

The supervising aspects for the architect or surveyor on the installation of a central heating system are included here, rather than later with other sub-contractor's works, since the system consists to a large extent of a series of pipe runs most of which are generally hidden within floors and partitions or run within casings. Accordingly, the architect or surveyor will have precisely those same elements to watch for as he has with a normal hot water installation. He will need to see that the pipes and fittings specified are being used and these, of course, with various alternatives, have already been dealt with earlier in this section. He will also need to ensure that he has either decided upon the layout of pipes himself, by preparing a drawing in advance, or will discuss with the engineer how they are proposed to be run. In this respect, some heating engineers can be as insensitive as some plumbers and, instead of a pleasingly neat arrangement being presented, an ill considered array of pipes will be fixed all over the place if the architect or surveyor exercises no control at all. At the same time, of course, care must be exercised over the often vexed question of cutting joists and other timbers for pipe runs and how this can be done to satisfy all the various requirements. All the necessary requirements for pipe fixings will also need to be considered.

A check will be needed on the running of expansion pipes and on the presence and proper installation of the balance tank, comprising a small cistern complete with ball valve and overflow pipe. The architect or surveyor will certainly wish to check that radiators are of the type and, in particular, of the size estimated for and securely fixed on the appropriate brackets with all control and regulating valves, thermostats and self venting air or "bleeding" valves as appropriate. Furthermore, that the boiler is of the make, type and size as specified, that it is undamaged as delivered, built in and complete in all respects, and properly installed on an incombustible base, with space around, all in accordance with the maker's instructions. Particular attention needs to be given to those aspects involving safety valves, draining down cocks and connection to flues, including all joints being gas tight, caulked as necessary, and sleeved where connected to the main flue, yet with proper access for cleaning. Pumps similarly need checking as being in accordance with the estimate and properly installed.

Most certainly the architect or surveyor will wish to be in attendance when the system is charged and tested before any covering up of any part of the installation is carried out, or any insulation is fixed. This will be done even though it will subsequently be necessary to take radiators down again for the decoration work or even more plastering, cap off pipes and radiators temporarily and then refix and test radiators again before the system is handed over on completion. The wise architect or surveyor's task will, of course, be greatly facilitated by the fact that he will have chosen a firm of heating engineers known to be reliable and whose staff, certainly at supervisory level, will be as keen as the architect or surveyor to see that all is well as to efficiency and for the safety of the client. In consequence the testing and examination stage will usually be more of a matter of joint reassurance, rather than an exercise in fault finding.

Drainage Installation

The provision of a system of pipes for the disposal of soil, waste and rainwater to the local authority sewer, to a private disposal plant, or to a storage cesspool for subsequent emptying is normally work for the general contractor. It must be admitted however, that this is an area where standards can fall considerably below the ideal and where the architect or surveyor, if he is not very careful, may well find that work is carried out and covered up very rapidly without him knowing whether it has been done properly or not. The work is analogous to a great extent to that of providing the foundations and lower courses of walling for a building and, in consequence, it is sensible to adopt much the same sort of procedures to control the sequence of events so as to ensure that each step is prepared and then seen before authorisation is given to put the next stage in hand. Coupled with checks on the materials being used and the workmanship of laying and jointing then, at the conclusion of the contract, the architect or surveyor will be able to provide any assurance necessary to his client that the work has been completed in accordance with the requirements of the specification and drawings, so far as he is able to do so, within the limits of the terms of his engagement.

The requirements for controlling the sequence of events will be dependant upon the type of drain pipe and method of bedding and jointing selected. The design of drainage systems is covered by British Standard Code of Practice CP 301: 1971 "Building Drainage", a document which recognises the viability of traditional ways of laying drains as well as newer methods advocated by the Building Research Establishment in the 1950's and 1960's. The Code of Practice was produced not so much as a compromise but as an indication that there were two schools of thought and no measure of agreement between the two. However, much of the literature provided by the Department of the Environment provides one viewpoint only and in advocating the case for flexible joints between lengths of drain pipe based on plastics and rubber, it provides no answer to the charge that such materials may deteriorate within a relatively short space of time, (despite the superficially favourable results of accelerated ageing tests to which some materials have been subjected), when compared with the anticipated life of the average building. While it must be acknowledged that in its study of traditional drainage systems the Establishment found many faults, it overlooked the experience of others who are well aware that many drains laid down 60–100 years ago are as sound today as they were when first laid. Clearly there are many design alternatives available to the architect or surveyor, particularly since there are substantial variations between the various materials for pipes and in the methods of laying. As long as he is aware of all the pros and cons of the various systems he should, if necessary in consultation with his client, be able to come to a reasoned decision as to which of the various alternatives to adopt. Sufficient to say that for work anticipated to be required for a relatively short while only, say 20–30 years, the use of long lengths of comparatively cheap flexible pipe, such as pitch fibre or unplasticised polyvinyl chloride, with flexible joints, laid and surrounded in granular material at a fairly shallow depth would seem to be all that is required and would probably last well enough. Any period above 20–30 years, where a degree of permanence is required, brings the aspect of choice more to the fore and rigid pipes with some semblance of proven durability would probably be the choice. On cheaper work, economies would probably be thought worthwhile and accepted as necessary and these could be achieved by the use of the cheaper pipes that come in long lengths, for example asbestos cement and, to a lesser extent, concrete. If these pipes were also to be laid at a shallow depth, it would be a reasonable risk, agreed in conjunction with the client, to bed these in granular material and with flexible joints, on the principle that if there is too much flexibility over the years, which results in frequent blockages, or the joints eventually leaked badly due to the perishability of the rubber rings, the cost of replacement would be acceptable. For medium quality work, drains may be taken as a desirable precaution to a greater depth, but still be made of the same materials and in as long lengths as possible but designed as a rigid pipe line with rigid joints. For top quality work, few architects or surveyors would, it is thought, have any hesitation in using the top quality long lasting proven materials, such as vitrefied clayware or cast iron, with traditional and long lasting rigid joints and would concentrate on ensuring that the construction of a sound, rigid, pipe line is completed at a proper depth below the surface, well away from the effects of climate or vegetation. The natural bed, or the natural bed coupled with a concrete base, perhaps reinforced as well, for a drain run of this nature, would have the same degree of attention devoted to it as the excavation and foundation work for the building itself, for the simple reason that it will be expected to produce the same sort of performance over the same number of years.

Research into the performance of flexible pipe lines, comprising the use of both pipes flexible in themselves and rigid pipes with flexible joints, continues, and the two parts of the Building Research Establishment's study of Drainage Pipelines, published in 1970, as Digests 130 and 131 are now considered out of date because of changes in the British Standards for the various types of pipe since then and subsequent further research. Transport and Road Research Laboratory Supplementary Reports No. 303 "The Structural Design and Laying of Small Underground Drains of Rigid Materials", published in 1977, and No. 375 "The Structural Design and Laying of Small Underground Drains of Flexible Materials", published in 1978, replace respectively Digests 130 and 131, until such times as they in turn are revised and brought up to date. There is an urgent need for this updating since the Supplementary Reports are, as one would expect, more orientated to the subject of drains in relation to roads and, for example, just do not take account of the requirements of the Building Regulations in regard to drains near buildings. Until more overall balanced information is prepared and published, the advice given in earlier publications needs to be followed. Regrettably also, it must be said that the advice in the Supplementary Reports is not as clearly presented as it might be and a greater concentration on fewer alternatives and more simplicity would have been beneficial.

Suitable flexible pipes for drains are produced in two materials, pitch impregnated fibre to BS 2760: 1973 for pipes up to 225mm nominal bore, and unplasticised polyvinyl chloride (UPVC) to BS 4660: 1973, as amended in 1978, for pipes of 100 and 150mm nominal bore and BS 5481: 1977, for pipes of 200mm nominal bore and above. Pipes produced in accordance with the respective Standards can be identified on site by the British Standard number clearly and durably marked on each pipe length, coupling or fitting, together with the name or identification mark of the manufacturer. The UPVC pipes in addition have the nominal size of the pipe marked thereon and are produced in a golden brown colour, so that they can be readily distinguished from other UPVC pipes produced under BS 4514: 1969, as amended in 1978, in black and grey which, although suitable for use as drain pipes, have a different range of couplings and which are not interchangeable with those produced for pipes made under BS 4660: 1973 or BS 5481: 1977 and are only suitable for above ground drainage purposes. It is curious that Transport and Road Research Laboratory Supplementary Report No. 375 seems to be in error in this respect by quoting BS 3505: 1968 and BS 3506: 1969, UPVC pipes for cold water services and for industrial purposes respectively, as being pipes suitable for drainage instead of those made under BS 4514: 1969.

Pitch fibre pipes now have polypropylene couplings and rubber ring seals for the 75, 100 and 150mm nominal bore pipes, superseding the earlier push fit taper joints, although the latter are still used on the 50, 200 and 225mm nominal bore size pipes. There are two separate systems of jointing UPVC pipes, one using compression ring seals in rubber and utilising a lubricant and the other formed merely with solvent cement. Since the sockets on the pipes are shaped according to the jointing system, it is important for the architect or surveyor to be sure that they are not confused. Neither the push fit taper joints for pitch fibre pipes or the welded solvent cement joints for UPVC pipes allow for telescopic movement in the pipe run and, accordingly, are not considered as adequate as the other methods of flexible jointing. Indeed they are considered unsuitable for use in ground where mining subsidence may occur or in situations where differential settlement may arise, for example where pipes pass into buildings.

As with all building materials, care in handling and storage is important, particularly in cold weather when, for example, UPVC pipes become brittle. Distortion must be prevented and pipes and fittings must be stored in accordance with the manufacturer's directions and protected from extremes of temperature. Rubber jointing rings should be stored away from direct sunlight and all pipes require to be examined for damage before laying.

The flexible characteristics of the pitch impregnated fibre and UPVC pipes and joints requires that they should only be bedded and surrounded in granular material to provide them with uniform but slightly flexible support from both below and at the sides throughout their length. The main emphasis accordingly is on the workmanship of bedding and backfilling. Trenches must be excavated to the size of the pipe plus not less than 150mm on either side in width and to a depth of at least 100mm below the proposed level of the pipe and cleared of all projecting stones, pieces of rock, or hard spots and all roots. In soft clays, silts, fine sands or mud it will be necessary to overdig to a further 50–75mm to prevent undue churning up and possible mixing of the granular bedding layer with the soil. In poor ground, where the cover depth exceeds 2–3 metres, it is necessary to double both the bedding thickness and the thickness of the side filling so that these become 200mm and the thickness of the pipe plus 600mm respectively. The architect or surveyor will therefore need to see that the excavation is satisfactory before the bedding layer is put down, both as to size and condition. This may, of course, involve more than one visit unless of course, as should generally be the case, the conditions below ground are accurately anticipated in advance.

At this stage, the architect or surveyor will clearly need to have other matters on his mind apart from the suitability of excavations for the imminent work of drainlaying. The estimate submitted by the contractor will have provided for certain widths and depths of excavation for the drain run in accordance with the specification. Accordingly, he will need to take, or have taken, levels, together with measurements, so as to be sure that not only is the depth of the proposed drain correct but, also, that the excavated widths and depth of excavation are as provided for in the specification and drawings, and if not, as is likely to be the case, what saving allowance or extra payment is due from or to the contractor. There is no need to dwell on this aspect further since it has already been discussed in regard to foundation work and precisely the same procedures require to be followed in relation to drain trenches.

The bedding material and the material proposed for packing to the side of the pipe will need to be checked since, for example, clay or soft chalk will not be suitable and neither will limestone be suitable in acid groundwater conditions. The material can be specified as either of the following:

(a) Nominal single sized aggregate to BS 882, 1201: Part 2: 1973 "Aggregate From Natural Sources for Concrete (including granolithic)" sized according to the pipe dimension thus:
10mm for 100mm nominal bore pipes.
10 or 14mm for 150 mm nominal bore pipes.
10 or 14mm or 20mm for 225 and 300mm nominal bore pipes.

(b) Graded aggregate to BS 882, as above, also sized according to the pipe dimenion thus:
Graded 14–5mm for 150mm nominal bore pipes.
Graded 14–5mm or 20–5mm for 225 and 300mm nominal bore pipes.

Alternatively, an Ease of Compaction Test is laid down in TRRL Supplementary Reports No. 303 and No. 375 and the architect or surveyor must require any other proposed material to be put to this test before authorising its use if it is not certified as being in accordance with either of the above specifications. If the "as dug" material from the site is not satisfactory, then gravel or broken stone is ideal. Coarse sand, or a mixture of sand and gravel, may also be suitable if it satisfies the test, but it will require more care in compaction. In all cases, however, the maximum size of the particles in the bedding material must not exceed those indicated in the two specifications above related to the size of drain, to be checked on a sieving test if necessary.

The material being satisfactory, the contractor can be authorised to lay the bedding material in the bottom of the trench, withdrawing any planking or sheeting as the work proceeds. The bedding material must be well compacted to the appropriate depth, providing it is not in excess of 150mm, otherwise the operation will have to be carried out in two separate layers. Since compaction by tamping is open to extensive skimping, the architect or surveyor is well advised to have the effectiveness of this labour only item demonstrated to him or, alternatively, to try some tamping down along the bedding layer himself to see that it has been thoroughly carried out. If at all possible for this very reason, the use of a granular bedding material which does not involve the extra compaction referred to in the Ease of Compaction Test is probably wise. Single size aggregate is obviously the best in this respect.

Once the bedding has been passed, authorisation can be given for the work to proceed on laying and jointing the drains. Although the use of flexible pipes does permit lengths of drains to be laid on gentle curves subject to the approval of the local authority, generally pipes are laid in straight runs to an even gradient. Socket holes are formed in the bedding of the granular material to provide even support to the barrels, throughout the length of the drain run, and this aspect of straightness and evenness can be tested with the aid of a torch and mirror as necessary. It is important that pipes and sealing components are thoroughly clean on jointing, that the correct lubricant is used and the manufacturer's directions followed implicitly. In regard to laying and jointing, the architect or surveyor may well consider it appropriate to make an unheralded visit during the course of the work to see that it is being carried out correctly.

Normally, with all the patent flexible joints, other than those made with solvent cement, testing can be carried out as soon as the drains have been laid and the drains on test will be the next stage that the architect or surveyor will have to see before authorising the first stage of backfilling. At the same time as the architect or surveyor is checking the soundness of the drains as laid, he will be able to check the external constructional details of inspection chambers if these are of traditional design. He will need to see that the proper bricks, to BS 3921: 1974, Part 2, Class B engineering, have been used and laid properly in English bond, frogs uppermost and flush pointed, that channels are properly bedded and jointed and benching properly formed. Other proprietory forms of inspection or access and junction chambers will, of course, need checking to see that they are in accordance with manufacturer's instructions and the local authority's requirements, particularly if these are made of plastic materials requiring bedding and jointing by non-traditional means. At this time also the local authority's inspector will be invited to pass the drains for Building Regulation or By-Law approval, to the pressures and over the time required as laid down in the Regulations or By-Laws, once the architect or surveyor is satisfied himself that this will be a mere formality. Generally new drains are subjected to a water test with a maximum pressure at the head of the drain of 1.2m head of water with no part of the drain subjected to more than a 2.4m head of water. An allowance for absorption must be made and the pressure held for 30 minutes.

The next succeeding stage which can be authorised in the laying of flexible pipes, once the drains have passed the water test, is the placing of further selected granular bedding to each side of the pipe in hard compacted layers not exceeding 100mm deep, well tamped into the lower quadrants of the pipe so as to eliminate any air pockets and continued until the crown of the pipe has been reached. In small scale domestic work this stage will be reached in one operation, since the drain is unlikely to be more than 100mm in bore, but on estate or commercial work it may involve two, or more, operations. However many operations are needed, the satisfactory completion of each will need to be checked by the architect or surveyor.

The side filling between the drain and the inside natural face of the trench having been satisfactorily completed, the placing of the top covering to the drain can be authorised. This consists of a further layer of selected granular material, to be hard compacted to a depth of 100mm above pipes of that size or for a depth of 150mm for pipes of 150mm bore and over. Here again, the architect or surveyor will need to see that this work has been carried out satisfactorily before normal backfilling of the trench above this level can proceed. If he does not see this, he will arrive later to see the filling completed to ground level and have little alternative but to accept the contractors bland assurance "of course it was completed properly". At this point, where the top of the drain is less than 600mm below ground level, but not under a road, it is necessary to provide concrete slabs along the length of the pipe, to the full width of the trench, so as to provide pitch fibre and UPVC pipes, which are very susceptible to impact damage, with protection from garden forks or pickaxes. This susceptibility to damage is a point to be borne in mind if the need should arise to use sharp ended implements, either machine or hand operated, to clear blockages subsequently.

Backfilling to the trench can proceed once the immediate top cover to the pipe has been passed. This is normally carried out using the excavated material and, to minimise settlement in the ground, must be done in layers not exceeding 300mm, well rammed by hand for the first two layers, although for subsequent layers mechanical means can be used. Occasionally, if the excavated material is poor, or difficult to compact, and surface settlement must be kept to the absolute minimum, it may be necessary to use layers of the selected granular material. If the architect or surveyor wishes to be sure that the work is being carried out properly then he will have to visit the site and check off each layer of 300mm before allowing the next to proceed. Assuming that the drain is some 1,200mm below ground level, the operation of laying, jointing and backfilling will involve the architect or surveyor in seven separate pre-arranged visits if he wishes to be sure that the work has been carried out to his requirements. While no doubt other matters will receive his attention during his visits apart from the drain and, on large estate or commercial work, he may have the benefit of a full time Clerk of Works on site, it remains a formidable amount of supervisory work related to but one comparatively small, but admittedly vitally important, part of a contract. The danger is that the supervision, in consequence, will receive rather less attention than it should. There is also a severe danger that if the architect or surveyor does not provide the degree of supervision necessary nobody else is likely to do so and it requires no wide stretch of the imagination to envisage that a good deal of shovelling of granular material into a trench will suffice to many building workers, as being entirely satisfactory for the purpose whatever the specification may say.

The desire to have a flexible drainage run may be partially frustrated by the Building Regulation requirement to encase drains in concrete where the side of the excavation for the drain is within 1m of any part of the foundations of a building and to extend such concrete casing at least to the level of the underside of the nearby foundation. Even if the distance is more than 1m but the underside of the drain is within an angle of 45° drawn from the nearest bottom corner of the foundation, then the drain must still be encased and the top of the concrete casing brought to a level equal to the distance from the side of the foundation, less 150mm. In consequence, care needs to be taken where there is a junction between encased drains and drains bedded on granular material. For a distance of 600mm beyond the face of the concrete, the drain should be surrounded by a minimum of 150mm of good quality selected granular material; a situation which should also be arranged at the junction with a traditionally constructed inspection chamber of concrete base and rigidly jointed channel sections. Obviously, at the junction itself, a fully flexible joint should be arranged on the drain and it is advisable for another flexible joint to be arranged at the next 600mm point. Being a Transport and Road Research Laboratory Publication, Supplementary Report No. 375 reminds architects and surveyors, as well as engineers, that generally the minimum cover for drains under roads should be not less than 1.2m. If it is absolutely essential for drains to be at a shallower depth below roads, then those at a depth of between 1.2m and 0.9m should be surrounded with the best of the granular materials, single size aggregate. If less cover than 0.9m is available, then drains should be encased in reinforced concrete to act as a beam, a suitable detail being provided in the Report, or protected by a reinforced concrete slab over a granular surround. A reminder is also given that the maximum depth for cover to drains should not exceed about 6m with all methods of bedding.

There are four materials used in the manufacture of rigid drain pipes which warrant consideration and, of these, vitrified clay is used to produce both plain ended pipes and spigot and socketed pipes. Although rigid pipes in all the materials available can be laid on granular beds with flexible joints, asbestos cement pipes, since they are available in long lengths and are relatively cheap, are the most likely candidates for laying in this manner at a comparatively shallow depth.

Asbestos cement pipes to BS 3656: 1973 are available in lengths of 3 and 4m, although smaller lengths are also available in multiples of 0.5m, from a minimum bore of 100mm upwards. Those pipes complying with the Standard have to be legibly and indelibly marked with the number of the Standard, the makers name or mark, the date of manufacture and the class of pipe, or fitting, according to crushing strength set out in Table 1 of the Standard. For the smaller job, the class is an irrelevance since pipes up to 250mm are available only to class H strength which requires the pipe to withstand a pressure 3,870kg per metre run. A certificate from the manufacturer is also available to warrant compliance with the Standard. Flexible rubber ring joints, employing separate asbestos cement sleeves, are provided for jointing.

Concrete pipes are another possibility for producing a drain run with flexible joints and on a bedding of granular material, as they too are relatively cheap. They are produced in lengths of 0.9m to 5.0m but the weight of longer lengths and the fact that the smallest bore pipe available is 150mm, however, does restrict their use to the larger domestic schemes involving the drainage of, perhaps, two or more properties. Indeed the main use for concrete pipes lies in sewerage work where the large bore pipes can be used to best advantage. The British Standard for concrete pipes is BS 556: Part 2: 1972 and pipes produced in accordance with the Standard bear the number indelibly stencilled or impressed, together with the letter "R" if the pipe or fitting is reinforced, the strength class of the pipe, the letter "S", "A" or "X" if sulphate resisting, High Alumina or Supersulphate resisting cement has been used in the manufacture and the day, month and year of manufacture. The strength class of the pipe relates to its minimum crushing strength under Test Loads and there are four classes available, Standard and Extra Strength classes "L", "M" or "H". However, there is only one strength class available for pipes of 150mm and 225mm nominal bore and only two for pipes of 300mm bore. Manufacturers are also prepared to certify that the pipes comply with the Standard. Spigot and socketed pipes are supplied now with flexible rubber ring joints. Plain pipes with ogee shaped ends for butt jointing which are also made are, of course, only suitable for surface water drainage.

Transport and Road Research Laboratory Supplementary Report No. 303, covering the laying of rigid pipes, provides for the use of the same types of selected granular material already described in relation to the laying of Flexible pipes and the use of aggregate size directly related to the nominal pipe bore, in precisely the same manner. Three classes of granular bedding, however, are described for rigid pipes, Class "S", the strongest, providing a 360° surround, Class "B" the next strongest, providing 180° support up to half the diameter the pipe and Class "Fss", the weakest of the three, providing a flat granular bedding layer. The thickness of the bedding and the cover to the pipe for Class "S" bedding, the 360° surround, will be related to the type of soil; in rock or mixed soils containing rock bands, boulders, large flints or stones or irregular hard spots which result in an uneven trench bottom, it should be a minimum of 200mm, while in soils that permit an even trench bottom to be excavated, it can be reduced to 100mm. In all cases the backfill above the selected granular material must be screened so as to be free of all large stones, building rubbish, tree roots, vegetable matter and clay lumps greater than 75mm in size to a height of 300mm above the crown of the pipes and, with Class "B" and Class "Fss", it must be put down in layers not exceeding 100mm at a time, all compacted by hand or by light plate vibrator, particularly at the sides. Trench back fill from the excavated material dug out on site can be used for the remainder of the depth up to ground level but, again, in layers not exceeding 300mm at a time, hand compacted until a cover 600 mm deep is provided over the crown of the pipe, when it is possible to use heavier compactors.

Tables 1 to 3, in the Supplementary Report No. 303, show the range, maximum to minimum, of cover depths for asbestos cement and concrete pipes for four sizes of pipe 100mm, 150mm, 225mm and 300mm, and in the strength classes available, when laid to fairly generous assumed trench widths on the three classes of bedding mentioned above. The depths considered extend from a minimum of 0.6m to a maximum of 6.0m. As Table 1 is provided for pipes laid under main roads it will be of more relevance to the highway engineer rather than the architect or surveyor, but Tables 2 and 3 for pipes laid under light roads and under fields, which are defined for the purpose of the Table to include gardens and lightly trafficked access areas respectively, are much more to the point. The Tables, of course, include values for rigid clay pipes laid on or in granular beds and the corollary of concrete and asbestos cement pipes laid on beddings other than granular.

Before proceeding to a consideration of rigid pipes made of other materials and the alternative beddings available for all rigid pipes, it is worth stressing that all the precautions in regard to the supervision required of the architect or surveyor on the laying of flexible pipes in granular beds, applies equally to the laying of rigid pipes in similar granular beds, particularly the need to approve the laying and compacting of each separate layer of material. There can be no suggestion that the choice of a satisfactory drainage system to solve the clients requirements, can be influenced in any way by the need for a greater or lesser amount of supervision by the architect or surveyor.

Burnt clay has, of course, provided the material for drain pipes since time immemorial and there is no questioning its long lasting properties when used for this purpose. The manufacturers, being well attuned to the market, produce a variety of pipes for both traditional jointing and for jointing in a flexible manner. BS 65 and 540: Part 1: 1971 (as amended in 1977) "Clay Drain and Sewer Pipes including Surface Water Pipes and Fittings" provides for the manufacture of pipes with plain ends and with different types of socket for use either with the makers own flexible joints or for jointing by the purchaser with his own preferred type of traditional joint. The flexible, mechanical joints are covered by Part 2 of the Standard dated 1972, also amended in 1977. The markings on pipes produced under the Standard are numerous as there are two varieties of pipes and different strengths within each variety with, furthermore, the provision for pipes to be supplied as tested. Before firing, each pipe has to be impressed or otherwise indelibly marked with the makers name, trade name or trade mark. After manufacture pipes have to be stamped or stencilled in black, before despatch, with the number of the British Standard and the licence number of the maker. No further markings would be an indication that the pipe was an ordinary Standard pipe, suitable for all purposes of soil, waste and surface water drainage. If the pipe was found suitable on manufacture only for surface water drainage, it would be stamped or stencilled "Surface Water". Both the "All Purpose" and "Surface Water Pipes", if of appropriate strength, will be stamped "Extra Strength" and the all purpose pipes may also be manufactured to a "Super Strength" class, and be stamped or stencilled accordingly. All pipes can be tested after manufacture and before delivery if required. "Surface Water" pipes stencilled "Tested" will withstand a 3.5m head of water, while the all purpose types, marked thus, will have been subjected to a 14m head of water. Just to add to the confusing possibilities for specification writing and, accordingly, for checking materials delivered to the site, it should be remembered that the Standard does not require pipes to be glazed, so that they can be supplied unglazed. If they are supplied glazed, however, they may be ceramic or salt glazed.

The situation in regard to iron drain pipes and fittings is even more confusing partly because the British Standards Institution produced BS 4622: 1970 "Grey Iron Pipes and Fittings" and BS 4772: 1971 "Ductile Iron Pipes and Fittings" to metric sizes on an International Standard with the intention that, eventually, all pipes would be produced to these new Standards instead of two earlier Standards which, even though updated, had merely converted Imperial sizes directly into metric units. However, pipes and fittings are still manufactured in quantity to the earlier Standards and although the National Building Specification, Small Jobs Version 1980, quotes from BS 4622: 1970, "Grey Iron Pipes and Fittings", to the exclusion of all others with a conscious view perhaps to speeding the metrication process, it is a fact that most drainage work is still carried out using pipes and fittings to BS 437: 1978 (which includes BS 1130) "Cast Iron Spigot and Socket Pipes and Fittings", the current version of a Standard first produced in the early 1900's. Pipes and fittings to this Standard are strong enough for most purposes but sometimes, if required, pipes and fittings to BS 78 "Cast Iron Spigot and Socket Pipes (vertically cast) and Spigot and Socket Fittings", Part 2: 1965 "Fittings" (being the only part of this Standard currently available) or BS 1211: 1958 "Centrifugally Cast (spun) Iron Pressure Pipes for Water, Gas and Sewerage" may be needed. Even although adaptors are made to connect drains made to the old Imperial Standards with drains made to the new International Standards, in the field of repairs to existing systems and new drain runs to extensions, this situation is likely to continue until such time as the manufacturers cease entirely the production of pipes to the old Imperial Standard sizes.

Cast iron drain pipes to BS 437: 1978 are marked comparatively simply, either in raised letters or numbers on the metal or, if centrifugally cast, in an otherwise legible manner. The nominal size of the pipe is given, the makers name or mark, the number of the British Standard and the letter "S", if centrifugally cast. The pipes and fittings are, of course, coated black. Pipes to BS 1211: 1958, in addition, would have not only the above markings but also either the letter "B", "C" or "D" denoting the class of pipe and indicating that on installation pipes of that class would withstand a maximum hydraulic pressure equivalent to 122, 183 or 244 metres head. They too are coated black with a tough bituminous protective solution.

Pipes made to the two International Standards have much more information marked on them than those manufactured under the metricised Imperial Standards. Thus pipes made to BS 4622: 1970 (as amended 1973), "Grey Iron Pipes and Fittings", which are made with bores from 80–700mm are marked with the makers name, initials or indentifying mark, the nominal internal diameter, the class reference of which there are three alternatives relating to the "mass" or strength of the pipe denoted by the numbers 1 to 3 for Standard pipes, class 3 being the heaviest, the British Standard number, the length of pipe if shorter than the appropriate standard length for the bore and the last two digits of the year of manufacture. Although called "Grey Iron Pipes" they are in fact given a black bituminous protective coating as for other iron drain pipes, and the "Grey" only refers to the type of iron used, where the carbon exists in flake form, not the colour. Ductile iron pipes and fittings made to BS 4772: 1971 (as amended 1973) are marked in precisely the same way, with all the above information, except that with pipes made to this Standard there are only two class designations to distinguish between spigot and socket pipes, marked class K9, and flange pipes marked Class K12. The makers can if they wish, however, draw more pronounced attention to the fact that the pipes are of ductile iron by painting the information to stand out indelibly in red. Pipes of this material are not prone to the risk of beam fracture, which is their main advantage over ordinary grey iron pipes where, in use, there is always a possible danger of fracturing with long lengths of small bore pipe, unless the support provided along the whole length of the barrel is reasonably uniform. These ductile pipes are also able to withstand distortion and impact damage better than ordinary grey iron pipes, so that they are particularly suitable for laying at shallow depths below roads. Pipes produced to this Standard are also coated black and flexible rubber ring joints are supplied for pipes made under both these International Standards.

Iron pipes, owing to their high strength, are not included in the Three Tables of Minimum and Maximum Cover Depth contained in Transport and Road Research Laboratory Supplementary Report No. 303 and they are suitable for use at any of the depths and on any of the beddings covered by the Tables, provided only that reasonable care is taken on installation. Where iron pipes are really useful is in very poor ground conditions, for example difficult waterlogged ground or where large ground movements are expected, or at relatively shallow depths under roads or below buildings, where their use is one of the alternative requirements under the Building Regulations and By-Laws. Another use is when suspended drain runs are required through basements, with a further innovation for their use in aggressive ground conditions when provided with a sleeve of polythene. As such they are probably less frequently used in new work than are other types of pipe but in the field of repair and extension to existing buildings they can be most useful.

As mentioned previously, all the rigid pipes under consideration as suitable for drainage purposes can be bedded on selected granular material in the classes described in Transport and Road Research Laboratory Supplementary Report No. 303 as Class "S" bedding, Class "B" or Class "Fss" and also provided with the appropriate type of flexible joint for the material concerned. However, all rigid pipes can also be laid on two other types of bedding covered by the Report one "stronger" and one "weaker" than the granular beddings previously described. The stronger bedding is, as might be expected, that of a concrete cradle and this is referred to as a Class "A" bedding in the Report.

A concrete bedding for drains may be required in heavily loaded situations under the requirements of the Building Regulations, or constructional by-laws in London, where the pipe line is near the foundations of a building, where the pipe line is near other services, where it may be disturbed by subsequent excavations or where, vis-a-vis granular beddings, it is not possible to remove the trench planking or sheeting until after completion of the bedding.

For concrete bedding where flexible jointing is being used between lengths of pipe, trenches should be the width of 300mm plus the size of the pipe, the same as required in normal circumstances for bedding in granular material. Once excavated, again not too far in advance of pipe laying, the bottom of the excavation should be immediately blinded with a 50mm layer of weak concrete. On this blinding, when hardened but still green, and when authorised by the architect or surveyor, a layer of concrete at least 100mm thick below the underside of the barrel of the pipes may be placed and the pipes gently bedded down as soon as the concrete is sufficiently set. Very careful setting out of the bedding is required since, at every flexible joint in the pipe run, it is necessary to form a construction joint in the concrete bed by the insertion of, for example, a 13mm compressible fireboard of expanded polystyrene sheet, cut to the full width of the trench and to the height of the proposed haunching with the profile of the drain cut out. The boards are left in situ so as to preclude the possibility of the bedding and haunching preventing the free movement at the pipe joint. The maximum spacing of such joints should not exceed 5m and clearly, in view of this necessity, the longer the length of each individual pipe the more economical the drain run. Concrete of a 1:2:4 mix should be used for the bedding, giving a maximum working strength of $20N/mm^2$ after 28 days, and the architect or surveyor will need to exercise the same control over materials, gauging, mixing, placing and compaction of concrete as described earlier in this Chapter including any necessary precautions in cold weather but, in particular, to ensure the right degree of consistency in the mix for this purpose of grading the pipes, neither too stiff so that collars are damaged when tapped down to the correct level, or too sloppy so that the pipes subsequently settle. This may not, however, add a great deal to the burden of supervision since obviously there is no reason why the checking of this work should not be directly related to other excavation or concrete work that may be proceeding at about the same time, for example for foundations to an extension of an existing building. The top of the concrete bed should be kept clean to ensure a good bond for subsequent work while the drains are being tested and approved. After testing the haunching of concrete should be placed, to prevent sideways displacement of the pipe, to the height specified, a minimum of a quarter the diameter of the pipe, although it is far preferable to extend this to half the diameter. Alternatively in the circumstances where required, the concrete will be extended to encase the pipe entirely with a minimum cover to the crown of the pipe or taken, for example, up to the level of the underside of nearby foundations.

Once the architect or surveyor has seen the concrete haunching or casing completed, backfilling can be authorised. This, as for back-filling above flexible pipes, must be carried out in layers. For a distance from the top of the haunching or casing to 300mm above the crown of the pipe layers of material no more than 100mm thick at a time and free of large stones, building rubbish, tree roots, vegetable matter or large lumps of clay over 75mm, must be carefully laid and hand compacted, particularly at the sides of the pipes as may be necessary if haunching only is adopted. Above the 300mm mark, layers of normal backfill material can be placed and com-pacted in the normal way, providing the layers do not exceed 300mm in depth.

Of course, as many architects and surveyors will know from their own experience, many drains in the past were laid directly on the natural bottom of the trench without any concrete bedding in the same way as the foundations of many old buildings were provided with no concrete base at all, but merely brick footings. In precisely the same way as many buildings with such foundations remain sound today, so there are many such drainage installations func-tioning perfectly satisfactorily and able, even to this day, to with-stand a water test to the pressure applied nowadays to new drains. It is possible and permissible to lay drains in this manner even today, provided the soil is suitable, even though it is no longer possible to provide foundations for buildings without a concrete base. The method is known as Class "D" bedding in the Transport and Road Research Laboratory Supplementary Report No. 303, although it is considered as the weakest of the five bedding classes covered in the Report. Soils classified as Types III to VI in the Table to Regulation D7 in the Building Regulations 1976 are likely to be suitable, as against the rock, compact sand or gravel covered by Types I and II or the very soft silt, clay or sandy clay or silty clay covered by Type VII provided that the soil at the trench bottom is not so hard or stony as to make it difficult to hand trim with a spade, nor so soft that a sample exudes between the fingers. The trench bottom must also be free of tree roots, rocks or large flints and must not become puddled when walked upon.

For bedding on the natural bottom of the trench, the excavation should be carried out slightly shallower than required so that hand trimming brings the bottom to the correct level with the barrels making continuous contact with the bottom and with holes dug out to give at least 50mm clearance below the sockets. Over-dug spots should be levelled up by filling with selected granular material and thorough compaction. The most important aspect is never to allow the pipe barrels to be propped up on hard packings such as pieces of timber or broken brick, as is the case with all drain laying, otherwise there can be severe danger of beam fractures due to severe concentration of load.

After testing trenches can be backfilled in precisely the same manner as previously described in 100mm layers of selected granular material to a height of 300mm above the crown of the pipe and then in 300mm layers up to ground level.

For bedding drains either on a concrete base or on the natural trench bottom at about 1,200mm below ground level, the architect or surveyor will be involved in about eight separate pre-arranged visits to the site, about the same number as would be required for bedding a drain in granular material at about the same depth if he is to see that excavation, laying, jointing, testing and backfilling has been carried out satisfactorily. It will be apparent that the need for so much supervision on the laying of drainage systems lies mainly in the requirements for backfilling above the drain in shallow layers, not only in the immediate vicinity of the pipe so as to avoid damage to the pipe itself by the careless tipping of unsuitable material, but also thereafter up to ground level so as to prevent subsequent settlement of pavings or the ground itself. For this reason the architect or surveyor's duties vary little whether drains are bedded on concrete, granular material or the natural trench bottom and whether joints are flexible or rigid. There is no way around this situation and the provision of a rigid drain line can involve more supervision owing to the need to traverse trench bottoms to ensure that there are no underlying pockets of weak soil as described in the earlier section of this Chapter dealing with foundations. Even the close supervision in setting out a concrete bed for a drain run with flexible joints necessitated by the requirement to provide a construction joint in the concrete at each flexible joint in the drain, cannot be ignored as similar joints must be provided at intervals of no more than 9m in a rigid drain line, otherwise there is a risk of cracking in the concrete base due to its expansion or contraction movements, which need to be accommodated in long lengths of strip concrete. Furthermore, of course, if it is necessary to reinforce the concrete then the architect or surveyor will become involved in those checks required to see that the reinforcement is as specified and placed, and retained, in the correct position.

Electrical Installation

Depending on the size and complexity of the proposed contract, the installation of an electrical system may be effected by one of three methods. For the smaller installation, the architect or surveyor will specify what is required and either the general contractor's own staff or an electrical sub-contractor to the general contractor will carry out the work. On a somewhat larger scheme, the architect or surveyor may approach an electrical contractor known to him and, in consultation with him, agree what is required and include his work as that of a nominated sub-contractor in the main contract, so that all the general contractor will have to do is attend upon the nominated electrical contractor, cut away and make good for him and eventually pay his account. On more complex jobs, the services of a consultant electrical engineer will be engaged by the client, through the architect or surveyor. In the latter case the consultant will be taking the responsibility, shouldered in the former two cases by the architect or surveyor, of ensuring that the materials specified are in fact used and that the workmanship is satisfactory. The relationship between the two professionals will be the same as it is in the employment of other consultants by the client.

The need for electrical work to be carried out by a team experienced in the work is self-evident in order to protect the client from the danger of shock and the risk of fire. Electrical faults are one of the most common causes of outbreaks of fire and these faults are by no means found solely in old installations due for renewal. Accordingly the architect or surveyor must ensure that if the general contractor's staff or a sub-contractor employed directly by the general contractor is to do the work that such staff are competent. If the team of men to do the work are of an entirely unfamiliar calibre to the architect or surveyor this can, perhaps, best be done by drawing the contractor's attention to the possibility of the need on completion to have the work tested independently, should there be any possible doubt of its satisfactory nature. The specification normally provides for the installation to be tested by the electrical contractor in the manner prescribed by the regulations of the Institute of Electrical Engineers, with the results recorded and, if satisfactory, a completion certificate issued by the contractor. In view of the lack of control over installation work exercised by the Electricity Boards, particularly in regard to extensions to systems already connected to the Board's supply where virtually anything can be done without any check being carried out on it whatsoever, and the lack of statutory controls on the materials used or the standard of workmanship, such a cosy self-certification system may be thought to leave a lot to be desired. At the hands of an unscrupulous contractor and at the mercy of an incompetent team of electricians, the client could only be protected by the architect or surveyor arranging for an independent test to be carried out and for the complete work, or any defective parts, to be done again. That this need arises very seldom, however, is a credit to the self-regulating aspects of the electrical contracting industry. In general, the task of supervising the installation of an electrical system is comparatively simple because it is rare to find staff of an established firm other than completely competent. Because of this, however, architects and surveyors can be lulled into a false sense of security and there are pitfalls of which they should be aware, since their responsibilities to the client in regard to the materials specified and the workmanship deployed remain precisely the same as for all other parts of the contract.

In the case of a full specification prepared by the architect or surveyor for work to be carried out by the general contractor, or a sub-contractor of the general contractor, in contrast to the outline specification which is usually sufficient when a nominated sub-contractor is to do the work, the architect or surveyor needs to take considerable care to specify his requirements in a manner which will eventually enable him to check, with as little difficulty as possible, that materials and workmanship are in accordance with the specification.

Although there is no British Standard Code of Practice governing the smaller electrical installation, there is guidance available from the Regulations published by the Institute of Electrical Engineers and the publication "Electrics" by the Electricity Council. Both "Specification", published by the Architectural Press, and the National Building Specification cover electrical installation in some detail and there are a wealth of British Standards dealing with the components and fittings in common use to make up the complete installation. The appearance of socket outlets, switch plates, control units, etc. is a matter on which most architects or surveyors take an interest, an interest very often shared by the client, so that selection of such fittings, complying with any relevant British Standard, from a reliable manufacturer by name and catalogue number, with the agreement of the client, is a sound practice leaving no doubt as to what is required and rendering identification on site a relatively simple matter. If this is not done and items are specified merely by the British Standard number, then the contractor will be perfectly entitled to estimate for and to supply the cheapest which although, because of the requirements of the Standard are fully serviceable, may well be below what the architect or surveyor, not to say the client, had in mind by way of design and finish.

If the practice of specifying by reference to manufacturer and catalogue number can be extended to items for the remainder of the installation, so much the better. However, as appearance is not so critical it is often usual to refer in the specification to British Standard numbers and relating these to, for example, different materials or gauges etc. and leave the contractor to obtain the items from whichever manufacturer he chooses. It is here, of course, that there is scope for the introduction of sub-standard materials and components, should the contractor be so minded and the architect or surveyor be unfamiliar with the markings on the materials and components made in accordance with the appropriate Standards. After all, if a contractor is of a mind to pass off inferior products in this manner he will certainly have the sense to use items which, superficially at any rate, resemble those made in accordance with the Standards.

As in all other aspects of building work, the specification for the electrical installation is very much related to the intended quality of the finished product. For example, there are ways of wiring which are cheaper than others and different qualities of cable for the same purpose. While initially all will happily fulfil the same function, over the years the more expensive method will prove less subject to damage, the more expensive cables longer lasting and, when the time comes to rewire the installation, it should be possible to do this without pulling the building apart. However, these are basic design decisions dependent on the economics of the proposition, to be taken in conjunction with the client and we are only concerned here with ensuring that what is specified is used, in relation to some of the more common materials in current use.

Cables for use in electrical installations are dealt with in a number of British Standards. Those with a polyvinyl chloride (PVC) sheathing, the most commonly used at present, are covered by BS 6004: 1975 "PVC Insulated Cables (non armoured) for Electric Power and Lighting". The Standard covers both PVC insulated cables under Table 1 for use in conduit only and PVC insulated and sheathed cables under Tables 4 and 5, which only need protection where there is a danger of impact damage by an enclosing channel. Cables manufactured under this Standard are provided with an indication of origin consisting either of an identification thread or threads or the continuous marking either by printing or legibly embossing or indenting of the makers name or trade mark. In the latter case the marking can be on a separate tape, on the insulation or on the sheath and counts as being continuous if it is at intervals not in excess of 200mm on the insulation or 500mm on the sheath. Thread colours are listed in a British Standard Publication PD 2379 "Register of Colours of Manufacturer's Identification Threads for Electric Cables and Cords". There is no requirement for the British

Standard number to be marked on the cables or for any other real and easily seen indication of compliance. In the face of these not very helpful requirements of the Standard, from the site supervision point of view if from no other, it would seem that the architect or surveyor is either faced with acquiring a copy of PD 2379 or of specifying a PVC cable with which he is familiar and can easily recognise.

For better quality installations, or where there is severe danger of impact or a lack of support, for example from concrete floors, or in aggressive conditions, the cables would be run entirely in conduit for which there are various British Standards providing a wide range of alternative types and materials. For the best quality work, steel would be used and there are early standards covering conduit in this material still extant but BS 4568 "Steel Conduit and Fittings with Metric Threads of ISO Form for Electrical Installations" Parts 1 and 2, both of 1970, is the latest. Conduits made under this Standard can be identified by the name or mark of the maker or "responsible vendor", a phrase to cover the marketing of products not actually made by the particular distributor, the number of the Standard and the class of finish (numbered 1–4, from a primer finish through to hot dip galvanised zinc coating), the markings being sited near to one end of each length. Fittings associated with this type of conduit are also marked on the fitting itself or on the package.

For cheaper installations "Non-metallic Conduits and Fittings for Electrical Installations" are covered by BS 4607 of which Parts 1 and 2 are dated 1970; Part 3, dealing with pliable conduit, 1971 and Part 5 dated 1973. Part 1 is entitled "Rigid PVC Conduits and Conduit Fittings" in metric units and Part 2 covers the same field in imperial units. Taking Part 1, the Standard requires that conduit be marked indelibly and legibly with the maker's name or trade mark, followed by a minus sign and the number 5 for conduits of Type "A" for use in temperatures not normally below 5°C, and the number 25 for conduits of Type "B" for use in situations not normally below 25°C. These markings on the conduit are to be at a distance not exceeding 50mm from one end and are to include the nominal size to enable an easy check to be made on site.

A more expensive form of wiring, likely to be much longer lasting, which can be buried without the protection of conduit and, because of its small size when compared with other cable of similar capacity, can be run on the surface and still appear comparatively neat yet does not need further protection by conduit is the mineral insulated type. British Standard 6207: "Mineral Insulated Cables", covers two types, Part 1: 1969, "Copper Sheathed Cables and

Conductors" and Part 2: 1973, "Aluminium Sheathed Cables with Copper Conductors". The latter are infrequently used but within Part 1, Table 7 provides for a type which is copper insulated but PVC sheathed and which, if specified, could result in confusion with other PVC covered cable. There are, however, no special indications for cables made to this Standard and even although close examination should enable easy differentiation to be made between copper insulated and PVC insulated cables, although both may be sheathed in PVC, it is clear that the cable makers rather than the user/clients had the greater influence on the deliberations of this particular Drafting Committee.

British Standards will also be found to cover other types of wiring, for example rubber insulated cables, and there is also a Standard for insulated flexible cords to which reference should be made for specific means of identification if required, although the requirements are basically the same as those for PVC insulated and sheathed cables.

As previously mentioned, selection of fittings should be by reference to manufacturer's products by name and catalogue reference number. However to give some idea of the extensive range of items covered by British Standards, in case the architect or surveyor does not wish to restrict the selection but is prepared to leave it to the contractor (subject, of course, to the client's agreement), to supply the cheapest consistent with a reasonable standard, it is pertinent to note that Consumer Control units, light switches (including dimmer switches), ceiling roses, lampholders, luminaires (or light fittings in ordinary parlance), lamps including both tungsten and fluorescent, socket outlets, cooker control units, shaver supply units, TV co-axial feeder connections, thermostats, immersion heaters, cookers, clocks, together with many other domestic appliances, such as door bells, are all covered by British Standards. If the procedure of specifying by British Standard only is adopted, then the architect or surveyor must still consult the appropriate Standard, not only for details but also for any information that it is necessary to supply on ordering as well as to ascertain the markings to distinguish British Standard appliances from others.

Ideally the architect or surveyor's drawings will show the position of every socket outlet, lighting point, switch or other control unit, including all the work required for the intake and connection to the main, should this be necessary and, if so, all as previously ascertained from the Board. It is often, however, not possible to show everything on drawings and it is therefore wise for the architect or surveyor to meet the electrician's foreman before work is commenced so that the positions of all electrical outlets can be agreed in advance. At the same time, it will probably be necessary to agree a starting date for the wiring to commence in conjunction with the main contractor, since on no account must this be commenced before the building is waterproof. On the other hand, it is equally important to get the work completed before the plastering is commenced, otherwise clients will be faced with the all too common sight of someone hacking away at completed work with a hammer and chisel, a procedure not likely to impress. It would be appropriate at this time also to settle the main runs of cabling in the various circuits since these must be arranged, in particular, to avoid close proximity to heating pipes; certainly never directly above such pipes and generally no nearer than 250mm. Other features may also need to be by-passed, which may not be immediately apparent to the electrician and to which his attention may need to be specially drawn. Any special provisions for cutting away and attendance by the general contractor can be settled at this stage, in particular the degree of drilling to timbers which will be permitted, bearing in mind that notching in no circumstances will be allowed, and that wires must be run through holes drilled in the neutral axis of beams. It is also useful to remind electricians at this time of the need to ensure that no conduits or wiring are placed within 75mm of the top surface of any flooring and, certainly, also never on the top surface of ceiling joists.

The architect or surveyor will need to be familiar with the current regulations of the Institute of Electrical Engineers, governing wiring on the looping in system, with wiring joints at switches and socket or lighting outlets only, and will need to look to see that its requirements are being followed on his unheralded inspections. However, to a great extent, it is inevitable, given the nature of the work, that some cover plates will be fixed as the work proceeds, preventing examination of connections unless a great deal of trouble is taken to require all covers to be unscrewed. This opening up may, or may not, be thought to be warranted according to circumstances. However, even if the finer points are not seen during the unheralded inspection, a general impression of the standard of workmanship will be obtained, sufficient for a decision to be taken as to whether a separate independent test will be required on completion. This is not to say that the architect or surveyor should come to this conclusion privately and without mentioning it to anyone else. A decision of this nature would only be taken after a considerable number of warnings had been issued to the electrical contractor's foreman and, if this failed to produce any improvement, warnings to the general contractor's foreman, confirmed in writing to the contractor's office.

On his unheralded inspections, the architect or surveyor will also look to see that cables are run flat and not twisted or bunched together, that they are properly secured, generally not in excess of one metre intervals, run truly vertically or horizontally and, when in roof or floor spaces, along the sides of joists or neatly at right angles and not diagonally. If crossing voids, cables must be supported on battens. Where cables enter metal boxes they require to be protected from damage against sharp edges by rubber bushes and on no account must the sheathing be pared before the cable enters the box. When conduit is used, bushing, if it is of steel or smoothing the ends, if it is of plastic, is another essential to avoid damage, as is the maintenance of a little slackness in the cable at changes of direction.

On completion of the wiring, it is important that all testing of the installation be carried out before any work is covered up and the architect or surveyor must arrange for this to be done, as in the case for all the service installations. Once tested, floors can be laid and walls plastered, leaving just the plates to be fitted afterwards. The thorough checking at the testing stage will have ensured that the boxes for these were all installed and secured truly horizontally and vertically so that they will be square with other features, architraves and skirtings for example, also to be fixed when the plastering and flooring has been completed. Sometimes slight irregularities in this respect can cause what seems a quite disproportionate amount of irritation in the client when he takes possession and this is always something best avoided in the interest of good relations.

Section C
The Finishings

Plastering

In view of the multitude of plasters available it is essential for the architect or surveyor to make special checks on site of the materials being used for plastering for both new work and replastering on existing buildings since the systems specified for each may be considerably different.

Portland cement and lime have already been covered earlier in this Chapter but in regard to sands for plastering these are covered by BS 1198: 1976, "Sands for Internal Plastering with Gypsum Plasters". The sands under this Standard are of different character-istics from those used in the mixing of concrete and mortar, dealt with in other Standards, and the architect or surveyor must see that they are not confused. It is necessary, since there are different types of sand in BS 1198: 1976, suitable for undercoats as distinct from finishing coats, for the architect or surveyor to see invoices and the certificate provided for in the Standard and to see that heaps of sand on site are kept entirely separate and identifiable. Better still, if the plastering system allows for an interval between coats or the job is sufficiently small, for materials for undercoats to be replaced by materials for finishing coats and the former removed from the site as being no longer required.

British Standard 1191: Part 1: 1973 covers Gypsum Building plasters, excluding premixed lightweight plasters which are dealt with in Part 2, also of 1973. Class "B" retarded hemihydrate plasters, the Thistle range for example, of undercoat and finishing coat plaster for gauging with sand or used neat or with lime as a finishing coat and Class C, anhydrous gypsum plaster, the Sirapite range of final coat plasters for use neat on sanded undercoats or with the addition of a little lime, are all delivered, in 50kg bags, labelled with the class and type, the BS number and whether intended as undercoat or finishing coat and also with the date of manufacture stamped thereon. This marking of manufacture date is provided for the very good reason that both types should be used within two months of the date of manufacture. The architect or surveyor will be looking therefore to see that not only is the right type of plaster being used but also that it is of suitably recent manufacture. Other classes of plaster, covered by the Standard are also delivered in 50kg bags, similarly labelled, but use times with these are not quite so critical.

Plasterboard is made to BS 1230: 1970 "Gypsum Plasterboard", and the paper surface is printed accordingly, so that no problem should arise in identifying the product, but it is important, nevertheless, to check that the correct thickness of board is being used according to the requirement of the span between the supports. Other gypsum board products used in plastering systems can, again, usually be identified on the surface with product and name of manufacturer enabling the architect or surveyor to be sure that his client is obtaining what has been specified on his behalf.

The adequate storage of materials has been referred to throughout this Chapter and it is as essential for the plasterer's materials as it is for any other trade. If, at the commencing stage, the bags of cement, lime or gypsum are produced caked, or partially set, and an examination shows that plasterboard is scuffed with damaged edges or corners or that metal lathing and corner beads are rusted, the architect or surveyor must order these to be returned and fresh supplies brought to the site. He will, after all, have pointed out to the foreman the need for adequate storage in the first place. Many of the defects in plastering are caused by the contamination of one material by another; gypsum plaster by Portland cement, for example, or the adulteration of materials, sand by clay or loam.

The architect or surveyor will be concerned to see that the fixing of plasterboard etc., and plastering, is not commenced too early. In the case of the former, boards are very prone to damage by other trades and can become dirty, greasy and dusty if left too long uncovered by plaster. The same comment applies to plastering on other surfaces, as to damage, and an early start can be counterproductive in the long run and not conducive to good workmanship. Accordingly the architect or surveyor should discuss and arrange with the foreman when a start should be made and, before this, should inspect and approve with him the backing and the preparation carried out before the plasterers attend; the foreman having previously been advised of this requirement. At the time of the inspection, both will be looking to see that all backgrounds are clear of dust, debris and efflorescence, all smooth backgrounds hacked, rather than reliance placed on bonding agents, that all cutting away and sleeving has been carried out so that difficult and untidy making good can be avoided, and that, all pipes where necessary are properly chased into walls and painted, if not galvanised, so that the full thickness of plaster provides cover without a risk of staining.

It is also necessary to see that all grounds are fixed to provide a proper non-ragged edging to the area to be plastered and that all plasterboard, gypsum lath for ceilings, or expanded metal lathing on framing, is fixed in accordance with the makers instructions and any reinforcement at joints of plasterboard with jute or galvanised scrim is provided, along with galvanised beads at external corners. In regard to the fixings, it is important that the correct type, length and spacing of nail is used for securing gypsum boards and that any boards likely to produce excessive suction should be given a coat of emulsion paint before being plastered. Junctions of dissimilar materials, which are to be covered by plaster, must be reinforced with heavy building paper and expanded metal lathing to avoid the risk of cracks if differential movement should occur between the two.

The backing passed and approval given for the undercoat, or in some cases the one and only coat, to be applied, the architect or surveyor, having gone over the requirements with the foreman in advance, should see work in progress and in particular watch that mixes are prepared to the correct proportions by volume batching, not by the shovelful unless, and preferably, the specification has sensibly called for the use of premixed plasters. Cleanliness, in the actual work of carrying out plastering, is as vital as it is in regard to the storage of materials. Contamination of gauging boxes, tools, unclean mixers and containers can seriously affect the setting time of gypsum plasters and the ultimate characteristics of the finished work. Sloppy workmanship, whereby more water is added to the mix after it has started to set and utilising an old mix as a basis for a new batch, can lead to disaster, as can the use of thick coats instead of a greater number of thinner coats. Backing coats must be left scratched, to provide a key before any subsequent coat is applied, and should be brushed down just prior to the application of a further coat.

Since undercoats for gypsum finishing coats need only to set hard before the finishing coat is applied, as distinct from complete drying out, it is not always a feasible proposition to insist that undercoats are left to be inspected by the architect or surveyor before the next coat is applied. The architect or surveyor merely has to see that undercoats are properly scratched and set and, accordingly, this aspect can be dealt with in the course of inspections of work in progress. On a fairly small job, the plasterers will probably complete all the undercoat work before proceeding with the finishing coat, but on longer jobs they will no doubt complete a section, perhaps a floor, entirely before proceeding to undercoat the next section. This is in contrast to the situation where plastering is being carried out on metal lathing, which is not considered to be a rigid background, or on undercoats of cement, lime and sand, or a slow setting Browning undercoat plaster. In these cases it is essential to allow undercoats to dry out thoroughly before proceeding with the next coat so that all shrinkage in the undercoat has taken place. Accordingly, it is entirely appropriate for the architect or surveyor to insist that he should be the decider of when it is appropriate to apply the finishing coat and that such work should not proceed without his authority, whether it be entirely new work or replacement plaster in an existing building. According to thickness and weather conditions, it is entirely conceivable that the interval between undercoats and finishing coat application could be to the order of two to three weeks.

In completing plastering, the architect or surveyor will need to see that the surface of the finishing coat is not overtrowelled to a mirror-like finish, as this will produce a dusty surface on the completed work, likely to break up subsequently. A matt, eggshell finish should be the aim. When all work has been completed, the architect or surveyor will wish to inspect the result shortly afterwards, so as to give ample opportunity at an early date for the correction of any areas of poor workmanship and if the temporary lighting provided for the plasterers has been tactfully taken away, he should ask for it to be reinstated. He should then closely examine the junction lines between all wall to wall and wall to ceiling surfaces, where no cornice is provided, and then stand back to see if they are true. A hand passed over the plaster may reveal unsuspected ripples, unsmoothed float lines and unsightly flecks of finishing coat. Good plastering should be smooth all over and truly flat and level under the straight edge. Visual inspection may reveal hasty finishing at door or window frames and above skirtings, or obvious junctions between one stage of the operation and another. It is at this point that a really skilful plasterer will be able to do much to tidy up many of the irregularities and imperfections which often occur, so that a finish to the satisfaction of the architect or surveyor can be achieved. Sometimes, however, whole areas may need replastering through some fault in workmanship and, if necessary, the architect or surveyor needs to be firm at an appropriate early stage after plastering has ostensibly been completed so that all faults are corrected before decoration is ready to commence, and not left until this process makes the faults more apparent, as it most surely will.

After the plastering is completed it is dangerous to induce too fast a drying out process as this will prevent proper hydration and setting. For drying, good natural ventilation and slight warmth is necessary. Too much warmth does the most damage, although it is also true that a long period of cold damp conditions will be equally harmful, weakening the plaster by delaying hydration too much. A happy balance must be struck and the surveyor or architect needs to bear this aspect very much in mind.

Screeds

Concrete floors and roofs require screeds to be laid by the plasterer before floor and roof coverings are applied. Defective screeds are common; the most usual defects being hollow areas and lifting at the edges of bays through a lack of adhesion to the base. The architect or surveyor therefore needs to see the base immediately before a screed is laid. If smooth, the concrete must be hacked to provide an adequate key but, if left rough, the application of a cement grout should suffice to provide adhesion. However, before application of either grout or screed, the concrete must be thoroughly swept clear of all dust and debris. On laying the screed, the mix used should be of the correct consistency, neither too dry or too wet, and the finish should be with either a screeding board for roofing work, or a board or steel float according to the type of flooring finish to be used. The richness of the mix necessary to provide the requisite strength requires protection after laying, so that the screed cures slowly to avoid surface crazing. This is achieved by covering the surface with tarpaulins, or polythene, for at least seven days before the commencement of the natural drying period, which would extend to at least four weeks for every 25mm thickness as previously discussed. Special care needs to be taken with lightweight screeds often used as insulation material on flat roofs, since in the mixing and laying these contain much more water than denser ordinary cement and sand screeds and, of necessity, having to be topped with a dense 13mm layer of screed, take far longer to dry out completely. Normal timings, quoted above, do not apply to these and it may be necessary to wait half as long again to be sure that the full thickness has dried out completely, with a check by moisture meter, as already described in the section on flat roof coverings, before dense impervious roof coverings are applied.

Ceramic wall tiling is an aspect of work also carried out by the plasterer and this is covered by British Standard 5385, "Code of Practice for Wall Tiling", Part 1: 1976 dealing with internal ceramic wall tiling and mosaics in normal conditions. The methods of fixing for tiles have changed over the years, (in particular so that the work can be completed quicker), in that tiles no longer need to be soaked before fixing and work is now done in a neater manner avoiding the thick backing beds of screed which were formerly necessary. Unfor-

622

tunately the new methods are often thought to overcome all problems and insufficient care is sometimes given to the limitations of the new products. Most new tiling fails through lack of adhesion to the backing and this in turn is usually due to entrapped moisture, although poor quality and incorrect use of adhesive are two further fairly frequent causes.

Tiles, are, of course, very much part of a decorative scheme and, certainly on domestic work, individual clients will often wish to make their own selection. Architects and surveyors should endeavour in these circumstances to steer clients towards tiles made in accordance with BS 1281: 1974, "Glazed Ceramic Tiles and Tile Fittings for Internal Walls". Unfortunately this Standard does not require manufacturers of tiles which comply to put either the kite mark or the number of the Standard on the unglazed side. The only markings required are the name of the manufacturer, or his identification mark, and the name of the country where the tile was made to be legibly and indelibly impressed. This is not really very helpful from the site supervision point of view and, although some makers do in fact indicate that their products are made in accordance with the Standard by a marking on the tile, it is usually necessary to establish that the manufacturer and supplier will provide a certificate of compliance. There are, however, many tiles available in the United Kingdom not made in accordance with the British Standard, some manufactured here but many also imported from abroad. They are not necessarily inferior to British Standard tiles and indeed some are probably made to higher standards. If selected from the catalogue or showroom of a long established supplier, it should be possible to obtain some form of certification or guarantee which in discussion with the supplier, and the client if necessary, may be considered as good as the assurance provided by the British Standard. On the other hand, if the client insists on selecting a tile which suits his decorative taste but which is unmarked, or otherwise unidentifiable as to type or maker and, accordingly, of unknown characteristics then it would seem wise that he should accept full responsibility for his choice in the event of subsequent early failure arising from the tiles themselves. It is not sufficient, however, for the architect or surveyor to allow such a situation to arise without full explanation in writing to the client. The possible consequences of the client's decision must be made absolutely clear to him and often, when this is done, the client will have second thoughts and revert back to a consideration of other tiles of known quality, when the full implications of his first decision sinks home.

It must be presumed that the architect or surveyor will have specified correctly where solid bed fixing is required, for example in shower compartments, on brickwork which is uneven, or externally on a cement and sand screed, as against normal current practice of thin bed fixing, used almost universally elsewhere. At the time it is proposed to commence tiling, it will remain for the architect or surveyor to ensure that the backing to the tiling is absolutely dry before work starts. The backing can, of course, consist not only of plaster or cement and sand rendering in areas likely to be damp, (shower compartments and wash rooms for example), but also of the brick or block work behind. For example new plaster must be allowed at least four weeks to dry out before being tiled, and, depressing though it may sound, when the client for whom a small extension is being built is anxious to have it completed as soon as possible, to tile a 225mm brick wall plastered both sides, which may have been saturated during the construction process, in under ten months is a recipe for failure. This provides further argument, if any is needed, for the use of temporary coverings to enable building works to proceed in the comparative comfort of dry and reasonably warm conditions, and also the need to consider the design and specification having due regard to the time scale necessary for drying out solid traditional construction, if the job is small and is required to be completed reasonably quickly by the client.

If the backing is passed, the tiling can proceed and the architect or surveyor will wish to see during the progress of the work that the adhesive is being used correctly; on the thin bed method, carefully ribbed with a notched trowel, and with the solid bed method, that a good 13mm layer is applied but with no ribbing. Joints should be even throughout, greatly facilitated by the lugs on tiles made to the British Standard, and the surface true and smooth. On completion, the tiling must be left for the adhesive to dry before grouting, 24 hours at least, but if the backing is non-porous, for example on an old oil painted surface, then 72 hours or even more may be required. If the tiles are being fixed externally, the ungrouted tiles would need in addition to be covered for this period. Proprietory grouts of reliable make are best used, or epoxy grout in conditions likely to be damp, well pressed in below the surface with any excess wiped off from the face of the tiles before they are polished to complete the whole operation. Externally, the work should be covered for fourteen days at least to protect it from any damaging effects of inclement weather and the extremes of either heat or cold.

Flooring and Paving

Mention has been made in the previous section of the plasterer's involvement on screeds for roof coverings and floors. Apart from cement screeds being laid to provide a base on structural concrete slabs for practically all types of flooring, the plasterer himself will be responsible for laying granolithic flooring. As with the cement screed, the best way of securing a good bond of flooring to the concrete slabs is to have it laid within twelve hours of the base being completed so that the two can form a unified whole. However, this is not generally practicable and, even it is possible, there are always the problems of subsequent protection to be overcome. Accordingly, in most cases, it is necessary to prepare the concrete base before the flooring can be laid. This will involve thorough cleaning of the surface of the slab, particularly to remove any oil or greasy matter, thorough hacking or roughening to produce a good key and the total removal of all dust and debris. The architect or surveyor will need to see the base at this stage before authorising the laying of the floor and will, no doubt, take the opportunity of reminding the foreman of the need, before laying actually commences, of thoroughly wetting the slab and applying a thick slurry of Portland cement grout. If the materials are on site, the architect or surveyor will need to see certification that the aggregate is in accordance with BS 1201: Part 2: 1973, "Aggregates for Granolithic Concrete Floor Finishes", to ensure that too much fine material is not to be incorporated, otherwise the wearing qualities may be seriously affected. Control of any movement in the flooring after laying will also need consideration with the foreman at this stage, so that no bays in excess of 15m square are formed while the appropriate ebonite or brass strips are set out in advance of laying at the appropriate thickness required, not less than 40mm, otherwise there is a distinct danger of subsequently lifting. On workmanship during laying, the architect or surveyor will look to see that the mix is well worked with the trowel, that excess laitance is removed and the surface polished with a steel float on completion. Vital to the success of the operation is the subsequent covering with polythene, and the keeping of the surface moist, for a period of at least seven days to allow for curing.

All the remarks in the above paragraph on preparing the concrete slabs before laying granolithic flooring apply also to the preparatory work prior to laying a screed. However, an equally important aspect in the final success of any floor finish, particularly if of an impervious nature laid on top of a cement screed, is the need to ensure that the screed is absolutely dry before laying begins. Sufficient has already been said, elsewhere in this Chapter, on the length of time necessary for this drying out to be completed, according to the thickness of the layer, but it is vital for the architect or surveyor to be thoroughly satisfied before authorising laying to begin. For thin flooring materials such as linoleum, rubber, thermoplastic or vinyl, whether in sheet or tile form, it is important to check also that the surface of the screed is smooth, that any bumps are rubbed down, any indentations brought up to the general level with latex, otherwise even the most minor imperfections can mar the finished appearance.

Floor finishes are generally well covered by British Standards and there are four Codes of Practice providing advice on choice and laying, CP 202: 1972 "Tile Flooring and Slab Flooring", CP 203: 1969 "Sheet and Tile Flooring (cork, linoleum, plastics and rubber)", Part 2: 1972, metric units, and CP 204 "In-Situ Floor Finishes", Part 2: 1970, metric units, with CP 201: 1951, "Timber Flooring", still applicable alongside a later edition entitled "Flooring of Wood and Wood Products" Part 2: 1972 "Wood Flooring (board, strip, block and mosaic)", metric units.

Some floor finishes are more typically laid on concrete and a screed than on, say, a wood sub-floor. Clay tiles are an example, but BS 1286: 1974, "Clay Tiles for Flooring", only provides for tiles made to this Standard to be legibly and indelibly impressed with the name of the manufacturer or the manufacturer's identification mark, together with the name of the country where the tile is made. This is insufficient and the architect or surveyor should require to see a certificate of manufacture in accordance with the Standard in view of the confusion which could result, particularly with so many imported tiles being available, marked thus, but not necessarily complying. Two types of tile are now covered by the Standard, in place of the Types "A" and "B" from earlier editions, and these are "Ceramic Floor Tiles" produced with a fine finish by compaction and firing and "Clay Floor Quarries", produced by extrusion and firing. Two methods are commonly adopted for laying, one on as thin a bed as possible, between 10mm and 13mm on a layer of polythene or building paper to separate the floor tiles from the screed or, alternatively, a thicker bed of about 35 to 40mm of cement and sand screed is used to bed the tiles on the slab direct. Proprietory adhesives are also available but must, of course, be used strictly in accordance with the manufacturer's directions. It is necessary to provide movement joints around the edge of any floor, at the junction of floor tiles and wall, or at the joint of the tile skirting and the general level of tiling.

Two Standards cover pitch mastic flooring which, again, is a possible choice for laying on concrete and these are BS 1450: 1963, "Black Pitch Mastic Flooring", and BS 3672: 1963, "Coloured Pitch Mastic Flooring", and the blocks from which the flooring is prepared are stamped or painted with the British Standard number, as appropriate, together with the manufacturer's identification mark, so that the architect or surveyor is able to check on the quality of material to be used when the material is delivered to the site or during laying. Care is necessary when laying on a concrete slab, in which expansion joints are provided, to ensure that an isolating sheathing is used to effectively separate the two. This is also necessary in domestic construction, where it is common practice to provide a single layer of less than 25mm. An isolating layer is also, of course, necessary should the flooring be laid on timber. The timing for laying mastic flooring is important in that accelerated cooling may take place and cause shrinkage and cracking if the floor is laid too soon before windows and external doors are installed and glazed and even then in cold weather, it is essential for some heating to be provided in the building.

The aspect of heating is also vital to the success of laying wood floors. Laying must be deferred until such time as windows and external doors are installed and glazed, but if it can also be deferred until such time as the central heating can be turned on low, so much the better. Timber can then be obtained at the moisture content appropriate to that anticipated for the building when in use, 10% to 14% for a building provided with central heating. If a form of underfloor heating is provided the level would be as low as 6% to 10%, but for a building only intended to have intermittent heating the appropriate level would be 12% to 16%. Later troubles will be avoided if, in the latter case, unit heaters can be introduced to provide a low background temperature on site and this is maintained from then on until completion. The architect or surveyor is wise to provide for this in the specification and insist on strict compliance by the contractor before, during and following the laying of any wood flooring.

Wood block and wood mosaic flooring are two types often laid on concrete provided with a damp proof membrane, if next to the ground, and levelled off smooth with a cement and sand screed, which must, of course, be dry and scrupulously clean before the architect or surveyor authorises laying the floor. Wood blocks are covered by BS 1187: 1959, "Wood Blocks for Floors", and suppliers of blocks, which are usually 25mm thick, must be required to certify that the blocks conform to the Standard, since no marking is provided for in the Standard itself. Nowadays such blocks are laid in cold latex bitumen emulsion adhesives, which are considered better than the bedding in hot bitumen formerly adopted, and the architect or surveyor will need to ensure that appropriate movement joints are included as appropriate. Movement joints to mosaic wood flooring are not required because the make up of so many small pieces can accommodate movement much more easily. Usually about 13mm thick and much cheaper than wood blocks, this type of flooring, laid in much the same way as wood blocks, is covered by BS 4050 "Specification for Mosaic Parquet Panels", Part 1: 1977, "General Characteristics", and Part 2: 1966, "Classification and Quality Requirements". Packages of panels made up in accordance with the Standard are marked by stamping on one side, in a waterproof and slightly penetrating manner, the information set out in clause 5 of the Standard covering wood species, nominal dimensions, number of fingers per panel and the International Standards Organisation Grade. At the purchaser's request, the country of origin can be added to the marking and the supplier's trade mark. Both wood block and mosaic wood panels, along with hardwood strip flooring, are intended to be left uncovered and therefore for effect. The architect or surveyor must, accordingly, insist on adequate protection after the flooring has been laid, otherwise the finished effect could so easily be ruined by physical damage from other trades. Used sheets of hardboard are much better protection than sheets of polythene or building paper which can be torn. It is far better to insist on protection rather than to have to call upon the contractor to replace damaged areas, since it can be very difficult to obtain a good match; later, of course, such floors will be lightly sanded and sealed almost as one of the very last jobs before completion.

To the extent, of course, that wood boards, battens or strips have to withstand loads, they are a structural element and their thickness depends upon the span between the centres of the floor joists. As for other structural timber, the architect or surveyor will accordingly need to check that the material delivered to the site is of the thickness, grade and moisture content as specified in relation to the Building Regulations and Constructional By-Laws. BS 1297: 1970, "Grading and Sizing of Softwood Flooring", provides for no marking system on the boards as flooring so that it will be necessary to obtain a certificate of compliance from the supplier. The main preoccupation for the architect or surveyor before authorising the laying of flooring, of whatever type, on wood joists, will be that all services are in position and fully tested, where applicable, properly secured, that all straps and anchors are fixed, all with the aim of ensuring that, once laid, it will not be necessary to disturb the flooring. With tongued and grooved flooring, it is necessary to well cramp before nailing, so as to minimise later movement, and to secure each 150mm board with two flooring brads at every joist, the brads being well punched home. This applies equally to secret nailed hardwood strip flooring except, of course, that there can only be one nail per support, since this is hidden on the tongueing although, because of the narrower width of strips as against normal boards, the number of nails is about the same over the equivalent area of flooring. The architect or surveyor needs also to see that head joints are well staggered and always made on a support.

A considerable saving can be achieved in flooring costs with the use of the large sheets available of 18mm tongued and grooved chipboard, with the spacing of joists arranged accordingly, and this may well be appropriate where economy is of paramount importance and even where in medium quality work, a conscious decision is taken with the client at an early stage to provide a more attractive floor finish on top of the chipboard. Resin bonded wood chipboard is covered by BS 2604: Part 2: 1970 and the type suitable for flooring complying with clause 15 of the Standard can be identified by the markings set out on Page 553 of this Chapter. Correct fixing of the chipboard is important and the architect or surveyor will need to see that this has been properly carried out at every point of support, to the recommended spacings. One prime advantage of chipboard is that it is stable and not subject to the movements commonly experienced with ordinary timber. On the other hand carpeting has to be loose laid, as tacks will not hold.

As mentioned earlier, a new wood or a new chipboard floor may well provide the base for another floor finish laid by the contractor. In both cases it will be necessary to sand to an even surface throughout, necessary also for that matter if the surface is to be sealed and left exposed, sweep or vacuum away all dust, coat with a wood primer and then the cork, rubber, linoleum, thermoplastic or vinyl flooring, as selected, can be laid with the appropriate adhesive on sheets of, dry, felt building paper. Old wood floors, because of the unevenness generated by the years of wear in the region of knots etc., require a different technique, in that it is necessary to punch down all nail heads, secure any loose boards and pin down sheets of hardboard or plywood, nailed overall at 150mm centres and along all edges, so as to provide a smooth base.

British Standards are available to cover all the flooring materials, except cork, mentioned in the foregoing paragraph and the architect or surveyor should have little difficulty in identifying that the correct material is being used since all the Standards, except that for rubber flooring, provide for materials manufactured in accordance with their requirements to be marked in a distinctive manner as follows:

Linoleum to BS 810: 1966, "Sheet Linoleum (Calendered types) cork, carpet and linoleum tiles": Sheets can be marked on the back with an adhesive label with the number of the Standard and the maker's name. Tiles preferably are marked in the same way but may only be marked on the package. Also to be included should be any special instructions for cleaning and maintenance.

Thermoplastic to BS 2592: 1973 "Thermoplastic Flooring Tiles": All containers for tiles are marked with the maker's product identification mark, the maker's batch number, the nominal size and thickness of the tile and the number of the Standard.

Vinyl to BS 3269: 1969 "PVC (Vinyl) Asbestos Floor Tiles": Containers for tiles are marked with the maker's identification mark, the maker's batch number, the nominal size and thickness of the tile and the number of the Standard.

Vinyl to BS 261: "Unbacked Flexible PVC Flooring", Part 1: 1973 "Homogeneous Flooring": Each container is marked with the maker's identification, the thickness, size of tile or width of roll, the maker's batch number and the number of the Standard.

Vinyl to BS 5085: "Backed Flexible PVC Flooring", Part 1: 1974: "Needle Loom Felt Backed Flooring", Part 2: 1976 "Cellular PVC Backing": Each container for these two types is marked with the batch number and the number of the Standard with the maker's identification mark, the colour, pattern and width of roll with, in addition for the cellular backed material, the overall thickness and the thickness of the wearing layer.

In the case of rubber flooring, BS 1711: 1975 "Solid Rubber Flooring", provides for the manufacture of both sheet and tiles in plain, ribbed or studded designs. As no marking requirement is made manufacturers and suppliers must be required to provide a certificate of manufacture in accordance with the Standard.

Cork should be selected by sample from a reputable supplier and the sample retained by the architect or surveyor for comparison with the material supplied. Thicknesses available range from 4.8mm upward and there are two qualities, "ordinary", which is suitable for domestic use, and "heavy duty" and three shades. Thinner tiles are butt jointed, the thicker tiles are tongued and grooved. Unlike the other coverings noted above, it is usual to pin the heavy duty tiles to ordinary wood floors in addition to using adhesive. On completion, fine sanding and sealing will improve the appearance and protect the surface, as with thermoplastic and all forms of vinyl floor covering.

External Paving

For external areas, paving can be of natural materials for preference, natural stone or slate, if the quality of the contract will extend to the expense or prepared products, such as precast stone, concrete slabs or brick, if economy is the order of the day. Natural materials are attractive because of the variations in colour and texture and if slate or natural stone are being selected, it will usually involve seeing completed work with the client, or stone at the quarry, or at least a range of samples which would need to be retained for comparison with the delivered material. Precast concrete flagstones, however, are covered by BS 368: 1971, so that a certain quality is assured if slabs are selected according to the requirements of the Standard. Flags made to this Standard will be certified as such by the maker, who will also certify date of manufacture if desired. The selection of bricks for paving requires considerable care and due regard must be had to durability, particularly resistance to saturation and freezing, as well as to appearance. British Standard 3921: 1974 provides guidance in this respect and, as for other brickwork described in this Chapter, the maker must supply a certificate in relation to the classification of the bricks delivered as to "variety", for example engineering, and "quality", probably "special quality" in this case, suitable for situations of extreme exposure.

In the case of all these heavy external paving materials, it is important for the architect or surveyor to ensure that the bed for paving is satisfactory before laying is commenced. In most cases, this will entail seeing that a suitable concrete base, in accordance with the specification, has been laid so that future settlement in the paving will be obviated, a method to be preferred to that of laying on sand or hardcore. For bedding on a concrete base, however, it is important to isolate paving from slab, so that the two can move independently if required.

Painting and Decorating

The long term function of painting, to preserve and enhance appearance, should ensure the architect or surveyor eschewing the blandishments of the makers of innovating products in the specification of paint systems. While fully admitting the possibility of long term success, and ultimate usefulness, the innovating products should be left for the DIY market and for time to prove their full value. This is most certainly the case for painting work to the exterior of buildings, where some of the non-drip paints have proved to be less than durable and some polyurethane paints have tended to chalk. Fortunately most of the points stressed on the labels of products in the DIY market concentrate on ease of application and speed but, since the client will not be doing the work himself, he is less likely to be tempted to interfere in the architect or surveyor's specification. Generally the finished appearance required by the client, particularly as to colour and texture, can in nearly all cases be achieved by traditional methods. Giving the advice to follow traditional practice in regard to painting, however, is easier to do than to follow in practice, as will be seen when it comes to examining the assistance available from British Standards. Should the client be drawn to the idea that a saving might be made, say, by missing out a coat of paint through utilising a new product that claims to enable this to be done, the architect or surveyor should resist the suggestion on the grounds that there is every likelihood of failure and of eventually much increased expenditure for the client. It is only if, perhaps, the client shows real signs of actually insisting on the use of the new product against all professional advice that the architect or surveyor should seriously consider his own position. Is this a case of reasonable experimentation, provided it is taken at the client's risk with full written acknowledgement, or is it a case where, if things go badly wrong, the reputation of the architect or surveyor is likely to be damaged, even though the fullest of indemnities is given by the client? It will be obvious that such likely sources of argument or friction between client and professional adviser need settling at an early date in the relationship and not be left either to the specification stage, or for the client's intervention on the site when the work is being put in hand, or even actually in progress.

Apart from the effect of conditions which cause eventual breakdown of the outer paint film on surfaces and thereby bring on the time for repainting after say 5–6 years, for example strong sunlight, rainfall or damp from condensation, most defects in comparatively new paintwork are caused by the presence of damp from behind the paint film, by chemical reaction, for example rusting of iron, or attack on the film from resins or oils, again from behind. All these faults are related to undue haste, to the materials used and to poor workmanship. It is sensible, therefore, for the architect or surveyor to specify a paint system that not only satisfies the requirements of the job but also one which consciously seeks to ease his task of ensuring that the materials he has specified are being used, the correct number of coats are being applied, and the standard of workmanship he requires, at various stages of the operation, are being followed. To this extent a great deal can be achieved by naming products and limiting the chosen selection to the smallest number of different items from, if possible, one manufacturer's range, whose advice must be followed in regard to compatibility with all the differing surfaces which have to be decorated. There is no harm in an architect or surveyor making use of the advisory services of particular manufacturers, if in doubt in regard to the selection of a paint system, provided the manufacturer chosen is long established in the business and has been making paints of a satisfactory nature for some considerable time. It is suggested that new arrivals on the scene should be avoided. Thought in this direction at the specification stage will be amply repaid in the long run, as will the inclusion and stressing of clauses relating to sections of the work not being carried out until backing surfaces are approved by the architect or surveyor. One of the reasons for suggesting stress on named products is that painters tend to move around the site carrying small unmarked cans into which has been tipped part of the contents of a large can, stored somewhere else. It is, accordingly, fairly easy for the architect or surveyor to wander around the site and never notice, in fact, what type of paint is being used. Consciously naming products will mean that he will wish to check the store to make sure that those present are indeed the paints specified. Anything present in the store and not included in the specification or not mentioned on the cans as a suitable thinner should immediately strike a jarring note and lead to further investigation.

Most architects or surveyors find it logical to start thinking of the painting system in terms of the ideal primers to be used on the various surfaces to be decorated. In fact, it is often far more sensible first of all to think in terms of the finish required both internally and externally for woodwork. If this finish, both inside and outside, can be the same then, immediately, it may be possible to eliminate one possible alternative, reduce the number of different cans on site and, accordingly, ease the task of supervision. For both internal and external use, an oil based gloss paint or an alkyd based gloss paint both from a good manufacturer, would probably be best since not many clients, if any, would wish to have the toxic white lead paints formerly included in BSs 2525-7: 1969 used indoors, even if still available and however durable they may be externally. Other newer types of paint, as mentioned before, have not all proved to date to be very successful when used externally.

Architects and surveyors will be surprised at this point by the sudden withdrawal of one of the main crutches on which they will have been taught, and generally have learnt, on which to rely. Out of the 1,400 or so British Standards relating to the building industry, at the time of writing, there is not a single Standard covering paints suitable for applying as an undercoat or a finishing coat on general surfaces of woodwork, plaster or metal. There are numerous Standards covering primers and some miscellaneous coatings, such as bituminous paints and powder cement paints, but none covering all that vast array of cans which the lay public, as well as architects and surveyors, can see adorning the shelves of the "do-it-yourself" shops and general stores. None of the makers of these massive selling ranges of paint wish their product to be thought of as "Standard" but more as "super", "wonderful" or "magic" or some other exaggerated adjective. The manufacturers are forever trying to steal a march on each other and cannot be brought to the table to agree something as mundane as a Standard, the adoption of which might inhibit the copy writers of the firms' advertising contractors. So much for the value placed on "Standards" by the general public. As most architects or surveyors have probably suspected for a long time, in the field of paints, the general public does not care a fig and will seek the soft option, nine times out of ten, and will fall for the blandishments of bright advertisements. The architect or surveyor, however, has to see through these as best he can and advise his client to the best of his ability on the most suitable products to use in the circumstances and he must clearly place a heavy reliance on the reputation of the manufacturer and, perhaps, also his own experience in the "do-it-yourself" field!

Examination of the main catalogues of the leading manufacturers, as distinct from the colour cards, and in particular that of the manufacturer of the chosen finishing coat, will certainly produce details of suitable compatible undercoats, in contrasting tints, for use below the top coat and for incorporation, where appropriate, in the specification. More often than not, it will also be apparent that the same finishing coat and undercoat are satisfactory for metalwork and plastered surfaces, subject to the previous application of satisfactory primers. Therefore, should it be required to paint wall and ceiling surfaces internally, there would be no need to select yet another paint, if a gloss finish was acceptable. This is unlikely, however, and as for bathrooms and kitchens it is likely that an eggshell finish would be required but, even so, there is almost bound to be an eggshell or silk finish version of the gloss paint in the manufacturer's range suitable for the purpose.

Further consideration of the manufacturer's catalogue will probably elicit the information that a range of primers is also available and compatible with the undercoats and finishing coats previously selected. It will be indicated in the catalogue that they can be used, as appropriate, on various surfaces such as wood, ferrous metals, galvanised metals or alkali prone surfaces. Those suggested for wood may be oil or alkyd based and the main claim for these will be that while they are not so durable as other wood primers, they have good water resistance. Accordingly it may be preferable to turn to the best of all primers for wood, namely pink primer formulated to BS 2521: 1966, containing a high proportion of white lead and some red lead, for both inside and outside work, since this may be acceptable as it will be covered over by subsequent coats of non-toxic paint. To overcome the problem of toxicity of lead a later Standard, BS 5358: 1976, governs the manufacture of "Low Lead Solvent Thinned Priming Paint" suitable for use on both exterior and interior softwood, Type "A" being for general use by brush application.

An important consideration in regard to the selection of a wood primer relates to made up joinery, the priming coat on which is invariably applied in the joiner's shop. It may be that in ordering joinery, the architect or surveyor will be able to specify the primer he requires and this would be all to the good, since he will be able to tie this requirement in with his specification for the painting system to be built up on site. On the other hand, if a purchase is being made from stock it may be that all the products of that particular joinery manufacturer come with a particular primer which cannot be varied. In this, admittedly unlikely, event, it may be that the joinery manufacturer's primer will have to govern the entire paint system.

Aluminium primer to BS 4756: 1971, "Ready Mixed Aluminium Priming Paints for Woodwork", provides another sound possibility for use on wood, being non-toxic and compatible with all types of paint, provided it is remembered that it acts as a vapour barrier and therefore it is important that all surfaces of the wood are coated. Its use is clearly a practical proposition on new work, as it can be used both internally and externally on both hardwoods as well as softwoods, while it has the further advantage that a two coat application eliminates the need for a separate initial coat of shellac knotting, on which it has always been difficult to get subsequent coats of paint to take, without special rubbing down. On repainting contracts, however, a coating on one side of a member can cause blistering on existing paintwork on the opposite face. Having selected aluminium primer, the architect or surveyor should not forget that there are two types covered by the Standard and he must remember to select the correct one according to the preservative treatment given to the timber. It is a matter of electrolytic corrosion again and Type 1 primer must not be used on woods treated with metallic napthenate preservatives; Type 2 is an all purpose material and accordingly much the safer to specify. Unlike the Standards covering lead based priming paints, not only those for woodwork but also the Standard covering primers suitable for iron and steel, BS 4756 provides for containers to be clearly marked with the maker's name or trade mark, the number of the Standard and the date of manufacture, and this gives aluminium primers a distinct advantage as far as site supervision is concerned.

Having selected the chosen manufacturer's alkali resisting primer, (a simple matter as there would probably be only one to choose from), for use on plastered or rendered surfaces, the specifier is then left with just the task of selecting suitable primers for the various types of metal being used on the contract and which are to be painted. Here, admittedly, there can be difficulty in achieving simplification since not all primers are suitable for all metals and, accordingly, it may be necessary to specify more than one, particularly when both ferrous and non-ferrous metals are involved. However, it is pertinent to note that some metal primers are compatible over a range of metals. Coupled with the use of chemically active etching primer, with an improved resistance to water and first applied to the metal to react with it to provide a coarse surface, it is possible, for example, to use zinc chromate primer on aluminium, zinc, or zinc coatings on other metals, and also, although perhaps not the very best primer for the purpose, for steel, or cast iron railings, rain water pipes and gutters provided they are in mild exposure conditions. Possible electrolytic action prevents the use of zinc chromate primer on copper, where an aluminium primer would have to be substituted, but, as already discussed, this type of primer has already been put forward as a sensible possible choice for all woodwork, so that its adoption as a primer for copper would not necessarily introduce another product on site.

Accordingly, with some thought along the lines above, it is possible to reduce substantially the number of different products being used on site and this must be advantageous not only from the architect or surveyor's supervisory function but, in itself, as an aid to the avoidance of mistakes. Of course, there will be circumstances where such simplification will not be possible and indeed where it would be incorrect to specify other than the most highly recommended primers for the metals concerned, particularly in instances of exposures to severe weather conditions, and where, for example, there may be substantial repairs and redecoration being carried out to existing premises as well as new work on an extension. In the latter case, of course, it may be advisable to adopt two distinct painting systems, while endeavouring to retain as much material as possible common to both. It remains, however, very necessary for the architect or surveyor to check the materials being used by the painters, whatever it is that may have been specified, and that the materials are being used in the correct context. Fortunately, most manufacturers of paints blazon the name of their products on the cans in bold designs, certainly for the undercoats and finishing coats. It is not always the case, however, with primers and it pays to examine the cans closely for the description of the product and confirmation that it has been produced to the appropriate British Standard.

It should hardly be necessary at this late stage to mention the need for adequate storage but paints can be damaged by the extremes of weather conditions and, accordingly, need to be stored in a dry and reasonably warm situation, which should be settled and agreed between the architect or surveyor and general foreman in advance of painting work commencing.

By the time thoughts turn to painting, towards the end of the contract, the items to be coated will vary considerably from new raw timber to rusty metal, although quite a number of the items will have been delivered already primed to the site. These items need careful examination, before building in, so that surfaces that are to be obscured are checked over and the priming touched up where damaged or missing. Since adequate priming is vital to the success of the entire paint system, the architect or surveyor will certainly need, and wish, to see that this operation has been completed entirely to his satisfaction before authorising the application of the first undercoat. Surfaces which have arrived already primed and which are still visible will need inspecting to see that the priming coat is still satisfactory and has not been damaged in transit, on unloading, or on building in. Damaged areas will need touching up to complete the coating, but items showing extensive signs of peeling, powdering or brittleness must be entirely stripped, surfaces scraped and rubbed down and then re-primed. Even before this stage, however, the architect or surveyor must take the opportunity, either with the general foreman or the foreman painter, to inspect surfaces which have not been primed before delivery, since it is vital that any contamination of bare wood, metal surfaces whether galvanised or not, or plaster by dirt, grease, rust, scale, efflorescence or dust, together with any moisture in excess of appropriate levels within the material, or any moisture at all on the surface, must be removed, otherwise there is no possibility of even primer adhering, let alone subsequent coats of paint. This site preparation, before priming, must be done in the case of metalwork before the application of the etching material to produce a roughened surface to which the appropriate metal primer will adhere and, in the case of woodwork, before the application of a coat of shallac knotting, or preferably, the application of a first coat of aluminium primer in lieu.

The preparatory work completed, priming coat or coats applied, holes stopped, cracks filled on wood, surfaces lightly rubbed down and dusted off, will be the time for the general foreman or foreman painter to inform the architect or surveyor that surfaces are now ready for his approval before the first undercoat is applied. At this stage, the architect or surveyor will wish to see that all surfaces, but timber in particular, presents a smooth surface for painting, otherwise the client is likely to be presented with poor uneven surfaces on completion which can be a continual source of irritation. Stopping holes and filling dents, and the indentations in grained surfaces of wood, must be carried out once the application of the priming coats enables these irregularities to be more easily seen, as it does in the case of plaster and metal surfaces. On wood, the best material for the purpose is a white lead oil paste and putty, but if the toxic nature of this material is not acceptable, then oil based or oleoresinous stoppings are available, but it is important to ensure that the oils do not leech out into the timber so that the stopping and filling shrinks and falls out. A thin coat of paint, to seal the area, may be a necessary first application before pressing the stopping or filling into the hole or indentation. The filling itself may also need a subsequent coating of thinned paint, to ensure uniform absorption over the whole area to be undercoated.

If all is found to be well after thorough examination, the next stage will be sanctioned and the painters can proceed with the first undercoat to the previously specified tint. On completion of this work, to include drying and lightly rubbing down, the architect or surveyor will make an arrangement to inspect to see that all surfaces have been covered before he gives authorisation to proceed with either the next undercoat or the first finishing coat, if a gloss or gloss two coat finish forms parts of the painting system. Whether the next coat is a second undercoat, or a first finishing coat it must be in a different tint so that, when it is dry and lightly rubbed down, it will be a straightforward matter for the architect or surveyor to see whether any area has been missed when he comes to make his inspection, by prior arrangement, before authorising work to proceed on the application of the final coat. For the same ease of checking on completion, the top coat must be in a contrasting tint to either the second undercoat or the first finishing coat. It may be thought that if the top coat is of high gloss paint over a second matt undercoat, the difference in character between the two would be sufficient to make checking, for total coverage, relatively easy. Some architects or surveyors may be prepared to accept work on this basis but, in fact, in the absence of angled reflected light, it can be quite difficult to tell whether a surface is matt or gloss at a glance, and from a distance. Apart from seeing that total coverage has been achieved, the architect or surveyor will be inspecting on completion to see that surfaces are dense, smooth and even and clear of brush marks, runs, sagging, or wrinkled areas, embedded dirt or brush hairs.

Up to now, painting of surfaces in oil paint only has been considered but, obviously, the principles of supervision apply equally to the use of other materials, such as the application of coats of emulsion paint on plastered walls or varnish or polyurethane on wood, particularly as to the drying out of surfaces and checking that the preparation has been satisfactorily completed, consistent with the requirements of the particular material to be used and also checking that the specified number of coats have been applied.

Apart from his set inspections at the various stages of the painting system, the architect or surveyor will need to be observant of the general standard of workmanship on his unheralded visits. In particular, if damp or misty conditions are prevailing, he should take the opportunity to attend one morning, rather early. Painters start at the same time as other members of the building industry and, if external painting is in hand, there is always the temptation to continue first thing in the morning irrespective of conditions. External painting must not be continued in very cold, damp and misty conditions, or in driving rain, as surfaces must be absolutely clear of moisture before the application of any painting material. Almost equally bad is painting in direct hot sunlight, or in areas where dust or grit is billowing about or, even, when a very high wind produces such conditions.

Paints must be thoroughly stirred and mixed properly before use and it is vital to ensure that in the comparatively rare circumstances when it is necessary to thin paint, it is with the architect or surveyor's express authority and that directions on the can are followed implicitly and never exceeded. It is obviously impossible for the architect or surveyor to be absolutely certain that such requirements are being adhered to by his site attendances on periodic inspections but he can, at least, stress such aspects to the painter foreman, or general foreman as the case may be, and keep his eyes fully open when he makes his inspections, particularly in coldish weather, when the temptation to thin paint unduly is at its greatest. A sense of bravado in some painters will induce them to do things they should not do under the very nose of the architect or surveyor, particularly if the architect or surveyor is young and relatively inexperienced, on the principle that he either does not know what is right or wrong or even if he does, he would not notice.

While the specification may allow for the application of under-coats and finishing coats by brush, spray or roller, the architect or surveyor must watch to see that primers are applied by brush only, as specified. Surfaces for priming are seldom entirely smooth and brush application forces the primer into hollows and indentations, particularly the end grain of timber, displacing air and ensuring good contact and adhesion to the entire exposed surfaces. Painters should be seen to be using clean good quality brushes, otherwise finished surfaces will be marred by detached hairs embedded in the surface or brush marks. Brushes should be loaded with paint carefully. "Fat" edges should be avoided in painting and the surface "laid off" in the direction of grain, or towards the light on walls and ceilings, so that brush marks disappear. Uniform coats can be achieved with the use of the roller with systematic light firm strokes because of the principle on which it is designed but, again, cleanliness of both rollers and trays is an essential basic requirement for good work. Spray application is, probably, only of real value on large areas and where a number of properties are involved in view of the need for specialised equipment, with protective shields for the operators, and the masking of surfaces, which is necessary. Much care in mixing the paint and adjusting the equipment is needed and considerable skill is required in the operator to prevent the build up of the paint film at the beginning and end of each stroke. As for all painting, dry conditions are vital to success.

The paper hangers traditional complaint has always been "the worse the quality of paper, the harder the job" and, as in most things, it pays to select as good a quality paper as possible. A cheap paper for example, when pasted, may come apart in the hands when used on high walls, such as staircase wells. Particular pains are required in preparing and making good surfaces that are to be hung with paper, whether expensive or otherwise. All holes must be filled, cracks repaired, loose areas of plaster removed and surfaces dry, smooth and clean. If surfaces have been damp, or there has been any suggestion of mould growth, the surfaces should be washed down with a proprietory mould inhibitor and allowed to dry. Badly cracked walls and those where surfaces have a variable degree of porosity, should be lined first and allowed to dry. This cross lining involves the paper being hung horizontally and butt jointed carefully, to produce a perfect surface. The architect or surveyor will wish to inspect the background, before paper hanging is commenced, to ensure adequate preparation and arrangements must be made with the general foreman to this effect.

Since wall and ceiling surfaces in old houses may not be truly horizontal or vertical, wallpaper may have to be cut to angles and allowance may have to be made for this in ordering. Occasions do arise when patterned paper is purchased from quantities, roughly calculated by the contractor, but when the amount is found to be inadequate the particular pattern has vanished from the market. Exotic wallpapers can have obvious disadvantages in this respect, or even peculiarities of their own, such as stretching or smudging, not encountered with paper purchased from a reputable manufacturer.

The paste used must be appropriate and compatible with the type of paper, but all pastes must now contain a fungicide, particularly necessary in the case of use with impervious wall coverings such as vinyl.

Rooms to be papered should have all items such as radiators, switch plates, etc., removed, otherwise a botch will be the result. With expensive patterned papers it is undoubtedly wise, say at the time the background is checked and approved, to discuss with the paper hanger how they are to be hung. For example with bold pronounced patterns on the paper, commencing in the centre of the wall is probably much more likely to produce a good effect and avoid a disappointment on completion and a discussion will ascertain how intrusions such as door openings or fireplace surrounds will affect the design or, indeed, influence the hanging. On completion the architect or surveyor will expect to see pieces hung so as to be properly matched with no horizontal joints, all edges carefully butted and the surfaces clear of stains, tears, bubbles or marks.

Part 5
Completion

Chapter 13
Normal Completion and the Settlement of Disputes

Contents

The time eventually arrives when the general contractor speaks quite hopefully of Practical Completion of the contract on the due date or, more probably, on the revised date, agreed following written notice under clause 23 of the JCT Standard Form of Building Contract 1963 or agreed under the "Relevant Event Procedure" under clause 25 of the JCT Standard Form of Contract 1980. By this time the site and building, or buildings, will be in what can only be described as an interesting condition. This would normally be described by the householder as one of total and complete chaos with no supervision, no one caring at all and everyone just coming and going as they please, while the general contractor, on his part, would describe matters as going according to plan. The opinion of the architect or surveyor may be less definite but might be generally found to be somewhere between the two other extremes. It must be said, in all conscience, that these last stages provide a trying time for any building owner and in particular his wife who remain in premises being refurbished or extended. She, in particular, is likely to be landed with the problem of living in a building while noise and confusion rages about her and groups of men who she has never seen in her life before suddenly descend without apology and, equally suddenly, disappear. What architect or surveyor has not had to deal with the type of situation where the lady of the house launches into a long and meticulous account of the mayhem that has occurred, with a talent for clarity and total recall that would impress (and indeed very often has impressed) a barrister. "The radiators have been taken off for the third time and no sooner have the doors been put up, after all the trouble in getting them delivered, when they have been actually taken down again. And to cap it all, when that nice young man took such pains to fit the light switches so neatly yesterday, today that horrible Mr. Smith, who you know I have never liked, told someone quite separately to take them all off again. It is really too ridiculous and who is going to pay for all this I really do not know."

It is always extremely difficult, at the best of times, to explain the activities of painters who inconveniently require that fixed items of equipment be removed so that they can get at the wall surfaces behind, just as it sounds rather lame to say that doors, once hung, then have to be re-hung after edges are shaved and fittings adjusted before the arrival of the painter. The lady of the house will, according to her temperament, telephone her husband repeatedly, engage in arguments with the various tradesmen or retire from the confusion completely and sun herself in the garden. The conduct of her husband will, according to his temperament, vary equally. It is simply that the lady of the house is more likely to be exposed to the mounting confusion that always seems to be a necessary prelude to practical completion and it is to these ladies that respectful sympathy always needs to be extended. How much better it would be, however, if they would just take a holiday at this time!

The exact day of practical or full completion of a contract for, say, the extension and repair of a house, may be of considerable importance for reasons that will be referred to later, but first one must have regard to what is meant by the term "completion". In Chapter 5 the subject of Entire Contracts has already been discussed, illustrated, as may be remembered, by the unfortunate case of the sailor who died on voyage thus being unable to complete his bargain, so that his personal representatives had no claim for wages. There are many other heartbreaking cases of such unfortunates in English case law, another being the printer who was unable to complete the full number of printed copies that he undertook to deliver due to a fire which consumed his premises. In accordance with the law he was unable to make any claim for money whatsoever, even in respect of those copies that he had in fact completed and delivered. Comments have already been made upon the essential characteristics of an Entire Contract and no apology is made for doing so again as it is as well to keep in mind that an Entire Contract not only covers cases where a lump sum is agreed in respect of certain specified work but also includes cases where a contract to construct the whole building or works is executed in consideration of a specified price made up of separate payments for each separate part of the whole. Moreover, a contract to construct the whole building or carry out works without mention of any price still comes within the definition of an Entire Contract as does a contract to construct the whole building or carry out works for a price to be subsequently ascertained on some fixed basis such as a Schedule of rates.

The Courts, in construing the conditions of any particular contract will, firstly, consider them as a whole in their ordinary and popular sense and, secondly, in any peculiar sense that they may have acquired by usage in the trades concerned. What constitutes completion, therefore, depends upon the terms of the contract and what might reasonably constitute fulfilment of it having regard to the intentions of the parties. It should be emphasised, however, that the Courts will pay attention to the true meaning of words printed or written above the signatures to a properly executed contract and no evidence may be adduced, however strong this may be, to prove an unexpressed intention. Neither the employer nor the general contractor would be able, for example, to call evidence to show that some different arrangement regarding completion was obvious to all parties at the outset of the contract since the Court will strictly interpret the actual words in the contract as they are set out. This is why it is so important that any amendments to the normal standard printed forms of contract are carefully made and validly executed.

The word "completion" has been judicially interpreted on a number of occasions and in different circumstances. Particularly apt was the Judge who said that "a contract for laying water pipes was completed when the water began to run through them". In normal circumstances, however, the term "completion" in relation to a dwelling-house connotes a readiness for immediate occupation. It may, however, generally be said that, within the field of this book, completion arises on that day and at that moment when the architect or surveyor, by inspection of the works, decides that he may with all reasonableness certify completion with its resulting payment, regard being had to the number of days latitude, if any, permitted by the contract, and when he is satisfied that the amount of retention money held is adequate to its particular purpose.

The term "practical completion" employed in the JCT Standard Forms of Contract (clause 15 in the 1963 version and clause 17 in the 1980 version) is not, in itself, defined. The question of whether works are "practically completed" is a matter for the architect or surveyor alone and his Certificate of Practical Completion decides the matter. It is therefore, to state the obvious, clear that this certificate is of vital importance, as issue of the certificate starts so many hares running together. Certification of Practical Completion affects, firstly, the question of the retention, secondly the period for Defects Liability, which commences from the date of issue, thirdly the period of Final Measurement and Valuation, fourthly, insurance and, fifthly, questions of arbitration under clause 35 of the 1963 JCT Form of Contract, but varied in the 1980 Edition. Finally, the issue of the certificate disposes of questions relating to the contractors liability to reinstate work affected by frost and liability for liquidated damages.

Under the JCT Standard Forms of Contract 1963 and 1980 (clause 15(2) and clause 17.2 respectively) "any defects, shrinkages or other faults which shall appear within the Defects Liability Period and which are due to materials or workmanship not in accordance with this Contract or to frost occurring before Practical Completion of the Works, shall be specified by the Architect in a Schedule of Defects which he shall deliver to the Contractor as an Instruction of the Architect not later than fourteen days after the expiration of the said Defects Liability Period and within a reasonable time after receipt of such Schedule the defects, shrinkages and other faults therein specified shall be made good by the Contractor and (unless the Architect shall otherwise instruct, in which case the Contract Sum shall be adjusted accordingly) entirely at his own cost".

What constitutes "defects, shrinkages or other faults" is a matter of interpretation but, obviously, matters cannot be included which depart widely from this terminology. The machinery to deal with such faults is triggered off by the architect producing and lodging his Schedule of Defects with the contractor who then, it is hoped, proceeds to put matters right with due dispatch in order to obtain the "Certificate of Completion of Making Good Defects". The importance of this rather clumsily worded certificate to the contractor is that it affects the question of retention monies on the one hand and its issue must have taken place before the period allowed for final certification can commence.

A number of architects and surveyors make use of the provision in the JCT Standard Forms of Contract (clause 15(3) 1963 Edition and 17.3 1980 Edition) to issue instructions regarding defects within the Defects Liability Period as an alternative to compiling a formal schedule at the end of the period. They say that this is a more flexible arrangement since it is impossible to ask the contractor to carry out any further remedial work once the formal Schedule of Defects has been served upon him and it it enables the architect or surveyor to see that some defects are put right or, if still further work is required, before the expiration of the period.

Whatever the preferences of individual architects or surveyors, a set procedure for inspection is favoured. Often under pressure of time such inspections become notorious for exasperating difficulties when scaffolding has been taken away, there are no ladders on the site and the helpful site agent has already departed to another job. A final check always reveals further irritations not present during interim inspections. Rubbish is left on roof surfaces or in lofts by the various trades or specialists, matters pointed out on previous surveys have not been remedied and damage has been caused, such as the painful case known on one site where a painter placed his steps in a bath to repaint the ceiling and scratched it; the bath, as might be expected, being a particularly valuable one, having taken months to obtain. Now is the time for matters which the contractor would rather forget about to be set down in writing. These may be small such as the need for balloon gratings to vent pipes ("more trouble than they are worth"), the need for pointing up flashings once the metalworkers have left the site ("it means that I will have to get Joe back and he has gone on holiday") and the need for access provisions such as ladders and duct boards for future maintenance ("ridiculous"); or they may be quite major items.

A set system for inspection should start internally at the top of the structure and should include an examination of each room from the ceiling, walls and floors, including windows, doors, electrical apparatus and other fittings generally, facts being written or being taken by hand recorder. Doors and windows should be tested, socket outlet points examined, doors to cupboards opened and shut and notes made accordingly. On numerous occasions, door handles or casement stays will be found to have been fitted by someone who is willing but inexpert, and who has galloped along at the last minute. It is highly desirable that the architect or surveyor picks up minor points such as this and other items such as clips to pipes or accessories, promised long ago but never delivered. WC chains should be pulled, taps opened and shut and everything that is supposed to work should be tested. The architect or surveyor must not shrink from insisting that the contractor cleans away dirt and rubbish to both the interior and the exterior of the property and cleans windows and floors no matter how unpopular insistence on such items will be. If rubbish is not cleared from gulleys, drains and inspection chambers, dire results can follow, just as the failure to provide a stop end to a gutter can have equally depressing consequences.

The problems which occur by way of shrinkage cracks, carelessness or neglect in finishings or damage caused by subsequent trades are demanding and should be taken extremely seriously. The architect or surveyor should remember that from the general contractor's point of view the contract is ended and his worries will now be centred upon other projects. The architect or surveyor will, it is hoped, have arranged matters so that sufficient retention monies are left to ensure that the work can be completed, even after the expenditure of time and argument has failed to do so. Many cases are known, however, where the retention money is abandoned by the contractor so that another candidate has to be found to finish the work, not always an easy task. The architect or surveyor should always remember, however, that it is the last stages of the contract that are the most frustrating for all the parties concerned, but particularly the Employer, and much good will built up over many months can be easily lost by neglect to look after small matters. The architect or surveyor also finds that when the heat is off, so to speak, because the main elements of the construction are complete, he himself, has a flood of more urgent matters to deal with and fails to employ energy and despatch to see the matter through. He may then, finally, be aggrieved to find that his client also lacks the necessary energy to deal with his account for fees.

The question of partial or sectional completion under clause 16 of the JCT Standard Form of Contract 1963, or clause 18 of the 1980 Edition, often causes problems for the architect or surveyor. Irrespective of the wise provisions set out in the Contract Forms, some Employers will clamour for possession of part of the premises prior to the recognised dates. The Employer who wishes to move a small team into three rooms in a newly refurbished office building, or the factory manager who wishes to utilise part of the warehouse space, will be deaf to reminders of everything that has been said before and will only see that empty space is available for occupation when it is urgently needed. If the contractor should agree to humour the client, although strictly he may refuse to do so, the architect or surveyor should act like lightning to carry out an immediate inspection and prepare a Schedule of Defects to regularise the whole position. The contractor might reasonably require the Employer to take partial possession at his own risk entirely under such circumstances but the architect or surveyor will know from his own experience that unless the state and condition of the part of the premises under consideration is recorded, problems may well follow. Complaints of the type that "Mrs. Smith found that such and such would not work and when she got on a chair to repair it, she fell and hurt herself" are best avoided if at all possible. Arrangements for partial possession, whether under the contract or by informal arrangement, sometimes work and sometimes do not. If matters go wrong all sorts of complications can present themselves. Sometimes, the clients employees, when business premises are involved, get on well with the contractors employees and sometimes they do not. On occasions, a row tends to develop when the Employer, spurred on by reported injustices from his employees, claims that nothing is right, while the contractor says that all will be well if he was not obstructed at every turn. The Employer then counters that the contractor never fulfilled his part of the bargain in the first place, whereupon the contractor retires to his office and compiles his master stroke. This is a claim for making good damage caused by the client's employees.

Whether full or partial possession is involved, it is best if the architect or surveyor deals with outstanding defects as quickly as possible following Practical Completion. Much will depend on the relationship he has formed with the contractor, the amount of the retention outstanding, the number of sub-contractors employed (who are probably proof against all blandishments) and other circumstances of a like nature. It is tempting to leave matters or slacken the tempo at this stage, but highly undesirable to do so.

651

The issue of a Certificate of Practical Completion under clause 15 of the JCT Standard Form of Building Contract 1963 marks the end of the regular interim certificates drawn under the provisions of clause 30(1). As we have seen in Chapter 5 however, clause 30 in the 1963 Edition has been extensively re-drafted in order to provide for amounts included in interim certificates to be set out in greater detail. This is so as to identify those amounts from which Retention can be deducted from those sums which the Employer is bound to pay without any deduction. Under the 1963 Form of Contract it becomes accepted practice for a Certificate of Practical Completion to be accompanied by a Certificate for the release of one moiety of the retention monies but this is no longer necessary. Now the retention deducted in each interim certificate is calculated at the full percentage of the total value of work which has not yet reached Practical Completion and on the value of all unfixed materials and goods; at half that percentage on the total value of work which has reached Practical Completion but for which a Certificate of Completion of Making Good Defects has not been issued, and at NIL % on work for which such a Certificate has been issued.

The new rules are designed to grasp the thorny problem of retention monies, thought by many in the past to have been unreasonably withheld, and to provide a much more firm yet flexible basis under the varying conditions which apply today. It is much more common now, for example, for the Employer, as we have seen, to take possession of part of the works before Practical Completion of the whole and nowadays where, as we have also seen, a Nominated Sub-Contractor is due for early final payment. The new provisions are designed to cope with such eventualities as well as dealing with the situation when Practical Completion of the whole of the works takes place and where defects in either the whole or part only of the works are made good.

The standard Retention Percentage of 5% may be varied where the Contract Sum exceeds £500,000, in which case it should be reduced to 3%. The rules governing the possession and control of the money have already been discussed as has the right of the Employer to deduct certain amounts from monies otherwise certi-fied as being due to the contractor, such as liquidated damages (clause 24) or the cost of rectifying defects following failure by the contractor to comply with the architect's or surveyor's instructions. He no longer however, has recourse to Retention for these amounts but may take any monies included in a Certificate, including any Retention already released (notwithstanding the fiduciary nature of his interest in the Retention). Included, however, is a new provision that requires the Employer to inform the Contractor of the reasons for any deduction and the manner in which he has deducted it (whether, for example, he has deducted it from the contractor's share or from any Nominated Sub-Contractor's share of the Retention as otherwise, if he did not do this, the position of the contractor would be impossible having regard to his own duties under the terms of the Sub-Contract Documents).

Under the JCT Standard Form of Building Contract 1980, provision is made for an Interim Certificate to be issued twenty-eight days before the Final Certificate which will set out the amounts finally due in respect of all Nominated Sub-Contract Work. The Final Certificate is reserved purely to deal with any amount due to the contractor from the Employer or the other way about. This clears the decks so to speak for the final balance of adjustment between the two parties.

Interim Certificates, drawn hitherto, have been merely in the nature of approximate estimates by the certifier of the value of work done, and are not evidence in favour of either party on the satisfaction of work carried out or as a determination of price. Interim Certificates are designed to oil the wheels of the contract from the financial point of view and are subject to readjustment upon final settlement. This is not to say that the architect or surveyor, in the absence of a quantity surveyor, should draw certificates lightheartedly or carelessly since, should he over-certify and the contractor go bankrupt, he is liable to be held to account for his actions by the Employer. It is for this reason that experienced architects and surveyors pay particular regard to the provisions of the contract in ascertaining how the amount of a Certificate is to be calculated; whether fixed or unfixed goods supplied are to be included in the payment or not and whether the "value of work done" means the actual cost to the contractor or, possibly a very different figure, the value of work done expressed as a percentage of the contract sum.

The issue of a Final Certificate ends the contract between the parties and thus the contractor's liability to carry out further work although this point is often misunderstood. The Certificate under most Standard Forms of Contract is designed to be final and conclusive, subject only to any matters referred to arbitration and subject, obviously, to the Certificate itself being valid; that is fully independent, not procured fraudulently and drawn strictly in accordance with the terms of the contract by the right person to the right party and at the right time. It should also obviously contain no reservations that might make it invalid.

A Final Certificate states that the work has been completed and the contract fulfilled to the satisfaction of the architect or surveyor and clause 30(7) of the JCT Standard Form of Building Contract 1963 has been substantially reproduced as clause 30.9 in the 1980 Edition. The Final Certificate is only to be "conclusive evidence that where the quality of the materials or standards of workmanship are to be to the reasonable satisfaction of the Architect the same are to such satisfaction . . .". while the Certificate is conclusive evidence that "any necessary effect has been given to all the terms of this contract . . .," it is also certainly conclusive so far as the architect or surveyor's signification of these matters is concerned, but only so far as his own function and duties extend. The issue of the Certificate does not override the basic contractual obligations between the Employer and the Contractor.

The question of time for completion often leads to difficulties in small cases where no particular time limit is specified within which the work is to be completed. The recognised Standard Forms deal with the question of time in such a way that the mere fact of non-completion before a specified date will not, in ordinary circumstances, release the Employer from the terms of the Contract but may instead, entitle him to damages. If there is undue delay in the work an Employer may give the contractor notice to complete within a fixed reasonable time limit and, upon further default, may be justified in allowing the Contractor to continue working, but where time is the essence of the contract such rules will not apply. It should be noted, however, that the mere insertion of words making time "of the essence of the contract" will not be effective if they are inconsistent with other terms of the contract. Time cannot, obviously, be of the essence of the contract where there is provision for the payment of a penalty or liquidated damages for delay nor, has it been found, where there is a bonus stated for expedition or where the parties contemplate beforehand a possible postponement of completion. When time is the essence of the contract, so that completion within a stated time limit is expressly made a condition precedent to payment, the Employer is released from the contract if the builder fails to complete the work on time. It is interesting to reflect that in former times the old rule of law was that time was always of the essence in a contract, but equity has now intervened to make such a provision extremely unusual so that in the event of a contract of this type going to Court, due to the fact that the builder was just unable to finish the work in time, one would imagine that the Judge (and possibly subsequent Judges) would have to be extremely satisfied that the circumstances warranted the truly terrible penalty of depriving the contractor of any remuneration whatsoever. The rule, now normally academic, that the builder had until midnight of the day fixed for completion to finish the work may assume a horrifying significance under such circumstances.

In small cases of jobbing work the architect or surveyor has to rely on the normal rule of law that, where no particular time limit is specified within which the work is to be completed, an agreement to complete within a reasonable time will be implied and a reasonable time for completion will be allowed. What constitutes reasonable time is, of course, the million dollar question. There is, obviously, a great deal of case law on the subject from which it can only be deduced that all the circumstances of the matter have to be taken into consideration, such as the nature of the work to be done, the time necessary to do the work, the ability of the contractor to carry out the work and the conduct of the parties. The test would probably be, under normal circumstances, the time which a reasonably diligent builder of the same class as the one involved would take to complete the work.

The tried and tested provisions made in most Standard Forms of Contract follow the rules of equity in that mere delay, particularly when this is due to the fault of no one in particular but, for example, adverse weather or unforeseen circumstances, does not frustrate the contract and provision is made for most eventualities, as we have seen. There will, however, be occasions, although it is hoped that these will be rare, when completion will not take place due, perhaps, to the fact that performance was impossible. Such a case may be, for example, where the building which was the subject of the contract, is burned to the ground by vandals after the contract has been entered into but before work commences due to no fault or lack of care on the part of either the Employer or the Contractor. Other valid reasons for non-completion of the contract by the contractor are where the employer may refuse access to the site in, say, a fit of insanity, or where the architect or surveyor simply fails to supply the necessary drawings so that the contractor has no directions. Such cases must of course be contrasted with waiver, when a new contract is substituted for the old one, either before or after the commencement of the work.

We have already seen how, under normal common law rules, the contractor is under a heavy obligation to complete an entire contract since, if he abandons the work, he has no right of action against the Employer for part payment, either in a specified sum or under a quantum meruit basis. Not only is he unable to recover payment for the incomplete work but he will also be liable in damages to the Employer for breach of contract to complete. This would obviously not apply, however, in cases where the contractor can show that non-completion of the work was due to the fault of the Employer. Moreover, if the contract has been discharged due to impossibility of performance, the contractor will be entitled to some payment if it can be shown that the Employer has obtained some valuable benefit and damages will not necessarily be awarded in consequence. Furthermore, if a contractor undertakes to carry out work in accordance with a specification which is divided into different parts, each of which is in respect of a distinct and separate price, the normal rules relating to an Entire Contract may be set aside when the contract is discharged by impossibility of performance or frustration so that some payment is then due to the contractor. It may also be the case that where provision for payment is made as each particular part of the work is completed, the contract may be envisaged as a severable one, each part of the work being seen as a separate contract so that payment may again be due.

In small cases where no payment is mentioned before the work is carried out, the employment of a builder implies an agreement to pay a reasonable remuneration for the work carried out, both in the form of labour and materials. The method of ascertaining the price would be by comparison with reasonable rates ruling at the time in connection with similar work. In the absence of any stipulation as to the standard of workmanship it is normally implied that the contract should be completed in a good and workmanlike manner and by workmen employed possessed of the ordinary amount of skill of tradesmen in the particular trades involved.

As we have already seen, the printed Forms of Contract in general use are designed, as the result of long experience, to cope with eventualities which might occur and in respect of which, had no provision been made, completion of the contract would not have been possible. There will, however, be cases where a breach of the contract occurs that is so serious and fundamental as to put matters in an altogether different light. If the Employer does not give possession of the site, for example, the contractor may be entitled to abandon the contract and claim damages for its breach by the Employer. Fundamental failure to perform a condition precedent to the contract may leave the contractor with no option but abandonment and, in certain cases, should he elect to proceed with the work he may well be relieved from conditions in the contract relating to the date for completion and liquidated damages while still preserving the right to initiate an action for damages.

The seriousness of any breach by the Employer during the progress of the work depends on whether it goes to the root of the contract or not. If it does not, the contractor is bound to continue with the work until completion and then sue for damages in addition to the contract price. As the contract continues, however, the chances of some breach occurring that is fundamental become less, although entire abandonment of the work by the contractor will entitle the Employer to repudiate the contract, just as formal notice by the Employer to the contractor requiring him not to do anything more will amount to a total breach and the contractor, on his part, may rescind the contract. The circumstances are obviously different, however, should the employer merely write to the contractor asking him to exclude two of his workmen from the site or where the Employer merely suggests a postponement in the work, rather than its total abandonment.

The remedy for a breach of contract in building matters is invariably damages, measured by the particular circumstances of the case. Evidence would be called upon to compute the difference between the price of the work as agreed under the contract and the actual cost that the employer is put to in having it completed by someone else, together with contingent damages such as loss of rent or compensation for the loss of use and occupation of the building suffered by the employer as a result of the delay in completion. In such a situation the rent or the appropriate computation of damages for the loss of the use of the building would not necessarily, if the contract was silent on the subject, be based upon the use contemplated by the employer but a purpose for which the contractor might reasonably have supposed the building would be likely to be used.

The main clauses in the JCT Standard Form of Building Contract 1963 that relate to the type of difficulties envisaged under normal circumstances, are clause 21 (possession, completion and post-ponement) clause 22 (damages for non-completion), clause 23 (extension of time) and clause 24 (loss and expense caused by disturbance of regular progress of the works). In the JCT Standard Form of Building Contract 1980 Edition, clause 21 is reproduced as clause 23, the only difference being the new defined term "completion date". Clause 22, however, is re-drafted as a new clause 24 but is similar to the old clause, while clause 23 has been substantially re-drafted as clause 25 incorporating a number of amendments. The phrase "exceptionally adverse" is inserted to replace "exceptionally inclement", in reference to weather, since the impact of one particular long hot summer caused confusion over the meaning of the old wording. The new defined phrase, "clause 22 perils", is now used as are the words "compliance with", in order to group together a number of matters referred to in other sections. Sub-clause 25.4.8.2 is new, dealing with the supply by the Employer of materials and goods which he has agreed to provide, as is clause 25.4.12 which deals with the failure of the Employer "to give in due time ingress to or egress from the site of the Works or any part thereof through or over any land, buildings, way or passage adjoining or connected with the site and in the possession and control of the employer . . .".

Clause 24 in the 1963 Contract Form has been replaced by clause 26 which has been substantially re-drafted, two further matters having been added to those dealing with entitlement to payment for direct loss and/or expense incurred by the contractor. The procedure for application for direct loss and/or expense has been changed by providing specifically for the supply of necessary information and details. Otherwise differences are due to use of the new terminology in the 1980 Edition while clause 26.2.6 repeats the clause relating to failure of the Employer to give in time due ingress to or egress from the site of the Works referred to under 25.4.12. A new provision, under clause 26.2.7, relates to the re-drafting of the old clause 11 as the new clause 13 (variations), while the new clause 26.3 in the 1980 Edition covers the new provision under which the architect is required to state what extensions of time he has given (Relevant Events). Clause 26.4 contains a further new provision dealing with applications for payment for direct loss and/or expense by nominated sub-contactors who apply through the Contractor under the terms of the Relevant Sub-Contract Documents.

Clause 25 of the JCT Standard Form of Building Contract 1963, (determination by Employer), has been substantially reproduced under clause 27 of the 1980 version with the amendment that the employer's right to pay any supplier or sub-contractor is now excluded if the reason for the contractor's employment being determined is bankruptcy or liquidation. The reason for this change is that the former provision was open to challenge by the Trustee-in-Bankruptcy or Liquidator of the Contractor and it was not considered proper to include this in the 1980 Edition. Clause 26 in the 1963 JCT Contract Form, (Determination by Contractor), is also substantially reproduced in clause 28 of the 1980 Edition but with the amendment that the concluding proviso to sub-clause (2) relating to a lien on unfixed goods and materials, the ownership of which had passed to the employer under clause 14, has now been deleted. As a lien depends upon possession, it hardly applies where the contractor has to give up possession by removing all his property, so that the sub-clause relating to lien was without value and even if it could have been exercised it would have been invalid unless registered as a charge.

One of the main reasons for determination of a contract are obviously that one or other of the parties has run out of money. The term "insolvency" merely means, in practical terms, the inability to pay debts but the effect of insolvency depends upon whether the debtor is an individual or a company. The laws of bankruptcy and of winding up companies with all the complicated provisions for the realisation and distribution of assets, certain debts having priority for payment, have been subject to changes lately and are the province of specialist lawyers as are the actions of the creditors as to whether they defer the enforcement of their rights or whether they agree to a formal arrangement by which the debtor attempts to pay off or reduce his debts. Bankruptcy under the terms of the Bankruptcy Act 1914 relates to individuals rather than incorporated companies. Possession of the property of a debtor is taken over for the benefit of his creditors and proceedings are set in train by a Bankruptcy Petition. The Court then appoints the Official Receiver who is empowered to act in relation to the property of the debtor, the creditors then considering at a general meeting as to what action they wish to take. If they do not agree either to accept part payment of debts or come to some scheme of arrangement, the debtor is then adjudicated bankrupt and may be subjected to public examination. His property then passes to a Trustee in Bankruptcy who may realise the assets and distribute the proceeds between creditors. The Trustee may, in particular, disclaim unprofitable contracts.

There is a distinct difference between bankruptcy on the one hand and winding up a company on the other. Bankruptcy is always conducted through the Courts, while winding up may be carried out by the company itself when it appoints its own liquidator, except in cases of insolvency where the creditors appoint their own liquidator, possibly subject to the Courts supervision. In most general cases, however, winding up on the grounds of insolvency will be ordered and conducted by the Court as the result of the Petition of Creditors and, in such cases, the Official Receiver acts initially as liquidator until other arrangements have been made. Assets do not vest in a liquidator as they do a trustee in bankruptcy. A Receiver, on the other hand, is a person appointed by the Court to administer property so as to keep it intact and soundly managed while a dispute is settled. A general practice chartered surveyor in private practice, specialising in management, is often selected for this role.

The consequences when one or other of the parties to the contract becomes insolvent can be severe upon the remaining party. The contractor may determine the contract due to non-payment of certificates and then claim the amount of his loss from the Employer but on the other hand any goods and materials already paid for by the Employer will have become the Employer's property and the contractor will not be able to repossess them. The Employer, on his part, may determine the contract if the contractor becomes bankrupt or has a winding up order made against him or a receiver of his business is appointed. The Employer may claim extra costs incurred in completing the contract but only has, as security, retention money and any performance bonds that may have been executed.

Should the Employer die during the term of the contract, his personal representatives, such as Executors or Administrators, are entitled to the benefit of the contract and are obviously liable to the contractor for the appropriate contract sum. In a similar manner the personal representatives of the contractor, should he die during the execution of the contract, may complete the work and recover due payment.

There will, of course, be occasions where the contract between the employer and contractor, was a personal one and, in the event of the death of the contractor, his personal representatives may claim entitlement either to any instalments of the contract sum which have become due on the one hand, or might formulate a claim on a quantum meruit basis on the other for work actually completed.

Finally, in this Chapter, it is necessary to discuss the procedure for settling disputes, common to most contract standard form documents, by the process known as Arbitration.

Arbitration

Since ancient times arbitration has been favoured as a process of settling trade or commercial disputes as against proceedings before the Courts. Two merchants who found that they were unable to agree over the terms of a bargain they had entered into would appoint a third merchant, known and trusted by each party as being highly knowledgeable in his field and totally trustworthy in personal terms, to decide the matter between them. It would be agreed beforehand that the decision arrived at by the third party would be binding and it was a matter of trust and good faith that neither of the parties to the dispute would dishonour the decision arrived at, even if one or other considered it to be mistaken. This system has flourished in England for centuries, running alongside and accepted by the Common Law only finally being subject to the clarification and restriction of Statute Law due to the increasing complexity of commercial disputes, in 1697. The main Act which now regulates arbitration proceedings is the Arbitration Act 1950, modified by the Arbitration Act 1979.

The reasons why the two merchants in the past selected a third in order to decide their dispute, remain as valid today to justify arbitration as against Court proceedings. In the first place they wished to settle the matter quickly so that disagreement would not hold up more important business matters. In the second place they wished to ensure that the dispute was heard by someone knowledgeable in their own specialist field of business affairs who would instantly understand what he was told and who could call upon his long experience in the field to decide the matter. Finally, and equally important, the dispute could be settled at a time and place convenient to all parties. This was, and still is, one of the main advantages of arbitration. The delay inseparable from Court proceedings and the inconvenience of travelling to the particular Court concerned, was, in medieval times, and still is, to some extent, one of the main reasons for preferring an arbitrator to a judge. The choice between the two is, of course, narrow, since an arbitrator has been defined as "a private extraordinary judge" between party and party, chosen by the parties by mutual consent, to determine controversies between them. An arbitrator could therefore act in an "arbitrary" way but this freedom is now, as we shall see, subject to the constraints of the Court.

Due to the long history of arbitrations for commerce it is hardly surprising that case law reports, in which the conduct of arbitrators is measured against the statutory provisions regulating their conduct, are mostly in the field of shipping, where the amount of money at stake and the need for quick decisions are factors which encourage the appointment and use of arbitrators. The parties and the experts in this particular field are so practised that they are apt to raise an eyebrow at arbitration proceedings in other specialist fields such as building and construction. If three men can meet in a room on the afternoon following a dispute, take their jackets off and hammer the matter out, there and then, what, it is often asked, is the need for the formal and protracted proceedings which usually arise in building disputes? The reason no doubt lies in the fact that the volume of arbitrations in this latter field is much less for one thing, the parties to any particular dispute more numerous and the legal complications more puzzling. Whatever the reasons, however, the reader of this volume is more likely to consider arbitrations in relation to two main areas; the settlement of disputes under the Landlord and Tenant Acts relating to commercial leases on the one hand and disputes under Building Contracts on the other. In the former field it has become necessary to distinguish between an arbitrator and an independent expert, either of whom might be appointed to decide the matter. The difference is fundamental. An arbitrator is regulated by the provisions of the Arbitration Acts and is appointed to decide a dispute which has either arisen already or may arise in the future. He makes his Award on the basis of evidence submitted to him and may or may not have specialist knowledge in the field to which the subject matter of the dispute relates. An independent expert on the other hand is just that. He is appointed because of his specialist knowledge and experience in the particular field of the dispute and he arrives at his own quite independent decision based on his knowledge and experience. He may invite submissions from the parties to the dispute but is not bound to do so. The two roles are therefore totally different in their fundamental characteristics. Building matters however are concerned with arbitration, provision for which can be made in a large number of different circumstances but usually arising out of a contract whether under the National House Building Council Scheme or under the Standard Building and Engineering Contract forms. While discussion in this section of the book is obviously related to building and construction matters, it should not be forgotten that the law relating to arbitrations is not in the least concerned with the particular field in which a dispute occurs. An arbitrator, properly appointed, who gives a decision in writing is bound under the provision of the Arbitration Acts and the case law which interprets those Acts. Architects and surveyors are therefore well advised to read the guidance notes published by the RIBA and RICS relating to arbitration practice and to profit from the articles written by chartered surveyors and chartered architects who are also members of the Chartered Institute of Arbitrators. Such articles are required reading in the area under consideration; those arbitrations which fall under the JCT Standard Forms of Building Contract, whether for major or minor works and whether for main or sub-contracts.

Before proceeding to describe arbitration procedure it is first necessary to explain the upheaval which led to the passing of the Arbitration Act 1979. This arose because a number of eminent lawyers and arbitrators (a considerable proportion being both lawyers and arbitrators combined in the same person) became increasingly dismayed as the last decade drew to a close to find, as one eminent barrister put it in an article to the New Law Journal on 7 December 1978, that "the attraction of England as a forum for international arbitration has become distinctly jaded . . .". The writer put forward as the reason for this trend the "lack of finality of decision in our system of arbitration". This, the writer went on to say, was due, in the main, to the entrenchment in the law of the "special case procedure" which provides for judicial supervision and review of arbitration proceedings. Parties to English arbitrations, said the writer, were unable to secure the swift, private and final adjudication they sought because of the difficulties the Courts faced in differentiating between Appeals instituted purely for the purposes of delay and those which were meritorious. Under section 21 of the Arbitration Act 1950, an arbitrator could, and indeed was, bound to state by way of a special case any point of law which had arisen during the hearing of the arbitration proceedings, for the guidance and determination of the High Court. The drawback to this was that while the Court had the power and duty to require the arbitrator to present such a reference, there was no similar procedure to enable the Court to know what particular question of law was in issue. Since, at the stage at which the High Court must decide whether or not an arbitrator should be ordered to state his Award in the form of a special case, the arbitrator had not, at that time, made any findings of fact upon the basis of which a decision could be made, the Court was not therefore able to determine clearly whether any point of substance in law was actually at stake.

Accordingly, after the 1 August 1979, section 21 of the Arbitration Act 1950 setting out the "case stated" procedure ceased to exist. Instead, a positive right of appeal was introduced in substitution. The purpose of the new procedure was to counteract delay in arbitration proceedings since the right of appeal could now only arise after the arbitrator had made his Award. While the right of appeal was still restricted to matters of law only, the new Act did provide a radical departure in stating that parties to an arbitration could exclude the right to appeal, should they wish to do so, provided that an "exclusion agreement" was entered into after the commencement of the arbitration. Perhaps however, the section of the new Act which has aroused the greatest controversy is that the High Court may now order an arbitrator to give reasons for his Award. It should be said, however, that such an order would not be made where an exclusion agreement is in force or where the parties agreed before the arbitrator arrived at his Award that no such requirement would be expected of him. Discussion over this particular section of the new Act has put lesser issues into the shade. The sensible provisions which give increased powers to arbitrators to deal with "reluctant litigants", much needed, have received little attention.

It is not easy for professional architects and surveyors unused to arbitrations to decide between one body of opinion that regards the 1979 Act as an excellent measure, long overdue, and the other body of opinion which regards it as an unmitigated disaster. Critics of those who uphold the benefits of the new Act point to the case of the Greek motor vessel "The Nema".[1] In this case Lord Denning set down guidelines for the operation of the new Appeal system based on the 1979 Act but, as a result of these, there have been seven Court Hearings since the arbitrator made his Award and the eighth, in the House of Lords, is awaited at the time of writing. It has been said that the matter could have been settled under the 1950 Act had the very experienced arbitrator been allowed to follow the previous procedure.

(1) *Pioneer Shipping Ltd.* v. *BTP Tioxide Ltd.*, "The Nema" (1980) 3 ALL ER 117.

Quite apart from the benefits or otherwise of the 1979 Act, professional feelings run high on the new requirement that an arbitrator should be expected to give a "reasoned" award. Section 1(5) of the Act gives little help on what is required from the arbitrator in this connection since it merely asks him to "state the reasons for his Award in sufficient detail to enable the Court . . . to consider any question of law arising out of the Award". Argument over what is meant by this clause has been considerable. Quite apart from this interpretation, however, it has aroused fundamental antagonisms. Those who support the point of view that an arbitrator should never give reasons for his decisions quote the well known saying of Lord Mansfield in the eighteenth century "Consider what you think justice requires and decide accordingly. But never give your reasons; for your judgement will probably be right, but your reasons will certainly be wrong". Against this however, experienced arbitrators who are both architects or surveyors and members of the Chartered Institute of Arbitrators consider it perfectly acceptable to give reasons and indeed not only have no hesitation in doing so but find it preferable so as to lay at rest any misgivings there may be as to whether the arbitrator has considered all aspects of the evidence or not. One point which comes through with total clarity are the advantages offered by those architects and surveyors who are prepared to act as arbitrators and who are also members of the Chartered Institute of Arbitrators, since they combine practical experience with skilled knowledge of procedure and conduct. The Institution has a set of rules to govern the conduct of arbitrations held by its members and although these rules are binding on members and not merely guide lines, they are binding only where the parties to the arbitration have agreed to adopt them. There is much force in the point that those members of the professional institutions from which arbitrators are selected should have previously passed the examinations of the Chartered Institute of Arbitrators and be a member of this particular Institution in addition to their own.

The selection of the appropriate arbitrator to decide a particular dispute is obviously all important since a wrong selection could have final and disastrous consequences whereas, in a Court hearing there is, at least in theory, always the opportunity of appeal. In a dispute involving both modern and traditional types of construction it might be difficult enough to know whether to appoint a chartered surveyor, chartered architect or chartered engineer without having to be sure that the arbitrator selected had the requisite knowledge in law and procedure as well which would be the case should the chosen arbitrator not be a member of the Chartered Institute of

Arbitrators. The arbitrator must have special knowledge, practical as well as theoretical, in the field of building and construction but must also have a basic knowledge of the general law of contract and tort and of building law and contracts in particular. Furthermore, he must be fully versed in the rules of evidence and of arbitration law and practice. He must be experienced in dealing with all types of personalities and be patient, impartial and sufficiently masterful to keep control of proceedings when clashes arise, as they frequently do. If this seems a lot to ask, any lack of these qualities is likely to point very quickly to the disadvantages of arbitration against Court proceedings. The first main disadvantage lies in the dangers from the selection of the wrong arbitrator while the second compounds the first in that his powers are limited so that he needs his long experience, knowledge and tact to ensure that he receives the information that he needs. A poor arbitrator lacks just these essential qualities. He has no power, for example, to summon all those who might be concerned in the dispute, such as third parties, before him, and if he is not clear sighted and precise in his procedural requirements, the actual hearing can result in a muddle.

The procedure at an arbitration hearing is worthy of consideration. The proceedings for settlement might for example be taken to arise under what is known at law as "an agreement to refer", either under clause 35 of the JCT Standard Form of Building Contract 1963 (revised July 1977) or Article 5 of the New JCT Standard Form of Building Contract 1980. As mentioned earlier in this Chapter, there are, of course, other agreements to refer to arbitration in contract documents; the most newly introduced being clause 10 of Form NSC/2 and Article 3 of Form NSC/4.

Initially, the parties proceed by way of submission, either agreeing upon the appointment of a specific arbitrator, or calling on some other person or body to make the appointment for them such as a professional institution. Where one of the parties only is anxious to start proceedings and the other party is reluctant the mere existence of the particular contract document is sufficient to compel arbitration proceedings to be put in hand. Generally, the initiating party sends a formal letter to the other party calling upon him to concur in the appointment of an arbitrator and usually suggests possible names, provided of course that it has first been established that the arbitrators suggested can, in fact, act. If this letter is ignored within the time scale stated in the particular contract form employed, an arbitrator is then appointed by the particular institution named in the contract. It is a pity in many ways if agreement on the appointment cannot be reached as the essential benefit of arbitration procedure is that both parties are convinced of its advantages

665

and if they cannot agree as to the selection of an arbitrator to decide between them, much of the basic value of the procedure is reduced.

While it is perfectly possible for both parties to agree upon a reduced procedure in order to save time and money, the majority of arbitrations follow a set procedure very like those adopted by the Courts. Initially, the claimant is required to set up the basis of his case in a document known as "the points of claim" which he then serves on the respondent. The respondent then replies with a similar document known as "the points of defence". Any cross-claim or "contra-charge" is set out by way of counter-claim as a supplement to the points of defence. The points of defence, and counter-claim, if any, are then served on the claimant, who is required to set out his answer in a further document called "the points of reply and defence to counter-claim". These documents, known as the "pleadings" form the basis of the dispute and thereafter neither party may step outside the scope of the pleadings as lodged without the consent of the arbitrator. Either party however, can press for further information on the basis of the existing pleadings by serving a further document termed "a request for further and better particulars". Examination of the works is, obviously, allowed to either party together with all relevant files and papers in the possession of the other side. The arbitrator is empowered to serve orders for "discovery" and "inspection" if there is any obstruction on this score. An order for discovery requires a particular party to list all the papers in his possession, while an order for inspection calls upon a party to make the listed papers available for scrutiny and copying by the other party.

A modern introduction into arbitration proceedings, and, for that matter, Court proceedings as well, is the exchange of expert's reports between the parties. The benefit of this is to reduce the area of disagreement between experts to the irreducible minimum.

In most cases the arbitrator will call for a "preliminary meeting". The value of such a meeting is that the parties are free to attend either by themselves or with solicitors and quickly, it is hoped, agree the procedure which is then confirmed by the arbitrator in an "order for directions". A time scale is usually set down with "Liberty to either party to apply", which allows a request for any particular provision in the order for directions to be amended if the party could show a good reason, such as illness for example. Whether the arbitrator calls a preliminary meeting, or whether the parties decide the preliminary issues between themselves, consent is required for the arbitrator to proceed. If one of the parties is obstructive or difficult he can be termed a "reluctant litigant" and while an arbitrator, obviously, cannot enforce compliance with his requirements or punish the particular party concerned, he can, if he thinks fit, proceed ex parte or award costs. The powers of the arbitrator are backed up by those of the High Court and an experienced arbitrator will ensure in his procedure that there is no possibility of a reluctant litigant unduly delaying or interferring with the arbitration and, ultimately, the award.

The power of the arbitrator to award costs against one party or the other, which is at his discretion, forms possibly his most powerful weapon. Generally speaking, "costs follow the event" which means that the unsuccessful party is responsible for all the costs in the case and those of the arbitrator. The Courts, however, keep a firm eye on the procedure in this connection as an arbitrator is expected on this aspect, as in so many others, to act as a Judge would. In 1953 Lord Goddard said "it is a curious circumstance – and one experiences it time and time again – that lay arbitrators always seem to think that parties should pay their own costs".

There has been some additional criticism of arbitration proceedings in regard to costs as the system of "payment into Court" cannot be adopted. When payments in are made on Court proceedings these affect the issue of costs since, if the judgement is far more than the defendant pays into Court he is responsible for the costs while the converse occurs since, should the judgement be less than the amount paid in, the plaintiff will be liable for costs. All legal authorities say that "payments-in" should not be permitted in arbitration proceedings, due to the problems involved, and some also say that the "sealed offer" procedure should also not be employed.

While the parties to an arbitration might appear in person it is more common, if there is a considerable sum of money at stake, for each party to be represented by a solicitor or Counsel. In defence of the often repeated cry of expense it must be said in fairness to the legal profession that the main essentials of the dispute can often be reduced to a minimum when solicitors and Counsel are involved whereas lay persons appearing before an arbitrator are apt to waste time by lengthy and off the point discourses, and tend to say what is, in essence, the same thing in a number of different ways. An arbitrator will allow some rope here so as not to give either party the impression that he is not being allowed to present his case.

The arbitrator will have arranged the hearing at a place convenient to all parties. This is normally on neutral territory such as the room hired in a professional institution or a conference room at a convenient hotel. At the time appointed the arbitrator opens the proceedings and invites the claimant to present his case as the burden of proof rests upon him. If Counsel are employed the usual

Court procedure of introduction of the parties, the background to the case, reference to documents and then to the issue or issues in dispute will be made, Counsel for the respondent correcting any errors while the arbitrator is then, as throughout the entire hearing, entitled to ask questions, although experienced arbitrators rarely intervene unless they have to.

Claimants' Counsel then sets out his client's case in detail making legal submissions and reviewing the supporting evidence. Aspects relating to any Counter-claim are also dealt with. This part of the procedure is apt to be lengthy since Counsel will be anxious to ensure that every aspect of his client's case is included, as otherwise the opportunity will be lost of introducing relevant matters that might affect the Award. Finally, Counsel will display the evidence in support of his case either by calling witnesses, referring to agreed experts reports or other documents, or referring to matters that are actually available for physical inspection. So far as witnesses are concerned, Counsel will be experienced in handling those who can speak as to fact and those who can speak as to opinion. This is where experience counts. Each witness is subject to examination-in-chief, cross-examination, and re-examination. Witnesses as to fact are expected to speak from memory but notes may be allowed if this is agreed and the notes are available to inspection by the other side. Counsel for the claimant will examine witnesses that he introduces and whose prepared proofs he has before him and then allow each witness to be cross-examined by Counsel for the respondent. Re-examination is then carried out by Counsel for the claimant in order to clear up the havoc wrought by his opponent. In cases where Counsel are employed, the arbitrator will take particular pains to see that the rules of the Courts are obeyed. The witnesses may be put on oath, be kept "incommunicado" and be kept from answering leading questions. It naturally takes an experienced arbitrator to cope with those Counsel who will always try to make use of any greater latitude permitted by an arbitrator than would be allowed by a Judge. Cross-examination, however, is a different matter and the arbitrator will generally allow Counsel to have total freedom in the questions that he asks; many witnesses surviving this ordeal either shaken or furious, depending upon the questions asked. It always amazes witnesses that Counsel on their side sits silent while they are asked questions of a personal or insinuating nature which seem to them to insult their character and cast doubt upon their qualifications and ability.

When re-examination of each witness is concluded, the arbitrator will be free to ask any questions which he himself may have and experienced arbitrators will make sure that these are put in a very neutral way otherwise one or other of the Counsel, seeing which way his mind may be working, will try to seize an advantage.

When Counsel for the claimant concludes his case, Counsel for the respondent will then rise to conduct his case upon similar lines as his opponent and then deliver his closing speach to which Counsel for the claimant has the final right of reply. Upon conclusion, the arbitrator will announce that the hearing is at an end and that he will now prepare and publish his Award.

Sometimes, due to the complexity of pleadings and the complications of the task of attempting to relate various items to each other in a large claim, the arbitrator will follow the practice of the Courts in requiring an "Official Referee's" or "Scott" Schedule. This schedule compiles in columns the allegations and counter-allegations in respect of each defect and while there is no standard form that such a "Scott" Schedule might take, it is easy to see the benefit that it provides at the hearing for all the parties and, not least of all, the arbitrator who is usually provided with a column for his own use in writing comments to assist him in reaching a decision on each item. Another area where experienced arbitrators in larger claims adjust the procedure to suit the circumstances, is where there is an unduly large number of items in dispute and these affect all parts of the structure from say, the steel portal frame to the finishings, he will divide the ground covered by the arbitration into a number of separate areas with the consent of the parties, only those witnesses being involved with each area being required to attend at predetermined times. This saves a good deal of wasted time but requires the consent of the parties and an experienced arbitrator to ensure that "natural justice" is seen to be done.

Once an arbitrator has prepared his Award, he is entitled to hold a lien upon it in respect of his charges. He will accordingly notify both parties that he has "made and published" his Award and that this may be "taken up" on payment of his charges amounting to so much. The party who pays the arbitrator's bill will obtain the original of the Award and a certified true copy will be sent to the other party. Sometimes, in cases of complexity or urgency, the arbitrator will issue an interim Award under the terms of Section 14 of the 1950 Act which permits this to be done. Once the Award is published and delivered the arbitrator becomes "functus officio" and drops out of jurisdiction. Any subsequent proceedings whether to enforce, set aside or remit the Award are made to the Courts.

The importance of arbitration procedure is highlighted by the drafting of a new Article 5 to the JCT Standard Form of Building Contract 1980. Under the new provisions, disputes related to extension of time and therefore presumably the question of liquidated damages are brought into a new field of early arbitration by permitting site inspections relating to serious defects and quality of work. Provision is also made for joinder applications to be made whereby the employer, the contractor and a nominated sub-contractor may join each other in arbitration proceedings, irrespective of which agreement to refer was first implemented.

Article 5 replaces the former Arbitration Agreement set out in clause 35 of the JCT Standard Form of Contract 1963. Under Articles 5.1.4 and 5.1.5 differences under the main contract which are substantially the same or are connected with issues raised in a related dispute under Agreement NSC/2, or 2A, or under NSC/4 and 4A or with a Nominated Supplier where the Contract of Sale provides for the matters referred to in Clause 36.4.8 (1980), then if such related dispute has been referred to an Arbitrator that Arbitrator is to decide the dispute under the Main Contract. The Arbitrator is given in Article 5.1.4 the same powers as are available in the High Court for the joining of parties in legal proceedings and Article 5.1.5 deals with the situation where the Employer or Contractor considers that the Arbitrator in the related dispute is not appropriately qualified to determine the dispute or difference under the main contract.

It has been stressed before, and will be stressed again, that time, effort and research will be amply repaid in the appointment of an experienced arbitrator skilled in the field to which the subject matter of the dispute relates. So far as the early procedure for arbitration is concerned, and, for that matter, the later conduct of the case, pride should not allow any of the parties to obstruct proceedings on the one hand or "go it alone" on the other unless they are absolutely certain of what they are doing. Arbitration is one of the fields where skilled and experienced help is invaluable.

Selected Bibliography

AJ Handbook of Building Structure, Allan Hodgkinson 2nd edition, 1980.

Arbitration for Builders, Peter J. Lord-Smith, 1980.

The Architect in Practice, A. J. Willis and Others, 6TH edition 1981.

Architects Job Book, RIBA, 3RD edition 1977.

Architectural Practice and Procedure, Hamilton H. Turner, 7TH edition 1981.

Architectural Supervision on Site, A. A. Macfarlane, 1974.

Briefing and Design Guides, 1 Libraries, Allan Konya, 1983.

Building and Civil Engineering Contracts and Law, Michael P. Barber, 1970.

Building Contracts, Donald Keating, 4TH edition 1978.

Building Contracts, Dennis F. Turner, 1977.

Building Contracts and Practice, W. H. Gill, 7TH edition.

Construction Law, John Uff, 3RD edition 1981.

Conversion, Improvement and Extension of Buildings, Richard and Sarah Catt, 1981.

Factories, Planning Design and Modernisation, Architectural Press, 1981.

Guide to the Building Regulations, A. J. Elder, 7th edition.

Handbook for Clerks of Works, Greater London Council, 1974.

Handbook of Architectural Practice and Management, RIBA, 4TH edition 1980.

Handbook of Sports and Recreational Building Design, Architectural Press, 1981.

Housing Rehabilitation Handbook. Architectural Press, 1980.

Hudson's Building and Engineering Contracts, I. N. Duncan Wallis, 10TH edition 1970.

Guide to the Standard Form of Building Contract, RIBA, 1980.

Manual for use with the JCT Form of Agreement for Minor Building Works, RICS.

National Building Specification, 2ND edition 1980.

Party Structure Rights in London, W. A. Leach, 1974.

Party Wall Legislation and Procedure, RICS, 1982.

Planning Office Space, Architectural Press, 1976.

Specification, Architectural Press, 80TH edition 1982.
Specification Writing for Architects and Surveyors, A. J. Willis and C. J. Willis, 7TH edition 1981.
Working Drawings Handbook, Keith Styles, 1982.
The publications of:-
The Building Research Establishment.
The Department of the Environment.
The British Standards Institution.
The Timber Research and Development Association.
The Brick Development Association.
The Joint Contracts Tribunal.
The National House Building Council.

Index

679